This BOOK HAS BEEN SENT TO YOU
AT THE SUGGESTION OF

EDMUND R. WYDER, JR.

Please accept it with our compliments

McGRAW-HILL BOOK COMPANY, Inc.

Ex Libris: _____

McGraw-Hill Series in Control Systems Engineering

JOHN R. RAGAZZINI AND WILLIAM E. VANNAH, *Consulting Editors*

RANDOM PROCESSES IN AUTOMATIC CONTROL

McGraw-Hill Series in Control Systems Engineering

JOHN R. RAGAZZINI AND WILLIAM E. VANNAH, *Consulting Editors*

LANING AND BATTIN . Random Processes in Automatic Control

RANDOM PROCESSES IN AUTOMATIC CONTROL

J. Halcombe Laning, Jr., Ph.D.

Deputy Associate Director
Instrumentation Laboratory
Massachusetts Institute of Technology

Richard H. Battin, Ph.D.

Assistant Director
Instrumentation Laboratory
Massachusetts Institute of Technology

McGRAW-HILL BOOK COMPANY, INC.

New York   Toronto   London

1956

RANDOM PROCESSES IN AUTOMATIC CONTROL

THE MAPLE PRESS COMPANY, YORK, PA.

PREFACE

The material presented in this text is the outgrowth of a set of lecture notes, first prepared in 1951, to meet the needs of a course on random processes in the field of automatic control given by the authors in the Aeronautical Engineering Department at M.I.T. At the time this project was started, there was need for an organized exposition of the foundations of the theory of random processes, including the basic probability theory, together with the techniques for applying these theories to the study of complex instrument systems. The authors hope that the present text has accomplished this objective.

The selection of suitable subject matter for a text in a field that overlaps several others and that is currently expanding at a rapid rate is not an easy one, and it would be impossible for everyone, including the authors, to be completely satisfied with the result. For example, the authors have completely ignored the vital field of information theory and its applications to radar, communications, and digital-data processing, despite the fact that an increasing number of control systems are being designed in which these elements play a basic part. On the other hand, they have devoted a whole chapter (Chap. 8) to optimum finite-data operations for which the principal purpose is the determination of limitations on control-system performance imposed by the intrinsic properties of the data to be processed. The application of this material to improved system design is at most indirect. In selecting topics for discussion, the authors have been motivated by their own experiences and interests in the design and analysis of systems in the fields of fire control and navigation. For the most part, the material presented has arisen in connection with studies of a concrete and practical nature in the M.I.T. Instrumentation Laboratory. In their writings, however, the authors are handicapped by the fact that most of these studies have been performed in connection with classified military projects. As a result, it has been impossible to include in the latter portions of the book as great a number and diversity of illustrative applications as the authors would have desired.

The material presented here is considerably in excess of that covered in the one-semester course for which it was originally designed. In particular, the whole of Chaps. 4 and 8 can be omitted from an abbreviated presentation without essential discontinuity. If this is done, Secs. 2.9 to 2.13 can be given a cursory discussion without great loss. In fact, the whole of Chaps. 2 and 3 can perhaps be given a much briefer treatment than is done here, provided that the applications in Chaps. 5, 6, and 7 are to be the principal subject matter stressed.

The authors owe a considerable debt of gratitude to Dr. W. L. Root, without whose collaboration the original version of this material would perhaps have never been prepared. They also wish to express their appreciation to Dr. C. S. Draper for his continued encouragement in this undertaking, to their students and colleagues at the Instrumentation Laboratory for their numerous constructive criticisms, and to the members of the Technical Publications group under Dorothy C. Ladd, who prepared the lecture notes from which this material was taken.

J. HALCOMBE LANING, JR.
RICHARD H. BATTIN

CONTENTS

CHAPTER 1

INTRODUCTION

1.1 General Nature of the Optimum Design Problem

The increasingly severe demands of modern technology on the speed and quality of performance of control equipment have created the need for a correspondingly more refined and accurate estimate of performance characteristics. In the communications field a high premium is placed on the successful discrimination between signal and noise. The design of an aircraft autopilot requires a high degree of stability, and at the same time requires a rapid response to eliminate effects of atmospheric turbulence. Precision thermostatic controls demand a rapid response to ambient temperatures in the surrounding environment, in the face of thermal lags within the controlled medium and sensing elements.

This situation is emphasized in the fire-control field. On the one hand, the increased mobility of military targets has brought into prominence the simultaneous problems of rapid generation of a correct result coupled with the automatic smoothing of fluctuating data. On the other, the continuous effort to extend the effective range of weapons has resulted in a demand for maximum accuracy of control systems under the most stringent operating conditions. In this and other fields the control-systems engineer is under pressure to obtain the maximum possible quality of performance from his system, compatible with the other requirements of the problem.

In many cases a change in operating characteristics of one portion of a control system produces results which are in part advantageous and in part disadvantageous for over-all operation. As a result, a balanced instrument design is composed of an endless series of compromise decisions. An example of this situation arises in the selection of smoothing or damping characteristics in a first-order system that receives as input a low-frequency signal in combination with a high-frequency interference. A lightly damped system may possess too great a response to the random interference in its input data, whereas a system which is heavily damped may respond too slowly to changes in the signal. An intermediate damping must therefore be employed which supplies an effective compromise between the two extremes.

In order to make such compromise decisions on a scientific rather than rule-of-thumb basis, a combination of theoretical analysis and experimental test is necessary.   On the one hand, experimental test is required to provide the basic performance characteristics of components under actual operating conditions as a starting point for analysis, to check the results of theoretical deductions, and to reveal the existence of practical problems and phenomona which would remain undiscovered in pencil-and-paper studies.   On the other hand, theoretical analysis is needed to provide a unified framework of design concepts and a systematic and quantitative mode of attack on the problem of securing the optimum performance from equipment.   For balanced design it is necessary both to develop operating components possessing a high quality of performance and to utilize those components in the most effective manner possible by a systematic study of over-all system performance characteristics.

One difficulty often encountered in experimental test of a completed control system is that of tracing an observed inaccuracy in performance back to its principal actuating cause.   There are, of course, many cases of unsatisfactory performance which are directly traceable to the malfunctioning of one component within the system, and these can generally be detected by means of a systematic check of each major component or subsystem.   In other cases, however, each component performs essentially as designed and yet the over-all system performance remains inaccurate.   In view of the great complexity of many present-day control systems and the large number of theoretical and practical compromises which must be incorporated in their design, this situation is hardly surprising.   For the same reason, the decomposition of an observed error into component parts, each of which may be ascribed to its separate cause, is an almost impossible task by experimental means alone.

In this respect, theoretical analysis possesses an important advantage over experimental measurement, in principle at least.   Provided that the necessary theory can be implemented by quantitative calculations, the interrelated phenomona present in a complex system can be studied in such a manner that the over-all effect of each may be given separate consideration.   It is feasible, for example, to study the net gain in over-all system operation to be expected from the improvement or modification of performance of a single component, and thereby to determine whether the gain in the over-all operation is worth the necessary effort.   By the same token it is possible to isolate those sources of inaccuracy which are the most important, permitting a concentration of further experimental development on those phases which seem to offer the maximum dividends. By experimental techniques alone, a program of this type can be directed only by the use of the highest degree of engineering judgment, and is still limited by a lack of quantitative evidence upon which decisions must be made. One role of theoretical analysis in the problem of securing optimum system design is thus that of determining in a systematic and quantitative way the contributions to over-all system performance of each potential source of inaccuracy present, in order to point the way toward those modifications which lead to improvement.

The practical interest in this type of effort, particularly in the area of the dynamic performance of systems, is magnified by the fact that the system performance may often be modified quite easily. The change of the value of a resistor or condenser at a critically located point, achieved with negligible cost and effort, can frequently alter the dynamic response of the system quite drastically. If a theoretical analysis can lead to optimum parameters which can be readily set into the system, the net result may be a significant improvement in performance with a disproportionately small expense.

1.2   The Role of Statistical Methods of Analysis

In investigations of this type a central position is held by the methods of statistical analysis. To begin with, many performance inaccuracies are essentially random functions of time, and cannot be prescribed a priori except in a general statistical sense. For example, because of fading and similar effects, the position of a target indicated by a radar unit contains components of roughness or *noise* which vary with time in an unpredictable way. Only by statistical techniques can such random interference effects be treated analytically. In addition, because of manufacturing tolerances in a system, the sensitivities and other fixed parameters of operating components are subject to variations, either in the form of slight fluctuations with time or in the form of variations from one system to another. To the extent that these variations are not corrected by calibration, they must be considered as subject to randomnicity within certain tolerance limits. Finally, an automatic control system is seldom designed to perform a single task which may be completely specified beforehand; instead, it is designed to perform a task selected at random from a complete repertory of possible tasks. For example, an antiaircraft fire-control system must be so designed as to score hits on targets possessing a wide variety of speeds and courses. Since the system performance is likely to vary from one course to the next, it is only by the calculation of a statistical average of performance quality over the various tactical situations, in which each situation is weighted in accordance with its tactical probability, that a summarized measure of the system performance can be obtained. In general, every phenomenon which is not amenable to exact a priori specification becomes the proper subject for study by the methods of statistical reasoning.

1.3   Stationary and Nonstationary Problems

For the special case of a linear operating system for which the performance is time-invariant (e.g., a system describable analytically by a linear differential equation with constant coefficients) there exists a well-developed body of techniques for characterizing and relating the random system input and output when these belong to the class of so-called stationary random processes. These techniques involve use of the operational calculus and harmonic analysis to relate the spectral distributions of input and output among various frequencies of oscillation, and permit a rapid evaluation of a statistical measure of output error. Techniques for reduction of output error to the minimum possible value for a given system have been developed, and in many cases permit an a priori characterization of the optimum form of linear system for a stated task as well as the optimum design parameters for that system.

There are many systems problems, however, for which these techniques possess at most a limited applicability. Although these methods possess the greatest mathematical elegance, the fundamental hypotheses on which they rest are often not satisfied. Leaving aside the question of nonlinearities which most systems possess in some degree, it frequently happens that the statistical characteristics of the problem change with time in a regular fashion. This can happen either because the input data to the system is changing its character or because the system itself contains parameters that vary with time. In the case of a guided-missile control problem, for example, it may be expected that both the coefficients of the control system and the data being processed may vary with the range to the target. Linear systems whose response characteristics vary with time may be termed linear time-variable systems, in contrast to linear time-invariant systems in which the response characteristics are fixed. Since an adequate harmonic analysis of linear time-variable systems has yet to be developed, at least in a form suited to the necessary design calculations, even the linear portions of a system are often not amenable to a complete analysis by the methods referred to above.

In the case of time-variable linear systems, approximate smoothing properties may often be determined by assuming that the frequencies associated with random interference are high relative to those associated with the rates of change of the variable coefficients. In this case, the smoothing properties of the system at each instant may be approximated by the smoothing properties of a corresponding constant-coefficient system. The frequencies associated with the signal, however, are usually of the same order as those associated with variations in coefficients, so that this quasi-static form of analysis cannot be used in studying errors in signal transmission. Thus the basis is lacking for a quantitative compromise on purely analytical terms between smoothing of interference and distortion of signal.

It is seen from the preceding discussion that a desirable requirement for the realistic analysis of over-all performance of many systems is an acceptable statistical method for treating the response of a linear time-variable system to random inputs. One objective of the material presented here is to develop such a method and illustrate its use by consideration of typical problems in instrumentation.

The methods developed for this purpose are analytical only to a limited extent; in fact, they rely quite heavily on the use of some form of analogue or digital computation in order to be practical. At the complete sacrifice of mathematical elegance, they do, however, appear to offer the possibility of machine solution of an important class of statistical problems which have not yet been found amenable to a direct analytical attack. The methods proposed are in no way concerned directly with the solution to the class of problems considered; rather, they constitute techniques whereby many of the basic statistical problems of system design can be translated into a form suited to analogue computation, or a combination of analogue computation and numerical analysis.

1.4 Performance Index of a System

By and large, the present development is concerned with processes of analysis rather than synthesis. With the exception of Wiener's work, and some of its extensions, no general techniques have as yet been discovered for the a priori characterization of optimum systems. A more practical difficulty, however, is that one seldom knows the characteristics of the data to be contended with in a complex control system until the system has actually been built and tested. There are many practical engineering reasons for this situation, and it would appear to be one that is not likely to be avoided for a long time to come, except in control problems which are essentially simple. Thus, even though the analyst would like to be able to tell the engineer what "optimum" system he should design for a given task, he is usually forced to study the properties of a system that actually exists, with numerous practical constraints that prevent the analyst from doing more than make a few last-minute parameter changes.

The effort here is concentrated on the determination of a number, which may be called a *performance index*, that gives a quantitative measure of the extent to which the performance of a system is regarded as satisfactory. The selection of a suitable performance index for a system is highly dependent upon the nature of the individual system and the function that it is called upon to perform.   It is not possible to give hard and fast rules for this selection; the two principal requirements are that the index should express the quality of the performance as closely as is practical, and that at the same time it should be a quantity that can be computed by existing techniques.

For a voice communication system.a suitable performance index might be the ratio of signal power to noise power at the output, with a standardized signal as input.   Assuming linearity of the system, a knowledge of the frequency distributions of the input signal and noise together with the system parameters would permit the calculation of this ratio by practical means.   Also, better performance would be expected if this ratio were high than if it were low, other things being equal, so that a correlation exists between this index and one's intuitive notion of quality of performance of the system.   A more refined point of view would perhaps take account of distortion in the signal, the probability of occurrence of various frequencies in randomly selected signals, and the response characteristics of the human ear and brain in translating the system output into intelligence.   Thus the performance index could be a relatively simple quantity, a fairly complicated quantity, or something of intermediate complexity.   The final choice would be dictated primarily by the available data and the amount of analysis which the designer felt that the problem justified, and would necessarily rest on a matter of engineering judgement.

In the case of a fire-control system, a performance index might be the survival probability of a target under stated tactical assumptions concerning the character of the attack and defense.   A somewhat simpler and more readily calculated index might be the time average, during a specified phase of the attack, of the root-mean-squared error in fire.   In an automatic aircraft navigation system such as might be used for blind landing, a performance index might be a specified function of rms vertical and lateral errors in position at the nominal instant of landing.

In the above examples and elsewhere in this material a prominent role is played by the rms error.   In the case of a random quantity following the so-called normal probability distribution, all statistical properties of the quantity may be found from its rms and mean values.   A much more fundamental reason for considering performance indices which are derivable from rms values, however, lies in the fact that the rms value of a random quantity can often be calculated practically under conditions in which many of its other statistical properties cannot.   This point should of course become much clearer at a later stage of the text; however, it must be emphasized that the widespread use of rms errors in design analysis is due less to the intrinsic worth of such criteria than to the convenience attached to their calculation.

1.5 Organization of Text

The analysis of random functions of time is quite naturally rooted rather deeply in the theory of probability. For much of the work to be done, only rudimentary concepts from this field are necessary, and many successful treatments of random processes have been made on the basis of a purely intuitive approach. It has been the feeling of the authors, however, that the application of much of this material to specific engineering problems has been inhibited by an inadequate foundation in probability theory. This is particularly true in the area of the translation of physical problems into a suitable analytical form for solution. It is for this reason that our technical discussion is prefaced in Chap. 2 by a brief introduction to the fundamental concepts of probability.

It can scarcely be claimed that our abbreviated treatment of the subject does it justice, or even attains its objective in providing the necessary background. A serious effort is nevertheless made to present fundamental principles, with the feeling that by frequent reference to these in later portions of the text a better appreciation for the whole material will result. The beginning student is not expected to become thoroughly familiar with the contents of Chap. 2 at first reading. By use of this material as a guide to further reading, and as a reference point in subsequent practical calculations, it is hoped that he can assimilate the foundations of the subject in spite of an inadequate allotment of space.

Chapter 3 treats the subject of the statistical properties of random functions of time in a somewhat similar spirit. At the expense of postponing until later chapters the practical application of this material to problems in systems analysis, Chap. 3 is chiefly concerned with the ways in which random processes can be analyzed and described per se. Portions of this material could perhaps be postponed until such later point as dictated by the applications. By a systematic study of the statistical properties of random processes in the beginning, however, later studies of their relation to systems analysis are considerably simplified.

Chapter 4 is concerned with the application of the concepts of Chaps. 2 and 3 to the study of the shot effect and the general Gaussian random process. These random processes have been studied fairly extensively in the literature and are among the very few for which any detailed mathematical properties have been derived to date. Their special importance arises primarily from this fact, as well as the fact that they represent mathematical models of certain natural phenomena. Since the description of the Gaussian process in particular is fairly complete, it is possible to use this model to advantage in the study of certain nonlinear problems. This material is somewhat advanced in character, and can be omitted upon first reading.

The first material relating directly to systems analysis appears in Chap. 5, which discusses stationary random processes as inputs to time-invariant linear systems. The subject is treated at this point from the standpoint of systems analysis rather than synthesis; consideration of the problem of optimum systems synthesis by the methods of Wiener is postponed until Chap. 7.

The material of Chap. 6 is concerned with the practical evaluation of rms errors in time-variable linear systems in response to stationary or nonstationary inputs. Primary emphasis is laid on analogue computation methods using functions in the time domain. In the case of a stationary random process, however, frequency methods are also employed. Particular attention is given to the role of a switch as a variable coefficient: for example, in the analysis of the transient period of operation of constant-coefficient systems that are inactive prior to a selected instant of time.

Whereas the theory of Wiener as developed in Chap. 7 is exclusively concerned with operations on stationary random processes and makes use of the complete past history of a set of data, the theories considered in Chap. 8 allow the signal to possess nonstationary components (e.g., a polynomial in time with arbitrary coefficients) and assume only a finite interval of past data to be known. Applications are given to the problem of determining an optimum filter with a prescribed solution time, and also to the problem of determining intrinsic limits of predictability of random data.

For a variety of reasons, the authors have elected to collect all bibliographical material in a single section at the end of the book. In certain chapters (e.g., Chap. 2) we are summarizing a large body of material that is available in any number of standard references. In other cases, material is presented which as a whole or in part has originated with the authors or their colleagues. In either extreme, it has seemed desirable to provide some sort of bibliographical commentary in which the whole chapter is considered as a unit. In many areas that we have not considered in detail, an effort has also been made to suggest directions for further reading.

CHAPTER 2

BASIC CONCEPTS OF PROBABILITY THEORY

2.1 Introduction

The usual intuitive concept of probability appears to center around the notion of "equal likelihood." Consider an experiment possessing n different possible outcomes, and assume that these have equal chances of occurring. Let a number m of these outcomes be singled out for consideration, and let the event E be said to occur if the outcome of the experiment is one of these. Then the probability of the event E, written $P(E)$, is equal to the ratio m/n. Thus in the single draw of a card from a bridge deck there are 52 "equally likely" outcomes. Let the four possible draws that result in a queen be defined as the event E. Then the probability of drawing a queen is $P(E) = 4/52$. This is the classical concept of probability; it is usually sufficient for games of chance where the number of possible occurrences n is finite and where the requirement of equal likelihood seems clearly to be met. Probability defined in this way is sometimes called *a priori* probability.

However, in many problems of an obviously probabilistic nature either the number of individual possible occurrences is not finite, or the notion "equal likelihood" is not meaningful, or both. For example, consider a coin-tossing experiment in which the toss is repeated until heads first appears. The possible outcomes of this experiment correspond to the sequences (H), (TH), (TTH), $(TTTH)$, and so on. Clearly the number of such sequences is not finite; moreover, it is fairly clear that the notion of "equal likelihood" is not directly applicable. The first of these difficulties can conceivably be overcome by the use of limiting processes. The second is more serious. One thing that can be done is to give up the idea of a priori probability and replace it with one of *statistical* or *empirical* probability. Roughly, one considers a situation in which an experiment has been performed a large number of times under like conditions and the results noted. If the ratio of number of occurrences of a specified event E to number of experiments is p, then one considers the probability that E will occur in the next trial to be p. Thus, if it has been observed that of a representative group of 1000 people aged 50, 30 have died in 1 year, it would be inferred that the probability of a person aged

50 dying within the year would be 30/1000.   This idea of probability can be formulated precisely to serve as the basis of a mathematical theory of probability, but we are not concerned with this fact here.

The conventional modern mathematical theory of probability is founded on a set of axioms.   These axioms state the rules for a basic calculus of probabilities, but do not concern themselves with how the probability of a given event is determined, whether from intuition or from experiment.   Thus the notions of a priori and empirical probability do not enter into the probability theory as such, but they are still necessary to connect the theory to actual problems.   The object in this mode of treatment is to frame a set of definitions and axioms that satisfy the requirements imposed by the intuitive notions of probability, and from these to deduce by rigorous mathematical means the various consequences of the theory.   In this way the mathematician has found it possible to treat the subject as a precise mathematical discipline, and to remove the aura of confusion and vagueness that previously surrounded it.   Our concern in the present text is much less with this process of rigorous deduction, however, than it is with the basic precisely defined notions which make this deduction possible.

The connection of this theory with the real world is much the same as that of any other mathematical theory that attempts to explain physical occurrences.   The theory as such is self-contained and self-consistent; to apply it, however, certain physical assumptions must be made and certain numerical data provided.   Clearly the success of the theory is closely related to the accuracy of these assumptions and data.   Probability theory, as considered here, has nothing to say about the philosophical question of why a well-balanced coin falls heads half the time, on the average.   Instead it accepts this datum, whether physically true or false, as the starting point for computing the probability of two heads in two independent tosses.   The calculus of probabilities is concerned exclusively with the rules and formal manipulative procedures that govern the combination of probabilities, and not at all with philosophical considerations.

2.2   Sets and Set Operations

As a prerequisite for a discussion of probability we need some definitions and some elementary facts concerning sets.   We do not attempt to define the term *set* except by illustration; we regard it as a synonym for *collection* and for *aggregate*.   Thus we may speak of the set of all positive integers, the set of all male citizens in the United States, the set of all straight lines passing through a prescribed point in a plane, or the set of all Ford automobiles manufactured during 1937.   In each such example we see that a set is a collection of certain elements possessing a common property. By means of this property it is always possible to determine whether an arbitrary entity is or is not an element of the set in question. For many purposes it is desirable to study characteristics of sets in general, that is, to consider definitions and properties associated with sets as such, without regard for the nature of their elements. The remainder of this section is devoted to such considerations. It is convenient to represent sets and their elements symbolically in this discussion; in general we use upper-case letters for sets and lower-case letters for elements. As a matter of terminology, we often use the word *point* as synonymous with *element;* this usage is carried over from geometry.

First, a set may be *finite* or *infinite;* that is, it may contain a finite or an infinite number of elements. If an infinite set has the property that (all) its elements can be placed in one-to-one correspondence with the (infinite) set of positive integers, we say it is *countable* or *enumerable.* An example of a countable set is the number of days in eternity; another is the set of all prime integers; another is the set of all rational numbers. An example of a noncountable set is the set of all points on a line segment. Another is the set of all continuous functions of a real variable. Essentially everything which follows in this section applies without distinction to both finite and infinite sets.

The *sum* or *union* of two arbitrary sets A and B, written $A + B$, is defined to be the set of all points contained in either A or B or both. The *product* or *intersection* of sets A and B, written AB, is defined to be the set of all points contained in both A and B. A set A is said to be a *subset* of B, written $A \subset B$, if every point of A is also a point of B. Sets A and B are said to be *equal*, $A = B$, if both $A \subset B$ and $B \subset A$; that is, if they comprise one and the same collection of elements. If $A \subset B$, the *difference* $B - A$ is defined to be the set of all points of B which are not contained in A. The *complement* A^* of a set A, with respect to a reference set $\mathfrak{S}$ which contains A, is defined by $A^* = \mathfrak{S} - A$. The *empty set* or *null set*, denoted by the symbol O, is the set which contains no elements. By convention the empty set is defined to be a subset of every set. Two sets A and B are said to be *disjoint* or *nonoverlapping* if $AB = O$, that is, if they have no common points.

Example 2.2-1. Let A = the set consisting of all men, B = the set consisting of all men and women who smoke, and $\mathfrak{S}$ = the set of all men and women. Then the set $A + B$ consists of all men, and all women who smoke; the set AB consists of all men who smoke; A^* with respect to $\mathfrak{S}$ (or $\mathfrak{S} - A$) consists of all women; B^* consists of all adults who do not smoke; $A - AB$ consists of all men who do not smoke.

For further work we need some elementary properties of the operations which have been defined above. For any sets A, B, C:

$$(A + B) + C = A + (B + C) \tag{2.2-1}$$
$$A + B = B + A \tag{2.2-2}$$
$$(AB)C = A(BC) \tag{2.2-3}$$
$$AB = BA \tag{2.2-4}$$
$$A(B + C) = AB + AC \tag{2.2-5}$$

All these properties may be proved immediately from the definitions.

To prove (2.2-1), we need show that $(A + B) + C \subset A + (B + C)$ and that $A + (B + C) \subset (A + B) + C$. The set $(A + B) + C$ is that which contains all elements belonging to the set $A + B$, to the set C, or to both. If x is any element of $(A + B) + C$, it must belong to C or to $A + B$, and hence must belong to at least one of the sets A, B, or C. This implies, however, that x belongs to either A or $(B + C)$ or both, and hence to $A + (B + C)$. We have thus shown that every element x contained in $(A + B) + C$ is also a member of $A + (B + C)$; in other words $(A + B) + C \subset A + (B + C)$. The relation $A + (B + C) \subset (A + B) + C$ can be established in like manner, and (2.2-1) is thus proved. The remaining relations (2.2-2) to (2.2-5) can be proved by similar reasoning.

Either of the expressions $(A + B) + C$ or $A + (B + C)$ stands for the set of all points belonging to one or more of the sets A, B, and C. Similarly, the expressions $(AB)C$ and $A(BC)$ both stand for the set of points common to A, B, and C. Because these properties hold it makes sense to talk about sums and products of an arbitrary number of sets; thus we may write $A + B + C$ and ABC without ambiguity. In fact, we even need infinite sums and products. If $\{A_i\}$ designates an infinite sequence of sets of which A_i is the ith member, then the *infinite sum* $A_1 + A_2 + A_3 + \cdots$ or ΣA_i is the set consisting of all elements which belong to any A_i, and the *infinite product* $A_1 A_2 A_3 \ldots$ or ΠA_i is the set consisting of all elements which belong to every A_i.

Example 2.2-2. As a second example of set operations, consider the set E of all possible outcomes of four successive throws of a single die. The set A_1 of all outcomes on which the first throw yields a three is a subset of E: $A_1 \subset E$. The set A of all outcomes in which any die gives a three is given by $A = A_1 + A_2 + A_3 + A_4$, where A_2, A_3, A_4 are the respective sets "three on second throw," "three on third throw," "three on fourth throw." The set "no threes appear" is the complement A^* of A. The set "two or more threes appear" is given by $A_1 A_2 + A_1 A_3 + A_1 A_4 + A_2 A_3 + A_2 A_4 + A_3 A_4$. Finally, the set "a three appears, but not on the first throw" is given by $A - A_1$. Note that $A - A_1$ and $A_2 + A_3 + A_4$ stand for somewhat different sets; in some respects the formal operations which we have defined for sets do not follow the laws of "elementary algebra." As a trivial example of this, $A + A = A$, for any set A.

For purposes of a further example, we require an auxiliary formula. Let X and Y be any two finite sets. Then the sets XY, $X - XY$, and $Y - XY$ are nonoverlapping, and

$$X + Y = (X - XY) + (Y - XY) + XY$$

For any finite set E, let $N(E)$ denote the number of elements in E. Since the terms on the right-hand side of this relation represent disjoint sets,

$$N(X + Y) = N(X - XY) + N(Y - XY) + N(XY) \quad (2.2\text{-}6)$$

However, since XY and $X - XY$ are disjoint and their sum is X, $N(XY) + N(X - XY) = N(X)$, giving

$$N(X - XY) = N(X) - N(XY)$$

Similarly
$$N(Y - XY) = N(Y) - N(XY)$$

Substitution of these results into (2.2-6) yields

$$N(X + Y) = N(X) + N(Y) - N(XY) \quad (2.2\text{-}7)$$

For three sets X, Y, and Z, we find by means of (2.2-7)

$$\begin{aligned}
N(X + Y + Z) &= N[X + (Y + Z)] \\
&= N(X) + N(Y + Z) - N(XY + XZ) \\
&= N(X) + [N(Y) + N(Z) - N(YZ)] \\
&\quad - [N(XY) + N(XZ) - N(XYZ)] \\
&= N(X) + N(Y) + N(Z) - N(XY) \\
&\quad - N(YZ) - N(XZ) + N(XYZ) \quad (2.2\text{-}8)
\end{aligned}$$

Example 2.2-3. As a somewhat more elaborate illustration of set operations, we consider the following problem. In a recent economic survey of 1000 male residents of a small town, it was reported that 579 earned less than \$3500 per year and that of these 502 were married. A total of 653 reported spending more than they earned, 317 were married and had incomes over \$3500, 217 had incomes over \$3500 and spent less than they earned, 382 were married and spent more than they earned, and 101 were single with incomes over \$3500 and spent more than they earned. Were these data mutually consistent?

To study this problem, let

M = the set of all males surveyed
A = the set of those who were married
B = the set of those earning more than \$3500
C = the set of those spending more than they earned

Let the complement A^* of A be referred to M; that is, $A^* = M - A$, with similar expressions for B^* and C^*. Considering our statements in order, we find that

$$\begin{array}{lll}
N(M) = 1000 & N(B^*) = 579 & N(AB^*) = 502 \\
N(C) = 653 & N(AB) = 317 & N(BC^*) = 217 \\
N(AC) = 382 & N(A^*BC) = 101 &
\end{array}$$

Since
$$A + B + C \subset M$$

we must have

$$N(A + B + C) \leq N(M) = 1000$$

To compute $N(A + B + C)$, using (2.2-8), we first require values for $N(A)$, $N(B)$, $N(BC)$, and $N(ABC)$ in addition to those specified above. We note that B and B^* are disjoint and $B + B^* = M$. Hence $N(B) + N(B^*) = N(M)$, or

$$N(B) = N(M) - N(B^*) = 1000 - 579 = 421$$

Also AB and AB^* are disjoint, $AB + AB^* = A(B + B^*) = AM = A$, whence

$$N(A) = N(AB) + N(AB^*) = 317 + 502 = 819$$

Similarly the sets BC and BC^* are disjoint, $BC + BC^* = B$, and

$$N(BC) = N(B) - N(BC^*) = 421 - 217 = 204$$

Finally, ABC and A^*BC are disjoint, $ABC + A^*BC = BC$, whence

$$N(ABC) = N(BC) - N(A^*BC) = 204 - 101 = 103$$

Combining these results, the relation (2.2-8) yields

$$N(A + B + C) = N(A) + N(B) + N(C) - N(AB) - N(BC) - N(AC) + N(ABC)$$
$$= 819 + 421 + 653 - 317 - 204 - 382 + 103 = 1093$$

According to this calculation, the set $A + B + C$ contains more elements than the total number of people surveyed; the data must therefore be in error. This calculation not only illustrates the use of certain set operations, but also gives a concrete example of ways in which set theoretic concepts can be used in guiding and clarifying complex thought processes.

For certain mathematical purposes the notion of a *class* of sets is useful. Consider, for example, the set M of all real numbers; a class of subsets of M is simply any collection of sets, each of which belongs to M. Thus we speak of the class $\mathfrak{S}$ of intervals belonging to M. Each interval of M is an element of $\mathfrak{S}$. Similarly, we may speak of the class $\mathfrak{R}$ of all sets of rational numbers, or the class $\mathfrak{F}$ of all finite subsets of M. In the first instance each point or element of $\mathfrak{R}$ is itself a set consisting of rational numbers; similarly, each point of $\mathfrak{F}$ is some finite set of points of M. For any set E, a trivial example of a class of sets is that comprising all subsets of E; a second is that comprising all sets that contain only one element of E. In each such illustration a class or aggregate of sets is a collection whose individual elements are themselves sets.

2.3   Point Functions and Set Functions

The notion of a function, as considered in elementary calculus, is one that can be generalized quite considerably. The essence of this concept is that of a correspondence from one set of numbers to another or of a dependence of one quantity upon another. Thus when we speak of the function $f(x)$ we imply that to each real number x for which $f(x)$ is defined there corresponds a number f depending upon x. If $f(x) = \sin x$, then to the number $x = 0$ corresponds $f = 0$, to $x = \pi/4$ corresponds $f = \sqrt{2}/2$, to $x = \pi/2$ corresponds $f = 1$, and so on. If $f(x) = 2 + x$, then to $x = 3$ corresponds $f = 5$ and to $x = -1$ corresponds $f = +1$. Alternately, we may consider the function $f(x)$ defined by the following statement: "$f(x)$ is sin x multiplied by the largest one of the sequence of numbers cos πx, cos $2\pi x$, cos $3\pi x$, ..." If x is a rational number then $f(x) = \sin x$; however, if x is irrational, then there is no "largest number" in the above sequence. (For irrational x, there are members of the sequence that lie arbitrarily close to unity, but no member of the sequence which actually equals unity.) Thus $f(x)$ is defined by the above statement only when x is rational, and we may choose to leave $f(x)$ undefined for irrational x. In this case the correspondence is established from a restricted set of numbers (the rational numbers) to a subset of real numbers.

It is convenient in the sequel to extend this notion of a function to include that of a general correspondence from a set of any elements whatever to a set of real numbers. In other words, we let $f(x)$ be a number whose value depends upon the selection of an element x from an arbitrary set S.

Definition. Let S be a set composed of any elements. We say that $f(x)$ is a real-valued *function* (or *point function*) defined over the set S, provided that to every point (element) x belonging to S there is assigned a corresponding real number denoted by $f(x)$.

Example 2.3-1. In a game of matching pennies, with two participants, let player A win if a match is obtained. Let S be the set of four possible outcomes (HH, HT, TH, TT). Then the gain to player A is a function $g(x)$ defined over S. Thus if x is the point HH, we may assign the value $+1$ to g. Similarly $g(HT) = g(TH) = -1$, and $g(TT) = +1$.

Example 2.3-2. Let S be the set of all people. With each point x of S (with each person) we may associate a number $a(x)$ representing the age of x in years. Thus $a(x)$ is a function defined over the set S. Two or more functions may often be considered simultaneously; for example, we may let $h(x)$ be the height of x in feet and $w(x)$ his weight in pounds. In a later section we shall consider the notion of expected or average value of a function such as $w(x)$, defined in terms of a suitable averaging process over all points x.

Example 2.3-3. It is often useful to construct certain functions artificially. In the above example let B be the subset of S consisting of all blue-eyed people. We then define a function $C_B(x)$ to equal $+1$ whenever x belongs to B and zero whenever x does not belong to B. In other words, to each blue-eyed person we arbitrarily assign the number $+1$ and to all others we assign the number 0. The function constructed in this way is called the *characteristic function* of B. For any set S and any subset E belonging to S, we define the characteristic function $C_E(x)$ to be that which takes on the respective values 1 or 0 for x in E or not in E.

An arbitrary function $f(x)$ can be approximated as closely as we please by a series involving characteristic functions. Let d be some small number, and for all positive and negative integers n let S_n be the set for which $nd \leqq f(x) < (n + 1)d$. The sets

S_n are disjoint; furthermore on S_n the difference between $f(x)$ and the number nd is no more than d.   A little reflection then shows that the function

$$f_1(x) = \sum_{n=-\infty}^{\infty} (nd) C_{S_n}(x) \qquad (2.3\text{-}1)$$

can differ from $f(x)$ by no more than d at any point of S.   By choosing d sufficiently small, we may thereby obtain an arbitrarily close approximation to $f(x)$.

Example 2.3-4.   Let R be the set of all intervals I of the form $I = (a < x < b)$, where a and b are real numbers with $a < b$.   To each such interval we attach the number $L(I)$ equal to its length; that is, $L(I) = b - a$.   Then $L(I)$ is a function defined over the set R of all open intervals.

Example 2.3-5.   Let S be the collection of all continuous functions $x(t)$.   To each such function we attach the number $f(x) = \int_0^1 x(t)^2 \, dt$.   Then $f(x)$ is a function defined over the set S.   Similarly the quantity $g(x) = x(0) + x(2)$ is a function over S.   In each case, the selection of an element of S [that is, the specification of a particular continuous function $x(t)$] determines corresponding values of f and g.   Here we have an application of the notion of a function in which the *independent variable* is itself a function (of t) in the ordinary sense.   Examples of this type occur quite frequently in our later work since it is necessary to study the properties of random functions of time in relation to characteristics of a set or ensemble of such functions.

In Example 2.3-4, the set R is chosen to be a collection of intervals I, and the *independent variable* in the function $L(I)$ is itself a set of real numbers.   In this case a correspondence is established between a class of sets (intervals) and real numbers.   Although this notion falls within the range of our extended definition of a function, we prefer to assign a special term to this type of function.

Definition.   Let E be an arbitrary set, and let $\Re$ be a class of subsets of E.   To each set A of the class $\Re$ let there be assigned a real number $F(A)$.   Then $F(A)$ is called a *set function* defined over the class $\Re$.

As an example of a set function, let a collection of 1-gram masses be placed at the points $x = 1, 2, 3, \ldots$ of the real axis.   Let E be the set of all positive real numbers and let the class $\Re$ consist of all subsets of E.   Then to each set A of positive real numbers we assign the number $m(A)$ which is the total (finite or infinite) mass contained in the points of A.

As another example, let E and $\Re$ again be the set of all real numbers and the class of all open intervals.   Let a continuous point function $f(x)$ be defined for $-\infty < x < \infty$.   Then to each interval A of $\Re$ we assign the number

$$F(A) = \int_A f(x) \, dx$$

Then $F(A)$ is a set function defined over the class $\Re$ of subsets of E.

As a further example of a set function, let the set E be a countable sequence $(x_1, x_2, \ldots)$ of arbitrary elements x_j.   To each such element

x_j let a positive number p_j be attached, such that

$$\sum_{j=1}^{\infty} p_j = 1$$

Let $\mathfrak{R}$ be the class of all subsets of E. For any subset A we set

$$P(A) = \Sigma p_j$$

where the summation is over all values of j for which x_j is in set A.

A final example of a set function is provided by the function $N(E)$ of Sec. 2.2, which assigns to each finite set E a number $N(E)$ equal to the number of elements contained in E.

2.4 Axioms of Probability

In the consideration of an experiment with an outcome depending upon chance, a fundamental set of elements is that consisting of all possible distinct outcomes of the experiment. We call this set the *sample space* for the experiment, using the term *space* as a synonym for the word *set* in this connection. The individual elements or points of the sample space are often called *sample points*.

The definition of a suitable sample space for an experiment is often not a simple question, and may depend in part upon the point of view adopted. In a complicated game of chance, for instance, the fundamental outcomes or sample points may each consist of a detailed description of one possible sequence of occurrences throughout the play. On the other hand, from the standpoint of a single player in the game, a very important sample space is the collection of real numbers representing his various possible winnings or losses. It may be necessary to refer to the first of these sample spaces in order to analyze the properties of the second; however, there may be a freedom of choice that depends upon the nature of the information desired. Thus the selection of a particular sample space for study is often a matter of convenience and the choice is seldom unique.

Considering further a game of chance, we shall be interested in what follows in assigning or analyzing probabilities associated with such statements as: "Player A wins more than \$2," "Player B draws two or more kings," "The sum of spots on two dice is seven," and so on. In a given experiment or game, there may be many different possible ways in which one of these statements can be realized. Thus with any such statement there generally may be associated a set E of fundamental outcomes or sample points such that the statement is true if and only if the outcome of the experiment is a sample point in the set E.

In the third case cited, the sample space may consist of all pairs of numbers (m,n), where m and n are integers in the range from one to six inclusive. To the statement "sum of spots is seven" corresponds the set of sample points $(1,6)$, $(2,5)$, . . . , $(6,1)$, which represent the various ways in which a sum of seven can be attained. Similarly in the deal of a single bridge hand, the sample space may consist of the collection of all possible 13-card hands. To the statement "the hand contains three honor tricks" corresponds the subset of the sample space consisting of all points (hands) possessing the stated property. We thus have frequent cause to associate with a given statement about the result of a random experiment the set of sample points for which the statement is valid. This becomes particularly important when the statement is of a complex character, and we have seen previously that the algebra of sets is often a powerful aid in resolving complex propositions into simpler components.

To place these matters on a more formal basis, let E be a subset of a suitable sample space $\mathfrak{S}$, and let x be an arbitrary point in $\mathfrak{S}$. We say that the *event* "x in E" or more concisely "*the event E*" occurs, on a given trial of the experiment, provided that the outcome x belongs to the set E on that trial. Each element in the sample space is called a *simple event*. Collections of simple events are subsets of the sample space and are called *compound events*. Note that to each element of a set there corresponds a subset consisting of that element alone, so that all events, simple and compound, may be regarded as subsets of the sample space. If the sample space is a finite or a countable set, we refer to it as a *discrete sample space*. It will transpire that many probability notions lose much of their technical difficulty when referred to discrete spaces, and discrete spaces will often be used to furnish examples. However, because of their practical importance, we cannot disregard sample spaces which are not discrete.

Returning to the experiment mentioned above, let $\mathfrak{S}$ represent the sample space of all possible outcomes. Assuming that the experiment is performed a large number of times N, then for any event A let n_A be the number of occurrences of A in the N trials and define

$$p_A = \frac{n_A}{N}$$

Clearly $0 \leqq n_A \leqq N$, so that $0 \leqq p_A \leqq 1$. Furthermore, let us assume that p_A tends to a limit as N becomes infinite. This limit, which we shall denote by $P(A)$, is a nonnegative real number and is defined for all sets of the sample space $\mathfrak{S}$. Thus $P(A)$ possesses the properties required of a set function and is called a *probability function* of $\mathfrak{S}$.

The function $P(A)$ must possess certain basic properties which are consistent with our intuitive notions of probability. For example, since every trial of the experiment must yield some outcome which belongs to

$\mathfrak{S}$, we have

$$n_O = 0 \qquad n_\mathfrak{S} = N$$

where n_O and $n_\mathfrak{S}$, respectively, represent the number of times the outcome belongs to the empty set O and to $\mathfrak{S}$. Thus, we find

$$p_O = 0 \qquad p_\mathfrak{S} = 1$$

and, in the limit

$$P(O) = 0 \qquad P(\mathfrak{S}) = 1$$

Furthermore, if A and B are mutually exclusive, i.e., disjoint, events, the number of occurrences of either the event A or the event B is the number of occurrences of A plus the number of occurrences of B. In symbols,

$$n_{(A+B)} = n_A + n_B$$

and thus

$$p_{(A+B)} = p_A + p_B$$

In the limit we find

$$P(A + B) = P(A) + P(B) \tag{2.4-1}$$

By induction, we may readily use the result (2.4-1) to show that for any finite collection of disjoint sets $A_1, A_2, \ldots, A_n$ we have

$$P(A_1 + A_2 + \cdots + A_n) = P(A_1) + P(A_2) + \cdots + P(A_n) \tag{2.4-2}$$

We now consider some examples. The first three are simple finite problems, but they illustrate the ideas presented above.

Example 2.4-1. One card is drawn from a bridge deck. The sample space $\mathfrak{S}$ contains 52 elements or simple events; each simple event is the drawing of a specified card. The probability function is defined by the statement that the probability of drawing any one card is $1/52$, and here, as in all finite problems, the probability function is defined on the class of all subsets of $\mathfrak{S}$. Let A = the compound event of drawing an ace. Let A_h = the event of drawing the ace of hearts, A_s, the ace of spades, etc. Then the probability of drawing an ace is given by

$$P(A) = P(A_c + A_d + A_h + A_s) = P(A_c) + P(A_d) + P(A_h) + P(A_s) = 4/52$$

Also the probability of drawing the ace of hearts and the ace of spades (on a single draw) is given by

$$P(A_h A_s) = P(O) = 0$$

Example 2.4-2. A coin is tossed four times. A simple event is a prescribed succession of heads and tails, as $HHTH$. There are $2^4 = 16$ simple events, and the probability of each is taken to be $1/16$. This defines the probability function. Then, for example, the probability of getting three heads, event A, is

$$P(A) = P(HHHT) + P(HHTH) + P(HTHH) + P(THHH) = 4/16 = \tfrac{1}{4}$$

Example 2.4-3. Two indistinguishable dice are rolled. A simple event is a prescribed sum of dots appearing on a single throw. The probability function is defined by the following probabilities of simple events: $P(2) = 1/36$, $P(3) = 2/36$, $P(4) = 3/36$, $P(5) = 4/36$, $P(6) = 5/36$, $P(7) = 6/36$, $P(8) = 5/36$, etc. It is clear even in this simple example that the notion of simple event is somewhat arbitrary, because here obviously a larger sample space could have been defined (using dice which were distinguishable) in which each simple event would have been equally likely.

Example 2.4-4. The tracking inaccuracy of a radar unit is observed over a time interval $t_1 \leq t \leq t_2$. A simple event is a real-valued function of time $f(t)$ defined over this interval. The sample space consists of all real-valued continuous functions. (This is only approximately true; some further restrictions on the functions are necessary if they are to represent realizable tracking errors.) The question as to how the probability function is defined cannot be answered yet; however, when the probability function for this type of problem is discussed, it will be found that the probability of any one tracking inaccuracy function is zero. This fact may be disturbing because although each simple event has probability zero, no one of them is impossible. However, in any uncountably infinite sample space (of which this example gives one) most of the simple events must have probability zero in order for the probability of the whole to be finite. A typical compound event A in this example might be represented by the relation

$$\int_{t_1}^{t_2} f(t)^2 \, dt \leq 2$$

In other words, every $f(t)$ satisfying this inequality would belong to the set A, and one could speak of the probability of this event.

In many problems it is found to be convenient to consider a countably infinite sequence of mutually exclusive events in place of a finite sequence. Our intuition suggests that the additive property, expressed by the relation (2.4-2), should hold when n is infinite. We simply postulate this condition rather than attempt any proof.

As an illustration, in a later study of the "shot effect" we shall have occasion to discuss the events E_0, E_1, E_2, . . . , where E_k is the event "exactly k electrons arrive at the anode of a vacuum tube during a stated time interval." Let A be the event "the output of the tube at time t exceeds 10 volts." The event $E_k A$ is expressed by the statement "exactly k electrons arrive at the anode during the prescribed interval, and also the tube output exceeds 10 volts at time t." The events $E_0 A$, $E_1 A$, $E_2 A$, . . . are mutually exclusive, and

$$A = E_0 A + E_1 A + E_2 A + \cdots$$

It is important that we be able to write a relation of this form without inquiry into the question of whether the event A defined by this infinite sum is an event of a type which we are considering. It is further important that we should be able to write with confidence the equation

$$P(A) = P(E_0 A) + P(E_1 A) + P(E_2 A) + \cdots$$

As a matter of fact we should suffer considerably if we were forced to terminate this series with a finite number of terms, since in the application given it happens to converge to a relatively simple closed expression.

It is important to realize that the relation (2.4-2) holds only when the events involved are all mutually exclusive. The expansion must be modified if the events are not disjoint. For example, let A and B be any two events, mutually exclusive or otherwise. We wish to calculate the probability $P(A + B)$ that one or the other of these events takes place. Since the events $A - AB$, AB, and $B - AB$ are mutually exclusive, and since

$$A + B = (A - AB) + AB + (B - AB)$$

we have

$$P(A + B) = P(A - AB) + P(AB) + P(B - AB) \qquad (2.4\text{-}3)$$

Also, since

$$(A - AB) + AB = A$$

we find

$$P(A) = P(A - AB) + P(AB) \qquad (2.4\text{-}4)$$

and similarly

$$P(B) = P(B - AB) + P(AB) \qquad (2.4\text{-}5)$$

Solving (2.4-4) and (2.4-5) for $P(A - AB)$ and $P(B - AB)$, respectively we find upon substitution into (2.4-3) the simplified relation

$$P(A + B) = P(A) + P(B) - P(AB) \qquad (2.4\text{-}6)$$

It will be noted that this derivation parallels quite closely that given in Sec. 2.2 for $N(A + B)$, the number of elements in $A + B$.

As an illustration, we compute the probability of obtaining one or more threes in the throw of two dice. Let A be the event "three on the first throw" and B the event "three on the second throw." Then $P(A) = P(B) = 1/6$. The event AB is "three on both throws," and $P(AB) = 1/36$. The event "one or more threes" is $A + B$. Thus the probability in question is

$$P(A + B) = \tfrac{1}{6} + \tfrac{1}{6} - \tfrac{1}{36} = \tfrac{11}{36}$$

The relation (2.4-6) can readily be extended to the sum of three or more sets; we leave this as an exercise.

The basic postulates, which form the foundation of the theory of probability, consist mainly of a formal statement of the intuitive ideas presented above. Before presenting these postulates, however, it is necessary to introduce the concept of an *additive class of sets*.

Definition. A class $\mathfrak{A}$ of subsets of a set M is called an *additive class of sets*, provided that the following conditions are met:

1. The empty set O belongs to $\mathfrak{A}$.
2. If E belongs to $\mathfrak{A}$ then the complement $E^* = M - E$ also belongs to $\mathfrak{A}$.
3. If each set E_n of a finite or countably infinite sequence of subsets $E_1, E_2, E_3, \ldots$, of M belongs to $\mathfrak{A}$, then the sum ΣE_n also belongs to $\mathfrak{A}$.

These conditions are sufficient to ensure that each finite or countably infinite algebraic combination of sets of the class $\mathfrak{A}$ is also a member of $\mathfrak{A}$. In our subsequent discussions of probability we shall require (usually implicitly) that all events (sets) under consideration shall belong to a suitable additive class of sets. The purpose in this is the purely mathematical one of providing a guarantee that all compound events that we may form are included in the class of events considered.

If now there is defined a nonnegative set function over a class of subsets of the sample space $\mathfrak{S}$ which satisfies the axioms to be listed below we call it a *probability function*. We define the probability of an event to be the value taken on by the probability function for the subset corresponding to this event. The conditions the probability function P must satisfy are as follows:

1. P must be defined on a class $\mathfrak{F}$ of subsets of $\mathfrak{S}$ which is an additive class.

2. P must be nonnegative, $P(O) = 0$, $P(\mathfrak{S}) = 1$.

3. If $\{A_i\}$ is any sequence of disjoint sets belonging to $\mathfrak{F}$, then

$$P(\Sigma A_i) = \Sigma P(A_i)$$

The basic postulates for a probability function go somewhat beyond the requirements that are encountered in most applications; however, we state them in this form so as to permit all further considerations to be freed from questions of the existence of various compound events and their probabilities. In requiring the definition of P over an additive class of subsets of $\mathfrak{S}$, we are simply stating that if probability is defined for a sequence of events E_1, E_2, E_3, . . . then it is also defined for any events formed from these by a finite or infinite sequence of steps.

As has been mentioned before, the theory starts with the existence of the probability function P. The determination of P for use in an actual problem requires separate considerations, which may themselves require mathematical techniques.

2.5 Independence of Events and Conditional Probability

Consider two events E_1 with probability p_1 and E_2 with probability p_2. What probability should be attached to the event that both E_1 and E_2 occur simultaneously? An answer to this question cannot be given without specifying further information, since the number $P(E_1 E_2)$ can, in a general case, take on any value between zero and the smaller of the numbers p_1 or p_2. A complete answer can be given, however, in the case in which E_1 and E_2 are "independent" events. Intuitively, we would expect two events to be independent if the occurrence or nonoccurrence of one is not affected by the occurrence or nonoccurrence of the other. This is not, of course, a precise statement, but the mathematical definition of independence, which shall be given presently, must be compatible with this intuitive notion if it is to be a useful concept.   Let us consider a few examples of independent events and their associated probabilities.

Example 2.5-1.   Two cards are chosen at random from a deck of playing cards. Let E_1 be the event that the first card drawn is an ace, and E_2 the event that the second card is an ace.   If the first card is replaced and the deck thoroughly shuffled before the second drawing takes place, the events E_1 and E_2 are independent.   However, if the first card is retained, the events are not independent because a knowledge of the outcome of the first drawing (the occurrence or nonoccurrence of E_1) has a very definite bearing on the outcome of the second drawing (the occurrence or nonoccurrence of E_2).

For the case in which E_1 and E_2 are independent, the appropriate sample space $\mathfrak{S}$ is the set of all pairs of cards (x,y), where x and y range independently over all cards of the deck (and may be equal).   The space $\mathfrak{S}$ thus contains a total of 52×52 points, and we assign equal probability to each of these.   The event E_1 is the set of all pairs of the form (a,y), with $a = $ ace and y arbitrary.   Similarly the event E_2 is the set of all pairs (x,a), with x arbitrary.   We note that E_1 contains 4×52 elements, as does E_2, and that the event E_1E_2 consisting of an ace on both draws contains 4×4 elements.   Then

$$P(E_1) = p_1 = \frac{4 \times 52}{52 \times 52} = \frac{1}{13}$$

$$P(E_2) = p_2 = \frac{4 \times 52}{52 \times 52} = \frac{1}{13}$$

and $$P(E_1E_2) = \text{Pr } (E_1 \text{ and } E_2 \text{ both occur})\dagger = \frac{4 \times 4}{52 \times 52} = p_1p_2$$

As a matter of fact this multiplication of probabilities holds in general whenever the events involved are independent.   To see this, we refer to the empirical notion of probability.   In a large number N of trials of a given experiment, let n_A be the number of occurrences of event A, n_B the number of occurrences of event B, and n_{AB} the number of occurrences in which both A and B take place.   The probability of occurrence of A is the limiting value of the ratio $p_A = n_A/N$; similarly, the probability of B is the limit of $p_B = n_B/N$.   We now temporarily confine our attention to those outcomes and only those in which event A takes place. If A and B are independent, then from this number of outcomes we may expect B to occur with an approximate relative frequency $p_B = n_B/N$. In other words, we may expect the number n_{AB} of joint occurrences of A and B to be in about the same ratio to the number n_A of occurrences of A as n_B is to the total number of trials N.   In symbols,

$$\frac{n_{AB}}{n_A} \cong \frac{n_B}{N} \quad \text{or} \quad \frac{p_{AB}}{p_A} \cong p_B$$

Taking the limit as the number N of trials becomes infinite, we obtain

$$P(AB) = \text{Pr } (A \text{ and } B) = P(A)P(B)$$

giving the multiplicative property as asserted.

† Here and elsewhere in this text we often use Pr to denote the probability of the statement or event indicated by the parentheses which follow.

For the special case in which E_1 and E_2 are events corresponding to two independent experiments, each of which possesses a finite number of equally likely outcomes, the product relation can be viewed in a different manner, as in Example 2.5-1. Let the first experiment possess n_1 different possible outcomes, of which s_1 give rise to the event E_1, with a similar notation for the second experiment. The sample space $\mathfrak{S}$ is again the set of all pairs of possible outcomes. Then the joint occurrence of E_1 and E_2 can take place in $s_1 s_2$ different ways, giving as before

$$\Pr\ (E_1 \text{ and } E_2) = \frac{s_1 s_2}{n_1 n_2} = \frac{s_1}{n_1}\frac{s_2}{n_2} = p_1 p_2 \qquad (2.5\text{-}1)$$

Example 2.5-2. The event E_1, tossing heads with a coin, and the event E_2, rolling a six with a die, are independent. The sample space consists of all possible outcomes of a single toss of a coin together with a single roll of a die. Each of these events is equally likely to occur and there are twelve in all. Thus, the probability of the simultaneous occurrence of the compound event $(E_1$ and $E_2)$ is $1/12$. Furthermore, it is clear that $p_1 = 1/2$ and $p_2 = 1/6$ so that again Eq. (2.5-1) is satisfied.

Example 2.5-3. A person is selected at random from a certain population. Let E_1 be the event that the person selected is male and let E_2 be the event that this person is a smoker. If it is known that precisely half of the population as well as half of the smokers is male, then the events E_1 and E_2 are independent. A knowledge of whether or not E_1 has occurred allows no inference to be drawn as to whether or not E_2 has also occurred. However, if there are twice as many men who smoke as women, then a knowledge that E_1 has occurred greatly increases the likelihood that E_2 has also occurred. Again, considering the case of independent events, let us suppose that half the population smokes. Then $p_1 = 1/2$ and $p_2 = 1/2$. The number of male smokers constitutes one-fourth of the entire population so that again we have Eq. (2.5-1) holding true.

From the examples it would seem that if events conform to the intuitive notion of independence, then the probability of their simultaneous occurrence is found by multiplying their individual probabilities of occurrence. We therefore formalize this concept by the following definition.

Definition. Two events E_1 and E_2 are said to be independent if and only if

$$\Pr\ (E_1 \text{ and } E_2) = \Pr\ (E_1)\ \Pr\ (E_2) \qquad (2.5\text{-}2)$$

If we wish to extend this definition to more than two events, it would seem, at first, that two possibilities present themselves. In the case of three events we might require

$$\Pr\ (E_i \text{ and } E_j) = \Pr\ (E_i)\ \Pr\ (E_j) \qquad i \neq j;\, i, j = 1, 2, 3 \quad (2.5\text{-}3)$$

to be satisfied if and only if E_1, E_2, and E_3 are to be independent. However, there are examples to show that the requirement of pairwise independence is not sufficient to satisfy the basic intuitive requirement of independence when more than two events are involved. The other alternative which might be considered is to require

$$\Pr\ (E_1 \text{ and } E_2 \text{ and } E_3) = \Pr\ (E_1)\ \Pr\ (E_2)\ \Pr\ (E_3) \qquad (2.5\text{-}4)$$

to be satisfied if and only if E_1, E_2, and E_3 are to be independent.   However, there is a serious objection to taking Eq. (2.5-4) as the complete definition of independence.   Intuitively, one would expect that if three events are independent then any two of them are also independent. Unfortunately, no such conclusion may be drawn from Eq. (2.5-4) alone. Therefore, in the case of three events, the requirements of both equations (2.5-3) and (2.5-4) shall be taken as the definition of independence.   In general we formulate the following definition.

Definition.   The events E_1, E_2, . . . , E_n are said to be independent if and only if the following $2^n - n - 1$ equations are satisfied:

$$\Pr\ (E_{i_1} \text{ and } E_{i_2} \text{ and } \ldots \text{ and } E_{i_m}) = \Pr\ (E_{i_1})\ \Pr\ (E_{i_2}) \cdots \Pr\ (E_{i_m})$$
$$(2.5\text{-}5)$$

where
$$m = 2, 3, \ldots, n$$
$$1 \leqq i_1 < i_2 < \cdots < i_m \leqq n$$

Example 2.5-4.   A ball is chosen at random from each of three boxes.   Box 1 contains one black and three white balls, box 2 contains two black and two white, and box 3 contains three black and one white.   What is the probability that the first and third balls will both be black?   What is the probability that all three balls will be black?

Let E_i ($i = 1, 2, 3$) be the event "black ball from box i and anything at all from the other two," and write $p_i = P(E_i)$.   Then $p_1 = 1/4$, $p_2 = 1/2$, and $p_3 = 3/4$. The events E_1, E_2, and E_3 are independent; therefore, the probability of black on the first and third draws is $p_1 p_3 = 3/16$.   Similarly, the probability of black on all three draws is $p_1 p_2 p_3 = 3/32$.

Let E_1, E_2, . . . , E_n be independent events according to the above definition.   If our intuitive ideas are correct, then we should be able to prove several consequences of the definition.   In the first place, if the occurrence of E_1 has no effect on E_2, . . . , E_n then the nonoccurrence of E_1 should also have no effect on the remaining events.   In other words, the events E_1^*, E_2, . . . , E_n should be independent.   More generally, the set of events formed by replacing any or all of the events E_1, . . . , E_n by their complements should be a set of independent events.   As a further proposition, let F be some compound event formed, say, from E_1, E_2, . . . , E_m and G be an event formed from E_{m+1}, . . . , E_n.   If the occurrence of no one of the events E_1 to E_m has any effect on the occurrence of the events E_{m+1} to E_n, then we should expect the occurrence of F to have no effect on the occurrence of G; in other words, F and G should be independent.   The proof of these matters is not difficult but is somewhat involved and is not included here.

In the case of events which are to some extent interdependent, the notion of conditional probability is often useful. Before defining this concept precisely, we consider a few examples.

Example 2.5-5. Consider the experiment of tossing a coin four times. Let the event E_1 be the compound event of obtaining exactly three heads and let the event E_2 be the event of obtaining a head on the first toss and anything on the three remaining tosses. Then if E_2 occurs, the probability of the occurrence of E_1 is certainly altered and in fact E_1 will be much more likely to occur. The experiment can result in sixteen different outcomes, four of which belong to the event E_1. If the event E_2 is known to have occurred, then there are only eight different possible outcomes of the experiment, three of which belong to the event E_1. Thus, the probability that E_1 will occur, with no hypothesis as to the occurrence of E_2, is $1/4$ while the probability that E_1 will occur, if it is known that E_2 has occurred, is $3/8$.

Consider again the random sampling described in Example 2.5-3. Suppose that the population consists of N people, n_M of which are males and n_S of which are smokers. Then from the a priori concept of probability and random choice we have

$$\Pr(E_1) = \frac{n_M}{N} \qquad \Pr(E_2) = \frac{n_S}{N} \qquad (2.5\text{-}6)$$

Now suppose that we require the probability that a man chosen at random should smoke. This probability is n_{MS}/n_M, where n_{MS} is the number of male smokers, and may be described by the phrase "the conditional probability of E_2 subject to the hypothesis E_1." The symbol that we use to denote this probability is $\Pr(E_2 \mid E_1)$ or simply $P(E_2 \mid E_1)$. Thus in this case

$$\Pr(E_2 \mid E_1) = \frac{n_{MS}}{n_M} = \frac{\Pr(E_1 \text{ and } E_2)}{\Pr(E_1)} \qquad (2.5\text{-}7)$$

and suggests the following definition.

Definition. If E_1 is an event of nonzero probability, then the *conditional probability* of E_2, subject to the hypothesis that E_1 has occurred, is given by

$$\Pr(E_2 \mid E_1) = \frac{\Pr(E_1 \text{ and } E_2)}{\Pr(E_1)} \qquad (2.5\text{-}8)$$

Equation (2.5-8) can be applied directly in the solution of the problem discussed in Example 2.5-5. The event (E_1 and E_2) is composed of three of the sixteen points in the sample space, while the event E_2 consists of one-half of the total sample points. Therefore

$$P(E_1 \mid E_2) = \frac{3/16}{1/2} = 3/8$$

which we obtained before.

Example 2.5-6.   Consider again the problem of Example 2.5-1 in which two cards are selected at random.   The probability of drawing two aces in succession from the pack (without replacing the first card drawn) is simply $P(E_1E_2)$.   Now

$$P(E_1) = \tfrac{4}{52} \quad \text{and} \quad P(E_2 \mid E_1) = \tfrac{3}{51}$$

so that from Eq. (2.5-8) we have

$$P(E_1E_2) = P(E_1)P(E_2 \mid E_1) = \tfrac{4}{52} \times \tfrac{3}{51} = \tfrac{1}{221}$$

It should be observed that when E_1 and E_2 are independent events, Eq. (2.5-8) reduces to

$$\Pr\,(E_2 \mid E_1) = \Pr\,(E_2) \tag{2.5-9}$$

which simply states that the probability that E_2 should occur, if it is known that E_1 has occurred, is unaffected by this information.

We conclude this discussion with two results which are frequently useful.   The first is

$$P(E_1E_2 \cdots E_n) = P(E_1)P(E_2 \mid E_1)P(E_3 \mid E_1E_2)$$
$$\cdots P(E_n \mid E_1E_2 \cdots E_{n-1}) \tag{2.5-10}$$

where $P(E_i) > 0$ for all i.   This relation may be proved by successive applications of Eq. (2.5-8).   The second result is obtained by the following argument.   Suppose the events $E_1, E_2, \ldots, E_n$ are mutually exclusive events which exhaust the sample space; that is, $\mathfrak{S} = \Sigma E_i$.   Then the occurrence of any event E is equivalent to the event $EE_1 + EE_2 + \cdots + EE_n$.   Thus by using Eq. (2.5-8) and the fact that the sets EE_j are disjoint, we obtain

$$P(E) = P(E_1)P(E \mid E_1) + P(E_2)P(E \mid E_2) + \cdots + P(E_n)P(E \mid E_n) \tag{2.5-11}$$

This result is clearly valid for a countably infinite sequence $\{E_j\}$ as well.

Example 2.5-7.   A gun fires shells at a target until the first hit is scored.   As a sample space for this experiment we could take the countable set of all finite sequences of the form $(H), (MH), (MMH)$, etc.; to do so, however, might involve difficulties in assigning probabilities to the sample points.   Instead, we choose the larger set of all infinite sequences $(X_1, X_2, X_3, \ldots)$ with $X_i = M$ or H.   Here we have a first example of a nondiscrete sample space.   If we replace M by zero and H by unity, and regard the sequence $(X_1, X_2, \ldots)$ as the binary expansion of a real number between zero and unity, then the sample space $\mathfrak{S}$ is placed by this means in a one-to-one correspondence with the interval $0 \leq u \leq 1$ of real numbers.   Since the latter set is noncountably infinite, so also is the sample space $\mathfrak{S}$.

Let A_k be the event "a hit is scored on round number k."   The elements of A_k are those sequences which possess an H in the kth position, with the letters in the remaining positions arbitrary.   We postulate that the events $A_1, A_2, A_3, \ldots$ are independent, and that $P(A_k) = p$ for each value of the index k.

Let $q = 1 - p$, and assume that neither p nor q is zero.   We may then show that the probability associated with each individual sample point is zero.   For example, let x denote the particular sequence $(HMMHMHH \ . \ . \ .)$. Then the point x is the intersection

$$x = A_1 A_2^* A_3^* A_4 A_5^* A_6 A_7 \ \cdot \ \cdot \ \cdot$$

and by the independence property, $P(x)$ is the infinite product

$$P(x) = pqqpqpp \ \cdot \ \cdot \ \cdot$$

Let r be the greater of the numbers p and q. For every positive integer n, we have

$$P(x) \leqq r^n$$

from which it follows that $P(x)$ must be zero. We thus have an example in which the probability of each individual sample point is zero, and yet certain (nonenumerable) sets of such points have nonzero probability.

Let E_k be the event "the first hit occurs on the kth round." Then E_k is the event "the first, second, . . . , and $(k - 1)$st rounds all miss, and the kth round hits." In symbols:

$$E_k = A_1^* A_2^* \ \cdot \ \cdot \ \cdot \ A_{k-1}^* A_k$$

By virtue of independence, we then have

$$P(E_k) = P(A_1^*) \ \cdot \ \cdot \ \cdot \ P(A_{k-1}^*)P(A_k) = q^{k-1}p$$

Suppose that the first shot fails to score a hit; that is, E_1 does not occur. We desire to calculate the probability, under this hypothesis, of the event E that more than two shots will be required to score a hit. The event EE_1^* is equivalent to the event E alone, so that

$$P(EE_1^*) = P(E) = P(E_3 + E_4 + \ \cdot \ \cdot \ \cdot)$$

Since the events E_k are mutually exclusive, we have

$$P(EE_1^*) = \sum_{k=3}^{\infty} P(E_k) = p(q^2 + q^3 + q^4 + \ \cdot \ \cdot \ \cdot) = \frac{pq^2}{1 - q} = q^2$$

since $p = 1 - q$. Also, $P(E_1^*) = 1 - p = q$, so that

$$P(E \mid E_1^*) = \frac{P(EE_1^*)}{P(E_1^*)} = q$$

This result is of course exactly what one would expect. If it is known that the first round is a miss, more than two rounds will be required if and only if the second round is a miss also (with probability q).

2.6   Random Variables

Consider all of the possible outcomes of a random experiment and to each of these outcomes or events let us assign a real number. Then, when the experiment is performed, we may identify the outcome solely by the associated real number rather than by giving a physical description of the event which has occurred. For example, in the coin-tossing experiment the sample space for a single toss consists of the two mutually exclusive events "heads" and "tails." Let us arbitrarily assign the number 1 to the event "heads" and 0 to the event "tails." Now when we discuss the outcome of a single performance of this experiment we need no longer use the descriptive phrases "toss a coin" and "heads or tails," but may simply say that the result is the number 1 or 0. Pursuing this idea further, we may introduce a variable X and define its values to be one and zero corresponding to each of the two possible results of the experiment. The quantity X is commonly called a *random variable* in probability theory. Thus, the term random variable is used to denote a real number whose value is determined by the outcome of a random experiment.

In many cases the sample space of the experiment is itself a set of real numbers, or can be immediately identified with a set of real numbers. For example, consider the experiment consisting of rolling a pair of dice. There are 11 possible outcomes or events in the sample space consisting of the numbers 2 to 12 appearing on the dice. These numbers themselves may be taken as the values of the random variable to be associated with the experiment although, of course, any other set of numbers could be used. Thus, we see that the notions of "random variable" and "sample point" may tend to fuse together. However, we wish to keep the distinction precise and, thereby, allow for more general situations.

We may extend the notion of a random variable to the case of a continuous sample space. The temperature in a room at any instant is an event or element of a continuous sample space. The reading of a thermometer may be taken as the random variable. Actually, of course, two different random variables may be quite naturally associated with this experiment since we could use either a centigrade or Fahrenheit thermometer in making the measurements.

Another example of a random variable defined over a continuous sample space is furnished by the experiment of a random selection of a point on the real line from zero to one. The sample space is the unit interval itself and the events or sample points are the points on the line. The function which assigns a number to each of these points in the usual way is a random variable. Another random variable defined over the same sample space is the function which has the value zero if the point selected corresponds to a rational number and the value one if the number is irrational.

In our later work we shall encounter sample spaces whose elements are functions of time $x_i(t)$, $i = 1, 2, \ldots, n$. Here n may be finite, infinite, or the number of elements in the sample space may even be nonenumerable. Now for a fixed value of $t = t_1$, the quantity $x_i(t_1)$ is a random variable in that it assigns a real number to each element of the sample space. Also, the function $\int_a^b x_i(t)\, dt$ is a random variable.

Each of these random variables takes on as many values as there are elements in the sample space.

Definition. A *random variable* is a real-valued point function $X(u)$ defined over the sample space $\mathfrak{S}$ of a random experiment, where u is an arbitrary element of $\mathfrak{S}$.

There may be a little confusion caused by the fact that what is called a "random variable" is really a function, but the term is kept because it has been widely used for a long time. The confusion is not lessened by the fact that the functional dependence of the number X on the sample point u is conventionally suppressed in the notation. Thus we speak of "the random variable X," where it is to be understood that we mean the function $X(u)$ in the sense of the definition above.

To be quite precise, there is one so-called "measurability condition" imposed upon $X(u)$ in order for it to be termed a random variable. This function must be such that for every real number x, the event $X(u) < x$ (that is, the set of points u for which this inequality is valid) must belong to the additive class of subsets of $\mathfrak{S}$ for which probability is defined. The reason for this restriction is to permit us to speak freely of the probability of the event "$X(u) < x$," or more generally, of the probability of any finite or countably infinite combination of such events. In practical applications the condition of measurability is almost always satisfied, and we give no further attention to this point.

In the case of a discrete sample space it is possible to enumerate all the values which a random variable may assume. To each of these may be assigned a number which represents the probability that the random variable assumes that value. For instance, in the coin-tossing experiment described above, if the coin is true, the random variable assumes the values one and zero, each with probability $1/2$. Again, in Example 2.5-7, the number k of shots required to score a hit is a random variable, taking on any positive integer value. Thus, to the number 1 we assign probability $p_1 = p$; to the number 2 we assign $p_2 = pq$; more generally, to the number n we assign the probability $p_n = pq^{n-1}$.

When the sample space is continuous, the problem of assigning a probability distribution to a random variable is more complicated. In the experiment consisting of the random selection of a point on a line, the first random variable defined assumes a nonenumerable number of values so that the probability of selecting any particular point at random is certainly zero. Therefore, it makes sense to speak only of the probability that the random variable assumes a value lying in some subinterval of the unit interval. Thus, we could say the probability of a randomly selected point belonging to the interval $1/4 \leq x \leq 3/4$ is $1/2$. For the random variable defined in the second part of this example, the appropriate probability distribution to assign is zero when the value of the function is zero, and one when the value of the function is one. This follows because although the rational numbers are everywhere dense in the real line, they constitute a set of *zero length*.

The usefulness of the notion of a random variable lies in the fact that it often permits us to replace a sample space of arbitrary objects by a new sample space consisting of real numbers, and thereby not only permits some of our concepts to be more simply expressed but also opens the door to arithmetic calculation. For instance, in Example 2.5-7, if our interest in this problem is centered solely about the number of rounds n required to score the first hit, we may consider the sample space to be the set of positive integers n with $p_n = pq^{n-1}$ as the probability attached to the nth sample point. We then may speak, for example, of the "average number of shots required for a hit" defined to be the sum $\sum_{n=1}^{\infty} np_n$. If we are considering an ensemble of functions of time $x(t)$ to be the sample space, and if we are interested in the value of x at a particular time t_1, then we may consider a new sample space consisting of real numbers corresponding to the possible values of the random variable $X = x(t_1)$. A knowledge of the quantity $F(x) = \Pr (X \leqq x)$ as a function of the variable x then permits us to compute $\Pr [-1 < x(t_1) \leqq +1]$ as the difference $F(+1) - F(-1)$. Also, as shown in Secs. 2.7 and 2.8, we may speak of the "average value of $x(t_1)$" defined by the integral $\int_{-\infty}^{\infty} x(dF/dx)\, dx$. In carrying out these calculations we are in effect forgetting about the original sample space, and are considering instead a new sample space of real numbers with appropriately defined probabilities.

The notion of independence of random variables follows immediately from the concept of independence of events considered in Sec. 2.5. Let X_1 and X_2 be two random variables defined over the same sample space. Intuitively, we should regard these variables as independent, provided that the value taken on by one has no influence on the value of the other. Since the probability is usually zero that a random variable takes on a single preassigned value, we must generalize this notion by specifying the events that X_1 and X_2 lie in preassigned sets S_1 and S_2 are independent in the sense of Sec. 2.5. In other words, we require that

$$\Pr (X_1 \text{ in } S_1 \text{ and } X_2 \text{ in } S_2) = \Pr (X_1 \text{ in } S_1) \Pr (X_2 \text{ in } S_2) \quad (2.6\text{-}1)$$

At the risk of repetition, we examine this concept in further detail. Let S_1 be a set of real numbers, and let E_1 be the event "X_1 in S_1." In other words, E_1 is the set of points u in the original sample space for which the value $X_1(u)$ lies in the set S_1. Similarly let S_2 be a set of real numbers, and let E_2 be the event "X_2 in S_2." For independence we require that

$$P(E_1 E_2) = P(E_1)P(E_2)$$

whatever the choice of sets S_1 and S_2.

In terms of a simple geometric picture, let S_1 and S_2 each be a pair of intervals as indicated in Fig. 2.6-1.

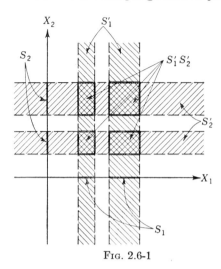

FIG. 2.6-1

Associated with the set S_1 is the set of points S_1' in the plane, described by the statement "X_1 in S_1 and X_2 arbitrary." Similarly with the set S_2 we associate the set S_2' "X_2 in S_2 and X_1 arbitrary." In terms of a new sample space defined as the set of all pairs of values (X_1, X_2), the event E_1 is described by "(X_1, X_2) in the set S_1'"; in other words, the event E_1 and the set S_1' are identical. Similarly E_2 is identical with S_2', and we require that

$$P(S_1'S_2') = P(S_1')P(S_2')$$

Turning to the case of several random variables, we introduce the following definition.

Definition. The random variables X_1, X_2, . . . , X_n are called *mutually*[1] *independent* if and only if

Pr $(X_1$ in S_1 and X_2 in S_2 and . . . and X_n in $S_n)$
$$= \text{Pr } (X_1 \text{ in } S_1) \text{ Pr } (X_2 \text{ in } S_2) \cdot \cdot \cdot \text{ Pr } (X_n \text{ in } S_n) \quad (2.6\text{-}2)$$

for all sets S_i of real numbers.

One should observe that the additional requirements of independence by pairs, triples, etc., is already contained in this definition. For example, if we let each of the sets except S_1 and S_2 be expanded to include all possible values of their associated variables, we obtain immediately, from (2.6-2),

$$\text{Pr } (X_1 \text{ in } S_1 \text{ and } X_2 \text{ in } S_2) = \text{Pr } (X_1 \text{ in } S_1) \text{ Pr } (X_2 \text{ in } S_2) \quad (2.6\text{-}3)$$

In many applications it is useful to consider a real-valued function of a random variable. One easily verifies that such a function is itself a random variable with a probability distribution derived from the distribution of the original variable. Also if X_1, X_2, . . . , X_n are independent random variables, it is immediately seen that the variables $f_1(X_1)$, $f_2(X_2)$, . . . , $f_n(X_n)$ are independent.

[1] The term *statistically independent* is also commonly used.

Example 2.6-1. Suppose that X_1, X_2, and X_3 are independent random variables each assuming the values ± 1 with probabilities $1/2$. The functions $X_1 + X_2$, $X_2 + X_3$ and $X_1 + X_3$ are also random variables, each assuming the values ± 2 with probabilities $1/4$ and 0 with probability $1/2$. These new variables are not, however, independent. If they were independent, then so would also be their squares $2(1 + X_1X_2)$, $2(1 + X_2X_3)$ and $2(1 + X_1X_3)$. However, if it is known that $2(1 + X_1X_2)$ and $2(1 + X_2X_3)$ each have the value 4, then the only possible value for $2(1 + X_1X_3)$ is also 4.

Example 2.6-2. A gun fires n rounds at a target. Let the aiming error e_j on the jth round be composed of two terms r_j and s_j:

$$e_j = r_j + s_j \qquad j = 1, 2, \cdots, n$$

The numbers r_j and s_j are restricted to the integer values -1, 0, $+1$ so that e_j can assume any integer value between -2 and $+2$ inclusive. We assume the target to be hit for a given round if and only if $e_j = 0$ for that round.

We wish to compute the probability that the target is hit one or more times during the n rounds, considering two separate sets of assumptions. In the first case to be examined, we assume that the $2n$ random variables $(r_1, \ldots, r_n, s_1, \ldots, s_n)$ are mutually independent, and that for each value of j

$$\begin{aligned}
\Pr\,(r_j = -1) &= \Pr\,(r_j = +1) = p \\
\Pr\,(s_j = -1) &= \Pr\,(s_j = +1) = p \\
\Pr\,(r_j = 0) &= \Pr\,(s_j = 0) = q = 1 - 2p
\end{aligned} \qquad (2.6\text{-}4)$$

In the second case we assume that the error s_j is systematic during any one set of n rounds, but random from one set to the next. In other words, we assume that $s_j = s$ for $j = 1, 2, \ldots, n$ where s is itself a single random variable. We further assume that the $n + 1$ random variables $(r_1, r_2, \ldots, r_n, s)$ are mutually independent, and again satisfy (2.6-4) with s_j replaced by s.

We may readily compute the probability that e_j takes on any particular one of its possible values. For example,

$$\begin{aligned}
\Pr\,(e_j = +1) &= \Pr\,[(r_j = 0 \text{ and } s_j = +1) \text{ or } (r_j = +1 \text{ and } s_j = 0)] \\
&= \Pr\,(r_j = 0 \text{ and } s_j = +1) + \Pr\,(r_j = +1 \text{ and } s_j = 0) \\
&= \Pr\,(r_j = 0)\,\Pr\,(s_j = +1) + \Pr\,(r_j = +1)\,\Pr\,(s_j = 0) \\
&= 2qp \\
&= 2p(1 - 2p)
\end{aligned}$$

Also we obtain by a similar calculation

$$\Pr\,(e_j = 0) = 2p^2 + q^2 = 1 - 4p + 6p^2 \qquad (2.6\text{-}5)$$

It is noted that these results do not depend upon whether case 1 or case 2 is under discussion. The random variable e_j has the same probability distribution in each of the two cases. The probability of obtaining a hit on round j does not depend on whether or not s_j is a systematic error for the set of n rounds; however, we proceed to show that the probability of obtaining one or more hits during the n rounds is distinctly different for the two cases.

Case 1. Let E be the event "one or more hits are scored." The complement E^* is the event "no hits are scored," and can be expressed in the form

$$E^* = M_1 M_2 \cdots M_n$$

where M_j is the event "miss on round j." Since M_j is equivalent to the event $e_j \neq 0$, and since the variables $(e_1, e_2, \ldots, e_n)$ are independent, we have, from (2.6-5),

$$
\begin{aligned}
P(E^*) &= P(M_1)P(M_2) \cdots P(M_n) \\
&= [\mathrm{Pr}\ (e_j \neq 0)]^n = [1 - \mathrm{Pr}\ (e_j = 0)]^n \\
&= (4p - 6p^2)^n
\end{aligned}
$$

Thus we find

$$
P(E) = 1 - P(E^*) = 1 - (4p - 6p^2)^n \tag{2.6-6}
$$

Case 2. Let E, E^*, and M_j have the same significance as before, and let A, B, and C denote the respective events $s = -1$, $s = 0$, and $s = +1$. The random variables e_j are no longer independent, so that we cannot proceed directly. Instead, we employ the relation

$$
P(E^*) = P(A)P(E^* \mid A) + P(B)P(E^* \mid B) + P(C)P(E^* \mid C) \tag{2.6-7}
$$

Under hypothesis $A(s = -1)$ the event M_j is equivalent to the statement that $r_j \neq +1$. Therefore, since the variables r_j are mutually independent,

$$
P(E^* \mid A) = P(M_1 M_2 \cdots M_n \mid A)
$$

$$
= \prod_{j=1}^{n} \mathrm{Pr}\ (r_j \neq +1) = (p + q)^n = (1 - p)^n
$$

In a similar manner we find that

$$
P(E^* \mid B) = (2p)^n \qquad P(E^* \mid C) = (1 - p)^n
$$

Substitution of these relations into (2.6-7), together with the expressions

$$
P(A) = P(C) = p \qquad P(B) = 1 - 2p
$$

gives $P(E^*) = 2p(1 - p)^n + (1 - 2p)(2p)^n$.

Therefore

$$
P(E) = 1 - 2p(1 - p)^n - (1 - 2p)(2p)^n \tag{2.6-8}
$$

A comparison of (2.6-6) and (2.6-8) shows that the probability of one or more hits in the n rounds does differ for the two cases. To examine the difference numerically (admittedly in a case chosen to accentuate this difference), let $p = 0.100$ and $n = 6$. We find from (2.6-6) the result $P(E) = 0.9985$, and from (2.6-8) $P(E) = 0.8937$. In other words, if s_j is random throughout each sequence of six rounds the target will escape without hits in less than 0.2 per cent of the cases, whereas if s_j is systematic, the target will escape without hits somewhat more than 10 per cent of the time. In either case, the probability that any single shot will constitute a hit is found from (2.6-5) to be $1 - 4p + 6p^2 = 0.66$.

2.7   Probability Distribution and Frequency Functions

Let X be a random variable which assumes values in a set S of real numbers. In Sec. 2.6 we observed that if the set S is not discrete it usually makes little sense to speak of the probability that X will have any particular value. Thus, we are obliged to consider the probability that X will assume a value lying in a subset of S. For this reason it is convenient to define the *distribution function* $F(x)$ as

$$
F(x) = \mathrm{Pr}\ (X \leqq x) \tag{2.7-1}
$$

If a and b are real numbers such that $a < b$, we have

$$\Pr(X \leq b) = \Pr(X \leq a) + \Pr(a < X \leq b) \qquad (2.7\text{-}2)$$

so that
$$\Pr(a < X \leq b) = F(b) - F(a) \qquad (2.7\text{-}3)$$

From this relation and the fact that the probability of any event is always nonnegative, we have

$$F(x_1) \leq F(x_2) \qquad \text{if } x_1 \leq x_2 \qquad (2.7\text{-}4)$$

In other words, $F(x)$ is a monotone nondecreasing function. [It is understood that $F(x)$ is constant in any interval that contains no points of S.] Also it is always true that

$$F(-\infty) = 0 \qquad \text{and} \qquad F(+\infty) = 1 \qquad (2.7\text{-}5)$$

Thus $F(x)$ is positive and has values between zero and one.

Henceforth we shall be primarily concerned with distribution functions rather than probability functions, because they lend themselves more readily to numerical computations; furthermore, in considering distribution functions, there is no loss in generality. From Eq. (2.7-3) we see that the probability associated with an arbitrary interval can be represented in terms of a difference between two values of the distribution function. Moreover, the probability function for a set of nonoverlapping intervals can be expressed as a sum of terms of this type. Generalizing the argument, the probability function associated with any set that is derivable from intervals by a countable number of algebraic operations can be found from the distribution function. In other words, a knowledge of the distribution function is sufficient in principle to determine the probability function for a certain general class of sets which is an additive class. The probability function and distribution function are thus equivalent in the sense that each can be found from the other.

We may also define a conditional probability distribution function of a random variable X. Thus, suppose that it is known that an event E has occurred which may affect the value assumed by X. Then we define the *conditional distribution function* of X by

$$F_E(x) = \Pr(X \leq x \mid E) = \frac{\Pr(X \leq x \text{ and } E)}{\Pr(E)} \qquad (2.7\text{-}6)$$

One may interpret the distribution function physically in terms of the distribution of one unit of mass over the real line $-\infty < x < \infty$. If the mass allotted to any set of points represents the probability that X will assume a value lying in that set, then $F(x)$ is the total mass associated with the point x and all points lying to the left of x. With this interpretation we may imagine concentrations of mass at certain points on the line in addition to or in place of the *continuous* mass distribution.

The latter condition is described as a *discrete* distribution, while the former characterizes the *mixed* type of distribution.

As an example of distribution functions of the discrete type, consider the random variable associated with the coin-tossing experiment described at the beginning of Sec. 2.6. This is illustrated in Fig. 2.7-1. The experiment described in Sec. 2.6 consisting of the random selection of a point in the unit interval offers an illustration of a continuous distribution.

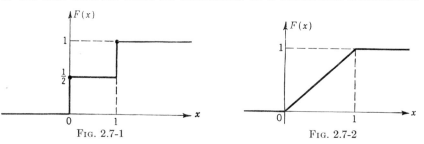

Fig. 2.7-1   Fig. 2.7-2

For the random variable defined first in that example, the distribution function is shown in Fig. 2.7-2. The second random variable described is defined over a continuous sample space but gives rise to a discrete distribution function. In fact, the distribution function is a unit step function with its jump at $x = 1$. Thus, care should be taken to distinguish between the concepts of a continuous distribution function and a continuous sample space. The two are *not* synonymous.

If $F(x)$ is differentiable, we define the *frequency function* or *probability density function* $f(x)$ by

$$f(x) = \frac{dF(x)}{dx} \tag{2.7-7}$$

Since $F(x)$ is monotone nondecreasing, for all x we have

$$f(x) \geq 0 \tag{2.7-8}$$

Also from the definitions we have the further properties:

$$F(x) = \int_{-\infty}^{x} f(u) \, du \tag{2.7-9}$$

$$\Pr\,(a < X \leq b) = \int_{a}^{b} f(x) \, dx \tag{2.7-10}$$

$$\int_{-\infty}^{\infty} f(x) \, dx = 1 \tag{2.7-11}$$

If the random variable X takes on only discrete values, say x_1, x_2, x_3, . . . , then the distribution function $F(x)$ is not differentiable in the ordinary sense. If we write $p_1 = \Pr\,(X = x_1)$, $p_2 = \Pr\,(X = x_2)$, etc., then $F(x)$ is given by

$$F(x) = \Sigma p_j \tag{2.7-12}$$

where the summation extends over all values of j for which $x_j \leq x$.

To handle this type of situation in a way consistent with the previous discussion, we may assign to each point x_j a probability density given by $p_j\delta(x - x_j)$. Here the function $\delta(x)$ is the so-called *delta function* or *unit impulse function*, defined by the properties

$$\delta(x) = 0 \qquad x \neq 0 \tag{2.7-13}$$

$$\int_a^b \delta(x)\, dx = 1 \qquad a < 0 < b \tag{2.7-14}$$

The delta function is not a mathematical function in the strict sense. In all legitimate applications, this function is visualized as a result of a limiting process involving a function $\delta(x,\epsilon)$ satisfying the following conditions.

$$\delta(x,\epsilon) \geq 0 \qquad -\infty < x < \infty \, ; 0 < \epsilon < \infty \tag{2.7-15}$$

$$\int_{-\infty}^{\infty} \delta(x,\epsilon)\, dx = 1 \qquad 0 < \epsilon < \infty \tag{2.7-16}$$

$$\lim_{\epsilon \to 0} \delta(x,\epsilon) = 0 \qquad x \neq 0 \tag{2.7-17}$$

Examples of such functions are given by

$$\delta(x,\epsilon) = \begin{cases} 0 & x < 0 \\ \dfrac{1}{\epsilon} e^{-x/\epsilon} & x \geq 0 \end{cases} \tag{2.7-18}$$

or

$$\delta(x,\epsilon) = \begin{cases} \dfrac{1}{2\epsilon} & -\epsilon \leq x \leq +\epsilon \\ 0 & |x| > |\epsilon| \end{cases} \tag{2.7-19}$$

Among the more useful properties of the delta function is the relation

$$\int_{-\infty}^{\infty} g(x)\delta(x - x_0)\, dx = g(x_0) \tag{2.7-20}$$

which is satisfied if $g(x)$ is continuous at $x = x_0$.

In terms of the delta function we may define the probability density for the discrete case by

$$f(x) = \sum_j p_j\delta(x - x_j) \tag{2.7-21}$$

Then

$$F(x) = \int_{-\infty}^{x+0} f(u)\, du = \sum_j p_j \int_{-\infty}^{x+0} \delta(u - x_j)\, du \tag{2.7-22}\dagger$$

† Here we mean by the upper limit $x + 0$ the limit

$$\lim_{\epsilon \to 0} \int_{-\infty}^{x+\epsilon} f(u)\, du \qquad \epsilon > 0$$

Whenever we use integrals involving delta functions in which one of the limits of integration may occur at one of the points x_j, we must clearly indicate whether or not this end point is to be included. We do this by the notation $x + 0$ or $x - 0$, interpreted as above.

If $x_j \leqq x$ then the term p_j is included in the above sums.   If $x_j > x$ then

$$\int_{-\infty}^{x+0} \delta(u - x_j) \, du = 0$$

and the term is missing.   Thus the relation (2.7-22) is equivalent to the previous definition (2.7-12).

For a mixed distribution, $F(x)$ may be written in the form

$$F(x) = F_1(x) + \sum_j p_j \int_{-\infty}^{x+0} \delta(u - x_j) \, du \qquad (2.7\text{-}23)$$

where $F_1(x)$ is continuous.   By use of delta functions, our previous formulas (2.7-1) to (2.7-12) may be carried through intact, with the possible exception of (2.7-7), and we no longer need be concerned as to whether our distribution is continuous or discrete.

The choice of the term *probability density function* is a consequence of our analogy between probability distribution functions and mass distributions.   In the regions in which the mass distribution $F(x)$ is continuous, the mass density $f(x)$ is the mass per unit length.   When discrete masses are attached to certain points, the mass density at these points is infinite.   In any case the function $F(x)$ specifies the total mass lying to the left of and including the point x.

Example 2.7-1.   At time $t = 0$ a particle is located at the point $X = 0$.   At a randomly selected time, uniformly distributed[1] over the interval $0 < t < 1$, the particle is suddenly given a velocity V in the positive X direction.   We seek to calculate the probability distribution and frequency functions of the particle position $X(t)$ at an arbitrary time t in the interval $0 < t < 1$.

Let values t and x be assigned, and let t_0 be the time at which the particle starts to move.   Then

$$\text{Pr} \,[X(t) \leqq x] = \text{Pr} \,[V(t - t_0) \leqq x] = \text{Pr} \left[t_0 \geqq t - \frac{x}{V} \right]$$

For $x > Vt$, we have $t - x/V < 0$ and

$$\text{Pr} \left(t_0 \geqq t - \frac{x}{V} \right) = \text{Pr} \,(t_0 \geqq 0) = +1$$

For $0 \leqq x \leqq Vt$,

$$\text{Pr} \left(t_0 \geqq t - \frac{x}{V} \right) = 1 - \left(t - \frac{x}{V} \right)$$

Combining these results, the plot of $F(x)$ against x for a fixed value of t in $0 < t < 1$ is given by Fig. 2.7-3.   It is noted that there is a definite probability (equal to $1 - t$) that the particle is still at the origin at time t.

The corresponding probability density function is given by

$$f(x) = (1 - t)\delta(x) + \frac{f_1(x)}{V}$$

[1] A random variable is *uniformly distributed* over an interval if its corresponding probability density function is constant over that interval.

where $f_1(x)$ is the step function

$$f_1(x) = \begin{cases} 0 & x < 0 \\ 1 & 0 \leq x \leq Vt \\ 0 & Vt < x \end{cases}$$

Example 2.7-2. Given that a vacuum tube has lasted x days, the probability of its failure within the next dx days is $0.01dx$, independent of x. If a certain tube is known to have lasted for 30 days, we wish to compute the probability of its failure within the next 10 days.

Let X be the random variable representing the life of a tube in days. Let A be the event that the tube has lasted x days, and B the event that it fails between x and $x + dx$. From the statement of the problem,

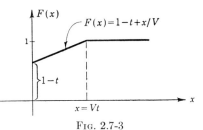

$F(x)=1-t+x/V$

FIG. 2.7-3

$$P(B \mid A) = 0.01dx$$

Since B is a subset of A, we have $AB = B$ and

$$P(B \mid A) = \frac{P(AB)}{P(A)} = \frac{P(B)}{P(A)}$$

In terms of the distribution function $F(x)$ and frequency function $f(x)$, however,

$$P(A) = \Pr\ (X > x) = 1 - \Pr\ (X \leq x) = 1 - F(x)$$
$$P(B) = \Pr\ (x < X \leq x + dx) = f(x)\ dx$$

The combination of these relations gives

$$\frac{f(x)\ dx}{1 - F(x)} = 0.01dx$$

or

$$f(x) = 0.01\left[1 - \int_0^x f(u)\ du \right]$$

The differentiation of this last relation with respect to x leads to the differential equation

$$\frac{df}{dx} + 0.01f = 0$$

whose solution is

$$f(x) = ce^{-0.01x} \qquad x \geq 0$$

To determine c, we note that

$$\int_0^\infty f(x)\ dx = 100c = 1$$

giving $c = 0.01$.

Now let G be the event that a tube lasts for 30 days (or more), and H the event that it fails between 30 and 40 days. Then $GH = H$, and

$$P(H \mid G) = \frac{P(GH)}{P(G)} = \frac{P(H)}{P(G)}$$

However,

$$P(G) = \Pr \ (X > 30) = 1 - F(30)$$
$$= 1 - \int_0^{30} 0.01 e^{-0.01x} \, dx = e^{-0.3}$$

and

$$P(H) = \Pr \ (30 < X \leq 40) = F(40) - F(30)$$
$$= 1 - e^{-0.4} - (1 - e^{-0.3}) = e^{-0.3} - e^{-0.4}$$

Thus the required probability is

$$P(H \mid G) = 1 - e^{-0.1}$$

We now wish to extend the notion of distribution and frequency functions to the case of two or more random variables. Considering first the case of two variables X and Y, the *joint distribution function* $F(x,y)$ is defined by

$$F(x,y) = \Pr \ (X \leq x \text{ and } Y \leq y) \tag{2.7-24}$$

for all x and y. Again we find the analogy with a mass distribution instructive. Let one unit of mass be distributed over the (x,y) plane in such a manner that the mass associated with any set S is the same as $\Pr \ [(X,Y) \text{ in } S]$. Then the distribution function $F(x,y)$ represents the total mass in the quadrant to the left of and below the point (x,y), including the boundaries of this region and the point (x,y) itself.

If $\partial^2 F / \partial x \, \partial y$ exists and is integrable

$$F(x_0, y_0) = \int_{-\infty}^{y_0} \int_{-\infty}^{x_0} \frac{\partial^2 F}{\partial x \, \partial y} \, dx \, dy \tag{2.7-25}$$

and we define the *frequency function* $f(x,y)$ by

$$f(x,y) = \frac{\partial^2 F}{\partial x \, \partial y} \tag{2.7-26}$$

Equation (2.7-25) then becomes

$$F(x_0, y_0) = \int_{-\infty}^{y_0} \int_{-\infty}^{x_0} f(x,y) \, dx \, dy \tag{2.7-27}$$

As in the one-dimensional case,

$$F(\infty, \infty) = 1 = \int_{-\infty}^{\infty} \int_{-\infty}^{\infty} f(x,y) \, dx \, dy \tag{2.7-28}$$

Also we note that

$$F(x, -\infty) = \Pr \ (X \leq x \text{ and } Y \leq -\infty) = 0 \tag{2.7-29}$$

and similarly

$$F(-\infty, y) = F(-\infty, -\infty) = 0 \tag{2.7-30}$$

The above definitions can all be extended in an obvious manner to the case of three or more variables.

The frequency function $f(x,y)$ can readily be visualized as a mass density in the plane at point (x,y). In considering distributions that are not continuous, however, an important distinction must be drawn between the case of one random variable and two or more. In the two-dimensional case we can imagine a positive mass associated with a single point of the plane, and this notion leads us to a concept of a two-dimensional delta function. In addition, however, we may imagine a positive mass associated with an arbitrary line in the plane, or in fact with any curve whatever. Similarly in three dimensions a positive mass may be associated with a discrete point, an arbitrary space curve, or an arbitrary surface. Thus an extended notion of a delta function is not of itself sufficiently general to include all discontinuous cases.

If we confine our attention to a mass density that is everywhere finite except at a discrete set of points corresponding to a countably infinite set of point masses, and give an appropriate definition of a two- or n-dimensional delta function to represent the mass density at these points, then Eq. (2.7-27) or its n-dimensional counterpart still makes sense. Since we have need for no greater degree of generality than this, we bypass the more difficult questions.

Calculations involving the distributions of two or more random variables are much simplified if the variables happen to be mutually independent. To begin with, let X and Y be independent, with distribution functions $F_1(x)$ and $F_2(y)$, respectively. The joint distribution function $F(x,y)$ is then given by (2.7-24) and (2.6-1) in the form

$$F(x,y) = \text{Pr } (X \leq x \text{ and } Y \leq y) = \text{Pr } (X \leq x) \text{ Pr } (Y \leq y)$$
$$= F_1(x)F_2(y) \qquad (2.7\text{-}31)$$

Also, by differentiation of (2.7-31),

$$f(x,y) = \frac{\partial^2 F}{\partial x \, \partial y} = f_1(x)f_2(y) \qquad (2.7\text{-}32)$$

where $f(x,y)$, $f_1(x)$, and $f_2(y)$ are, respectively, the joint frequency function for X and Y and the frequency functions for X and Y considered separately. Similar relations are of course valid for the general case of n variables.

The two equivalent product relations (2.7-31) and (2.7-32) are not only necessary consequences of the independence of X and Y; they are also sufficient conditions for independence. This statement is a direct consequence of our remark in Sec. 2.6 concerning the equivalence of distribution and probability functions.

From the joint distribution of two variables X and Y it is possible to compute the distribution of each variable separately. Thus

$$\text{Pr } (X \leq x) = \text{Pr } (X \leq x \text{ and } Y \leq +\infty) = F(x, \infty) \qquad (2.7\text{-}33)$$

with a similar relation for $\Pr(Y \leq y)$.   Writing $F_1(x)$ and $F_2(y)$ for the respective distribution functions for X and Y separately, we obtain

$$F_1(x) = F(x, \infty) \qquad F_2(y) = F(\infty, y) \qquad (2.7\text{-}34)$$

In terms of the probability frequency functions $f_1(x)$, $f_2(y)$, and $f(x,y)$, the relation (2.7-34) yields

$$f_1(x) = \frac{d}{dx} F(x, \infty) = \frac{d}{dx} \int_{-\infty}^{x} dx \int_{-\infty}^{\infty} f(x,y)\, dy$$

$$= \int_{-\infty}^{\infty} f(x,y)\, dy \qquad (2.7\text{-}35)$$

Similarly $f_2(y)$ is given by

$$f_2(y) = \int_{-\infty}^{\infty} f(x,y)\, dx \qquad (2.7\text{-}36)$$

The extension of these results to the general case of n random variables is immediate.   Thus, the joint distribution of the random variables X_1, X_2, . . . , X_n is defined by

$$F_n(x_1, x_2, \ldots , x_n) = \Pr(X_1 \leq x_1 \text{ and } X_2 \leq x_2 \text{ and } \ldots \text{ and } X_n \leq x_n) \qquad (2.7\text{-}37)$$

with a corresponding joint frequency function given by

$$f_n(x_1, x_2, \ldots , x_n) = \frac{\partial^n}{\partial x_1\, \partial x_2 \cdots \partial x_n} F_n(x_1, x_2, \ldots , x_n) \qquad (2.7\text{-}38)$$

If we select a subset $X_1, X_2, \ldots , X_k$ $(k < n)$ of these random variables, their joint density function $f_k(x_1, x_2, \ldots , x_k)$ is given by

$$f_k(x_1, x_2, \ldots , x_k) = \int_{-\infty}^{\infty} dx_{k+1} \int_{-\infty}^{\infty} dx_{k+2}$$

$$\cdots \int_{-\infty}^{\infty} dx_n f_n(x_1, x_2, \ldots , x_n) \qquad (2.7\text{-}39)$$

The sum of a set of n random variables is itself a random variable and its distribution is determined by the distribution of the original variables. In particular if the variables are independent we have, for the case of two variables X and Y where $Z = X + Y$,

$$\Pr(a < Z \leq b) = \int_{a}^{b} f_3(z)\, dz = \iint_{\Gamma} f(x,y)\, dx\, dy \qquad (2.7\text{-}40)$$

where Γ is the region, a diagonal strip, in which $a < X + Y \leq b$, and where $f_3(z)$ is the frequency function for Z.   Then

$$\int_{a}^{b} f_3(z)\, dz = \int_{-\infty}^{\infty} dx \int_{a-x}^{b-x} f_1(x) f_2(y)\, dy$$

$$= \int_{-\infty}^{\infty} dx \int_{a}^{b} f_1(x) f_2(z - x)\, dz$$

$$= \int_{a}^{b} dz \int_{-\infty}^{\infty} f_1(x) f_2(z - x)\, dx \qquad (2.7\text{-}41)$$

Since this holds for any a and b, the frequency function for Z is

$$f_3(z) = \int_{-\infty}^{\infty} f_1(x) f_2(z - x) \, dx \qquad (2.7\text{-}42)$$

which is the convolution integral.

Example 2.7-3. A ship is shelling a target on an enemy shore line, firing n inde-pendent shots all of which may be assumed to fall on a straight line and to be dis-tributed according to the probability frequency function $f(x)$ or the distribution func-tion $F(x)$. If we define the *span of the attack* as the interval between the location of the two extreme shells, we desire to find the probability distribution of the span.

Let $X_1, X_2, \ldots, X_n$ be independent random variables representing the coordi-nates locating the position of the n shots. We define two auxiliary random variables[1]

$$U = \min (X_1, X_2, \ldots, X_n) \qquad V = \max (X_1, X_2, \ldots, X_n)$$

which are clearly not independent. Then the span of the attack is given by

$$S = V - U$$

We carry out the calculation in several distinct steps.

1. The probability that any selected one of the X's will be less than an arbitrary number v is simply

$$\Pr (X_i \leqq v) = F(v)$$

If the variable V is to be less than v, then each of the variables X_i must be less than v also. Thus since the variables are independent

$$\Pr (V \leqq v) = \Pr (X_1 \leqq v \text{ and } X_2 \leqq v \ldots \text{ and } X_n \leqq v) = [F(v)]^n$$

which is the distribution function for V. Similarly we find

$$\Pr (U > u) = [1 - F(u)]^n$$

giving

$$\Pr (U \leqq u) = 1 - [1 - F(u)]^n$$

as the distribution function for U.

2. We next compute the joint probability distribution function for U and V. This function is $\Pr (U \leqq u \text{ and } V \leqq v)$ which is a difficult quantity to compute directly. For this reason we resort to the following artifice. The event $(V \leqq v)$ is decomposable into two mutually exclusive events $(V \leqq v; U \leqq u)$† and $(V \leqq v; U > u)$. Thus

$$\Pr (V \leqq v) = \Pr (V \leqq v; U \leqq u) + \Pr (V \leqq v; U > u)$$

giving

$$\Pr (U \leqq u; V \leqq v) = [F(v)]^n - \Pr (V \leqq v; U > u)$$

From the definition of U and V, the event $(V \leqq v; U > u)$ requires that each of the random variables X_i shall satisfy $u < X_i \leqq v$. If $u \geqq v$, the probability of the event is zero. On the other hand, if $u < v$ the probability that any selected X_i should lie in the interval from u to v is simply $[F(v) - F(u)]$. Since the X's are independent,

---

[1] The abbreviations max and min denote, respectively, the maximum and minimum of the quantities which follow.

† For convenience, here and elsewhere, we often use the notation "$(\ldots ; \ldots)$" in place of the more cumbersome notation "$(\ldots \text{ and } \ldots)$."

the probability that they should all lie in the interval is $[F(v) - F(u)]^n$. **Therefore**

$$\Pr\ (V \leq v;\ U > u) = \begin{cases} 0 & \text{if } u \geq v \\ [F(v) - F(u)]^n & \text{if } u < v \end{cases}$$

Hence the desired joint distribution function is

$$\Pr\ (U \leq u;\ V \leq v) = \begin{cases} [F(v)]^n & \text{if } u \geq v \\ [F(v)]^n - [F(v) - F(u)]^n & \text{if } u < v \end{cases}$$

3. Let $w(u,v)$ be the joint density function for U and V. This quantity is found by differentiating the distribution function with respect to u and v. We thereby obtain

$$w(u,v) = \begin{cases} 0 & \text{if } u > v \\ n(n - 1)[F(v) - F(u)]^{n-2}f(u)f(v) & \text{if } u < v \end{cases}$$

If $n > 2$ the function $w(u,v)$ is continuous, but for $n = 2$ this function is discontinuous along the line $u = v$.

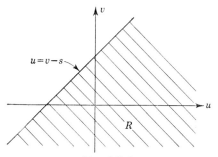

FIG. 2.7-4

4. To compute the distribution function for the span $S = V - U$, we wish to find

$$\Pr\ (V - U \leq s)$$

as a function of s. This is accomplished by integrating $w(u,v)$ over the region R in the (u,v) plane for which $v - u \leq s$, or $u \geq v - s$, as shown in Fig. 2.7-4.

$$\Pr\ (V - U \leq s) = \iint\limits_{R} w(u,v)\ du\ dv = \int_{-\infty}^{\infty} dv \int_{v-s}^{\infty} w(u,v)\ du$$

$$= \int_{-\infty}^{\infty} dv \int_{-\infty}^{s} w(v - u,\ v)\ du = \int_{-\infty}^{s} du \int_{-\infty}^{\infty} w(v - u,\ v)\ dv$$

Differentiating with respect to s, the density function for the span is

$$\int_{-\infty}^{\infty} w(v - s,\ v)\ dv$$

which is analogous to a generalized form of the convolution integral (2.7-42). From the previously calculated expression for $w(u,v)$, this quantity is zero if $u > v$. Thus $w(v - s, v) = 0$ if $v - s > v$ or in other words if $s < 0$. Hence the probability density function for the span of the attack is given by

$$\begin{cases} 0 & \text{for } s < 0 \\ n(n - 1) \int_{-\infty}^{\infty} [F(v) - F(v - s)]^{n-2}f(v - s)f(v)\ dv & \text{for } s > 0 \end{cases}$$

2.8 Expectation, Mean, Variance, and Moments

Consider a random variable X which can assume any one of the discrete set of values x_1, x_2, . . . with respective probabilities p_1, p_2, ... If the value assumed by X corresponds to the outcome of a certain experiment, and the experiment is repeated a large number N of times, we wish to estimate the numerical average of X over the N trials. Let the event $X = x_i$ occur m_i times; then the average in question is given by

$$\frac{1}{N} (m_1 x_1 + m_2 x_2 + \cdot \cdot \cdot) = \frac{m_1}{N} x_1 + \frac{m_2}{N} x_2 + \cdot \cdot \cdot$$

However, according to the empirical notion of probability, the ratio m_i/N approaches the probability p_i in the limit as the number of trials becomes infinite. We therefore define the *average, mean,* or *mathematical expectation* $E[X]$ of the random variable X in this case by the limiting expression

$$E[X] = p_1 x_1 + p_2 x_2 + \cdot \cdot \cdot \tag{2.8-1}$$

Thus the expectation of a random variable is a probability-weighted average of the values which the variable can take on, and represents the anticipated numerical average of the observed values of this variable in a very large number of trials. To calculate the mathematical expectation of a random variable X in the discrete case, we multiply each of the values which X can assume by the corresponding probabilities with which they are assumed and sum over all possible cases.

Although we refer to the empirical theory of probability to motivate this discussion, the relation (2.8-1) is taken as a postulated definition and not something to be proved. As a matter of fact the definition (2.8-1) together with our previous postulates makes it possible to prove quite rigorously that in a large number of independent trials the numerical average of observed values of X actually does approach $E[X]$, as defined above. The precise statement is that

$$\lim_{n \to \infty} \text{Pr} \left\{ \left| \frac{1}{n} (X_1 + X_2 + \cdot \cdot \cdot + X_n) - E[X] \right| > \epsilon \right\} = 0$$

where X_i is the observed value on the ith trial and ϵ is any fixed small positive number.

Example 2.8-1. A coin is tossed twice. A pays B \$2 for the event HH, A pays B \$1 for the events HT or TH, and B pays A \$3 for the event TT. The problem is to calculate A's average winnings (or losings) per game if the game is played a large number of times. For a sufficiently large number of games, the total number of occurrences of each simple event will be proportional to its probability. Hence in n games we have, from (2.8-1),

$$\text{Average winnings} = \frac{\text{total winnings}}{N}$$

$$= \frac{1}{N}\left[-2\left(\frac{N}{4}\right) - 1\left(\frac{N}{4}\right) - 1\left(\frac{N}{4}\right) + 3\left(\frac{N}{4}\right) \right]$$

$$= -2 \times \tfrac{1}{4} - 1 \times \tfrac{1}{4} - 1 \times \tfrac{1}{4} + 3 \times \tfrac{1}{4} = -\tfrac{1}{4} \text{ dollars}$$

Thus A may expect to lose an average of 25 cents per game.

Example 2.8-2.   An experiment is made in which a pair of dice are rolled repeatedly until a seven appears.   Assuming the successive trials to be independent, what is the average number of trials required?

From Example 2.4-3 the probability p of a seven on any one trial is $p = 1/6$.   Let X be a random variable defined as the number of trials required to produce the first seven.   The event $X = n$ is realized by $n - 1$ throws in which a seven does not appear, followed by one throw on which a seven does appear.   Thus

$$\Pr\,(X = n) = (1 - p)^{n-1}p = \frac{5^{n-1}}{6^n}$$

The mathematical expectation of X is given by the sum of the various possible values of X (i.e., the integers $n = 1, 2, 3, \ldots$) multiplied by their respective probabilities of occurrence.   Thus

$$E[X] = \sum_{n=1}^{\infty} n\,\Pr\,(X = n) = \sum_{n=1}^{\infty} np(1 - p)^{n-1} = \frac{1}{p} = 6$$

OMIT **Example 2.8-3.**   The mathematical expectation of a random variable as defined by (2.8-1) is not necessarily a finite quantity.   To illustrate this point, we consider briefly the following problem.   A game of matching pennies between two players, each of which possesses infinite capital resources, proceeds until they "break even"; i.e., until the winnings of each player total zero.   The first time that this occurs, the game terminates.   What is the average duration of the game?

The game will terminate if and only if each player has won on exactly half of the tosses.   Thus, termination on the nth toss is possible only if n is even.   To compute the average number of tosses per game, let us define a random variable X to be equal to $2n$ if the game terminates on the $2n$th toss and denote by p_{2n} the probability associated with this event.   Then the average number of tosses is given by

$$E[X] = \sum_{n=1}^{\infty} 2np_{2n}$$

The computation of the probability p_{2n} is not a trivial one, and for this purpose we shall employ a rather powerful and frequently useful method.   Let us define y_{2n} to be the probability that the players break even in $2n$ tosses whether for the first time or not.   (Note that p_{2n} is the probability that they break even for the first time in $2n$ tosses.)   The event "the players break even in $2n$ plays" can be broken down into the sum of the n mutually exclusive events "the players break even for the first time in $2k$ plays and also break even on the remaining $2n - 2k$ plays" for $k = 1, 2, \ldots n$. Thus

$$y_{2n} = \sum_{k=1}^{n} p_{2k}y_{2n-2k}$$

(Observe that $y_0 = 1$, since neither player had the advantage before the game began.) The quantity y_{2n} is the probability of obtaining exactly n wins in $2n$ plays and this is shown in the section on the binomial distribution (Sec. 2.10) to be given by

$$y_{2n} = \frac{(2n)!}{(n!)^2 2^{2n}}$$

Thus, the quantities p_{2n} may be computed in succession by placing $n = 1, 2, 3, \ldots$ in the recurrence formula relating the y's and the p's.

To obtain a general expression for p_{2n}, we introduce the following so-called "generating functions"

$$P(x) = \sum_{k=1}^{\infty} p_{2k} x^{2k} \qquad Y(x) = \sum_{j=0}^{\infty} y_{2j} x^{2j}$$

It follows that

$$Y(x)P(x) = \sum_{j=0}^{\infty} \sum_{k=1}^{\infty} y_{2j} p_{2k} x^{2(j+k)}$$

$$= \sum_{n=1}^{\infty} \left(\sum_{k=1}^{n} p_{2k} y_{2n-2k} \right) x^{2n}$$

$$= \sum_{n=1}^{\infty} y_{2n} x^{2n} = Y(x) - 1$$

Hence

$$P(x) = 1 - \frac{1}{Y(x)}$$

The series representation for $Y(x)$ may be summed in closed form using the binomial theorem. Thus

$$Y(x) = \sum_{n=0}^{\infty} \frac{(2n)!}{(n!)^2} \left(\frac{x}{2}\right)^{2n} = (1 - x^2)^{-\frac{1}{2}}$$

so that

$$P(x) = 1 - (1 - x^2)^{\frac{1}{2}}$$

If, in turn, this closed form expression for $P(x)$ is expanded using the binomial theorem, the quantities p_{2n} are obtained immediately as the coefficients of x^{2n} in the resulting series. We obtain

$$p_{2n} = \frac{1}{n} \frac{(2n-2)!}{[(n-1)!]^2 2^{2n-1}}$$

as the probability that the original game will terminate after exactly $2n$ plays. To obtain the average number of plays per game, we observe that

$$E[X] = \left[\frac{d}{dx} P(x) \right]_{x=1} = \left[\frac{x}{(1-x^2)^{\frac{1}{2}}} \right]_{x=1} = \infty$$

i.e., the average duration of the game is infinite. Using Stirling's formula for factorials, one can show that $p_{2n} \sim n^{-\frac{3}{2}}$ for large n so that the probability of the game not terminating in a finite number of plays is zero. However, we find that the average duration is infinite simply because the expectation admits of infinitely many very large values of the variable X, each occurring with a probability which is not small enough to result in a convergent series.

We may extend this notion of mathematical expectation in a natural way to include the case of continuous distributions. Let X be a random variable with frequency function $f(x)$. Then the probability that X will assume a value in the interval $(x, x + dx)$ is approximately given by

$$\Pr\ (x < X \leqq x + dx) \cong f(x)\ dx$$

Thus, if we regard the continuous distribution function as the limit of a suitable discrete distribution, we are tempted to write $xf(x)\ dx$ as the value expected multiplied by the probability with which it is to be expected and to integrate rather than sum over all possible values. In this way we are led to the following definition.

Definition. Let X be a random variable with frequency function $f(x)$. The mathematical expectation or mean of X is defined by

$$E[X] = \int_{-\infty}^{\infty} xf(x)\ dx \tag{2.8-2}$$

For the case of a mixed distribution the expectation is defined in the obvious way to include both types of expressions appearing in Eqs. (2.8-1) and (2.8-2). Thus if the frequency function $f(x)$ is allowed to include terms of the delta-function type, it is clear that all three cases (continuous, discrete, or mixed) are included within the single definition (2.8-2).

In Sec. 2.6 the notion of an arbitrary function $g(X)$ of a random variable X was introduced, and it was pointed out that $g(X)$ is itself a random variable. The probability distribution for $g(X)$ can be calculated from the distribution of X and $E[g]$ thus computed by the appropriate form of (2.8-2). In many cases, however, the following procedure proves to be much simpler. The expectation of $g(X)$ is a probability-weighted average of the various values which g can assume. If we consider the contribution to this average arising from the event $(x < X \leqq x + dx)$, it is seen to be given approximately by

$$g(x)\ \Pr\ (x < X \leqq x + dx) = g(x)f(x)\ dx$$

Summing (i.e., integrating) over the various values which X can assume, we are led to the following proposition.

THEOREM.   For any real-valued function g, $g(X)$ is a random variable with

$$E[g(X)] = \int_{-\infty}^{\infty} g(x)f(x)\ dx \tag{2.8-3}$$

provided the integral exists.

It is to be noted that we present this result as a theorem rather than a definition. Although the preceding discussion is not a strict proof, the proposition is nevertheless capable of rigorous proof from our previous postulates and definitions.

For a given function g, $E[g(X)]$ depends on $f(x)$ and hence helps to characterize $f(x)$. For this reason one sometimes refers to an expectation generated by a certain function g as a *statistical parameter*. We now define the most common of these parameters. Similar definitions apply to the discrete and mixed distributions.

Mean (or average) value of $X = E[X] = \bar{X} = \int_{-\infty}^{\infty} x f(x)\, dx$ (2.8-4)

Mean-squared value of $X = E[X^2] = \overline{X^2} = \int_{-\infty}^{\infty} x^2 f(x)\, dx$ (2.8-5)

Variance of $X =$ mean-squared value of X about the mean

$$= E[(X - \bar{X})^2] = \int_{-\infty}^{\infty} (x - \bar{X})^2 f(x)\, dx$$

$$= \int_{-\infty}^{\infty} x^2 f(x)\, dx - 2\bar{X} \int_{-\infty}^{\infty} x f(x)\, dx$$

$$+ \bar{X}^2 \int_{-\infty}^{\infty} f(x)\, dx$$

$$= \overline{X^2} - \bar{X}^2$$ (2.8-6)

nth moment of $X = E[X^n] = \alpha_n = \int_{-\infty}^{\infty} x^n f(x)\, dx$ (2.8-7)

We observe that $\alpha_0 = 1$, $\alpha_1 = \bar{X}$, $\alpha_2 = \overline{X^2}$. The term *standard deviation* is also used and is usually denoted by σ. It is defined as the square root of the variance.

$$\sigma = \sqrt{E[(X - \bar{X})^2]}$$ (2.8-8)

There are a few obvious facts to be noted about the interpretation of these statistical parameters. First, if $f(x)$ is an even function, that is, $f(x) = f(-x)$, the mean, and indeed all of the odd-numbered moments, are zero. Second, if $f(x)$ is symmetric about any value x_0, then $\bar{X} = x_0$ and the odd-numbered moments about the mean, i.e., the values

$$\int_{-\infty}^{\infty} (x - \bar{X})^n f(x)\, dx$$

are zero. Third, if $f(x)$ is a curve sharply peaked at $\bar{X}$, the variance will be much smaller than if the curve is flattened out.

One sees that the moments tend to determine the frequency function and hence the distribution function. It can be proved in the particular case where the series $\sum_{0}^{\infty} \dfrac{\alpha_n}{n!} r^n$ is absolutely convergent for some $r > 0$ that the sequence of moments $(\alpha_0, \alpha_1, \alpha_2, \ldots)$ uniquely determines the distribution function.

The preceding statements can be extended in a fairly obvious manner to the case of two or more random variables. Thus, in particular, for a random variable g that is itself a function of two random variables X

and Y whose joint frequency function is $f(x,y)$, we have

$$E[g(X,Y)] = \int_{-\infty}^{\infty} dx \int_{-\infty}^{\infty} g(x,y)f(x,y) \, dy \qquad (2.8\text{-}9)$$

As a consequence of this relation, we observe that the expectation of the sum $X + Y$ of two random variables is the sum of their separate expectations. Writing $g(X,Y) = X + Y$, Eqs. (2.8-9), (2.7-35), and (2.7-36) yield

$$\begin{aligned}
E[X + Y] &= \int_{-\infty}^{\infty} dx \int_{-\infty}^{\infty} (x + y)f(x,y) \, dy \\
&= \int_{-\infty}^{\infty} x \left[\int_{-\infty}^{\infty} f(x,y) \, dy \right] dx \\
&\qquad + \int_{-\infty}^{\infty} y \left[\int_{-\infty}^{\infty} f(x,y) \, dx \right] dy \\
&= \int_{-\infty}^{\infty} xf_1(x) \, dx + \int_{-\infty}^{\infty} yf_2(y) \, dy \\
&= E[X] + E[Y] \qquad (2.8\text{-}10)
\end{aligned}$$

The extension of this relation to the case of n random variables follows at once by mathematical induction.

As a particular application of (2.8-9), we define the moments α_{jk} of the distribution of X and Y by

$$\alpha_{jk} = E[X^j Y^k] = \int_{-\infty}^{\infty} dx \int_{-\infty}^{\infty} x^j y^k f(x,y) \, dy \qquad (2.8\text{-}11)$$

for $j, k = 0, 1, 2, \ldots$. We observe that α_{n0} and α_{0n} are the respective nth moments of X and Y taken separately; in particular, α_{10} and α_{01} are simply the respective mean values.

Referring again to our notion of the probability density function, $f(x,y)$, as determining a mass density over the plane, it is noticed that the first moments α_{10} and α_{01} are the same as the x and y components of the center of gravity of the plane mass specified by $f(x,y)$. If we refer moments to this point $(\alpha_{10}, \alpha_{01})$, we have the *central moments* μ_{jk}:

$$\mu_{jk} = E[(X - \alpha_{10})^j (Y - \alpha_{01})^k] \qquad (2.8\text{-}12)$$

In particular,

$$\mu_{20} = E[(X - \alpha_{10})^2] = E[X^2 - 2X\alpha_{10} + \alpha_{10}^2] = \alpha_{20} - \alpha_{10}^2 \qquad (2.8\text{-}13)$$
$$\mu_{02} = E[(Y - \alpha_{01})^2] = \alpha_{02} - \alpha_{01}^2 \qquad (2.8\text{-}14)$$

and

$$\begin{aligned}
\mu_{11} &= E[(X - \alpha_{10})(Y - \alpha_{01})] \\
&= E[XY - Y\alpha_{10} - X\alpha_{01} + \alpha_{10}\alpha_{01}] = \alpha_{11} - \alpha_{10}\alpha_{01} \qquad (2.8\text{-}15)
\end{aligned}$$

μ_{20} and μ_{02} are the variances of X and Y, while μ_{11} is called the *covariance* of X and Y. The normalized covariance, denoted by ρ, is called the *correlation coefficient* of X and Y and is given by

$$\rho = \frac{\mu_{11}}{\sqrt{\mu_{20}\mu_{02}}} \tag{2.8-16}$$

The notion of the correlation between two random variables is one that is of particular importance, both in our later applications to random processes and more generally throughout the whole field of statistical analysis. To place this concept on a more concrete basis, we consider a random experiment possessing n distinct possible outcomes with probabilities $p_i(i = 1, 2, \ldots, n)$. With each of these outcomes let there be associated a pair (X,Y) of random variables. As an illustration, X might be a thermometer reading, Y the measured resistance of a resistor, and the n possible outcomes might be the finite collection of possible test results arising from the discrete scale subdivisions on the thermometer and ohmmeter. As a suitable sample space for this experiment we may choose the collection of n pairs of values (x_i,y_i) which the random variables (X,Y) may take on.

As noted previously, if we associate with each point (x_i,y_i) a mass equal to the probability p_i, the center of gravity of the resulting mass distribution is located at the point $(\bar{X},\bar{Y})$. In addition, the quantities $E[X^2]$, $E[Y^2]$, and $E[XY]$ are the respective moments of inertia and product of inertia of the mass distribution. For simplicity, we assume the center of gravity to be located at the origin of coordinates, so that $\bar{X} = \bar{Y} = 0$, and now wish to consider the possible interdependence of X and Y.

A common technique of empirical analysis used in attempting to approximate one set of data in terms of another is that of least squares. In the present application, we seek to determine that linear function $aX + b$ of the random variable X which gives the best fit to the variable Y in the sense of least squares. To be more specific, we seek those values of a and b which minimize the expression $E[(Y - aX - b)^2]$.

By a simple calculation we have

$$E[(Y - aX - b)^2] = \overline{Y^2} - 2a\overline{XY} + a^2\overline{X^2} - 2b\bar{Y} + 2ab\bar{X} + b^2 \tag{2.8-17}$$

Since $\bar{X} = \bar{Y} = 0$, however, the only term in this expression depending upon b is the quantity b^2. For any value of a, the best selection of b is therefore $b = 0$. To determine a, we differentiate (2.8-17) with respect to a, set the resulting expression equal to zero, and solve for a, obtaining

$$a = \frac{\overline{XY}}{\overline{X^2}}$$

Substitution of this value for a then gives

$$E[(Y - aX)^2] = \overline{Y^2}\left[1 - \frac{(\overline{XY})^2}{\overline{X^2}\,\overline{Y^2}}\right] \tag{2.8-18}$$

as the minimum attainable value for (2.8-17). Since the mean values of X and Y are zero, however, the quantities $\overline{X^2}$, $\overline{Y^2}$ and $\overline{XY}$ are simply the variances of X and Y and the covariance of these two variables, respectively. The expression (2.8-18) may therefore be rewritten in terms of the correlation coefficient (2.8-16) in the form

$$E[(Y - aX)^2] = \overline{Y^2}(1 - \rho^2) \qquad (2.8\text{-}19)$$

Examining this expression, we find that the correlation coefficient ρ is directly related to the minimum mean-squared error in fitting Y by a linear function of X. Consider, in the first instance, a case in which the points (x_i,y_i) all fall on a single straight line, so that Y is expressible in terms of X as a unique linear function. Then the minimum attainable value of (2.8-17) is zero, giving, by (2.8-19), $\rho = \pm 1$. If, on the other hand, we consider a case in which $\rho = 0$, (2.8-19) shows that the minimum attainable mean-squared error is the quantity $\overline{Y^2}$. Speaking loosely, this implies that the spread of the points (x_i,y_i) is such that no straight line gives a reasonable fit to the data. Thus, the correlation coefficient may be interpreted as a measure of the interdependence of X and Y.

In the special case in which the variables X and Y are statistically independent, the covariance is zero. To show this, we note from (2.8-4), (2.8-11), and (2.7-32) that

$$\begin{aligned}
\alpha_{11} &= \int_{-\infty}^{\infty} dx \int_{-\infty}^{\infty} xy f_1(x) f_2(y)\, dy \\
&= \int_{-\infty}^{\infty} x f_1(x)\, dx \int_{-\infty}^{\infty} y f_2(y)\, dy \\
&= \bar{X}\bar{Y} = \alpha_{10}\alpha_{01} \qquad (2.8\text{-}20)
\end{aligned}$$

Therefore, by (2.8-15),

$$\mu_{11} = \alpha_{11} - \alpha_{10}\alpha_{01} = 0 \qquad (2.8\text{-}21)$$

as asserted.

We have stated above that the correlation coefficient is a measure of the interdependence of X and Y. It should be carefully pointed out, however, that the correlation coefficient does not, of itself, completely determine the statistical dependence or independence of two random variables. To see this, we consider two special cases. In the first case, Y is chosen to be a nonlinear function of X; for example, $Y = X^2$. Then the value of Y is clearly determined completely by the value of X. Since, on the other hand, a parabola cannot be approximated by a straight line without error, clearly the value of ρ cannot be unity.

In the second case, we let X be an arbitrary random variable possessing a symmetric probability distribution about the origin, and let $Y = |X|$. Here, again, Y is completely determined by X. Since $f(x)$ is an even function and $\bar{X} = 0$, we have

$$E[(X - \bar{X})(Y - \bar{Y})] = E[X(Y - \bar{Y})] = E[XY] - \bar{X}\bar{Y}$$
$$= E[XY] = \int_{-\infty}^{\infty} x|x|f(x)\, dx = 0$$

The last step follows because the integrand is an odd function of x. Here, then, we have a case in which the covariance and hence the correlation coefficient are zero, and yet Y is functionally related to X. Thus a zero value for ρ does not of itself imply independence.

The calculations of (2.8-20) establish the two-dimensional case of the following theorem.

THEOREM.   Let the n random variables X_1, X_2, . . . , X_n be statistically independent.   Then

$$E[X_1 X_2 \cdots X_n] = E[X_1]E[X_2] \cdots E[X_n] \qquad (2.8\text{-}22)$$

The following theorem also follows immediately.

THEOREM.   The variance of the sum of a finite number of independent random variables is equal to the sum of the individual variances.   A similar statement applies to the third moments about the mean.

Example 2.8-4.   A coin is tossed with the events "heads" and "tails" occurring with probabilities p and q, respectively, where $p + q = 1$.   We wish to calculate the average number of heads and the mean-squared number of heads if the coin is tossed n times.   This problem may be easily solved if we introduce a random variable X_k to represent the outcome of the kth toss.   To be precise, let us define

$$X_k = \begin{cases} 1 & \text{if ``heads'' occurs on } k\text{th toss} \\ 0 & \text{if ``tails'' occurs on } k\text{th toss} \end{cases}$$

Then the variable X defined by

$$X = X_1 + X_2 + \cdots + X_n$$

has the desirable property that its value for each experiment is the total number of heads occurring in the n tosses.   The average of X_k is obtained by

$$E[X_k] = 0 \times \Pr(X_k = 0) + 1 \times \Pr(X_k = 1) = p \qquad k = 1, 2, \ldots, n$$

Therefore $\bar{X} = E[X] = E[X_1] + E[X_2] + \cdots + E[X_n] = np$

To compute $E[X^2]$, we note that

$$X^2 = \sum_{k=1}^{n} X_k^2 + 2 \sum_{j=1}^{n-1} \sum_{k=j+1}^{n} X_j X_k$$

Since $E[X_k^2] = 0^2 \times \Pr(X_k = 0) + 1^2 \times \Pr(X_k = 1) = p$

and since by the independence of X_j and X_k for $j \neq k$

$$E[X_j X_k] = E[X_j]E[X_k] = p^2$$

we have

$$E[X^2] = nE[X_k^2] + (n^2 - n)E[X_jX_k]$$
$$= np + (n^2 - n)p^2 = np(1 - p) + n^2p^2$$
$$= npq + n^2p^2$$

The variance of X is immediately given by

$$\sigma^2 = E[(X - \bar{X})^2] = E[X^2] - \bar{X}^2 = E[X^2] - (np)^2 = npq$$

Example 2.8-5. A ship is shelling a target on an enemy shore, firing n independent shots all of which may be assumed to fall on a straight line and to be distributed according to the probability frequency function $f(x)$ or the distribution function $F(x)$. If each shell has a lethal interval of length 2δ, we wish to find the average of the total lethal length of the attack.

This problem is most efficiently solved by means of characteristic set functions. Let X_1, X_2, . . . , X_n be independent variables representing the positions of the n shots along the line. For the moment, let the random variables X_i take on a fixed set of values. Then the function

$$C_i(x) = \begin{cases} 1 & \text{if } |X_i - x| < \delta \\ 0 & \text{otherwise} \end{cases}$$

is the characteristic function of the set consisting of the interval of length 2δ centered about X_i. The characteristic function of the complement of this set is $1 - C_i(x)$. The quantity

$$\prod_{i=1}^{n} [1 - C_i(x)]$$

is the characteristic function of the set of points which do not fall in any of the lethal intervals. Finally,

$$1 - \prod_{i=1}^{n} [1 - C_i(x)]$$

is the characteristic function of the set of points covered by at least one of these intervals and it is precisely this set whose average length we desire.

For any fixed value of x, the quantity $C_i(x)$ depends upon the random variable X_i, although this fact is not emphasized by our notation. The quantity $C_i(x)$ is therefore itself a random variable. Further, since the quantity $C_i(x)$ is dependent only upon the one random variable X_i, and since the variables X_i are independent, it follows that the random variables $C_i(x)$ are also independent.

Denoting the average total length by $\bar{L}$, we proceed in a formal manner as follows

$$\bar{L} = E\left[\int_{-\infty}^{\infty} \left\{ 1 - \prod_{i=1}^{n} [1 - C_i(x)] \right\} dx \right]$$

$$= \int_{-\infty}^{\infty} E\left[1 - \prod_{i=1}^{n} \{1 - C_i(x)\} \right] dx$$

$$= \int_{-\infty}^{\infty} \left\{ 1 - \prod_{i=1}^{n} E[1 - C_i(x)] \right\} dx$$

Now

$$E[1 - C_i(x)] = 1 - E[C_i(x)]$$
$$= 1 - \Pr(x - \delta < X_i < x + \delta)$$
$$= 1 - \int_{x-\delta}^{x+\delta} f(u) \, du$$
$$= 1 - [F(x + \delta) - F(x - \delta)]$$

Thus we have

$$\bar{L} = \int_{-\infty}^{\infty} \{1 - [1 - F(x + \delta) + F(x - \delta)]^n\} \, dx$$

This result can be put in a more compact form if the number n of shots fired is very large and the lethal interval 2δ is very small. If we define

$$\lambda = 2\delta n$$

then

$$F(x + \delta) - F(x - \delta) = \int_{x-\lambda/2n}^{x+\lambda/2n} f(u) \, du \cong f(x) \frac{\lambda}{n}$$

Now

$$\left[1 - f(x) \frac{\lambda}{n}\right]^n \cong e^{-\lambda f(x)}$$

so that the average may be written approximately as

$$\bar{L} \cong \int_{-\infty}^{\infty} (1 - e^{-\lambda f(x)}) \, dx$$

A concept that is frequently useful is that of the conditional expectation of a random variable subject to a specified hypothesis. Let A be an arbitrary event of positive probability. For the random variable X, we have defined the conditional distribution function

$$F_A(x) = \Pr(X \leq x \mid A) = \frac{\Pr(X \leq x \text{ and } A)}{P(A)} \tag{2.8-23}$$

Let $f_A(x)$ denote the corresponding frequency function

$$f_A(x) = \frac{dF_A(x)}{dx} \tag{2.8-24}$$

We then introduce the following definition.

Definition. The *conditional expectation* of a quantity $g(X)$, subject to hypothesis A, is given by

$$E[g(X) \mid A] = \int_{-\infty}^{\infty} g(x) f_A(x) \, dx \tag{2.8-25}$$

The nature of the conditional expectation of a random variable can be seen from the following discussion. Let a random experiment be performed with a probability function $P(E)$, and let $P(A)$ be positive. We consider a second experiment that is identical with the first in all respects except that every trial is rejected in which event A does not occur. Let $P_A(E)$ be the probability function for this second experiment. It is verified without difficulty that $P_A(E) = P(E \mid A)$. Since

$P_A(E)$ is a probability function, the set function $P(E \mid A)$, considered as a function of E for fixed A, is itself a probability function. It is immediately evident that the conditional functions $F_A(x)$ and $f_A(x)$ are precisely the distribution and frequency functions pertaining to our second experiment. Consequently $E[g(X) \mid A]$ is simply the numerical average of $g(X)$ under the same conditions; i.e., for the modified experiment in which all trials are rejected for which A does not occur.

Example 2.8-6. Let the event A be $(a < X \leq b)$. Then

$$F_A(x) = \Pr\ (X \leq x \mid a < X \leq b)$$
$$= \frac{\Pr\ (X \leq x \text{ and } a < X \leq b)}{\Pr\ (a < X \leq b)}$$

Thus
$$F_A(x) = \begin{cases} 0 & \text{if } x \leq a \\ \dfrac{F(x) - F(a)}{F(b) - F(a)} & \text{if } a < x \leq b \\ 1 & \text{if } b < x \end{cases}$$

Consequently $f_A(x) = 0$ unless $a < x \leq b$, and

$$f_A(x) = \frac{f(x)}{\displaystyle\int_a^b f(x)\ dx} \qquad a < x \leq b$$

We thus find

$$E[g(X) \mid A] = \frac{\displaystyle\int_a^b g(x)f(x)\ dx}{\displaystyle\int_a^b f(x)\ dx}$$

We conclude this section with the derivation of a useful relation involving conditional expectation. Let A_1, A_2, A_3, . . . be a finite or countably infinite sequence of mutually exclusive events, each of which has positive probability of occurrence, such that $\Sigma A_i = \mathfrak{S}$ is the complete sample space. Then for any random variable X,

$$E[X] = \Sigma P(A_i)E[X \mid A_i] \tag{2.8-26}$$

To establish this relation, we note that since the events A_i are mutually exclusive,

$$F(x) = \Pr\ (X \leq x) = \Pr\ (X \leq x \text{ and } \mathfrak{S})$$
$$= \Sigma\ \Pr\ (X \leq x \text{ and } A_i)$$
$$= \Sigma P(A_i)\ \Pr\ (X \leq x \mid A_i)$$
$$= \Sigma P(A_i)F_{A_i}(x)$$

Differentiation with respect to x yields

$$f(x) = \Sigma P(A_i)f_{A_i}(x)$$

We thus find

$$E[X] = \int_{-\infty}^{\infty} xf(x)\ dx = \Sigma P(A_i) \int_{-\infty}^{\infty} xf_{A_i}(x)\ dx$$
$$= \Sigma P(A_i)E[X \mid A_i]$$

as asserted.

2.9 Characteristic Functions

The *characteristic function* $\phi(t)$ of a random variable X with frequency function $f(x)$ is defined by

$$\phi(t) = E[e^{jtX}] = \int_{-\infty}^{\infty} e^{jtx} f(x) \, dx \qquad (2.9\text{-}1)$$

where t is an arbitrary real-valued parameter and $j = \sqrt{-1}$. Equation (2.9-1) also defines $\phi(t)$ as the inverse Fourier transform of $f(x)$, but it is customary in statistical theory to refer to it as the characteristic function. The characteristic function always exists; that is, the integral defining $\phi(t)$ converges for every frequency function $f(x)$. Furthermore it is known that $f(x)$ is uniquely determined by its characteristic function; no two frequency functions can have the same characteristic function. This fact follows from the inversion formula (2.9-7).

The inversion formula corresponding to Eq. (2.9-1) follows immediately from the theory of Fourier transforms, but it is interesting to derive this relation directly from a probabilistic point of view.

A standard formula which may be found in any table of integrals is

$$\frac{1}{\pi} \int_{-\infty}^{\infty} \frac{\sin au}{u} \, du = \begin{cases} 1 & \text{if } a > 0 \\ 0 & \text{if } a = 0 \\ -1 & \text{if } a < 0 \end{cases} \qquad (2.9\text{-}2)$$

The function $(1 - \cos au)/u$ is an odd function of u so that its integral over a symmetric range vanishes. Using these facts, it is easy to establish the equation

$$\frac{1}{2} - \frac{1}{2\pi} \int_{-\infty}^{\infty} \frac{\sin au + j(1 - \cos au)}{u} \, du = \begin{cases} 0 & \text{if } a > 0 \\ \frac{1}{2} & \text{if } a = 0 \\ 1 & \text{if } a < 0 \end{cases} \qquad (2.9\text{-}3)$$

If we replace a by $X - x$ and introduce complex exponentials in place of the sine and cosine appearing in Eq. (2.9-3) we obtain

$$\frac{1}{2} - \frac{j}{2\pi} \int_{-\infty}^{\infty} \frac{1 - e^{j(X-x)u}}{u} \, du = \begin{cases} 1 & \text{if } X < x \\ \frac{1}{2} & \text{if } X = x \\ 0 & \text{if } X > x \end{cases} \qquad (2.9\text{-}4)$$

For a fixed value of x this quantity is a function of X and may therefore be regarded as defining a new random variable $Y(X)$ over the same sample space as the one associated with X. The random variable Y takes on the discrete values 0, $\frac{1}{2}$, and 1. Thus, we may write

$$E[Y] = 1 \times \Pr\,(X < x) + \tfrac{1}{2} \times \Pr\,(X = x) + 0 \times \Pr\,(X > x)$$

$$\text{(2.9-5)}$$

If x is a point of continuity of the distribution function $F(x)$, then $\Pr\,(X = x) = 0$. Proceeding formally, we may write the expectation of Y from Eqs. (2.9-4) and (2.9-5) as

$$E[Y] = \Pr\,(X < x) = F(x) = \frac{1}{2} - \frac{j}{2\pi} \int_{-\infty}^{\infty} \frac{1 - E[e^{i(X-x)u}]}{u}\, du$$

$$= \frac{1}{2} - \frac{j}{2\pi} \int_{-\infty}^{\infty} \frac{1 - e^{-jxu}\phi(u)}{u}\, du \qquad \text{(2.9-6)}$$

using Eq. (2.9-1). If we differentiate Eq. (2.9-6) with respect to x, we obtain the desired inversion formula

$$f(x) = \frac{1}{2\pi} \int_{-\infty}^{\infty} e^{-jxu}\phi(u)\, du \qquad \text{(2.9-7)}$$

For the case of discrete distributions we may apply these results by proceeding in a formal manner using the delta-function concept introduced in Sec. 2.7. Thus, the characteristic function of $\delta(x,\epsilon)$ defined in Eq. (2.7-19) may be found directly by using Eq. (2.9-1) to obtain

$$\phi_\epsilon(t) = \int_{-\epsilon}^{\epsilon} \frac{1}{2\epsilon} e^{jtx}\, dx = \frac{\sin \epsilon t}{\epsilon t} \qquad \text{(2.9-8)}$$

Passing to the limit as ϵ approaches zero, we obtain $\phi(t) = 1$ as the characteristic function of $\delta(x)$. Similarly we find the characteristic function of $\delta(x - x_1)$ to be e^{jtx_1}. Therefore, if we wish to make use of the inversion formula (2.9-7), at least in a formal way, we must have

$$\delta(x - x_1) = \frac{1}{2\pi} \int_{-\infty}^{\infty} e^{-j(x-x_1)u}\, du \qquad \text{(2.9-9)}$$

One of the most important uses of characteristic functions follows from the inversion formula (2.9-7). In many problems when it is required to find the frequency function of a certain random variable, it is easier to compute the characteristic function first and from this find the density function, using (2.9-7).

The following theorem follows immediately from the definition of a characteristic function and from the theorem on products of independent random variables. The proof is left as an exercise.

THEOREM. The characteristic function of a sum of independent random variables is equal to the product of the characteristic functions of the individual variables.

Example 2.9-1. Let us consider as an illustration of the application of characteristic functions the two-dimensional random walk problem. A man starts at the origin and takes a step in any direction of length Δ. He then stops, selects a new arbitrary direction, and proceeds to take another step of length Δ in this new direction. He continues his walk for n steps. The angles through which he proceeds on the n steps are chosen independently and at random and thus may be taken as independent random variables. Therefore, let α_k be a random variable whose value determines the angle made with the x axis in the kth step and assume that it is uniformly distributed from 0 to 2π (that is, the frequency function is $1/2\pi$ for $0 \leq \alpha_k \leq 2\pi$ and zero elsewhere). The problem is to find the probability frequency function of the x coordinate of the man's position after n steps.

Let X be the random variable whose frequency function is desired. Then

$$X = \Delta \sum_{k=1}^{n} \cos \alpha_k$$

and the characteristic function of X is

$$\phi(t) = E[e^{jtX}] = E\left[\exp\left(jt\Delta \sum_{k=1}^{n} \cos \alpha_k \right) \right]$$

Since the steps are independent, $\phi(t)$ may be written as

$$\phi(t) = \prod_{k=1}^{n} E[\exp (jt\Delta \cos \alpha_k)]$$

Since the variable α_k is uniformly distributed over the interval $(0,2\pi)$, we have

$$E[\exp (jt\Delta \cos \alpha_k)] = \frac{1}{2\pi} \int_0^{2\pi} \exp (jt\Delta \cos \alpha)\, d\alpha$$

which is precisely the Bessel function of the first kind of order zero with argument $t\Delta$ and denoted by $J_0(t\Delta)$. Thus, the characteristic function of X is simply

$$\phi(t) = [J_0(t\Delta)]^n$$

Since this is an even function, we may express the frequency function in the form

$$f(x) = \frac{1}{2\pi} \int_{-\infty}^{\infty} [J_0(u\Delta)]^n \cos xu\, du$$

using Eq. (2.9-7).

A tremendous simplification results when the number of steps n is large and the length of each step is of the order of $1/\sqrt{n}$. For if we write

$$\Delta = \frac{m}{\sqrt{n}}$$

where m is a fixed constant, we have

$$\phi(t) = \left(1 - \frac{m^2t^2}{2^2 n} + \frac{m^4t^4}{2^2 4^2 n^2} - \cdots \right)^n \cong e^{-m^2t^2/4}$$

for large n. Thus

$$f(x) \cong \frac{1}{2\pi} \int_{-\infty}^{\infty} e^{-m^2u^2/4} \cos xu\, du$$

which reduces to

$$f(x) \cong \frac{1}{m \sqrt{\pi}} e^{-x^2/m^2}$$

This last result is an illustration of the central-limit theorem which will be discussed at the end of this chapter.

Another of the important uses of the characteristic function is in the determination of the moments of a distribution. If we expand $\phi(t)$ in its MacLaurin series, we have

$$\phi(t) = \phi(0) + \phi'(0) + \phi''(0) \frac{t^2}{2!} + \cdots + \phi^{(n)}(0) \frac{t^n}{n!} + \cdots \quad (2.9\text{-}10)$$

where
$$\phi(0) = \int_{-\infty}^{\infty} f(x) \, dx = 1$$

$$\phi'(0) = \int_{-\infty}^{\infty} jx f(x) \, dx = j\bar{X} = j\alpha_1 \quad (2.9\text{-}11)$$

$$\phi^{(n)}(0) = \int_{-\infty}^{\infty} \left(\frac{\partial^n}{\partial t^n} e^{jtx}\right)_{t=0} f(x) \, dx = j^n \alpha_n$$

Thus
$$\phi(t) = 1 + \sum_{n=1}^{\infty} \frac{(jt)^n \alpha_n}{n!} \quad (2.9\text{-}12)$$

Equation (2.9-12) gives the moments of the distribution in terms of the coefficients of the expansion for $\phi(t)$. Specifically

$$\alpha_n = j^{-n} \phi^{(n)}(0) \quad (2.9\text{-}13)$$

Another expansion which we shall find useful in our later work is the power series development for the logarithm of the characteristic function. Thus, suppose we have

$$\log \phi(t) = \sum_{k=1}^{\infty} \frac{\lambda_k}{k!} (jt)^k \quad (2.9\text{-}14)$$

Then by forming the exponential of $\log \phi(t)$, expanding this in a power series in jt, and equating coefficients to those of corresponding powers in (2.9-12), we obtain the following relations between the α's and λ's.

$$\begin{aligned}
\lambda_1 &= \alpha_1 \\
\lambda_2 &= \alpha_2 - \alpha_1^2 \\
\lambda_3 &= \alpha_3 - 3\alpha_1\alpha_2 + 2\alpha_1^3 \\
\lambda_4 &= \alpha_4 - 3\alpha_2^2 - 4\alpha_1\alpha_3 + 12\alpha_1^2\alpha_2 - 6\alpha_1^4
\end{aligned} \quad (2.9\text{-}15)$$
$$\cdots \cdots \cdots \cdots \cdots \cdots \cdots \cdots \cdots$$

Thus, we see that λ_1 is the first moment or mean value, λ_2 is the second moment about the mean or the square of the standard deviation, while λ_3 is the third moment about the mean. The other λ's are related to the higher central moments but not in such a simple fashion.

Turning to the case of two random variables, the *joint characteristic function* of X and Y is defined by

$$\phi(s,t) = E[e^{j(sX+tY)}] = \int_{-\infty}^{\infty} \int_{-\infty}^{\infty} e^{j(sx+ty)} f(x,y) \, dx \, dy \qquad (2.9\text{-}16)$$

The corresponding inversion formula is found to be

$$f(x,y) = \frac{1}{(2\pi)^2} \int_{-\infty}^{\infty} \int_{-\infty}^{\infty} e^{-j(sx+ty)} \phi(s,t) \, ds \, dt \qquad (2.9\text{-}17)$$

and may be derived in essentially the same way as in the one-dimensional case.

As in the case of one variable, the power series expansion of $\phi(s,t)$ in terms of s and t at once gives the moments of the distribution. Thus we see that

$$\left[\frac{\partial^{m+n}}{\partial s^m \partial t^n} \phi(s,t) \right]_{s=t=0}$$
$$= \int_{-\infty}^{\infty} dx \int_{-\infty}^{\infty} \left[\frac{\partial^{m+n}}{\partial s^m \partial t^n} e^{j(sx+ty)} \right]_{s=t=0} f(x,y) \, dy$$
$$= \int_{-\infty}^{\infty} dx \int_{-\infty}^{\infty} [(jx)^m (jy)^n] f(x,y) \, dy = j^{m+n} \alpha_{mn} \qquad (2.9\text{-}18)$$

Thus
$$\phi(s,t) = \sum_{m=0}^{\infty} \sum_{n=0}^{\infty} \frac{s^m t^n}{m! n!} \left[\frac{\partial^{m+n}}{\partial s^m \partial t^n} \phi(s,t) \right]_{s=t=0}$$
$$= \sum_{m=0}^{\infty} \sum_{n=0}^{\infty} \frac{\alpha_{mn}}{m! n!} (js)^m (jt)^n \qquad (2.9\text{-}19)$$

Let us consider now a *random vector* $\mathbf{Z}$ (in two dimensions) whose components are two random variables X and Y. We say that the random vectors $\mathbf{Z}_1$ and $\mathbf{Z}_2$ are *independent*, provided that for any pair of two-dimensional sets S_1 and S_2,

$$\Pr (\mathbf{Z}_1 \text{ in } S_1 \text{ and } \mathbf{Z}_2 \text{ in } S_2) = \Pr (\mathbf{Z}_1 \text{ in } S_1) \Pr (\mathbf{Z}_2 \text{ in } S_2) \qquad (2.9\text{-}20)$$

A similar definition applies to the mutual independence of n random vectors. Note that the independence of $\mathbf{Z}_1$ and $\mathbf{Z}_2$ implies the independence of the x components X_1 and X_2, and the independence of the y components also. The converse proposition is false, in general, as evidenced by the vectors $\mathbf{Z}_1 = (U,W)$ and $\mathbf{Z}_2 = (W,U)$, where U and W are independent random variables.

The characteristic function of the vector $\mathbf{Z}$ is defined to be the function $\phi(s,t)$ given by (2.9-16). The following proposition is stated without proof.

THEOREM. The characteristic function of the sum of n independent random vectors is the product of their separate characteristic functions.

The extension of these various notions to the case of n random variables (or n-dimensional random vectors) follows without difficulty, and is not considered further.

2.10   The Binomial Distribution

Consider an experiment which can have but two results, e.g., tossing a coin, one of which we shall call success and the other failure. Denote the probability of success by p and the probability of failure by $q = 1 - p$. Let this same experiment be performed n times so that the individual trials are independent, and let the random variable X be the total number of successes in n trials. The distribution function for X, which we shall find, is the binomial distribution function.

One phase of this problem has been considered in Example 2.8-4. There we were interested in finding the average number of successes in n trials rather than the actual distribution of these successes. The latter problem in most practical instances is a rather formidable one and usually one must be satisfied with a computation of a few of the various statistical parameters such as the mean or standard deviation. However, for this simple problem the distribution is relatively easy to find. We shall carry through the computation in both a direct and indirect manner, the latter method illustrating the use of characteristic functions.

The random variable X may assume the values 0, 1, 2, . . . , n. The probability that $X = k$ is precisely the probability of k successes and $n - k$ failures in n trials. Now since the trials are independent and the probability of success in each is the same, the probability of k successes and $n - k$ failures occurring in a particularly prescribed order is $p^k q^{n-k}$. The number of distinct ways of obtaining precisely k successes is $\binom{n}{k}$†, and therefore the probability of k successes and $n - k$ failures is $\binom{n}{k} p^k q^{n-k}$. Then, from Eq. (2.7-21),

---

† The symbol $\binom{n}{k}$, where n and k are positive integers such that $k \leq n$, is used to denote the number of subsets of k items contained in a set of n items (with the order of the items in the subsets disregarded), or, in classical terminology, "the number of combinations of n things taken k at a time." It is easy to show that

$$\binom{n}{k} = \frac{n!}{k!(n-k)!}$$

whence $\binom{n}{k} = \binom{n}{n-k}$. It may also be shown that $\binom{n}{k}$ is the kth coefficient in the expansion of $(a + b)^n$, so that it is customary to refer to the values $\binom{n}{k}$ as the *binomial coefficients*.

$$f(x) = \sum_{k=0}^{n} \binom{n}{k} p^k q^{n-k} \delta(x - k) \tag{2.10-1}$$

The distribution function is then found from Eq. (2.7-22) so that

$$F(x) = \sum_{k=0}^{[x]} \binom{n}{k} p^k q^{n-k} \tag{2.10-2}$$

Here we use the symbol $[x]$ to denote the greatest integer less than or equal to x.

The same result may be obtained in a more routine fashion using characteristic functions. Using the notation of Example 2.8-4, we first calculate the characteristic function of X_k. The distribution function of X_k is given by

$$f_k(x) = p\delta(x - 1) + q\delta(x) \tag{2.10-3}$$

so that the characteristic function is, by Eq. (2.9-1),

$$\phi_k(t) = \int_{-\infty}^{\infty} e^{itx}[p\delta(x - 1) + q\delta(x)]\, dx \tag{2.10-4}$$

To carry out the integration, we refer to Eq. (2.7-20) and thereby obtain

$$\phi_k(t) = pe^{it} + q \tag{2.10-5}$$

Since the X_k's are mutually independent random variables, the characteristic function of their sum is given by

$$\phi(t) = E[e^{itX}] = \prod_{k=1}^{n} \phi_k(t) = (pe^{it} + q)^n \tag{2.10-6}$$

This expression may be expanded by means of the binomial theorem to give

$$\phi(t) = \sum_{k=0}^{n} \binom{n}{k} p^k q^{n-k} e^{itk} \tag{2.10-7}$$

We may now apply the inversion formula (2.9-7) and interpret the integrals by means of Eq. (2.9-9). The result is again Eq. (2.10-1). The mean, the mean-squared value, and the standard deviation of the random variable X were computed in Example 2.8-4.

2.11 The Poisson Distribution

We wish in this section to consider a mathematical model of a problem whose physical counterpart is the random emission of electrons from the filament of a vacuum tube, or the spontaneous decomposition of radioactive atomic nuclei. In particular, we wish to determine the probability distribution of the number of electrons emitted (or of the number of nuclei disintegrating) in a specified interval of time.

Let $E_k(t_1,t_2)$ be the event that exactly k electrons are emitted during a time interval $t_1 < t < t_2$; for simplicity we write

$$p_k(t_1,t_2) = \Pr [E_k(t_1,t_2)] \qquad (2.11\text{-}1)$$

To study this problem we make the following three assumptions:

1. The numbers of electrons emitted in any finite collection of non-overlapping time intervals form a set of independent random variables. Stated another way, the events $E_j(t_1,t_2)$, $E_k(t_3,t_4)$, $E_m(t_5,t_6)$, . . . , are independent for any indices j, k, m, . . . , where $t_1 < t_2 < t_3 < t_4 < t_5 < \cdots$.

2. For sufficiently small Δt,

$$p_1(t, t + \Delta t) = \lambda(t) \Delta t + o(\Delta t) \qquad (2.11\text{-}2)$$

where $o(\Delta t)$ stands for terms in Δt such that

$$\lim_{\Delta t \to 0} \frac{o(\Delta t)}{\Delta t} = 0 \qquad (2.11\text{-}3)$$

The quantity $\lambda(t)$ is the average density or rate of emission at time t. In most treatments λ is chosen to be constant; however, there is no difficulty in allowing it to vary with time, and we can thereby study certain transient problems.

3. We further assume that for Δt sufficiently small, the probability of emission of two or more electrons in an interval of length Δt is negligibly small. In symbols,

$$\sum_{k=2}^{\infty} p_k(t, t + \Delta t) = o(\Delta t) \qquad (2.11\text{-}4)$$

From (2.11-2) and (2.11-4) we thus find

$$p_0(t, t + \Delta t) = \Pr [E_0(t, t + \Delta t)] = 1 - \lambda(t) \Delta t + o(\Delta t) \quad (2.11\text{-}5)$$

On the basis of these assumptions we may readily derive a differential equation for p_0. Let t_0 be fixed and t variable. Then the event "no electrons emitted in $(t_0, t + \Delta t)$" is equivalent to the simultaneous events "none in (t_0, t)" and "none in $(t, t + \Delta t)$." In other words, $E_0(t_0, t + \Delta t)$ can be expressed as the intersection of the events $E_0(t_0, t)$ and $E_0(t, t + \Delta t)$. Thus since these events are independent,

$$\begin{aligned} p_0(t_0, t + \Delta t) &= \Pr [E_0(t_0, t)] \Pr [E_0(t, t + \Delta t)] \\ &= p_0(t_0, t)[1 - \lambda(t) \Delta t + o(\Delta t)] \end{aligned}$$

giving

$$\frac{p_0(t_0, t + \Delta t) - p_0(t_0, t)}{\Delta t} = -\lambda(t)p_0(t_0, t) + \frac{o(\Delta t)}{\Delta t} \qquad (2.11\text{-}6)$$

In the limit as $\Delta t \to 0$, this relation becomes

$$\frac{\partial}{\partial t} p_0(t_0, t) = -\lambda(t) p_0(t_0, t) \tag{2.11-7}$$

Since $p_0(t_0, t_0) = 1$, we readily obtain

$$p_0(t_0, t) = \exp\left[-\int_{t_0}^{t} \lambda(\tau)\, d\tau \right] \tag{2.11-8}$$

Turning to the calculation of p_1, we observe that exactly one electron can be emitted in $(t_0, t + \Delta t)$, either by having one emission in (t_0, t) and none in $(t, t + \Delta t)$, or vice versa. Thus

$$E_1(t_0, t + \Delta t) = E_1(t_0, t) E_0(t, t + \Delta t) + E_0(t_0, t) E_1(t, t + \Delta t) \tag{2.11-9}$$

and, taking probabilities, we have

$$p_1(t_0, t + \Delta t) = p_1(t_0, t)[1 - \lambda(t)\, \Delta t] + p_0(t_0, t)\lambda(t)\, \Delta t + o(\Delta t) \tag{2.11-10}$$

We therefore find

$$\frac{\partial}{\partial t} p_1(t_0, t) = -\lambda(t) p_1(t_0, t) + \lambda(t) p_0(t_0, t) \tag{2.11-11}$$

We now define a new variable μ by the relation

$$\mu = \int_{t_0}^{t} \lambda(\tau)\, d\tau \tag{2.11-12}$$

Then (2.11-11) becomes

$$\frac{\partial p_1}{\partial \mu} = -p_1 + p_0 = -p_1 + e^{-\mu} \tag{2.11-13}$$

possessing the solution

$$p_1(t_0, t) = \mu e^{-\mu} = \left[\int_{t_0}^{t} \lambda(\tau)\, d\tau \right] \exp\left[-\int_{t_0}^{t} \lambda(\tau)\, d\tau \right] \tag{2.11-14}$$

There is no difficulty in establishing the general result

$$p_k(t_0, t) = \frac{1}{k!} \left[\int_{t_0}^{t} \lambda(\tau)\, d\tau \right]^k \exp\left[-\int_{t_0}^{t} \lambda(\tau)\, d\tau \right] \tag{2.11-15}$$

We assume this relation to be true for $k = 0, 1, 2, \ldots, n - 1$, and proceed to establish it for $k = n$ also. We note that

$$E_n(t_0, t + \Delta t) = \sum_{k=0}^{n} E_k(t_0, t) E_{n-k}(t, t + \Delta t) \tag{2.11-16}$$

In this sum of mutually exclusive events, all terms but the last two possess negligible probability for small Δt; thus

$$p_n(t_0, t + \Delta t) = p_{n-1}(t_0, t)\lambda(t)\, \Delta t + p_n(t_0, t)[1 - \lambda(t)\, \Delta t] + o(\Delta t)$$

Letting Δt approach zero as before, and using μ as the independent variable,

$$\frac{\partial p_n}{\partial \mu} = -p_n + p_{n-1}$$

$$= -p_n + \frac{1}{(n-1)!}\, \mu^{n-1} e^{-\mu} \tag{2.11-17}$$

where we use (2.11-15) with k replaced by $n - 1$. Then

$$p_n = \frac{1}{n!}\, \mu^n e^{-\mu} \tag{2.11-18}$$

and our result is established by induction.

For the special case in which λ is a constant and the interval length is t, we have $\mu = \lambda t$, and

$$p_n(t) = \frac{1}{n!}\, (\lambda t)^n e^{-\lambda t} \tag{2.11-19}$$

If we define a random variable $X(t)$ which can assume the values $n = 0$, $1, 2, \ldots$ with probabilities p_n, then the distribution function of $X(t)$ is

$$F(x,t) = e^{-\lambda t} \sum_{n=0}^{[x]} \frac{(\lambda t)^n}{n!} \tag{2.11-20}$$

and represents the probability that no more than $[x]$ electrons are emitted from the filament in time t. $F(x,t)$ is called the Poisson distribution function. The mean and standard deviation of $X(t)$ are both found to be

$$\overline{X(t)} = \sigma^2 = \lambda t \tag{2.11-21}$$

The Poisson distribution can be derived from a somewhat different viewpoint in the following manner. Suppose that n points $(t_1, t_2, \ldots, t_n)$ are distributed independently along the time axis, each with the probability frequency function $f(t)$. Let a time interval $t' < t < t''$ be selected, and let a random variable X_k be defined to be unity if t_k lies in this interval and zero otherwise. The total number of points in this interval is the random variable

$$X = \sum_{k=1}^{n} X_k \tag{2.11-22}$$

and it is the distribution of X that we wish to study.

We first note that

$$\overline{X_k} = E[X_k] = 1 \times \Pr\,(t' < t_k < t'') = \int_{t'}^{t''} f(t)\, dt$$

Thus from (2.11-22),

$$\bar{X} = n \int_{t'}^{t''} f(t)\, dt = np \qquad (2.11\text{-}23)$$

where p is the probability that a single point t_k falls within the interval.

To compute the distribution of X, we observe from Eq. (2.11-22) that X is the total number of "successes" in the n independent experiments which consist in examining each point t_k in succession to determine whether $t' < t_k < t''$. The distribution in question is thus the binomial distribution, and we have, from Sec. 2.10,

$$\Pr\,(X = m) = \binom{n}{m} p^m (1 - p)^{n-m} \qquad (2.11\text{-}24)$$

We now wish to let n become infinite, and simultaneously let p approach zero, in such manner that the product $np = \mu$ remains fixed. It is noted from (2.11-23) that μ is the average number of points falling between t' and t''; thus this quantity has the same significance as previously.

From (2.11-24),

$$\Pr\,(X = m) = \binom{n}{m} \left(\frac{\mu}{n}\right)^m \left(1 - \frac{\mu}{n}\right)^{n-m} \qquad (2.11\text{-}25)$$

In the limit, as n becomes infinite, we find

$$\Pr\,(X = m) = \frac{\mu^m}{m!}\, e^{-\mu} \qquad (2.11\text{-}26)$$

in agreement with (2.11-18). The limit can readily be established by expressing $\binom{n}{m}$ in terms of factorials, using the Stirling approximation for $n!$ and $(n - m)!$, and using the relation $\lim_{n \to \infty} (1 + x/n)^n = e^x$. The details are left as an exercise.

2.12   The Normal Distribution and the Central-limit Theorem

A random variable X is *normally distributed* if it has a frequency function given by

$$f(x) = \frac{1}{\sigma \sqrt{2\pi}}\, e^{-(x-m)^2/2\sigma^2} \qquad (2.12\text{-}1)$$

where m is any real constant and σ is any positive constant. The parameters m and σ are introduced in (2.12-1) in such fashion that the mean value of X is m and the standard deviation is σ. The constant $1/\sigma \sqrt{2\pi}$ is a normalizing factor which makes the infinite integral of (2.12-1) equal to one. Obviously the equation $Y = (X - m)/\sigma$ defines a normally distributed random variable Y with mean of zero and standard deviation of unity.

We have encountered the normal distribution previously in the random walk problem discussed in Sec. 2.9. This normal distribution resulted when the number of steps taken was very large, while the length of each step was itself very small. A similar result is obtained in many practical applications when we are dealing with a large number of observations, each of which contributes only a small amount to the outcome of an experiment. This statement is verified on one hand by statistical experience. Indeed, it is a fact that many distributions which are encountered in the physical world are either normal or approximately normal. This remarkable state of affairs has some basis mathematically in the so called central-limit theorem which we shall now discuss.

Let X_1, X_2, . . . , X_n be independent random variables and denote by m_i, σ_i, μ_i the mean, the standard deviation, and the third moment about the mean of X_i. Then the sum

$$X = \sum_{i=1}^{n} X_i \tag{2.12-2}$$

will have a mean m, variance σ^2, and third central moment μ given by

$$m = \sum_{i=1}^{n} m_i \qquad \sigma^2 = \sum_{i=1}^{n} \sigma_i^2 \qquad \mu = \sum_{i=1}^{n} \mu_i \tag{2.12-3}$$

We now form a new normalized variable Y so that

$$Y = \frac{X - m}{\sigma} \tag{2.12-4}$$

Since the X_i's are independent, it is easy to verify that the characteristic function of Y is

$$\phi(t) = E[e^{jtY}] = e^{-jmt/\sigma} \prod_{i=1}^{n} \phi_i\left(\frac{t}{\sigma}\right) \tag{2.12-5}$$

where $\phi_i(t)$ is the characteristic function of X_i. Taking the logarithm of Eq. (2.12-5) we have

$$\log \phi(t) = -\frac{jmt}{\sigma} + \sum_{i=1}^{n} \log \phi_i\left(\frac{t}{\sigma}\right) \tag{2.12-6}$$

and it follows from Eq. (2.9-14) that

$$\log \phi_i\left(\frac{t}{\sigma}\right) = \sum_{k=1}^{\infty} \frac{\lambda_{ik}}{k!}\left(\frac{jt}{\sigma}\right)^k \tag{2.12-7}$$

where $\qquad \lambda_{i1} = m_i \qquad \lambda_{i2} = \sigma_i^2 \qquad \lambda_{i3} = \mu_i \tag{2.12-8}$

Substituting Eqs. (2.12-7) and (2.12-8) into Eq. (2.12-6) and using Eqs. (2.12-3), we obtain

$$\log \phi(t) = -\frac{t^2}{2} - \frac{j\mu t^3}{6\sigma^3} + \sum_{k=4}^{\infty} \frac{\lambda_k}{k!}\left(\frac{jt}{\sigma}\right)^k \tag{2.12-9}$$

where we have defined $\lambda_k = \sum_{i=1}^{n} \lambda_{ik}$.

The central-limit theorem states that under certain circumstances

$$\lim_{n \to \infty} \log \phi(t) = -\frac{t^2}{2} \tag{2.12-10}$$

However, the characteristic function of a normal distribution with mean zero and standard deviation one is

$$\begin{aligned}
\phi(t) &= \frac{1}{\sqrt{2\pi}} \int_{-\infty}^{\infty} e^{jxt}e^{-x^2/2}\, dx \\
&= \frac{1}{\sqrt{2\pi}} \int_{-\infty}^{\infty} e^{-(x-jt)^2/2}e^{-t^2/2}\, dx \\
&= e^{-t^2/2} \frac{1}{\sqrt{2\pi}} \int_{-\infty}^{\infty} e^{-z^2/2}\, dz \\
&= e^{-t^2/2} \tag{2.12-11}
\end{aligned}$$

It would then follow from the uniqueness property of characteristic functions that Y in the limit would be normally distributed.

The truth of the theorem may be made quite plausible for the case in which the X_i's are identically distributed. We would then have

$$\sigma^2 = n\sigma_1^2 \qquad \mu = n\mu_1 \qquad \lambda_k = n\lambda_{1k}$$

so that each of the terms in Eq. (2.12-9) except the first would be of order $1/\sqrt{n}$ or higher and would each tend to zero as n approached infinity.

When the X_i's are not identically distributed, the theorem may be proved under the following requirement. Define β_i to be the third absolute moment of X_i about the mean, that is,

$$\beta_i = E[|X_i - m_i|^3] \tag{2.12-12}$$

and let

$$\beta = \sum_{i=1}^{n} \beta_i \tag{2.12-13}$$

Then a sufficient condition for the truth of the central-limit theorem is that

$$\lim_{n \to \infty} \frac{\beta}{\sigma^3} = 0 \tag{2.12-14}$$

Example 2.12-1. Consider again the coin-tossing experiment described in Example 2.8-4. The random variables X_k all have the same distribution with mean p and standard deviation $\sqrt{pq}$. The arithmetic mean of the variables X_k is X/n so that the new normalized variable Y defined in the central-limit theorem is

$$Y = \frac{(X/n) - p}{\sqrt{pq}/\sqrt{n}} = \frac{X - np}{\sqrt{npq}}$$

Using the procedure of Sec. 2.10, it follows that the characteristic function for Y is

$$\phi_n(t) = \left[p \exp\left(\frac{qjt}{\sqrt{npq}} \right) + q \exp\left(-\frac{pjt}{\sqrt{npq}} \right) \right]^n$$

Thus, in order to prove the theorem for this case, we must show that

$$\lim_{n \to \infty} \phi_n(t) = e^{-t^2/2}$$

It would then follow from Eq. (2.12-11) and the uniqueness of characteristic functions that the limiting distribution of Y is, indeed, normal. The verification of this limit is left as an exercise.

Example 2.12-2. Let $X_1, X_2, \ldots, X_n$ be a set of independent random variables, each possessing a Poisson distribution defined by Eq. (2.11-26). It is left as an exercise to show that the sum

$$X = \sum_{i=1}^{n} X_i$$

has a Poisson distribution with $m = \sigma^2 = n\lambda$. The characteristic function of the variable

$$Y = \frac{X - n\lambda}{\sqrt{n\lambda}}$$

is given by

$$\phi(t) = E\left[\exp \frac{jt(X - n\lambda)}{\sqrt{n\lambda}} \right]$$

$$= \sum_{k=0}^{\infty} e^{-n\lambda} \frac{(n\lambda)^k}{k!} \exp \frac{jt(k - n\lambda)}{\sqrt{n\lambda}}$$

$$= e^{-n\lambda} \exp\left(-jt \sqrt{n\lambda} \right) \sum_{k=0}^{\infty} \frac{[n\lambda \exp\,(jt/\sqrt{n\lambda})]^k}{k!}$$

$$= e^{-n\lambda} \exp\left(-jt \sqrt{n\lambda} \right) \exp\left[n\lambda \exp\left(\frac{jt}{\sqrt{n\lambda}} \right) \right]$$

$$= \exp\left[n\lambda \left(-\frac{t^2}{2n\lambda} + \cdots \right) \right]$$

Therefore

$$\lim_{n \to \infty} \phi(t) = e^{-t^2/2}$$

as would be expected from the central-limit theorem.

Example 2.12-3. We consider here a simplified form of the Brownian motion problem in one dimension; i.e., the motion of a particle along a line under the influence of numerous random impacts from other particles. To study this problem, we assume that the particle is at the origin of the x axis at $t = 0$, and let its position at any later time t be $x(t)$. We assume the impacts to be applied at random and independent times with uniform average density λ. We further assume the effect of a single impact on the particle is a change of its position by the fixed amount α and that the impacts are random and independent in their sign with equal probability of positive or negative direction.

These assumptions are sufficient to define completely the distribution of the random variable $X = x(t)$. Given that n impacts have occurred in the interval from 0 to t, the distribution of X is found from the binomial distribution. However, the probability of precisely n impacts in this interval is computable from the Poisson distribution, and the combination of these properties permits us to write a formal series expression for the distribution function of X. Our interest in this problem is centered about the limiting form of this distribution for the case of an infinite density of impacts, as the magnitude of each approaches zero. Although we could compute the desired limit by this means, the details are cumbersome and we employ a somewhat more subtle procedure.

To begin with, let $0 < t_1 < t_2$. The random variables $X_1 = x(t_1)$ and $X_2 = x(t_2)$ are not independent. However, the changes in particle position over any two nonoverlapping intervals are independent; thus X_1 and $X_2 - X_1$ are independent. In addition, the distribution of $X_2 - X_1$ considered by itself depends only on the interval length $t_2 - t_1$, and not on t_1 and t_2 separately. Let $\sigma(t)$ be the standard deviation of $x(t)$. Then, noting that X_1 and $X_2 - X_1$ both have zero mean values, we have

$$\begin{aligned} \sigma(t_2)^2 &= E[X_2^2] = E[\{X_1 + (X_2 - X_1)\}^2] \\ &= E[X_1^2] + E[(X_2 - X_1)^2] \\ &= \sigma(t_1)^2 + \sigma(t_2 - t_1)^2 \end{aligned}$$

Writing $u(t) = \sigma(t)^2$, and setting $t_1 = t$, $t_2 = t + \tau$ in the above expression, we have

$$u(t + \tau) = u(t) + u(\tau)$$

Since this relation is valid for all positive numbers t and τ, it can be shown that $u(t)$ must be of the form

$$u(t) = a^2 t$$

for some constant a. Thus we find that

$$\sigma(t) = a \sqrt{t}$$

The above arguments make use only of the independence of changes in $x(t)$ over two nonoverlapping time intervals, and are equally valid for finite or infinite density of impacts λ. As a matter of fact, the changes in $x(t)$ over any set of nonoverlapping intervals form a set of independent random variables. This fact suggests the following construction. We could divide the interval from 0 to t into n subintervals of equal length. Then $X = x(t)$ would be represented as the sum of n independent and identically distributed random variables, as seen from the relation

$$x(t) = [x(t_1) - x(t_0)] + [x(t_2) - x(t_1)] + \cdots + [x(t_n) - x(t_{n-1})]$$

where $x(t_0) = x(0) = 0$ and $x(t_n) = x(t)$. We are tempted to let n approach infinity and to invoke the central-limit theorem to conclude that $x(t)$ is normally distributed.

It is easy to show that this reasoning is incorrect. In the case of finite density λ the quantity $x(t)$ can assume only the discrete values $k\alpha$, where k is an arbitrary positive or negative integer. Thus the distribution of $x(t)$ cannot possibly be described by the normal distribution, which is continuous. The explanation is that as n

changes, so also does the distribution of each random variable in the sum (since the interval length is inversely proportional to n). The application of the central-limit theorem is thus not valid. Although we shall establish the normal distribution of $x(t)$ in the case of an infinite density of impacts, we must do so by other means.

The distribution function of the random variable $X = x(t)$ depends parametrically upon α and λ as well as upon x and t, and only upon these variables. Thus

$$\Pr (X \leqq x) = G(x,t,\alpha,\lambda)$$

Since the probability in question is a dimensionless quantity, it can be expressed as a function of dimensionless combinations of the indicated variables. The quantity x has dimensions of distance, as does the quantity α [the change in $x(t)$ for a single impact]. The quantity λ has dimensions of reciprocal time, since it is the average number of impacts per unit time. It can be shown from these facts that there are precisely two independent dimensionless variables involved. These may be taken to be x/α and λt. A more fruitful choice, however, is the pair $x/\alpha \sqrt{\lambda t}$ and λt, obtained by dividing the first quantity above by the square root of the second. Thus we write

$$\Pr (X \leqq x) = H \left(\frac{x}{a \sqrt{t}}, \lambda t \right)$$

where $a = \alpha \sqrt{\lambda}$. To consider the case of an infinite density λ, we now let $\lambda \to \infty$ and $\alpha \to 0$ in such manner that the quantity a remains constant. If we assume that H remains finite in this process, then it must clearly depend upon λt in such a way that the effect of this parameter disappears in the limit; the quantity H cannot depend upon an infinite number. Thus in the limit,

$$F(x) = \Pr (X \leqq x) = K \left(\frac{x}{a \sqrt{t}} \right)$$

for some function K. The frequency function of X is given by

$$f(x) = \frac{1}{a \sqrt{t}} K' \left(\frac{x}{a \sqrt{t}} \right)$$

and the characteristic function $\phi(u)$ by

$$\phi(u) = E[e^{iuX}] = \frac{1}{a \sqrt{t}} \int_{-\infty}^{\infty} K' \left(\frac{x}{a \sqrt{t}} \right) e^{iux} \, dx$$

$$= \psi(ua \sqrt{t})$$

where ψ is the Fourier transform of K'.

As before, we now observe that $x(t_1)$ and $x(t_2) - x(t_1)$ are statistically independent, and that the distribution of $x(t_2) - x(t_1)$ is the same as that of $x(t_2 - t_1)$. We thus have $x(t_2)$ given as the sum of independent variables, and may therefore multiply characteristic functions to obtain

$$\psi(ua \sqrt{t_2}) = \psi(ua \sqrt{t_1})\psi(ua \sqrt{t_2 - t_1})$$

We now define a new function v by

$$v(x^2) = \log \psi(x)$$

Then
$$v(u^2a^2t_2) = v(u^2a^2t_1) + v[u^2a^2(t_2 - t_1)]$$

If this relation is to hold for all values t_1, t_2 for which $0 < t_1 < t_2$, v must be a linear function.   We may therefore write

$$v(u^2 a^2 t) = -\mu u^2 t$$

where μ is a suitable constant.   From this it follows that

$$\phi(u) = \psi(ua \sqrt{t}) = e^{-\mu u^2 t}$$

so that $x(t)$ is normally distributed.

The above treatment does not enable us to relate the standard deviation of X to the quantity $\alpha \sqrt{\lambda}$; however this can be done by other means.   In Chaps. 3 and 4 a much more thorough examination is given for this type of problem, and it is shown that the joint distribution of $x(t_1)$, $x(t_2)$, . . . , $x(t_n)$ is an n-dimensional normal distribution, as defined in Sec. 2.13.

2.13   The Multidimensional Normal Distribution

Let us consider the following example to motivate the general discussion of the multidimensional normal distribution.

Example 2.13-1.   A game is played between two men A and B by tossing a true coin a number of times.   For the event "heads" B pays A a dollar and for the event "tails" A pays B a dollar.   Suppose the coin is tossed $3n$ times.   Let X be the amount A wins in the first $2n$ tosses and Y be the amount A wins in the last $2n$ tosses.   We wish to determine $f(x,y)$, the joint probability frequency function of $X/\sqrt{n}$ and $Y/\sqrt{n}$ for large values of n.

It is convenient to define the auxiliary variable X_k to represent the outcome of the kth toss.   Specifically, let X_k assume the values one and minus one with equal probabilities for the mutually exclusive events "heads" or "tails" on the kth toss.   Then

$$
\begin{aligned}
X &= X_1 + X_2 + \cdots + X_{2n} \\
Y &= X_{n+1} + X_{n+2} + \cdots + X_{3n}
\end{aligned}
\tag{2.13-1}
$$

The characteristic function of $X_k/\sqrt{n}$ is

$$\phi(t) = E\left[\exp \frac{jtX_k}{\sqrt{n}}\right] = \frac{1}{2}\exp\left(\frac{jt}{\sqrt{n}}\right) + \frac{1}{2}\exp\left(-\frac{jt}{\sqrt{n}}\right) = \cos\left(\frac{t}{\sqrt{n}}\right) \tag{2.13-2}$$

and the joint characteristic function of $X/\sqrt{n}$ and $Y/\sqrt{n}$ is

$$
\begin{aligned}
\phi_n(s,t) &= E\left[\exp\left\{j\left(\frac{sX}{\sqrt{n}} + \frac{tY}{\sqrt{n}}\right)\right\}\right] \\
&= E\left[\exp\left\{\frac{j}{\sqrt{n}}\left[s\sum_1^n X_k + (s+t)\sum_{n+1}^{2n} X_k + t\sum_{2n+1}^{3n} X_k\right]\right\}\right] \\
&= [\phi(s)\phi(s+t)\phi(t)]^n
\end{aligned}
\tag{2.13-3}
$$

The last step in the calculation indicated in Eq. (2.13-3) is justified by the fact that the individual events X_k are independent.   From Eq. (2.13-2) it follows that

$$
\begin{aligned}
[\phi(t)]^n &= \left(1 - \frac{t^2}{n\,2!} + \frac{t^4}{n^2 4!} - \cdots\right)^n \\
&\simeq e^{-t^2/2}
\end{aligned}
\tag{2.13-4}
$$

for large n.   Hence, from Eq. (2.13-3) we have, for large n,

$$
\begin{aligned}
\phi_n(s,t) &\simeq e^{-s^2/2} e^{-(s+t)^2/2} e^{-t^2/2} \\
&\simeq e^{-(2s^2+2st+2t^2)/2} = \phi(s,t)
\end{aligned}
\tag{2.13-5}
$$

as the limiting form of the joint characteristic function of $X/\sqrt{n}$ and $Y/\sqrt{n}$. The function $\phi(s,t)$ is an example of the characteristic function of what we shall call a bivariate normal distribution. The frequency function may be determined from Eq. (2.9-17).

Before carrying through the computation to determine the explicit form taken by the frequency function of the normal distribution let us make the following important observation. From Eq. (2.13-3) we may write

$$\phi_n(s,t) = E\left[1 + j\left(s\frac{X}{\sqrt{n}} + t\frac{Y}{\sqrt{n}}\right) - \frac{1}{2}\left(s\frac{X}{\sqrt{n}} + t\frac{Y}{\sqrt{n}}\right)^2 + o(s^2 + t^2) \right] \quad (2.13\text{-}6)$$

using the series expansion for the exponential. If the expectation of the individual terms is taken, we obtain

$$\phi_n(s,t) = 1 - \frac{1}{2}(m_{11}s^2 + m_{12}st + m_{21}ts + m_{22}t^2) + E[o(s^2 + t^2)] \quad (2.13\text{-}7)$$

where $m_{11} = \alpha_{20}$, $m_{12} = m_{21} = \alpha_{11}$, $m_{22} = \alpha_{02}$ are the second moments of the variables $X/\sqrt{n}$ and $Y/\sqrt{n}$. This expression may be compared with a similar expansion of Eq. (2.13-5), i.e.,

$$\phi(s,t) = 1 - \frac{1}{2}(2s^2 + 2st + 2t^2) + o(s^2 + t^2) \quad (2.13\text{-}8)$$

Thus, we see that in the limit for large n

$$m_{11} = 2 \qquad m_{12} = m_{21} = 1 \qquad m_{22} = 2$$

It is instructive to verify these results directly. We have

$$m_{11} = E\left[\frac{X^2}{n}\right] = \frac{1}{n}\left\{E\left[\sum_{k=1}^{2n} X_k^2\right] + E\left[\sum_{j \neq k} X_j X_k\right]\right\} = \frac{1}{n}(2n + 0) = 2$$

$$m_{12} = m_{21} = E\left[\frac{XY}{n}\right] = \frac{1}{n}\left\{E\left[\sum_{k=n+1}^{2n} X_k^2\right] + E\left[\sum_{j \neq k} X_j X_k\right]\right\} = \frac{1}{n}(n + 0) = 1$$

$$m_{22} = E\left[\frac{Y^2}{n}\right] = \frac{1}{n}\left\{E\left[\sum_{k=2n+1}^{3n} X_k^2\right] + E\left[\sum_{j \neq k} X_j X_k\right]\right\} = \frac{1}{n}(2n + 0) = 2$$

which checks the previous results.

The joint frequency function corresponding to $\phi(s,t)$ is found from Eq. (2.9-17).

$$f(x,y) = \frac{1}{(2\pi)^2} \int_{-\infty}^{\infty} \int_{-\infty}^{\infty} e^{-j(sx+ty)} e^{-(s^2+st+t^2)} \, ds \, dt \quad (2.13\text{-}9)$$

This integral cannot be evaluated immediately because the integrand does not factor into two separate functions, one of s and one of t. This condition is a result of the lack of independence between the variables X and Y. However, by a linear transformation of coordinates it is possible to obtain a separable integrand.

From analytic geometry it is known that the equation

$$s^2 + st + t^2 = 1 \quad (2.13\text{-}10)$$

represents an ellipse in the st plane. By a rotation of coordinates it is possible to remove the cross-product term and thus align the principal axes of the ellipse with the coordinate axes. The appropriate change in variable is

$$s = \frac{1}{\sqrt{2}} (s' - t') \qquad t = \frac{1}{\sqrt{2}} (s' + t') \tag{2.13-11}$$

which represents a rotation through an angle of 45°. Equation (2.13-10) becomes

$$\tfrac{3}{2}s'^2 + \tfrac{1}{2}t'^2 = 1 \tag{2.13-12}$$

We now introduce the change of variable defined by Eq. (2.13-11) into Eq. (2.13-9). The limits of integration remain unchanged since the integration extends over the entire plane. Thus Eq. (2.13-9) becomes

$$f(x,y) = \frac{1}{(2\pi)^2} \int_{-\infty}^{\infty} \int_{-\infty}^{\infty} \exp \left\{ -\frac{j}{\sqrt{2}} [x(s' - t') + y(s' + t')] \right.$$
$$\left. - \left(\frac{3}{2} s'^2 + \frac{1}{2} t'^2 \right) \right\} ds' \, dt' \tag{2.13-13}$$

The double integral now separates into the product of two integrals. Equation (2.13-13) becomes

$$f(x,y) = \frac{1}{(2\pi)^2} \exp \left[-\frac{(x + y)^2}{12} - \frac{(x - y)^2}{4} \right]$$
$$\times \int_{-\infty}^{\infty} \exp \left\{ -\frac{3}{2} \left[s' + \frac{j}{3\sqrt{2}} (x + y) \right]^2 \right\} ds'$$
$$\times \int_{-\infty}^{\infty} \exp \left\{ -\frac{1}{2} \left[t' + \frac{j}{\sqrt{2}} (x - y) \right]^2 \right\} dt' \tag{2.13-14}$$

so that

$$f(x,y) = \frac{1}{2\pi \sqrt{3}} \exp \left[-\frac{1}{2} \left(\frac{2}{3} x^2 - \frac{2}{3} xy + \frac{2}{3} y^2 \right) \right] \tag{2.13-15}$$

is obtained as the required joint frequency function of $X/\sqrt{n}$ and $Y/\sqrt{n}$ which holds for large values of n.

The preceding example suggests the following definition of the multi-dimensional normal distribution.

Definition. Let $X_1, X_2, \ldots, X_n$ be n random variables with zero mean values.[1] The joint distribution is said to be an n-dimensional normal distribution if the associated characteristic function is of the form

$$\phi(s_1, s_2, \ldots, s_n) = \exp \left(-\tfrac{1}{2} \sum_{j=1}^{n} \sum_{k=1}^{n} m_{jk} s_j s_k \right) \tag{2.13-16}$$

The quantities m_{jk} are the second moments of the variables.

If the variables $X_1, X_2, \ldots, X_n$ are algebraically independent (i.e., no linear combination of these variables can vanish identically unless all coefficients in the combination are zero), then the quadratic form

$$Q = \sum_{j=1}^{n} \sum_{k=1}^{n} m_{jk} s_j s_k \tag{2.13-17}$$

---

[1] For simplicity, we consider here only the case in which the random variables have zero mean values. The extension of this definition and related results to the general case is easily achieved.

is positive definite.   In other words, Q is zero only if

$$s_1 = s_2 = \cdots = s_n = 0$$

and is otherwise positive.   This follows from the fact that Q may be expressed as

$$Q = E[(X_1 s_1 + X_2 s_2 + \cdots + X_n s_n)^2] \qquad (2.13\text{-}18)$$

The condition for algebraic independence is that the determinant $|m_{jk}|$ of the second moments is different from zero.

In the case in which the X's are algebraically dependent, there exist one or more linear algebraic equations relating them.   Consequently, the X's can all be expressed as linear combinations of a smaller number m of algebraically independent variables.   The probability distribution of the X's is therefore not continuous, since the range of values which they can take on is confined to a space of only m dimensions.

We shall now derive an explicit expression for the frequency function in the continuous case, following the method used in the preceding example.   However, the discussion is greatly simplified if certain properties of matrices may be assumed.

Let us use $\mathbf{s}$ to denote the n-dimensional row vector $(s_1, s_2, \ldots, s_n)$ and $\mathbf{s}^T$ its transpose which is a column vector.   Let M be the moment matrix of the X's, that is, the element in the ith row and kth column of M is m_{ik}.   Then the positive definite quadratic form Q may be written as

$$Q = \mathbf{s} M \mathbf{s}^T \qquad (2.13\text{-}19)$$

It is known that under these circumstances an orthogonal matrix P may be found such that

$$PMP^T = D \qquad (2.13\text{-}20)$$

where D is a diagonal matrix given by

$$D = \begin{Vmatrix} \lambda_1 & 0 & \cdots & 0 \\ 0 & \lambda_2 & \cdots & 0 \\ \multicolumn{4}{c}{\dotfill} \\ 0 & 0 & \cdots & \lambda_n \end{Vmatrix} \qquad (2.13\text{-}21)$$

and the λ's are the characteristic roots of the matrix M.   Therefore, if we introduce the transformation

$$\mathbf{s} = \mathbf{s}'P \qquad (2.13\text{-}22)$$

then Eq. (2.13-19) may be written as

$$Q = \mathbf{s}' P M P^T \mathbf{s}'^T = \mathbf{s}' D \mathbf{s}'^T$$

$$= \sum_{i=1}^{n} \lambda_i s_i'^2 \qquad (2.13\text{-}23)$$

The equation analogous to Eq. (2.9-17) for computing the frequency function from the characteristic function is

$$f(x_1, x_2, \ldots, x_n)$$
$$= \frac{1}{(2\pi)^n} \int_{-\infty}^{\infty} \cdots \int_{-\infty}^{\infty} e^{-jx \cdot s^T} \phi(s_1, s_2, \ldots, s_n) \, ds_1 \, ds_2 \cdots ds_n$$

(2.13-24)

Introducing the change in variable defined by Eq. (2.13-22), we may write this as

$$f(x_1, x_2, \ldots, x_n)$$
$$= \frac{1}{(2\pi)^n} \int_{-\infty}^{\infty} \cdots \int_{-\infty}^{\infty} \exp\left(-jx P^T s'^T - \frac{1}{2} s' D s'^T \right) ds_1' \cdots ds_n'$$

(2.13-25)

If we define a vector $\mathbf{c}$ by

$$\mathbf{c} = \mathbf{x} P^T \qquad (2.13\text{-}26)$$

then we have

$$f(x_1, x_2, \ldots, x_n)$$
$$= \frac{1}{(2\pi)^n} \int_{-\infty}^{\infty} \cdots \int_{-\infty}^{\infty} \exp\left[-\sum_{1}^{n} \left(jc_i s_i' + \frac{1}{2} \lambda_i s_i'^2 \right) \right] ds_1' \cdots ds_n'$$
$$= \frac{1}{(2\pi)^n} \exp\left(-\frac{1}{2} \sum_{1}^{n} \frac{c_i^2}{\lambda_i} \right)$$
$$\times \int_{-\infty}^{\infty} \cdots \int_{-\infty}^{\infty} \exp\left[-\frac{1}{2} \sum_{1}^{n} \lambda_i \left(s_i' + \frac{jc_i}{\lambda_i} \right)^2 \right] ds_1' \cdots ds_n'$$
$$= \frac{1}{(2\pi)^n} \exp\left(-\frac{1}{2} \sum_{1}^{n} \frac{c_i^2}{\lambda_i} \right) (2\pi)^{n/2} \prod_{1}^{n} \lambda_i^{-\frac{1}{2}}$$

(2.13-27)

Observe that

$$\sum_{i=1}^{n} \frac{c_i^2}{\lambda_i} = \mathbf{c} D^{-1} \mathbf{c}^T = \mathbf{x} \, P^T D^{-1} P \mathbf{x}^T \qquad (2.13\text{-}28)$$

and from Eq. (2.13-20), that

$$M^{-1} = P^T D^{-1} P \qquad (2.13\text{-}29)$$

Now since the determinant of the matrix M is simply

$$|M| = \prod_{i=1}^{n} \lambda_i$$

we may write Eq. (2.13-27) as

$$f(x_1, x_2, \ldots, x_n) = \frac{1}{(2\pi)^{n/2} \sqrt{|M|}} \exp\left(-\frac{1}{2} \mathbf{x} M^{-1} \mathbf{x}^T \right) \qquad (2.13\text{-}30)$$

If we denote the general element of M^{-1} by m_{ik}^{-1}, we may write Eq. (2.13-30) in the form

$$f(x_1, x_2, \ldots, x_n) = \frac{1}{(2\pi)^{n/2} \sqrt{|M|}} \exp\left[-\frac{1}{2} \sum_{i=1}^{n} \sum_{k=1}^{n} m_{ik}^{-1} x_i x_k\right] \qquad (2.13\text{-}31)$$

which gives us finally the joint frequency function of the n normally distributed random variables $X_1, X_2, \ldots, X_n$. (Note that m_{ik}^{-1} does not mean the reciprocal of m_{ik}.)

We now prove the following important theorem.

THEOREM. Let $X_1, X_2, \ldots, X_n$ be n normally distributed random variables (not necessarily independent). Then the variables $Y_1, Y_2, \ldots, Y_m$, where

$$Y_i = \sum_{k=1}^{n} C_{ik} X_k \qquad i = 1, 2, \ldots, m \qquad (2.13\text{-}32)$$

are themselves normally distributed.

For the proof we first define the second moments of the X's and Y's by

$$\lambda_{ik} = E[X_i X_k] \qquad (2.13\text{-}33)$$
$$\mu_{ik} = E[Y_i Y_k] \qquad (2.13\text{-}34)$$

A relationship between the λ's and μ's may be found immediately and is given by

$$\mu_{ik} = \sum_{r=1}^{n} \sum_{s=1}^{n} C_{ir} \lambda_{rs} C_{ks} \qquad (2.13\text{-}35)$$

Since the X's are normally distributed, their joint characteristic function is

$$E\left[\exp\left(j \sum_{i=1}^{n} X_i s_i\right)\right] = \exp\left(-\frac{1}{2} \sum_{i=1}^{n} \sum_{k=1}^{n} \lambda_{ik} s_i s_k\right) \qquad (2.13\text{-}36)$$

To obtain the characteristic function for the Y's, we introduce the following change of variable

$$s_i = \sum_{r=1}^{m} C_{ri} t_r \qquad (2.13\text{-}37)$$

into (2.13-36) to obtain

$$E\left[\exp\left(j \sum_{r=1}^{m} Y_r t_r\right)\right] = E\left[\exp\left(j \sum_{i=1}^{n} \sum_{r=1}^{m} C_{ri} X_i t_r\right)\right]$$

$$= \exp\left(-\frac{1}{2} \sum_{i=1}^{n} \sum_{k=1}^{n} \sum_{r=1}^{m} \sum_{s=1}^{m} \lambda_{ik} C_{ri} t_r C_{sk} t_s\right)$$

$$= \exp\left(-\frac{1}{2} \sum_{r=1}^{m} \sum_{s=1}^{m} \mu_{rs} t_r t_s\right) \qquad (2.13\text{-}38)$$

which shows that the Y's are also normally distributed random variables.

Analogous to the central-limit theorem discussed in Sec. 2.12 for one dimension there is a similar theorem for the multidimensional case. Here we shall consider only the two-dimensional case but the generalization to n dimensions follows almost immediately.

Let $\mathbf{Z}_1$, $\mathbf{Z}_2$, . . . , $\mathbf{Z}_n$ be n independent random two-dimensional vectors. We use the notation

$$\mathbf{Z}_i = (X_i, Y_i) \qquad i = 1, \ldots, n \qquad (2.13\text{-}39)$$

to display the components. The mean and second moments of $\mathbf{Z}_i$ are

$$\overline{\mathbf{Z}}_i = (\overline{X}_i, \overline{Y}_i) = (m_{xi}, m_{yi}) \qquad (2.13\text{-}40)$$

$$\sigma_{xi}^2 = \overline{X_i^2} - m_{xi}^2 \qquad \sigma^2 = \overline{Y_i^2} - m_{yi}^2$$
$$\mu_{xyi} = \overline{X_i Y_i} - m_{xi} m_{yi} \qquad (2.13\text{-}41)$$

The vector sum

$$\mathbf{Z} = \sum_{i=1}^{n} \mathbf{Z}_i = \left(\sum_{i=1}^{n} X_i, \sum_{i=1}^{n} Y_i \right) = (X, Y) \qquad (2.13\text{-}42)$$

will then have the following mean and second moments.

$$\overline{\mathbf{Z}} = \left(\sum_{i=1}^{n} m_{xi}, \sum_{i=1}^{n} m_{yi} \right) = (m_x, m_y) \qquad (2.13\text{-}43)$$

$$\sigma_x^2 = \sum_{i=1}^{n} \sigma_{xi}^2 \qquad \sigma_y^2 = \sum_{i=1}^{n} \sigma_{yi}^2 \qquad \mu_{xy} = \sum_{i=1}^{n} \mu_{xyi} \qquad (2.13\text{-}44)$$

We now form a new normalized random vector $\mathbf{W}$ given by

$$\mathbf{W} = \left(\frac{X - m_x}{\sigma_x}, \frac{Y - m_y}{\sigma_y} \right) \qquad (2.13\text{-}45)$$

Now following the procedure of the one-dimensional case, we calculate the joint characteristic function of the components of the vector $\mathbf{W}$.

$$\phi(s,t) = E\left[\exp\left\{ j \left(s \frac{X - m_x}{\sigma_x} + t \frac{Y - m_y}{\sigma_y} \right) \right\} \right]$$

$$= \exp\left[-j \left(\frac{m_x}{\sigma_x} s + \frac{m_y}{\sigma_y} t \right) \right] \prod_{i=1}^{n} \phi_i\left(\frac{s}{\sigma_x}, \frac{t}{\sigma_y} \right) \qquad (2.13\text{-}46)$$

where $\phi_i(s,t)$ is the joint characteristic function of X_i and Y_i.

The logarithm of ϕ_i may be expanded in a double series as follows:

$$\log \phi_i\left(\frac{s}{\sigma_x}, \frac{t}{\sigma_y} \right) = \sum_{q=0}^{\infty} \sum_{r=0}^{\infty} \frac{\lambda_{iqr}}{q!r!} \left(\frac{js}{\sigma_x} \right)^q \left(\frac{jt}{\sigma_y} \right)^r \qquad (2.13\text{-}47)$$

where

$$\begin{array}{ll} \lambda_{i00} = 0 & \lambda_{i20} = \sigma_{xi}^2 \\ \lambda_{i10} = m_{xi} & \lambda_{i11} = \mu_{xyi} \\ \lambda_{i01} = m_{yi} & \lambda_{i02} = \sigma_{yi}^2 \end{array} \qquad (2.13\text{-}48)$$

Substituting Eqs. (2.13-47) and (2.13-48) into Eq. (2.13-46), we obtain

$$\log \phi(s,t) = -\tfrac{1}{2}(s^2 + 2\rho st + t^2)$$
$$+ \sum_{i=1}^{n} \sum_{q} \sum_{r} \frac{\lambda_{iqr}}{q!\,r!} \left(\frac{js}{\sigma_x}\right)^q \left(\frac{jt}{\sigma_y}\right)^r \qquad (2.13\text{-}49)$$

where the summation is to be extended over all values of q and r but omitting those listed in (2.13-48). Here ρ is the correlation coefficient of X and Y and is defined by

$$\rho = \frac{\mu_{xy}}{\sigma_x \sigma_y} \qquad (2.13\text{-}50)$$

The central-limit theorem for this case states that

$$\lim_{n \to \infty} \phi(s,t) = -\tfrac{1}{2}(s^2 + 2\rho st + t^2) \qquad (2.13\text{-}51)$$

under certain restrictions, so that from Eq. (2.13-16) it follows that in the limit the random vector $\mathbf{W}$ is distributed according to the normal law. For the two-dimensional case one sufficient condition for the truth of the central-limit theorem is that

$$\lim_{n \to \infty} \frac{1}{\sigma_x^3} \sum_{i=1}^{n} E[|X_i - m_{xi}|^3] = 0$$
$$\lim_{n \to \infty} \frac{1}{\sigma_y^3} \sum_{i=1}^{n} E[|Y_i - m_{yi}|^3] = 0 \qquad (2.13\text{-}52)$$

which is analogous to the sufficient condition in the one-dimensional case, as expressed by Eq. (2.12-14). The central-limit theorem can also be stated in an analogous form for the case of vectors in n dimensions.

The example considered at the beginning of this section is a special case of the two-dimensional central-limit theorem; however, it is necessary to exercise a little caution in demonstrating this. At first we would be tempted to define the random vectors $\mathbf{Z}_i$ by $\mathbf{Z}_i = (X_i, X_{n+i})$, where the X's are defined in the example and $i = 1, 2, \ldots, 2n$. In this way $\mathbf{Z} = \sum_{i=1}^{2n} \mathbf{Z}_i = (X,Y)$ from Eq. (2.13-1) and we would then apply the central-limit theorem to this vector sum $\mathbf{Z}$. However, this line of reasoning is completely incorrect because the vectors $\mathbf{Z}_i$ defined in this way are not independent. Fortunately, we can circumvent this difficulty by defining our random vectors $\mathbf{Z}_i$ as

$$\mathbf{Z}_i = (X_i + X_{n+i}, X_{n+i} + X_{2n+i}) \qquad i = 1, 2, \ldots, n \qquad (2.13\text{-}53)$$

These vectors are independent and

$$\mathbf{Z} = \sum_{i=1}^{n} \mathbf{Z}_i = (X, Y) \qquad (2.13\text{-}54)$$

is a vector sum to which the central-limit theorem may be applied.

The means of $\mathbf{Z}_i$ for this case are easily seen to be zero and the standard deviations σ_x and σ_y are each equal to $\sqrt{2n}$. Hence, the vector $\mathbf{W}$, whose limiting distribution we desire, is simply

$$\mathbf{W} = \left(\frac{X}{\sqrt{2n}}, \frac{Y}{\sqrt{2n}} \right) \qquad (2.13\text{-}55)$$

It is easy to show that the correlation coefficient defined by Eq. (2.13-50) is

$$\rho = \frac{\mu_{xy}}{2n} = \frac{n}{2n} = \frac{1}{2} \qquad (2.13\text{-}56)$$

so that the limiting characteristic function for $\mathbf{W}$ is

$$\phi(s,t) = e^{-(s^2 + st + t^2)/2} \qquad (2.13\text{-}57)$$

If this is compared with Eq. (2.13-5), we find a difference of a factor of two in the exponent which results from the fact that the variables in the example were not normalized. A normalization can be carried out on the characteristic function of Eq. (2.13-5) by introducing a change in notation. Thus if we define $s' = \sqrt{2}\, s$ and $t' = \sqrt{2}\, t$, Eq. (2.13-5) becomes

$$\phi(s',t') = e^{-(s'^2 + s't' + t'^2)/2} \qquad (2.13\text{-}58)$$

which is now in complete agreement with the characteristic function obtained from application of the central-limit theorem, i.e. Eq. (2.13-57).

A second example of the application of the central-limit theorem is the two-dimensional random walk problem considered in Sec. 2.9. In our previous discussion we showed that the x component of the random walk is normally distributed in the limit; it follows similarly that the y component is also normal. We cannot, however, conclude from these facts that the joint distribution is normal. We could do so if the x and y components were independent; however, they are not except in the limit.

The position in the plane at the end of n steps is the sum of n independent random two-dimensional vectors. The distribution of each of these vectors is discontinuous, and is most conveniently visualized in terms of the distribution of one unit of probability around the circumference of a circle centered at the origin and of radius Δ. Since the vectors all have the same distribution, Eqs. (2.13-52) can be shown to be satisfied. The central-limit theorem thus permits us to conclude that the joint distribution is normal after all.

One of the most useful characteristics of the multivariate normal distribution is the fact that all its properties are determined once the second moments are known. This is of course obvious from the fact that the characteristic function and frequency function are completely specified by the second moments. It is of interest, however, to show explicitly how the general moments may be computed. In passing, we establish the fact that the quantities m_{ik} used in defining the characteristic function actually are the second moments as was asserted.

Since

$$\phi(s_1, s_2, \ldots, s_n) = E[\exp\{j(X_1 s_1 + \cdots + X_n s_n)\}]$$

we have for any set of integers $r_1, r_2, \ldots, r_n$,

$$\frac{\partial^{r_1 + \cdots + r_n}}{\partial s_1^{r_1} \partial s_2^{r_2} \cdots \partial s_n^{r_n}} \phi(s_1, \ldots, s_n)$$
$$= j^{r_1 + \cdots + r_n} E[\{X_1^{r_1} X_2^{r_2} \cdots X_n^{r_n}\} \exp\{j(X_1 s_1 + \cdots + X_n s_n)\}]$$

In particular, setting $s_1 = s_2 = \cdots = s_n = 0$

$$E[X_1^{r_1} X_2^{r_2} \cdots X_n^{r_n}]$$
$$= j^{-(r_1 + \cdots + r_n)} \left[\frac{\partial^{r_1 + \cdots + r_n}}{\partial s_1^{r_1} \partial s_2^{r_2} \cdots \partial s_n^{r_n}} \phi(s_1, \ldots, s_n) \right]_{s_1 = \cdots = s_n = 0} \quad (2.13\text{-}59)$$

It is noted that this relation is true for any distribution for which the indicated moments exist, whether or not it is normal.

For the case of the normal distribution, we have, by a power series expansion of the exponential function,

$$\phi(s_1, \ldots, s_n) = \exp\left(-\frac{1}{2} \sum_{i=1}^{n} \sum_{k=1}^{n} m_{ik} s_i s_k\right)$$
$$= \sum_{p=0}^{\infty} \frac{(-1)^p}{2^p p!} \left(\sum_{i=1}^{n} \sum_{k=1}^{n} m_{ik} s_i s_k\right)^p \quad (2.13\text{-}60)$$

The term in this expansion of index p is a homogeneous polynomial of degree $2p$ in the variables $s_1, \ldots, s_n$. Upon differentiation a total of $r_1 + \cdots + r_n$ times, it is clear that all terms in the above expansion disappear for which $2p < r_1 + \cdots + r_n$. Upon the subsequent substitution $s_1 = \cdots = s_n = 0$, it is also clear that all terms disappear for which $2p > r_1 + \cdots + r_n$. In particular, if $r_1 + \cdots + r_n$ is an odd integer,

$$E[X_1^{r_1} \cdots X_n^{r_n}] = 0 \qquad \Sigma r_i \text{ odd} \qquad (2.13\text{-}61)$$

If Σr_i is even, we see from the above argument that the only contributing term from (2.13-60) is that for which $2p = \Sigma r_i$. Hence

$$E[X_i^{r_1} \cdots X_n^{r_n}] = \frac{1}{2^p p!} \frac{\partial^{r_1 + \cdots + r_n}}{\partial s_1^{r_1} \partial s_2^{r_2} \cdots \partial s_n^{r_n}} \left(\sum_{i=1}^{n} \sum_{k=1}^{n} m_{ik} s_i s_k \right)^p \quad (2.13\text{-}62)$$

Setting $r_1 = r_2 = 1, r_3 = \cdots = r_n = 0$, we have

$$E[X_1 X_2] = \frac{1}{2} \frac{\partial^2}{\partial s_1 \partial s_2} \sum_{i=1}^{n} \sum_{k=1}^{n} m_{ik} s_i s_k = m_{12}$$

Similarly $E[X_i X_k]$ is found to be m_{ik}, establishing these quantities as the second moments.

In the general case, we may write

$$\left(\sum_{i=1}^{n} \sum_{k=1}^{n} m_{ik} s_i s_k \right)^p$$

$$= \sum_{i_1=1}^{n} \sum_{k_1=1}^{n} \sum_{i_2=1}^{n} \cdots \sum_{k_p=1}^{n} m_{i_1 k_1} m_{i_2 k_2} \cdots m_{i_p k_p} s_{i_1} s_{k_1} \cdots s_{i_p} s_{k_p} \quad (2.13\text{-}63)$$

In carrying out the differentiation indicated by (2.13-62), only those terms contribute for which s_1 occurs precisely r_1 times, s_2 occurs precisely r_2 times, and so on. Any such term is of the form

$$m_{i_1 k_1} m_{i_2 k_2} \cdots m_{i_p k_p} s_1^{r_1} s_2^{r_2} \cdots s_n^{r_n}$$

where r_1 of the numbers $(i_1, k_1, i_2, \ldots, i_p, k_p)$ are equal to unity, r_2 of them are equal to two, and so on. Further, the contribution of such a term to (2.13-62) is

$$\frac{1}{2^p p!} (m_{i_1 k_1} \cdots m_{i_p k_p}) \frac{\partial^{r_1 + \cdots + r_n}}{\partial s_1^{r_1} \cdots \partial s_n^{r_n}} (s_1^{r_1} \cdots s_n^{r_n})$$

$$= \frac{r_1! r_2! \cdots r_n!}{2^p p!} m_{i_1 k_1} m_{i_2 k_2} \cdots m_{i_p k_p}$$

Thus

$$E[X_1^{r_1} X_2^{r_2} \cdots X_n^{r_n}] = \frac{r_1! r_2! \cdots r_n!}{2^p p!} \sum (m_{i_1 k_1} m_{i_2 k_2} \cdots m_{i_p k_p}) \quad (2.13\text{-}64)$$

where the summation is to be carried out over all sets of indices $(i_1, k_1, \ldots, i_p, k_p)$ such that r_1 of the indices are unity, r_2 of them are two, etc.

As it stands, the sum in (2.13-64) is somewhat unmanageable; in particular, it may contain a very large number of terms even in a relatively simple case. In general we are not able to assign any simpler formal expression to this sum; however, we show by illustration how it may be computed in practice. Suppose, for example, that we wish to compute

$$E[X_1 X_2^3 X_3^2 X_4^2]$$

Then $r_1 = 1$, $r_2 = 3$, $r_3 = 2$, $r_4 = 2$, and $p = 4$. Now let us consider a typical term in the sum, for example $(m_{12}m_{23}m_{24}m_{34})$. Here the index 1 appears once, the index 2 appears three times, and the indices 3 and 4 appear twice each; thus the term does in fact belong to the sum. Now let us permute the four symbols m_{12}, m_{23}, m_{24}, m_{34} in any way (for example, m_{23}, m_{34}, m_{12}, m_{24}). Clearly the resulting product is equal to the original one and is also a distinct term of the sum. Since there are $4! = 24$ such permutations, all of which give distinct terms of the sum that are equal in value, we may include them all by writing

$$24m_{12}m_{23}m_{24}m_{34}$$

In addition, however, we may take account of the symmetry of the moments by noting that $m_{12} = m_{21}$, etc. Thus for each of the 24 combinations considered above, we may interchange subscripts on any one of the symbols to obtain new terms of the sum, or in fact on any combination of the symbols. Thus, for example, $m_{21}m_{23}m_{42}m_{34}$ is a new term obtained in this way. Since $2^4 = 16$ such interchanges are possible on each of the $4! = 24$ distinct permutations, the sum of all terms of this basic type is

$$2^4 \times 4!m_{12}m_{23}m_{24}m_{34} = 384m_{12}m_{23}m_{24}m_{34}$$

Now let us consider another typical term, for example, $m_{12}m_{23}m_{23}m_{44}$. Here there are not $4!$ distinguishable permutations to be made, since the middle two symbols are identical. Instead, we require the number of permutations of four objects of which two are identical: namely, $4!/2! = 12$. Also, when we examine the subscript interchanges on each symbol, we see that the interchange for m_{44} gives rise to no new term. Thus there are only $2^3 = 8$ such interchanges possible, and the sum of all terms of this basic type is

$$2^3 \times \frac{4!}{2!} \, m_{12}m_{23}m_{23}m_{44} = 96m_{12}m_{23}m_{23}m_{44}$$

Continuing in this manner, we obtain 11 distinct types of terms as represented by the sum below. Thus we find that

$$E[X_1X_2^3X_3^2X_4^2] = \frac{1! \times 3! \times 2! \times 2!}{2^4 \times 4!} \Bigg[(m_{12}m_{22}m_{33}m_{44}) \times 2 \times 4!$$

$$+ (m_{12}m_{23}m_{24}m_{34}) \times 2^4 \times 4! + (m_{12}m_{23}m_{23}m_{44}) \times 2^3 \times \frac{4!}{2!}$$

$$+ (m_{12}m_{33}m_{24}m_{24}) \times 2^3 \times \frac{4!}{2!} + (m_{12}m_{22}m_{34}m_{34}) \times 2^3 \times \frac{4!}{2!}$$

$$+ (m_{13}m_{22}m_{23}m_{44}) \times 2^2 \times 4! + (m_{13}m_{22}m_{24}m_{34}) \times 2^3 \times 4!$$

$$+ (m_{13}m_{23}m_{24}m_{24}) \times 2^4 \times \frac{4!}{2!} + (m_{14}m_{22}m_{24}m_{33}) \times 2^2 \times 4!$$

$$+ (m_{14}m_{22}m_{23}m_{34}) \times 2^3 \times 4! + (m_{14}m_{24}m_{23}m_{23}) \times 2^4 \times \frac{4!}{2!} \Bigg] \quad (2.13\text{-}65)$$

It may well be asked, in this calculation, how we can be certain that all the desired terms have been included. The total number of terms appearing in (2.13-64), however, is equal to the number of distinct ways in which a total of $r_1 + r_2 + \cdots + r_n$ objects can be placed in n boxes with r_i objects in the ith box $(i = 1, 2, \ldots, n)$. This number is given by

$$\frac{(r_1 + \cdots + r_n)!}{r_1! r_2! \cdots r_n!}$$

and in the present case turns out to be 1680. Addition of the numerical coefficients in (2.13-65), however, shows that exactly 1680 terms have been included; thus a check is provided on our work.

The general rule to be followed in computing the numerical coefficient for a particular term can be stated as follows:

1. The number of factors are counted in which the two subscripts differ. This number represents the power to which 2 is raised.

2. If there are m factors involved, and if there is one set of m_1 of them which are identical, another set of m_2 which are identical, and so on, the number of distinct permutations is $m!/(m_1! m_2! \cdots)$.

Thus, for example, a term such as

$$m_{11} m_{11} m_{11} m_{23} m_{23} m_{24} m_{33} m_{33} m_{34}$$

would have as coefficient $2^4 \times (9!/3! 2! 2!)$. Clearly this method is confined in its usefulness to moments of very low order. It is interesting to note, however, that to obtain the results of (2.13-65) by means of a

detailed expansion of $\left(\sum_{i=1}^{4} \sum_{k=1}^{4} m_{ik} s_i s_k \right)^4$, we should have to examine a

total of $2^{16} = 65{,}536$ terms instead of the 11 used above.

One final remark seems to be appropriate before concluding this section. It is possible for two random variables to each be distributed according to the normal law and yet not have a normal joint distribution. This may be seen from the following (admittedly rather artificial) example.

Let X and Y be two random variables with a joint probability density given by

$$f(x,y) = \frac{1}{2\pi} e^{-(x^2+y^2)/2} + a g(x,y)$$

where
$$g(x,y) = \begin{cases} xy & \text{for } |x| \leq 1 \text{ and } |y| \leq 1 \\ 0 & \text{otherwise} \end{cases}$$

and a is any constant chosen so that $f(x,y)$ is everywhere positive. Then the joint distribution of X and Y is obviously not normal. However, the density functions of X and Y considered separately and denoted by $f_1(x)$ and $f_2(y)$ are normal since

$$f_1(x) = \int_{-\infty}^{\infty} f(x,y) \, dy = \frac{1}{\sqrt{2\pi}} e^{-x^2/2}$$

$$f_2(y) = \int_{-\infty}^{\infty} f(x,y) \, dx = \frac{1}{\sqrt{2\pi}} e^{-y^2/2}$$

PROBLEMS

2-1. Let A, B, and C be arbitrary sets. Determine which of the following relations are correct and which are incorrect.

a. $(A + B + C) - C = A + B$
b. $(ABC)^* = A^* + B^* + C^*$
c. $(A - AB)C^* = A(B + C)^*$
d. $A(B + C)^* = AB^* + AC^*$
e. $AB^* \subset A + B$

2-2. Let A, B, C be three arbitrary events. Find expressions for the events that of A, B, C:
a. At least one occurs.
b. A occurs and either B or C occurs but not both.
c. Not more than one occurs.
d. Two and no more occur.

2-3. From three dozen eggs one dozen is selected. If it is known that there are four bad eggs in the three dozen, what is the probability that the one dozen selected will all be good?

2-4. What is the probability of being dealt a full house in a five-card poker hand?

2-5. Consider a sample space $\mathfrak{S}$ composed of four mutually exclusive events E_1, E_2, E_3, and E_4, each occurring with probability $1/4$. Define three compound events as follows:

$$A = E_1 + E_2 \qquad B = E_1 + E_3 \qquad C = E_1 + E_4$$

Show that

a. $P(AB) = P(A)P(B)$
b. $P(AC) = P(A)P(C)$
c. $P(BC) = P(B)P(C)$

but

d. $P(ABC) \neq P(A)P(B)P(C)$

2-6. Three dice are rolled. Given that no two faces are the same, what is the probability that one of the faces is a four?

2-7. A game is played in which two men each toss a coin in turn, the one obtaining "heads" first being the winner. Find the probability that the man who plays first will win.

2-8. Three urns are filled with a mixture of black and white balls. The first urn contains six black balls and three white ones. The second contains six black and nine white, while the third contains three black and three white. An urn is picked at random, and a ball is selected at random from this urn.
a. What is the probability that the chosen ball is black?
b. If it is known that the chosen ball is black, what is the probability that it came from the first urn?

2-9. A machine can fail if any of three independent parts fail.   If the probabilities of failure during a year's operation of parts A, B, and C are 1/3, 1/4, and 1/5, respectively, what is the probability of the machine failing within the year.

2-10. Two men decide to meet between 12 o'clock and 1 o'clock, each not waiting more than 10 minutes for the other.   If all times of arrival within the hour are equally likely for each person, and if their times of arrival are independent, find the probability that they will meet.

2-11. In the interval $(0,1)$ n points are distributed uniformly and independently. Find:

a. The probability that the point lying farthest to the right is to the right of the number X.

b. The probability that the point lying farthest to the left is to the left of the number Y.

c. The probability that the point lying next farthest to the right is to the left of Z.

2-12. In a study of genetics, the following data were found.   Of the people surveyed, 52 per cent were female, 24 per cent were female and had blue eyes, 14 per cent were blue-eyed and had a blue-eyed parent, 13 per cent were males who had blue eyes but had no blue-eyed parent, and 54 per cent either were male, or were blue-eyed with a blue-eyed parent, or both.   According to these data, what is the probability that a randomly chosen blue-eyed person is also male?

2-13. Let X_1, X_2, X_3 be independent random variables, each assuming the values ± 1 with probability 1/2.   Consider the random variables defined by

$$Y_1 = X_1 X_2 \qquad Y_2 = X_1 X_3 \qquad Y_3 = X_2 X_3$$

Show that any two of these new variables are independent but that Y_1, Y_2, Y_3 are not independent.

2-14. X and Y are independent random variables uniformly distributed in the interval $(0,1)$.   Find the probability that XY is less than 1/2.

2-15. A gun is fired at a target.   Taking the origin of coordinates as the point of aim, it is known that due to dispersion effects the x and y coordinates of the point of hit are independent and each may be specified in a probabilistic sense by the same frequency function f where

$$f(x) = \frac{1}{\sigma \sqrt{2\pi}} e^{-x^2/2\sigma^2}$$

Show that the probability of a point of hit lying within a circle of radius R centered at the origin is

$$1 - e^{-R^2/2\sigma^2}$$

2-16. Let X and Y be independent random variables which are uniformly distributed in the interval $(-1,1)$, i.e., the frequency function for both X and Y is zero outside the interval and equal to 1/2 inside.   Find the frequency function for the variable $X + Y$.

2-17. The random variables X and Y are statistically independent and are confined to the integer values $n = 0, 1, 2, \ldots$.   Let $a_n = \Pr(X = n)$, $b_n = \Pr(Y = n)$, and write $A(s) = \sum_{n=0}^{\infty} a_n s^n$, $B(s) = \sum_{n=0}^{\infty} b_n s^n$.   Show that $\Pr(X + Y = n) = c_n$, where $C(s) = \sum_{n=0}^{\infty} c_n s^n = A(s)B(s)$.

2-18. Compute the frequency function for the random variable $X = \tan \theta$, where θ is a random variable uniformly distributed over the interval $\left(-\frac{\pi}{2} < \theta < \frac{\pi}{2} \right)$.

2-19. Let X be a random variable uniformly distributed in the interval (a,b) and let $Y = G(X)$ be a function of X such that the inverse function $X = G^{-1}(Y)$ is a single-valued function of Y in the interval $[G(a),G(b)]$. Show that the density function for the random variable Y is given by

$$ f(y) = \begin{cases} \dfrac{1}{b-a} \left\{ \dfrac{1}{G'[G^{-1}(y)]} \right\} & \text{if } G(a) < y < G(b) \\ 0 & \text{otherwise} \end{cases} $$

where $G'(x) = dG(x)/dx$.

2-20. Let X and Y be statistically independent random variables, with respective frequency functions $f_1(x)$ and $f_2(y)$. Compute the frequency function of the random variable $Z = |X - Y|$.

2-21. A die is tossed n times. Find the average number of occurrences of the event "a six is followed by a number no smaller than three."

2-22. Let $X_1, X_2, \ldots, X_n$ be statistically independent random variables, and let σ_j^2 and μ_j denote the respective variance and third central moment of X_j. Let σ^2 and μ be the corresponding quantities for X, where $X = X_1 + X_2 + \cdots + X_n$. Show that

$$ \sigma^2 = \sigma_1^2 + \sigma_2^2 + \cdots + \sigma_n^2 $$
$$ \mu = \mu_1 + \mu_2 + \cdots + \mu_n $$

Show also that this additive property is false for the fourth central moments.

2-23. A commuter is accustomed to leaving his house between 7:30 and 8:00 A.M., the drive to the station taking between 20 and 30 minutes. It is assumed that the departure time and length of trip are independent random variables, uniformly distributed over their respective intervals. There are two trains which he can take: the first leaves precisely at 8:05 A.M. and takes exactly 35 minutes for the trip, and the second leaves at 8:25 A.M. and takes 30 minutes. Assuming that he makes one of these trains, what is his average arrival time at the destination? What is the probability that he misses both trains?

2-24. A coin is tossed n times with equal probabilities for heads and tails. Show that the average and the average square of the number of times a head is followed by a tail are given by $\dfrac{n-2}{4}$ and $\dfrac{n-2}{4} + \dfrac{(n-4)(n-3)}{16}$, respectively.

2-25. Three urns contain a collection of coins, distributed as follows. The first contains two dimes and a quarter, the second contains a silver dollar and a half dollar, and the third contains two dimes and three quarters. An urn is selected at random and a single coin drawn at random from this urn. What is the average value drawn?

2-26. Let $X_1, X_2, \ldots, X_n$ be mutually independent random variables, each possessing the frequency function $f(x) = 1/\pi(1 + x^2)$. By means of characteristic functions, compute the frequency function for $S_n = X_1 + X_2 + \cdots + X_n$, and thus show that the distribution of the random variable $Y_n = (1/n)S_n$ is independent of n. Note that the application of the central-limit theorem is not valid since the moments of X_k do not exist.

2-27. Show that if the random variables $X_1, X_2, \ldots, X_n$ are independent, then the characteristic function of their sum is the product of their individual characteristic functions.

2-28. Use the method of characteristic functions to solve Prob. 2-16, and use the two results to show that

$$\int_{-\infty}^{\infty} \frac{\sin^2 x}{x^2} \, dx = \pi$$

2-29. In Example 2.9-1 show that the joint probability density function for the x and y components is

$$f(x,y) = \frac{1}{(2\pi)^2} \int_{-\infty}^{\infty} \int_{-\infty}^{\infty} e^{j(ux+vy)}[J_0(\Delta \sqrt{u^2 + v^2})]^n \, du \, dv$$

2-30. In each of the two cases considered in Example 2.6-2, compute the probability distribution of the number of hits scored; i.e., compute Pr (exactly k hits are scored) as a function of k and of the number n of rounds fired.

2-31. In Example 2.8-5, what is the average length of the set of points x which are covered by two or more lethal shots?

2-32. Let X and Y be random variables with zero mean values. From consideration of the roots of the quantity $E[(X + \lambda Y)^2]$ as a quadratic function of the real variable λ, show that the correlation coefficient ρ defined by (2.8-16) is always such that $|\rho| \leq 1$.

CHAPTER 3

THE STATISTICAL DESCRIPTION
OF RANDOM PROCESSES

3.1 Introductory Remarks

As suggested in Chap. 1, much of the succeeding material relates to the study of random functions of time in a role as possible inputs, wanted or otherwise, to automatic control or information-processing systems. Numerous examples of random functions suggest themselves immediately. In an antiaircraft fire-control problem the path of the target is random. This is true both in the sense that it generally contains components of roughness due to atmospheric turbulence and also in the sense that, even though the path be regular, it is not known beforehand. In addition, a fire-control system may have to contend with random roughness in radar data.

In a communication system both the desired message and the interfering noise are random; one need never consider a system called upon to transmit only a single and completely describable item of information. A regulated power supply receives as its input an unregulated line voltage which contains fluctuations that might be computed in theory but which are properly regarded as random from a practical standpoint. In each such example we wish a useful and quantitative statistical manner of describing properties of a *random function*.

In the present chapter we study the manner in which statistical properties of random functions can be defined and analyzed, without reference to control applications. In seeking to apply the probabilistic considerations of Chap. 2 to this problem, we are immediately confronted with a dilemma. As long as we remain in the realm of abstract theory, everything appears relatively simple. When we attempt a practical calculation, however, we are at once presented with a formidable array of obstacles. In principle, we start by defining an ensemble or sample space whose elements are functions of time, together with a probability function defined over this space. How do we phrase our definition so as to include those functions and only those which might plausibly be associated with our problem? Since we shall undoubtedly wish to speak of an infinite sample space, we are effectively prevented from using notions of equal a priori probability. How, then, do we proceed in assigning a probability distribution in any intelligent way? Having supposedly overcome these problems, however, we compute the probability of the particular subset of functions whose members possess the properties in which we are interested. Even this step is filled with serious difficulties that cannot be resolved by mere technical computation. In the face of this situation, how do we apply the methods of probability theory which our conscience indicates are necessary?

The answer, of course, is that we must rest content with much less than the complete information that the above steps would provide. There are very few nontrivial instances (although we shall have occasion to consider one in Chap. 4) in which any significant portion of the above program can be carried out successfully. In this type of analysis the material of Chap. 2 serves more as a guide to our reasoning processes than as a specific computational technique. We draw quite heavily on this material for the concepts of distributions, random variables, mathematical expectation, and statistical independence. In general, however, the more elaborate and abstract portions of probability theory are primarily of value in helping us to set up our problems in a precise manner. If we can assign a well-defined meaning to the statements and calculations which we set down, then we can assess both the value and the limitations of these calculations from a practical viewpoint.

For the most part we are forced to work with statistical parameters, i.e., quantities that can be expressed as the expectations of certain random variables in which we are interested. The parameters with which we deal are in general directly observable by the statistical analysis of empirical data. They do not, of course, completely characterize the probability distributions of the sample spaces to be studied; as indicated in Sec. 2.8, however, they do convey a limited amount of information about these distributions. The standard deviation of a random variable, for example, gives at least some index of the spread of the distribution about the mean, even though it does not specify the distribution uniquely.

Our main problem, then, is the selection of statistical parameters which meet three important requirements. In the first place, they must be calculable, either from a theoretical model of our problem or directly from the analysis of empirical data, without a prohibitive amount of effort. In the second place, they must be of such nature that a knowledge of their values for the inputs to a control system enables us to compute their values for the output as well. We postpone a detailed examination of this point until later chapters. Finally, they must be useful to us in the sense that they afford the opportunity for making significant statements concerning the quality of performance of the system studied. The remainder of this chapter is therefore devoted to the discussion of such statistical parameters, and related topics using the material of Chap. 2 as a guide.

3.2   Random Processes

By the term *random process* we mean a sample space or ensemble comprised of functions of time as the fundamental elements. We assume as an integral part of this notion the existence of a probability distribution defined over an appropriate class of sets in this sample space, so that we may speak with confidence of the probability of various events even though we may find many such probabilities difficult to compute. It is to be noted that we have not specified that the individual functions under discussion are "random" in the accepted sense; they may be completely regular and predictable if this suits our purpose. As a trivial example, the sample space consisting of the functions $A \cos (\omega t + \phi)$ with the quantities A, ω, and ϕ satisfying an assigned three-dimensional probability distribution, is a case in point. The essential randomnicity here is not in the character of the individual functions, but in the particular choice of a set of values (A, ω, ϕ).

We may conveniently visualize the sample space as being generated by a large number of independent repetitions of the same experiment under conditions which are essentially identical. In studying the fluctuations in the output of a vacuum tube, for example, we may assume the simultaneous testing of an indefinitely large number of tubes as a conceptual model for our problem. The function of time which is the output of a particular tube of the collection is then one point of the sample space. In discussing time-dependent phenomona, we may have to exercise a certain amount of care in the selection of a common time origin for the experiments; however, this point usually offers no difficulties.

Example 3.2-1.   As a simple and concrete example of a random process, we consider the collection of all functions $f(t)$ generated for positive t by flipping a coin at times $t = 0, 1, 2, \ldots$ and setting $f(t) = 1$ or 0 over the next time interval for heads or tails, respectively. To the sequence $HTHHT \ldots$, for example, corresponds the function

$$f(t) = \begin{cases} 1 & 0 < t \leqq 1 \\ 0 & 1 < t \leqq 2 \\ 1 & 2 < t \leqq 3 \\ 1 & 3 < t \leqq 4 \\ 0 & 4 < t \leqq 5 \\ \cdots \cdots \cdots \end{cases}$$

The sample space is then the collection of all functions consisting of zero's and one's over the successive unit intervals.

Each function of time in this example can be adequately represented by the particular infinite sequence of zeros and ones which it takes on; e.g., the sequence $(1, 0, 1, 1, 0, \ldots)$. To each such sequence, however, there corresponds a real number u

expressed in the binary notation[1] and lying between zero and unity (for example, $u = 0.10110 \cdots$). The converse is also true; to each number u in the interval $(0 \leq u \leq 1)$ there corresponds a function $f(t)$ of the type considered. The sample space can thus be equally well chosen to be the set of all real numbers in the unit interval. If we define the probability of an arbitrary set A of functions $f(t)$ as identical to the length of the corresponding set of real numbers u, we find, first of all, that the probability of obtaining heads on the nth toss is precisely $1/2$, as it should be. To see this, we note that the set A_n of points u for which $f(t) = 1$ over the interval $n - 1 < t \leq n$ is the set of binary numbers whose nth digit is a one. This set consists of a collection of nonoverlapping intervals, each of length 2^{-n}. Each such interval is the set of all numbers u with the nth digit unity and the first $n - 1$ digits fixed. Since the first $n - 1$ digits can be assigned in 2^{n-1} different ways, there are 2^{n-1} such intervals. Their total length is therefore $2^{n-1} \times 2^{-n} = 1/2$, as asserted.

We can also reconcile the interpretation of probability as interval length with the notion of independence of successive tosses of a coin. If $n > k$, the intersection $A_k A_n$ is a set of 2^{n-2} intervals, each of length 2^{-n}. Therefore

$$P(A_k A_n) = 2^{n-2} \times 2^{-n} = \tfrac{1}{4}$$

However
$$P(A_k)P(A_n) = \tfrac{1}{2} \times \tfrac{1}{2} = P(A_k A_n)$$

establishing the independence of the kth and nth tosses.

Two points are worth noting in this example. In the first place, since the points of any interval of positive length are noncountable, the sample space contains a noncountable infinity of elements. This situation is the usual one in the study of random processes; we seldom deal with discrete sample spaces except as a convenience. In the second place, there are included in our sample space particular functions $f(t)$ with peculiar properties. For example, the function $f(t)$ which is identically equal to one is a member, as is the function $f(t) \equiv 0$, and neither of these would normally be regarded as random. They are, however, possible results of the coin-flipping experiment and must therefore be included in our study. We have here to distinguish between those events which are impossible and those which merely have zero probability. The latter, according to the empirical interpretation of probability, occur sufficiently seldom so

[1] Any number u between zero and one may be expanded in a series of the form

$$u = \frac{a_1}{2^1} + \frac{a_2}{2^2} + \cdots + \frac{a_n}{2^n} + \cdots$$

where the a's are either zero or unity. The expression

$$u = .a_1 a_2 \cdots a_n \cdots$$

is called the binary expansion of u and is analogous to the decimal expansion

$$u = \frac{b_1}{10^1} + \frac{b_2}{10^2} + \cdots + \frac{b_n}{10^n} + \cdots$$
$$= .b_1 b_2 \cdots b_n \cdots$$

where the b's are any integers from zero to nine.

that they can be neglected in a very large number of trials. It can be shown precisely in our example that all functions $f(t)$ enjoying special properties such as periodicity or any regularity whatsoever can be lumped together in a set of zero probability.

Example 3.2-2.   As a second and less trivial example of a random process, we consider a simple case of the shot effect in a vacuum-tube circuit.   We assume a certain average rate of flow of electrons from the cathode to the anode of the tube, and wish to study the effects of fluctuations about this mean.   Let the times at which the individual electrons arrive be arbitrarily labeled t_0, t_1, t_{-1}, t_2, t_{-2}, etc.   At a specified point of the circuit, let $F(t - t_k)$ be the current or voltage at time t resulting from the arrival of the kth electron at time t_k.   Assuming linearity of the circuit, so that the effects of the individual electrons may be superimposed, we then study the ensemble of functions of the form

$$I(t) = \sum_{k=-\infty}^{\infty} F(t - t_k) \tag{3.2-1}$$

in which the quantities t_k are random.   Here we find it necessary to specify an infinite number of "coordinates" (the numbers t_k) to determine a point of our sample space.

3.3   Probability Distributions and Statistical Parameters

Let a random process be comprised of a set of functions $\{x(t)\}$.† For a fixed value of t, say $t = t_1$, the quantity $X_1 = x(t_1)$ is a random variable. We use the term *random variable* strictly in the sense of Sec. 2.6; i.e., to each element of the sample space there corresponds a number X_1 which is the value taken on by that element $x(t)$ at the particular instant t_1. The "variability" here is with respect to different elements of the sample space and not with respect to time; the quantity t_1 simply appears as a parameter. We thus define the distribution function of $x(t_1)$ by the relation

$$\begin{aligned} F_1(x_1,t_1) &= \Pr\ (X_1 \leqq x_1) \\ &= \Pr\ [x(t_1) \leqq x_1] \end{aligned} \tag{3.3-1}$$

In defining the distribution function we indicate specifically in our notation that it depends upon the parameter t_1. We also append the subscript 1 to this function to distinguish it from certain joint distribution functions to be defined later.

Correspondingly we may define a probability density $f_1(x_1,t_1)$ by

$$f_1(x_1,t_1) = \frac{\partial F_1(x_1,t_1)}{\partial x_1} \tag{3.3-2}$$

We have further,

$$\Pr\ [x_1 < x(t_1) \leqq x_1 + dx_1] = f_1(x_1,t_1)\ dx_1 \tag{3.3-3}$$

† We often use the notation $\{x(t)\}$ to denote the random process of which the function $x(t)$ is a representative member.

The relations (3.3-2) and (3.3-3) assume implicitly that $F_1(x_1, t_1)$ is differentiable with respect to x_1. We call the function $F_1(x_1, t_1)$ the *first probability distribution function* of the random process.

In terms of f_1 we define the following statistical parameters:

$$
\begin{aligned}
\overline{x(t)} &= \text{mean value of } x(t) \\
&= E[x(t)] \\
&= \int_{-\infty}^{\infty} x f_1(x, t)\, dx
\end{aligned}
\tag{3.3-4}
$$

$$
\begin{aligned}
\overline{x(t)^2} &= \text{mean-squared value of } x(t) \\
&= E[x(t)^2] \\
&= \int_{-\infty}^{\infty} x^2 f_1(x, t)\, dx
\end{aligned}
\tag{3.3-5}
$$

$$
\begin{aligned}
\overline{x(t)^n} &= n\text{th moment of } x(t) \\
&= E[x(t)^n] \\
&= \int_{-\infty}^{\infty} x^n f_1(x, t)\, dx
\end{aligned}
\tag{3.3-6}
$$

$$
\begin{aligned}
\phi_1(u, t) &= \text{characteristic function of } x(t) \\
&= E[e^{jux(t)}] \\
&= \int_{-\infty}^{\infty} e^{jux} f_1(x, t)\, dx
\end{aligned}
\tag{3.3-7}
$$

Other parameters such as variance can of course be similarly defined. We reserve the use of the bar over a quantity, here and later, to denote the ensemble average or expectation of that quantity. This type of averaging process is to be carefully distinguished from the time average of a quantity, performed with respect to a single function $x(t)$, which will be discussed later on in the chapter. Thus quantities such as $\overline{x(t)}$, etc., are in general functions of time.

In a similar way we may study the joint distribution of the two random variables $X_1 = x(t_1)$ and $X_2 = x(t_2)$, where t_1 and t_2 are arbitrary fixed values of t. The *second probability distribution function* is defined by

$$
\begin{aligned}
F_2(x_1, t_1; x_2, t_2) &= \Pr\,(X_1 \leqq x_1; X_2 \leqq x_2) \\
&= \Pr\,[x(t_1) \leqq x_1; x(t_2) \leqq x_2]
\end{aligned}
\tag{3.3-8}
$$

and the corresponding probability density is

$$
f_2(x_1, t_1; x_2, t_2) = \frac{\partial^2}{\partial x_1\, \partial x_2} F_2(x_1, t_1; x_2, t_2)
\tag{3.3-9}
$$

when this derivative exists. Clearly F_2 and f_2 are symmetric in the pairs of variables (x_1, t_1) and (x_2, t_2); that is,

$$
F_2(x_2, t_2; x_1, t_1) = F_2(x_1, t_1; x_2, t_2)
\tag{3.3-10}
$$

Since

$$
\Pr\,[x(t_1) \leqq x_1] = \Pr\,[x(t_1) \leqq x_1; x(t_2) < +\infty]
\tag{3.3-11}
$$

we must have for consistency

$$F_2(x_1,t_1; +\infty,t_2) = F_1(x_1,t_1) \tag{3.3-12}$$

for all values of x_1, t_1, and t_2. In terms of the probability densities, this leads to the integral relation

$$f_1(x_1,t_1) = \int_{-\infty}^{\infty} f_2(x_1,t_1; x_2,t_2)\, dx_2 \tag{3.3-13}$$

As in Sec. 2.8 we may define the general moments α_{ik} by

$$\begin{aligned}
\alpha_{ik} &= E[x(t_1)^i\, x(t_2)^k] \\
&= \int_{-\infty}^{\infty} dx_1 \int_{-\infty}^{\infty} dx_2\, x_1^i x_2^k f_2(x_1,t_1; x_2,t_2)
\end{aligned} \tag{3.3-14}$$

For α_{20} we find, by (3.3-13),

$$\begin{aligned}
\alpha_{20} &= \int_{-\infty}^{\infty} dx_1 \int_{-\infty}^{\infty} dx_2\, x_1^2 f_2(x_1,t_1; x_2,t_2) \\
&= \int_{-\infty}^{\infty} x_1^2 f_1(x_1,t_1)\, dx_1 \\
&= \overline{x(t_1)^2}
\end{aligned} \tag{3.3-15}$$

and similarly

$$\alpha_{02} = \overline{x(t_2)^2} \tag{3.3-16}$$

One of these moments, α_{11}, is of sufficient importance in later calculations to justify a special name and symbol. We define the *correlation function* of x, $\phi_{xx}(t_1,t_2)$, by

$$\begin{aligned}
\phi_{xx}(t_1,t_2) &= E[x(t_1)x(t_2)] \\
&= \int_{-\infty}^{\infty} dx_1 \int_{-\infty}^{\infty} dx_2\, x_1 x_2 f_2(x_1,t_1; x_2,t_2)
\end{aligned} \tag{3.3-17}$$

We indicate by the notation the specific dependence of the correlation function upon t_1 and t_2 as parameters; we further indicate by the double subscript xx that the correlation of $x(t)$ with itself is intended, to distinguish this quantity from various cross correlations discussed later.[1] In one respect we deviate from Sec. 2.8 in that we do not utilize the correlation coefficient; we prefer not to normalize this quantity in the present applications. We also remark that the correlation function is symmetric in the variables t_1 and t_2; that is, $\phi(t_1,t_2) = \phi(t_2,t_1)$.

One of the more important properties of the correlation function is revealed when t_1 and t_2 are both assigned the same value t. Then

$$\phi_{xx}(t,t) = E[x(t)x(t)] = \overline{x(t)^2} \tag{3.3-18}$$

Thus the mean-squared value of x may be obtained from a knowledge of the correlation function.

---

[1] However, we often drop the double subscript xx or change it to a single subscript x when no confusion is likely.

Example 3.3-1. As a somewhat trivial application of these definitions, we compute the correlation function $\phi_{ff}(t_1,t_2)$ for the random step function considered in Sec. 3.2. If t_1 and t_2 lie in the same interval ($n < t_1, t_2 \leqq n + 1$), then $f(t_1) = f(t_2)$ and

$$\phi_{ff}(t_1,t_2) = E[f(t_1)f(t_2)] = E[f(t_1)^2]$$
$$= 1^2 \times \tfrac{1}{2} + 0^2 \times \tfrac{1}{2} = \tfrac{1}{2}$$

On the other hand, if t_1 and t_2 lie in different intervals, then $f(t_1)$ and $f(t_2)$ are independent random variables so that

$$\phi_{ff}(t_1,t_2) = E[f(t_1)]E[f(t_2)]$$
$$= \tfrac{1}{2} \times \tfrac{1}{2} = \tfrac{1}{4}$$

Thus the correlation function assumes only two discrete values.

Example 3.3-2. Let a and b be a pair of random variables. Then the ensemble of functions

$$x(t) = at + bt^2$$

forms a random process. Writing $f(a,b)$ for the joint frequency function of a and b, the first distribution function for $x(t)$ is

$$F_1(x_1,t_1) = \iint_R f(a,b) \, da \, db$$

where R is the region in the ab plane for which $at_1 + bt_1^2 \leqq x_1$.

The function $F_2(x_1,t_1; x_2,t_2)$ is given by a similar integral over the intersection RS, where S is region for which $at_2 + bt_2^2 \leqq x_2$. Clearly the computation of F_1 and F_2 is somewhat complicated, even though $f(a,b)$ may have a simple form.

In spite of this fact, we can readily compute the mean value and correlation function for $x(t)$. We have

$$\overline{x(t)} = \bar{a}t + \bar{b}t^2$$
$$\phi_{xx}(t_1,t_2) = E[(at_1 + bt_1^2)(at_2 + bt_2^2)]$$
$$= \overline{a^2}t_1t_2 + \overline{ab}(t_1t_2^2 + t_1^2t_2) + \overline{b^2}t_1^2t_2^2$$

If a random process is such that the individual functions are "random" in the accepted sense, then when $t_2 - t_1$ is large it often happens that $x(t_1)$ and $x(t_2)$ are statistically independent random variables. In the case of the random voltage fluctuations in the output of a vacuum tube, for example, there is little reason for supposing that fluctuations observed 10 minutes apart are in any way related. Under these conditions

$$E[x(t_1)x(t_2)] \cong E[x(t_1)]E[x(t_2)] \tag{3.3-19}$$

so that

$$\phi_{xx}(t_1,t_2) \cong \overline{x(t_1)} \times \overline{x(t_2)} \qquad t_2 - t_1 \text{ large} \tag{3.3-20}$$

In particular, if the mean value of $x(t)$ is zero for all t, then as $|t_2 - t_1|$ becomes infinite

$$\phi_{xx}(t_1,t_2) \to 0 \tag{3.3-21}$$

In addition to the first and second probability distributions discussed above, we may study more general distributions of an arbitrary order n, defined by

$$F_n(x_1, t_1; x_2, t_2; \; \ldots \; ; x_n, t_n)$$
$$= \text{Pr} \, [x(t_1) \le x_1; x(t_2) \le x_2; \; \ldots \; ; x(t_n) \le x_n] \quad (3.3\text{-}22)$$

where $t_1, t_2, \; \ldots \; , t_n$ is an arbitrary sequence. The corresponding probability density is given by

$$f_n(x_1, t_1; \; \ldots \; ; x_n, t_n) = \frac{\partial^n}{\partial x_1 \, \partial x_2 \; \cdots \; \partial x_n} F_n(x_1, t_1; \; \ldots \; ; x_n, t_n) \quad (3.3\text{-}23)$$

Each of these functions is symmetric in all pairs of variables (x_i, t_i), (x_j, t_j). Also, for self-consistency,

$$f_m(x_1, t_1; \; \ldots \; ; x_m, t_m)$$
$$= \int_{-\infty}^{\infty} dx_{m+1} \; \cdots \; \int_{-\infty}^{\infty} dx_n \, f_n(x_1, t_1; \; \ldots \; ; x_m, t_m; \; \ldots \; ; x_n, t_n) \quad (3.3\text{-}24)$$

for all positive integers m and $n > m$.

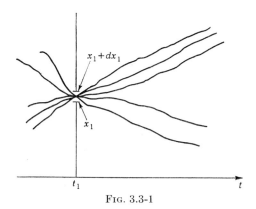

FIG. 3.3-1

The functions $f_1(x_1, t_1)$, $f_2(x_1, t_1; x_2, t_2)$, $\ldots$,$f_n(x_1, t_1; \; \ldots \; ; x_n t_n)$ specify the statistical properties of a random process in increasing detail. For example, the quantity $f_1(x_1, t_1) \, dx_1$ gives the probability of functions passing through a certain "slit" in the xt plane, as illustrated in Fig. 3.3-1. The quantity $f_2(x_1, t_1; x_2, t_2) \, dx_1 \, dx_2$ gives the probability of functions passing through this same slit and simultaneously passing through a second slit, as in Fig. 3.3-2. The more of these density functions we specify, the more completely informed we are concerning the statistical characteristics of the random process. This is evident mathematically from (3.3-24), since a knowledge of f_n implies that of $f_{n-1}, f_{n-2}, \; \ldots \; , f_1$.

It can in fact be proved in a very general sense that the infinite sequence of functions $f_1, f_2, \; \ldots$ completely defines the statistical properties of our random process. This gives at least one clue to the manner in which theoretical analyses of random processes can be made, and considerations of this sort play an important part in Chap. 4. For the most part, however, we consider only the first and second probability distributions. As a matter of fact, in a large proportion of problems we remain content with the calculation of the mean value, mean-squared value, and the correlation function. The specification of these statistical parameters does not, of course, always give all of the information which we would like to possess. Later calculations will show, however, that these quantities satisfy, at least in part, the general requirements for usefulness set down in Sec. 3.1.

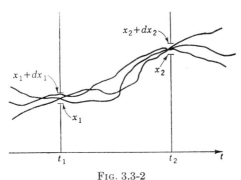

FIG. 3.3-2

Example 3.3-3. In Example 2.12-3, we studied the random process representing the Brownian motion of a particle which starts from the origin $x = 0$ at zero time, and which moves under the influence of an infinitely dense collection of infinitesimal impacts. Under suitable assumptions, we found that $x(t)$ was normally distributed with zero mean value; also that the variance of $x(t)$ was linear in t so that $\sigma^2 = a^2 t$.

To compute the correlation function of x, we temporarily assume $t_2 > t_1$ and note that

$$\phi_{xx}(t_1,t_2) = E[x(t_1)x(t_2)]$$
$$= E[x(t_1)^2 + x(t_1)\{x(t_2) - x(t_1)\}]$$

However, our previous results showed that $x(t_1)$ and $x(t_2) - x(t_1)$ are independent. Thus

$$\phi_{xx}(t_1,t_2) = \overline{x(t_1)^2} + \overline{x(t_1)} \times \overline{[x(t_2) - x(t_1)]}$$
$$= \overline{x(t_1)^2} = a^2 t_1$$

Since $\phi_{xx}(t_1,t_2) = \phi_{xx}(t_2,t_1)$, we may express this result in the form

$$\phi_{xx}(t_1,t_2) = a^2 \min (t_1,t_2)$$

We also may compute the general frequency function for $x(t)$. Let $0 < t_1 < t_2 < \cdots < t_n$; then $\{x(t_1), x(t_2) - x(t_1), \ldots, x(t_n) - x(t_{n-1})\}$ are a set of normally distributed and independent random variables. By our previous results,

$$f_1(x_1,t_1) = \frac{1}{\sqrt{2\pi}\, a \sqrt{t_1}} \exp\left(-\frac{x_1^2}{2a^2 t_1}\right)$$

Now

$$f_2(x_1, t_1; x_2, t_2)\, dx_1\, dx_2$$
$$= \Pr\,[x_1 < x(t_1) < x_1 + dx_1;\ x_2 < x(t_2) < x_2 + dx_2]$$
$$= \Pr\,[x_1 < x(t_1) < x_1 + dx_1;\ x_2 - x_1 < x(t_2) - x(t_1) < x_2 - x_1 + dx_2]$$
$$= \Pr\,[x_1 < x(t_1) < x_1 + dx_1] \times \Pr\,[x_2 - x_1 < x(t_2) - x(t_1) < x_2 - x_1 + dx_2]$$
$$= f_1(x_1, t_1)\, dx_1\, f_1(x_2 - x_1, t_2 - t_1)\, dx_2$$
$$= \frac{1}{\sqrt{2\pi}\, a\, \sqrt{t_1}}\ \frac{1}{\sqrt{2\pi}\, a\, \sqrt{t_2 - t_1}}\ \exp\left[-\frac{x_1^2}{2a^2 t_1} - \frac{(x_2 - x_1)^2}{2a^2(t_2 - t_1)} \right] dx_1\, dx_2$$

Thus, writing $t_0 = x_0 = 0$, for convenience, we have

$$f_2(x_1, t_1; x_2, t_2) = \frac{1}{2\pi a^2} \prod_{i=1}^{2} (t_i - t_{i-1})^{-\frac{1}{2}} \exp\left[-\frac{1}{2a^2} \sum_{k=1}^{2} \frac{(x_k - x_{k-1})^2}{t_k - t_{k-1}} \right]$$

The generalization to the nth frequency function follows without difficulty, giving

$$f_n(x_1, t_1;\ \cdots\ ; x_n, t_n) = (2\pi)^{-n/2} a^{-n} \prod_{i=1}^{n} (t_i - t_{i-1})^{-\frac{1}{2}} \exp\left[-\frac{1}{2a^2} \sum_{k=1}^{n} \frac{(x_k - x_{k-1})^2}{t_k - t_{k-1}} \right]$$

3.4   Joint Distributions for Two or More Random Processes

In many practical problems one has to give simultaneous consideration to two or more random processes; the concepts of Sec. 3.3 must therefore be extended to cover this situation. In a communications problem, for example, both signal and noise may be random. Since the task of a well-designed filter is to separate the signal from the noise as effectively as possible, it is clearly necessary to study the way in which the two random processes may be interrelated statistically, as well as their separate statistical properties. Similarly in a complex automatic control system both signal and interference may be random; one may also have to consider several different sources of interference simultaneously. A further example is provided by the problem of forecasting weather. Clearly the random processes representing temperature, wind velocity, humidity, and barometric pressure are in part related to each other. Also, today's weather in Boston is in a statistical sense related to yesterday's weather in Baltimore and Chicago. The methods of Sec. 3.3 permit study of the properties of each such random process by itself, but do not of themselves provide a way of analyzing statistical interrelations which may exist between them.

The necessary extension in ideas is achieved quite easily. Let $x(t)$ and $y(t)$ denote members of the random processes E_x and E_y. Since the primary experiment is the observation of a pair of functions (x, y), it is natural to regard the basic probability distribution as defined over the sample space consisting of all such pairs. We define the general *joint distribution function* by the following relation

$$F_{mn}^{(x,y)}(x_1,t_1; \ . \ . \ . \ ; x_m,t_m; y_1,t_1'; \ . \ . \ . \ ; y_n,t_n')$$
$$= \Pr\left[x(t_1) \leq x_1; \ . \ . \ . \ ; x(t_m) \leq x_m; y(t_1') \leq y_1; \ . \ . \ . \ ; y(t_n') \leq y_n\right]$$
$$(3.4\text{-}1)$$

where $t_1, \ . \ . \ . \ , t_m, t_1', \ . \ . \ . \ , t_n'$ is any set of values of t.
Clearly the functions

$$F_m^{(x)}(x_1,t_1; \ . \ . \ . \ ; x_m,t_m)$$
$$= F_{mn}^{(x,y)}(x_1,t_1; \ . \ . \ . \ ; x_m,t_m; +\infty,t_1'; \ . \ . \ . \ ; +\infty,t_n') \quad (3.4\text{-}2)$$

and

$$F_n^{(y)}(y_1,t_1'; \ . \ . \ . \ ; y_n,t_n')$$
$$= F_{mn}^{(x,y)}(+\infty,t_1; \ . \ . \ . \ ; +\infty,t_m; y_1,t_1'; \ . \ . \ . \ ; y_n,t_n') \quad (3.4\text{-}3)$$

respectively, represent the distribution functions for the random processes E_x and E_y considered separately. Thus a knowledge of $F_{mn}^{(x,y)}$ for all m and n implies a knowledge of all distributions associated with each random process by itself.

Associated with the joint distribution function is the *joint density function*

$$f_{mn}^{(x,y)}(x_1,t_1; \ . \ . \ . \ ; x_m,t_m; y_1,t_1'; \ . \ . \ . \ ; y_n,t_n')$$
$$= \frac{\partial^{m+n}}{\partial x_1 \cdots \partial x_m \, \partial y_1 \cdots \partial y_n} F_{mn}^{(x,y)} \quad (3.4\text{-}4)$$

The mathematical expectation of any function $g(x_1, \ . \ . \ . \ ,x_m; y_1, \ . \ . \ . \ ,y_n)$ that depends upon the $m + n$ variables $x_1 = x(t_1), \ . \ . \ . \ , x_m = x(t_m), y_1 = y(t_1'), \ . \ . \ . \ , y_n = y(t_n')$ is given by

$$E[g] = \int_{-\infty}^{\infty} dx_1 \cdots \int_{-\infty}^{\infty} dy_n \, g f_{mn}^{(x,y)} \quad (3.4\text{-}5)$$

In particular, we may define general moments in much the same way as in Sec. 3.3.

For practical applications, our interest is almost entirely centered about the most elementary joint density function $f_{11}^{(x,y)}(x_1,t_1; y_1,t_1')$, and the moment

$$E[x(t_1)y(t_2)] = \int_{-\infty}^{\infty} dx \int_{-\infty}^{\infty} dy \, xy f_{11}^{(x,y)}(x,t_1; y,t_2) \quad (3.4\text{-}6)$$

We call this quantity the *cross-correlation function* of x and y, and denote it by the symbol $\phi_{xy}(t_1,t_2)$:

$$\phi_{xy}(t_1,t_2) = E[x(t_1)y(t_2)] \quad (3.4\text{-}7)$$

Where necessary, we use the term *autocorrelation function* to distinguish $\phi_{xx}(t_1,t_2)$ from the cross-correlation function. It is clear from (3.4-7) that the cross-correlation function is generally not symmetric in t_1 and t_2;

however, we have

$$\phi_{xy}(t_1,t_2) = \phi_{yx}(t_2,t_1) \tag{3.4-8}$$

The concepts of joint distribution and frequency functions can readily be extended to the case of three or more random processes. We do not consider this point in detail. It is nevertheless worth remarking that if we have several random processes represented by $x(t)$, $y(t)$, $z(t)$, . . . , $w(t)$, the joint distributions for any pair may be obtained from the joint distributions for the complete set. Thus, for example, if we consider three random processes x, y, and z,

$$f_{11}^{(x,y)}(x,t;y,t') = \int_{-\infty}^{\infty} dz\, f_{111}^{(x,y,z)}(x,t;y,t';z,t'') \tag{3.4-9}$$

We therefore find

$$\begin{aligned}
\phi_{xy}(t,t') &= E[x(t)y(t')] \\
&= \int_{-\infty}^{\infty} dx \int_{-\infty}^{\infty} dy \int_{-\infty}^{\infty} dz\, xy f_{111}^{(x,y,z)}(x,t;y,t';z,t'') \\
&= \int_{-\infty}^{\infty} dx \int_{-\infty}^{\infty} dy\, xy f_{11}^{(x,y)}(x,t;y,t') \tag{3.4-10}
\end{aligned}$$

It is thus immaterial in calculating ϕ_{xy} whether we consider the sample space of triplets (x,y,z) or of pairs (x,y).

Example 3.4-1. For an arbitrary random process represented by the function $x(t)$, it is relatively simple to calculate the autocorrelation function of the derivative $y(t) = dx(t)/dt$ and the cross correlations between $x(t)$ and $y(t)$, in terms of the autocorrelation function of $x(t)$. By differentiation of $\phi_{xx}(t_1,t_2)$, we find

$$\begin{aligned}
\frac{\partial}{\partial t_1} \phi_{xx}(t_1,t_2) &= \frac{\partial}{\partial t_1} E[x(t_1)x(t_2)] \\
&= \lim_{h \to 0} \frac{E[x(t_1 + h)x(t_2)] - E[x(t_1)x(t_2)]}{h} \\
&= E\left[\lim_{h \to 0} \frac{x(t_1 + h) - x(t_1)}{h} x(t_2) \right] \\
&= E\left[\frac{\partial}{\partial t_1} \left\{ x(t_1)x(t_2) \right\} \right] = E[y(t_1)x(t_2)] \\
&= \phi_{yx}(t_1,t_2) \tag{3.4-11}
\end{aligned}$$

Similarly

$$\frac{\partial}{\partial t_2} \phi_{xx}(t_1,t_2) = \phi_{xy}(t_1,t_2) \tag{3.4-12}$$

and

$$\frac{\partial^2}{\partial t_1\, \partial t_2} \phi_{xx}(t_1,t_2) = \phi_{yy}(t_1,t_2) \tag{3.4-13}$$

The extension of this procedure to higher-order derivatives is quite simply achieved. In effect, we are here considering $\{x(t)\}$ and $\{dx(t)/dt\}$ to be different, though closely related, random processes.

In many applications it is necessary to study the statistical properties of the sum of two or more random processes. As an example, the net inaccuracy in the output of a complicated linear control system may be composed of a sum of terms, each of which arises from one particular source of inaccuracy in the system.   We confine our attention here to the calculation of the correlation function for such a sum.

Consider, for simplicity, the case of three random processes $\{x(t)\}$, $\{y(t)\}$, $\{z(t)\}$ and let

$$w(t) = x(t) + y(t) + z(t)$$

We then find

$$
\begin{aligned}
\phi_{ww}(t_1,t_2) &= E[w(t_1)w(t_2)] \\
&= E[\{x(t_1) + y(t_1) + z(t_1)\} \{x(t_2) + y(t_2) + z(t_2)\}] \\
&= E[x(t_1)x(t_2)] + E[x(t_1)y(t_2)] + E[x(t_1)z(t_2)] \\
&\quad + E[y(t_1)x(t_2)] + E[y(t_1)y(t_2)] + E[y(t_1)z(t_2)] \\
&\quad + E[z(t_1)x(t_2)] + E[z(t_1)y(t_2)] + E[z(t_1)z(t_2)] \\
&= \phi_{xx}(t_1,t_2) + \phi_{xy}(t_1,t_2) + \phi_{xz}(t_1,t_2) \\
&\quad + \phi_{yx}(t_1,t_2) + \phi_{yy}(t_1,t_2) + \phi_{yz}(t_1,t_2) \\
&\quad + \phi_{zx}(t_1,t_2) + \phi_{zy}(t_1,t_2) + \phi_{zz}(t_1,t_2) \quad (3.4\text{-}14)
\end{aligned}
$$

Thus the autocorrelation of the sum of x, y, and z can be represented as the sum of all autocorrelations and cross correlations formed from pairs of these functions.   Clearly this result is also valid for cases involving more than three random processes.

Many of the above results can be simplified when the random processes involved are statistically independent.   If $x(t_1)$ and $y(t_2)$ are statistically independent random variables,

$$E[x(t_1)y(t_2)] = E[x(t_1)]E[y(t_2)]$$

Therefore in this case

$$\phi_{xy}(t_1,t_2) = \overline{x(t_1)} \; \overline{y(t_2)} \qquad (3.4\text{-}15)$$

If, in addition, one or both of the random processes has a zero mean value, then

$$\phi_{xy}(t_1,t_2) = 0 \qquad (3.4\text{-}16)$$

It is worth noting specifically that if neither random process has a zero mean value, the cross-correlation function does not vanish even though the two may be statistically independent.   Also, the vanishing of the cross-correlation function does not of itself imply independence, as we have seen in Chap. 2.

In the particular case in which we have a sum of random processes, which are mutually independent and which possess zero mean values, the cross-correlation functions all disappear.   In this case, the correlation function for the sum is simply the sum of the individual autocorrelation functions. In the case studied previously, for example, Eq. (3.4-14) takes on the simplified form

$$\phi_{ww}(t_1,t_2) = \phi_{xx}(t_1,t_2) + \phi_{yy}(t_1,t_2) + \phi_{zz}(t_1,t_2) \qquad (3.4\text{-}17)$$

The additive property represented by (3.4-14) or (3.4-17) is quite fundamental in studying complicated problems. It means, from the practical standpoint, that one does not always have to consider a complicated problem involving several sources of random inaccuracy as a single unit. Instead, one may consider each source of inaccuracy by itself (or each pair if the sources are not independent) and superimpose results at the end of the calculation. In particular, for the case treated in (3.4-17), mean-squared values are additive:

$$\overline{w(t)^2} = \overline{x(t)^2} + \overline{y(t)^2} + \overline{z(t)^2} \qquad (3.4\text{-}18)$$

Example 3.4-2. We wish to consider the following problem in the interpolation of data. Let $\{x(t)\}$ represent a random process for which we desire to obtain the value $x(0)$ by averaging over an interval $(-T < t < T)$. The data that we are given contain a random inaccuracy represented by the random process $\{y(t)\}$. We wish to determine the length of interval $2T$ that gives us a minimum mean-squared error.

The computed average is defined by

$$a = \frac{1}{2T} \int_{-T}^{T} [x(t) + y(t)] \, dt$$

and the error ϵ is the difference between the computed average and the true value $x(0)$. Thus

$$\epsilon = a - x(0)$$
$$= \frac{1}{2T} \int_{-T}^{T} [x(t) + y(t) - x(0)] \, dt$$

To compute the mean-squared error, we first note that

$$\epsilon^2 = \frac{1}{4T^2} \left\{ \int_{-T}^{T} [x(t_1) + y(t_1) - x(0)] \, dt_1 \right\} \left\{ \int_{-T}^{T} [x(t_2) + y(t_2) - x(0)] \, dt_2 \right\}$$

where we have replaced t by t_1 and t_2, respectively, as the dummy variable of integration. The product of two integrals occurring in this expression can be written as a double integral, however, to give

$$\epsilon^2 = \frac{1}{4T^2} \int_{-T}^{T} dt_1 \int_{-T}^{T} [x(t_1)x(t_2) + x(t_1)y(t_2) - x(t_1)x(0) + y(t_1)x(t_2) + y(t_1)y(t_2)$$
$$- y(t_1)x(0) - x(0)x(t_2) - x(0)y(t_2) + x(0)^2] \, dt_2$$

We now form the mathematical expectation of this quantity, to obtain

$$\overline{\epsilon^2} = \frac{1}{4T^2} \int_{-T}^{T} dt_1 \int_{-T}^{T} [\phi_{xx}(t_1,t_2) + \phi_{xy}(t_1,t_2) - \phi_{xx}(t_1,0) + \phi_{yx}(t_1,t_2) + \phi_{yy}(t_1,t_2)$$
$$- \phi_{yx}(t_1,0) - \phi_{xx}(0,t_2) - \phi_{xy}(0,t_2) + \phi_{xx}(0,0)] \, dt_2$$

A knowledge of the autocorrelation and cross-correlation functions for $x(t)$ and $y(t)$ then permits us to compute $\overline{\epsilon^2}$ as a function of T to determine the optimum value.

One more class of problems deserves comment, although the concepts involved are trivial extensions of those considered above. In analyzing the transient behavior of linear systems that are placed in operation at a prescribed time instant (for example, $t = 0$), we often must give consideration not only to random imputs but also to transients arising from random initial conditions. For example, we may wish to study the first-order system

$$T \frac{dx}{dt} + x = f(t)$$

for $t > 0$, where $f(t)$ is random and where $x(0)$ is itself a random variable. The quantity $x(t)$ may be expressed in the form

$$x(t) = x(0)e^{-t/T} + \frac{1}{T} \int_0^t e^{-(t-\tau)/T} f(\tau) \, d\tau$$

From this relation it can be shown that

$$\overline{x(t)^2} = \overline{x(0)^2} e^{-2t/T} + \frac{2}{T} e^{-t/T} \int_0^t e^{-(t-\tau)/T} \overline{x(0)f(\tau)} \, d\tau$$
$$+ \frac{4}{T^2} \int_0^t d\tau_1 \int_0^t \exp\left[-\frac{(2t - \tau_1 - \tau_2)}{T} \right] \phi_{ff}(\tau_1, \tau_2) \, d\tau_2$$

where

$$\overline{x(0)^2} = E[x(0)x(0)]$$
$$\overline{x(0)f(\tau)} = E[x(0)f(\tau)]$$

In effect, the second quantity is a cross correlation between the initial condition and the forcing function, and may differ from zero if the initial condition is in any way influenced by the forcing function.

3.5 Stationary and Ergodic Random Processes

Let $x(t)$ be a representative member of a random process E, and let τ be an arbitrary number. With each function $x(t)$ of the ensemble we may associate a new function $y_\tau(t)$ defined by

$$y_\tau(t) = x(t - \tau) \tag{3.5-1}$$

We term this quantity the *translation* of $x(t)$ by the amount τ. The function $y_\tau(t)$ is simply the function $x(t)$ displaced to the right along the time axis by the amount τ. The ensemble of functions $y_\tau(t)$ may be considered as a new random process which we may term the *translation* by amount τ of the original random process.

In many practical situations, it can be expected that the translation in time of the functions of a random process will do little to alter their statistical characteristics. Consider, for example, an experiment in which one observes the voltage fluctuations in the outputs of a large collection of vacuum tubes. Let an arbitrary time instant be labeled $t = 0$, and let each output be recorded with respect to that instant as the time origin. The collection of records thus obtained is the ensemble to be studied.   Now let a new time origin be chosen for the same set of records; the result will be equivalent to a translation of each of the original functions.   Under the supposition that all tubes are adequately warmed up at the time of test, and that aging effects are negligible, one expects that all statistical quantities derived from the two sets of records will be essentially identical.   The same situation prevails whenever the general conditions under which an experiment is performed are time-independent.

If $x(t)$ is a function belonging to the random process E, the translated function $y_\tau(t)$ may or may not belong to E.   However, in many situations it is desirable to assume that all functions belonging to E are transformed by the translation operation into other functions of E.   Assuming this to be the case, let S be an arbitrary event, or in other words an arbitrary set of functions $\{x(t)\}$ belonging to E.   For example, let S be the set of functions for which $x(0) < 0$ and $x(1) > 4$.   If every function in S is translated by the same fixed amount τ, the result is a new set of functions which we may designate by S_τ.   In the example considered, taking $\tau = -2$, the event or set S_{-2} is the collection of functions satisfying $x(2) < 0$ and $x(3) > 4$.   Now if the external environment surrounding our random experiment is essentially unchanging with time, we would infer that the events $[x(0) < 0$ and $x(1) > 4]$ and $[x(2) < 0$ and $x(3) > 4]$ should have equal probability, since the distinction between the two is simply a matter of choice of time origin.   We express this symbolically by saying that

$$P(S_\tau) = P(S) \tag{3.5-2}$$

To give this general concept of time-invariance a name and a precise formulation, we introduce the following definition.

Definition.   A random process E is said to be *stationary* if every translation in time carries E into itself in such manner that probability is preserved.   In other words, every translation of every function in E also belongs to E, and Eq. (3.5-2) is valid for all translations τ and for all sets S for which probability is defined.

An important property of a stationary random process is that each probability distribution function (or frequency function) of the process depends upon the time instants involved only through their differences; that is, for each n,

$$F_n(x_1,t_1; x_2,t_2; \ \ldots \ ; x_n,t_n) = F_n(x_1,0; x_2,t_2 - t_1; \ \ldots \ ; x_n,t_n - t_1) \tag{3.5-3}$$

identically in all variables.   Another is that every translation in time carries the set of functions comprising the random process into itself in such a way that all its statistical parameters are unchanged.   These propositions can readily be derived as consequences of the definition that we have given; conversely, each of these statements essentially implies our definition, and could therefore have been used as the defining property.

In the remainder of this chapter and in Chap. 4 we shall have occasion to study several stationary random processes that represent various physical situations. When one is confronted with a new physical problem, however, it may be somewhat difficult to decide whether the stationary property should be assumed. As a general proposition, a given physical random process may be judged to be stationary when the environment

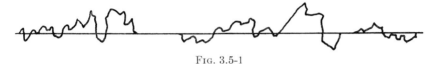

FIG. 3.5-1

surrounding the experiment is essentially unchanging. However, even this criterion is not always easily applied except through empirical analysis.

It should be kept in mind that, as in every branch of applied mathematics, we are attempting to construct mathematical models of physical situations, and that various models may often be used with varying degrees of success to describe the same situation. For example, if one considers an automatic radar tracking problem and plots against time the radar noise as various targets are tracked in sequence, the result

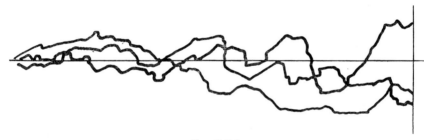

FIG. 3.5-2

might resemble Fig. 3.5-1. The random process involved could quite legitimately be regarded as stationary. On the other hand, for each target let a separate time origin be chosen, e.g., the instant at which the target is at its closest point of approach to the radar. In this case the same data might resemble Fig. 3.5-2. The plot in this figure suggests that the amplitude of the noise might depend upon the range of the target. If significant use can be made of this property, then the assumption of a nonstationary random process would perhaps be advisable. In this case one cannot say precisely that the original physical situation is or is not stationary; the answer given depends upon the precise question asked and the point of view of the one doing the asking.

Practical tests can, of course, be applied to empirical data to ascertain whether the assumption of a stationary random process is reasonable. If such statistical parameters as the mean value, mean-squared value, and correlation function are independent of a translation in time, and if further these parameters are all that are used in subsequent analysis (as is usually the case), then the assumption of the stationary property is certainly legitimate.   Even when this is not the case, it may be reasonable to assume that the random process can be approximated at any instant by one that is stationary.   This is particularly the case in the analysis of a high frequency noise for which the statistical parameters are changing with time only slowly.

Several simple but important consequences of the stationary property can be derived quite easily.   In the first place, for all τ we have

$$E[x(t + \tau)] = E[x(t)] \tag{3.5-4}$$

The particular choice $\tau = -t$ gives

$$E[x(0)] = E[x(t)] \tag{3.5-5}$$

Thus for all t, $\overline{x(t)}$ equals the fixed constant $\overline{x(0)}$.   We may similarly show that the mean-squared value of $x(t)$ is independent of time, also.

For the correlation function of a stationary random process

$$\phi_{xx}(t_1 + \tau, t_2 + \tau) = \phi_{xx}(t_1, t_2) \tag{3.5-6}$$

for every τ.   Choosing $\tau = -t_1$, we find

$$\phi_{xx}(t_1, t_2) = \phi_{xx}(0, t_2 - t_1) \tag{3.5-7}$$

The correlation function thus depends only upon the correlation interval $t_2 - t_1$, and not on t_1 and t_2 separately.   We simplify notation in this case by writing

$$\phi_{xx}(t_1, t_2) = \phi_{xx}(t_2 - t_1) \tag{3.5-8}$$

In an alternate notation

$$\phi_{xx}(t, t + \tau) = \phi_{xx}(\tau) \tag{3.5-9}$$

Since

$$\phi_{xx}(t_1, t_2) = \phi_{xx}(t_2, t_1) \tag{3.5-10}$$

we find

$$\phi_{xx}(-\tau) = \phi_{xx}(\tau) \tag{3.5-11}$$

so that the correlation function is an even function of τ.   For the case of the cross correlation between two stationary random processes we also have

$$\phi_{xy}(t_1, t_2) = \phi_{xy}(0, t_2 - t_1) = \phi_{xy}(t_2 - t_1) \tag{3.5-12}$$

Therefore

$$\phi_{xy}(\tau) = E[x(t)y(t + \tau)] \tag{3.5-13}$$

Here, we have no symmetry condition analogous to (3.5-11); however, we can write

$$\phi_{xy}(-\tau) = \phi_{yx}(\tau) \tag{3.5-14}$$

Example 3.5-1. In Example 3.2-2 we considered briefly the ensemble of functions

$$\sum_{k=-\infty}^{\infty} F(t - t_k)$$

corresponding to the voltage output of a linear vacuum-tube circuit, with the numbers t_k representing the arrival times of different electrons at the anode. Assuming the numbers t_k to be independent and distributed over the time axis with a constant average density, it is clear that any translation of a function of this type yields a function of the same type. It is further evident intuitively that the probability associated with any set of these functions is unchanged upon translation; in fact this is an intrinsic part of the notion of a uniform and independent distribution of the numbers t_k. We may thus conclude that this random process is stationary.

Example 3.5-2. The random process derived from the coin-tossing experiment in Example 3.2-1 is not stationary as it stands, since the process is considered to start at a definite time ($t = 0$) and since the time instants at which discontinuities can occur bear a definite relation to this time origin. We may form a stationary process in much the same way, however, by the following construction. Let t_0 and u be a pair of independent random variables, distributed uniformly over the intervals ($0 \leq t_0 < 1$) and ($0 \leq u < 1$). Let the binary expansion of u be

$$u = .u_1u_2u_3 \cdots$$

For a particular pair of numbers (t_0, u), we define $f(t)$ by

$$f(t) = \begin{cases} u_1 & t_0 < t \leq t_0 + 1 \\ u_2 & t_0 - 1 < t \leq t_0 \\ u_3 & t_0 + 1 < t \leq t_0 + 2 \\ u_4 & t_0 - 2 < t \leq t_0 - 1 \\ u_5 & t_0 + 2 < t \leq t_0 + 3 \\ u_6 & t_0 - 3 < t \leq t_0 - 2 \\ \cdots \cdots \cdots \cdots \cdots \end{cases}$$

By this process we obtain the collection E of all functions describable by the property that they consist of zeros and ones over successive unit intervals of time.

Clearly every translation of such a function yields one of the same type. Since t_0 is uniformly distributed over the unit interval, from our discussion in Example 3.2-1 it is natural to define the probability associated with every set of these functions as equal to the area of the corresponding set of points in the t_0u plane. Then it is clear that for at least some sets S and some translations τ probability is preserved. A case in point is indicated in Fig. 3.5-3, for $\tau = 1/2$. Actually the stationary property can be established in its full generality for this example.

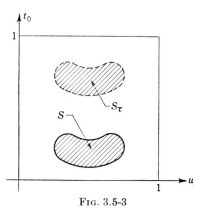

FIG. 3.5-3

Example 3.5-3.   We consider an ensemble of functions of the form

$$x(t) = \sum_{n=1}^{\infty} (a_n \cos n\omega t + b_n \sin n\omega t) \tag{3.5-15}$$

in which the coefficients $(a_1, b_1, a_2, b_2, \ldots)$ form a set of mutually independent random variables, each possessing a zero mean value. We assume the respective distributions for the coefficients to be such that the probability is zero that the series does not converge; we also assume that the various operations which are performed on this series are legitimate.

No attempt is made to compute the various distribution functions for $x(t)$; however, we can readily calculate the correlation function by a direct approach. We first write $x(t_1)x(t_2)$ in the form

$$x(t_1)x(t_2) = \left[\sum_{m=1}^{\infty} (a_m \cos m\omega t_1 + b_m \sin m\omega t_1) \right]\left[\sum_{n=1}^{\infty} (a_n \cos n\omega t_2 + b_n \sin n\omega t_2) \right]$$

$$= \sum_{m=1}^{\infty} \sum_{n=1}^{\infty} (a_m a_n \cos m\omega t_1 \cos n\omega t_2 + a_m b_n \cos m\omega t_1 \sin n\omega t_2$$

$$+ a_n b_m \cos n\omega t_2 \sin m\omega t_1 + b_m b_n \sin m\omega t_1 \sin n\omega t_2)$$

Upon averaging, we note that since all a's are independent of all b's,

$$\overline{a_i b_k} = \overline{a_i}\,\overline{b_k} = 0$$

For the average of the remaining terms, we have

$$E[x(t_1)x(t_2)] = \sum_{m=1}^{\infty} \sum_{n=1}^{\infty} \{E[a_m a_n] \cos m\omega t_1 \cos n\omega t_2 + E[b_m b_n] \sin m\omega t_1 \sin n\omega t_2\}$$

However, for those terms in which $m \neq n$,

$$E[a_m a_n] = E[b_m b_n] = 0$$

Thus

$$\phi(t_1, t_2) = \sum_{n=1}^{\infty} (\overline{a_n^2} \cos n\omega t_1 \cos n\omega t_2 + \overline{b_n^2} \sin n\omega t_1 \sin n\omega t_2)$$

In the special case for which

$$\overline{a_n^2} = \overline{b_n^2} \tag{3.5-16}$$

for all values of n, the expression for ϕ can be simplified as follows:

$$\phi(t_1, t_2) = \sum_{n=1}^{\infty} \overline{a_n^2} (\cos n\omega t_1 \cos n\omega t_2 + \sin n\omega t_1 \sin n\omega t_2)$$

$$= \sum_{n=1}^{\infty} \overline{a_n^2} \cos n\omega(t_2 - t_1)$$

Thus the correlation function depends only upon the difference $t_2 - t_1$. We note also that the function

$$\phi(\tau) = \sum_{n=1}^{\infty} \overline{a_n^2} \cos n\omega\tau \qquad (3.5\text{-}17)$$

is a periodic function of τ containing precisely the frequencies contained in $x(t)$, with amplitudes $\overline{a_n^2}$ representing the average squared amplitudes of the corresponding terms in $x(t)$. In fact, if we average the expression $(a_n \cos n\omega t + b_n \sin n\omega t)^2$ with respect to the coefficients a_n, b_n and subsequently with respect to t over a full period of the oscillation, we obtain precisely $\frac{1}{2}(\overline{a_n^2} + \overline{b_n^2}) = \overline{a_n^2}$.

The random process is clearly nonstationary unless (3.5-16) is satisfied for all values of n. If this condition is satisfied, however, the correlation function depends upon t_1 and t_2 only through their difference $t_2 - t_1$, and we might be tempted to conclude that (3.5-16) is a sufficient condition for the process to be stationary. Actually, as we shall now show, additional and much more stringent conditions must be imposed before our definition for a stationary process is satisfied. The necessary condition is in fact that the distribution of a_n and b_n be the normal distribution, for all n. To see this, let us fix upon an arbitrary value of n and consider the set of functions S such that the pair of coefficients (a_n, b_n) lies in an assigned set A in the ab plane. If the process is to be stationary, then an arbitrary translation τ should leave probability unchanged. Since

$$a_n \cos n\omega(t - \tau) + b_n \sin n\omega(t - \tau)$$
$$= (a_n \cos n\omega\tau - b_n \sin n\omega\tau) \cos n\omega t + (a_n \sin n\omega\tau + b_n \cos n\omega\tau) \sin n\omega t$$
$$= a_n' \cos n\omega t + b_n' \sin n\omega t \qquad (3.5\text{-}18)$$

the effect of translation on any single function is to replace its coefficients (a_n, b_n) by new coefficients (a_n', b_n') defined by the above relation.

It is seen from (3.5-18) that the point (a_n', b_n') is related to (a_n, b_n) by a rotation about the origin through an angle $n\omega\tau$. Consequently, if (a_n, b_n) lies in the set A, (a_n', b_n') must lie in the set A_τ shown in Fig. 3.5-4, which is the set A rotated by the angle $n\omega\tau$. If the random process is to be stationary, it is necessary for the probability associated with the set A_τ to be identical to that associated with A, for every translation τ and for every set A. In other words,

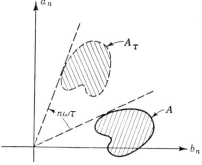

FIG. 3.5-4

$$\text{Pr } [(a_n, b_n) \text{ in } A_\tau] = \text{Pr } [(a_n, b_n) \text{ in } A]$$

for all τ and all A.

It should be fairly evident that if this relation is to be satisfied, the joint probability density function of a_n and b_n can only be a function of the radial distance from the origin. We indicate this by the notation

$$f(a_n, b_n) = g(a_n^2 + b_n^2)$$

where it is convenient to use the square of the radius $(a_n^2 + b_n^2)$ rather than the radius itself, and where g is a function to be determined. Now let $f_1(a_n)$ and $f_2(b_n)$ be the respective density functions for a_n and b_n separately. By the postulated independence of these variables, we have

$$f(a_n,b_n) = f_1(a_n)f_2(b_n)$$

Writing, for convenience,

$$f_1(a_n) = h_1(a_n^2) \qquad f_2(b_n) = h_2(b_n^2)$$

we thus obtain

$$g(a_n^2 + b_n^2) = h_1(a_n^2)h_2(b_n^2)$$

as a relation that must hold identically in a_n and b_n.

Writing $b_n = 0$, $a_n^2 = \alpha$, we have

$$g(\alpha) = h_1(\alpha)h_2(0)$$

and similarly

$$g(\alpha) = h_1(0)h_2(\alpha)$$

Thus the h's are proportional to g, and we must have

$$g(\alpha + \beta) = cg(\alpha)g(\beta)$$

where $\alpha = a_n^2$, $\beta = b_n^2$, and c is some constant of proportionality.

Then

$$\log g(\alpha + \beta) = \log c + \log g(\alpha) + \log g(\beta)$$

for all positive α and β, and this can be true only if $\log g$ is a linear function of its argument. We may thus write

$$\log g(\alpha) = -\mu\alpha + c'$$

for some constants μ and c', obtaining

$$f(a_n,b_n) = g(a_n^2 + b_n^2) = c'' \exp\left[-\mu(a_n^2 + b_n^2)\right]$$

Thus a_n and b_n are independent and normally distributed random variables as asserted. Since the above demonstration is valid for any value of n, we have established the fact that each coefficient must be normally distributed in order that the process shall be stationary.

A second property, which is quite often assumed in the analysis of stationary random processes, is the so-called ergodic property. In general terms, this property permits one to equate ensemble averages and averages with respect to time performed on a single "representative" function of the ensemble. Suppose, for example, that one is again observing the output fluctuations in vacuum tubes, and let it be assumed that the environmental conditions allow the experiment to run an infinite length of time without change. Now let the record of the output of a single tube be cut into a sequence of strips each of length T, where T is large. Then in effect this sequence of samples drawn from a single function can be taken as an ensemble, and according to the ergodic hypothesis this latter ensemble possesses the same statistical properties as the original ensemble.

As a matter of fact, it is not necessary to cut the record into a set of nonoverlapping strips. The ergodic property can also be expressed by saying that the expectation of any random variable is equal to the average of that variable over all translations in time of a single function; i.e.,

$$E[V\{x(t)\}] = \lim_{T \to \infty} \frac{1}{2T} \int_{-T}^{T} V[x(t + \tau)] \, d\tau \qquad (3.5\text{-}19)$$

Here $V[x]$ is any random variable associated with $x(t)$, such as $x(t)^2$, $x(t_1)x(t_2)$, etc. We adopt the following definition.

Definition. A stationary random process is said to possess the *ergodic property*, provided that for every random variable $V[x]$ the relation (3.5-19) is valid for all functions $x(t)$, with the possible exception of a set of functions of zero probability.

One remark is appropriate on the definition of the ergodic property. We have deliberately allowed for the possible existence of a set of exceptional functions, of zero probability, for which this property fails. The reasons are suggested by the example of the step function generated by coin flipping, as discussed previously. Exceptional functions can occur, such as the function $f(t) \equiv 1$ of that example, and time averages performed on such functions cannot be expected to yield results representative of the whole ensemble. As long as the probability is zero that a random selection would yield any such exceptional function, however, their existence is not a matter of practical concern.

As examples of the application of this property, when it is valid, we consider the following:

1. *Mean Value of x*

$$\overline{x(t)} = E[x(t)] = \lim_{T \to \infty} \frac{1}{2T} \int_{-T}^{T} x(t + \tau) \, d\tau$$

$$= \lim_{T \to \infty} \frac{1}{2T} \int_{-T}^{T} x(t) \, dt \qquad (3.5\text{-}20)$$

2. *Mean-squared Value of x*

$$\overline{x(t)^2} = E[x(t)^2] = \lim_{T \to \infty} \frac{1}{2T} \int_{-T}^{T} x(t + \tau)^2 \, d\tau$$

$$= \lim_{T \to \infty} \frac{1}{2T} \int_{-T}^{T} x(t)^2 \, dt \qquad (3.5\text{-}21)$$

3. *Correlation Function*

$$\overline{x(t)x(t + \tau)} = E[x(t)x(t + \tau)]$$

$$= \lim_{T \to \infty} \frac{1}{2T} \int_{-T}^{T} x(t + \tau_1)x(t + \tau + \tau_1) \, d\tau_1$$

$$= \lim_{T \to \infty} \frac{1}{2T} \int_{-T}^{T} x(t)x(t + \tau) \, dt \qquad (3.5\text{-}22)$$

In each of these relations, use is made of the fact that for functions $f(t)$ which satisfy suitable conditions,

$$
\lim_{T \to \infty} \frac{1}{2T} \int_{-T}^{T} f(t + t') \, dt'
$$

$$
= \lim_{T \to \infty} \frac{1}{2T} \int_{-T+t}^{T+t} f(t') \, dt' = \lim_{T \to \infty} \frac{1}{2T} \int_{-T}^{T} f(t') \, dt'
$$

$$
+ \lim_{T \to \infty} \frac{1}{2T} \left[- \int_{-T}^{-T+t} f(t') \, dt' + \int_{T}^{T+t} f(t') \, dt' \right] \quad (3.5\text{-}23)
$$

and that in the limit the last terms approach zero and can be discarded.

The relations (3.5-20) to (3.5-22) form a very convenient tool for numerical calculations since, under conditions in which the ergodic hypothesis may reasonably be assumed, they eliminate the necessity for taking large numbers of experimental records to form an ensemble. Most of the recent devices for computing correlation functions, for example, are based upon an instrumental calculation of the type of average found in (3.5-22), or the equivalent average

$$
\lim_{T \to \infty} \frac{1}{T} \int_{0}^{T} x(t) x(t + \tau) \, dt \quad (3.5\text{-}24)
$$

Some of these devices replace the integral by a sum of the form

$$
\phi_{xx}(n \, \Delta\tau) = \lim_{N \to \infty} \frac{1}{N + 1} \sum_{k=0}^{N} x(k \, \Delta\tau) x(k \, \Delta\tau + n \, \Delta\tau) \quad (3.5\text{-}25)
$$

for a small value of $\Delta\tau$. As a matter of fact, the relationship (3.5-25) is not merely an approximate way of evaluating the integral form of average given by (3.5-24). According to the ergodic hypothesis it is also true that

$$
E[V\{x(t)\}] = \lim_{N \to \infty} \frac{1}{N + 1} \sum_{k=0}^{N} V[x(t + k\tau)] \quad (3.5\text{-}26)
$$

for any $\tau > 0$. This property is not derived from our basic definitions, but is true under the same set of conditions.

It should be noted that we have frequently referred to the ergodic property as a "hypothesis." Precise mathematical conditions can be stated for this property to be valid; in most applications, however, it is not easy to verify that these conditions are satisfied. Trivial examples (e.g., a random process for which each member is a constant) show that this property is not a consequence of the fact that a random process is stationary, so that a careful distinction between these properties is necessary. In practice, there is generally a sound intuitive basis for assuming the ergodic property, and its convenience in permitting interchange of time and ensemble averages offers a considerable appeal. We therefore make this assumption, where convenient, without apology.

Example 3.5-4. The concept of the ergodic property was first introduced in classical statistical mechanics in the following way. Suppose that there are n molecules in a container. A total of $3n$ numbers are required to specify the simultaneous positions of all molecules, and another $3n$ numbers are required to specify all velocities or momenta. Thus the *state* of the system at any instant can be specified in terms of $6n$ numbers that can be considered as coordinates of a single point in a $6n$-dimensional space called *phase space*. By this device the changing state of the system with time is visualized in terms of the motion through phase space of the point representing the system.

Now consider an ensemble of systems of this nature with an assigned probability distribution, e.g., the collection of all systems possessing a total energy E lying between fixed bounds $E_1 \leq E \leq E_2$. There will then exist a corresponding ensemble of points in phase space, and the motion of each such point with time will represent the progressive changes in the state of that system. Since any property or quantity associated with the system can be represented as a function of its $6n$ generalized coordinates, the successive values of such a quantity constitute a random function of time and the ensemble of such functions form a random process. Under suitable conditions the ergodic hypothesis can then be used to show that the average properties of a particular system with time are the same as the ensemble average at any instant.

Roughly speaking, the idea in this example is that of a continual mixing of the ensemble of points in phase space. This takes place in such manner that almost all points ultimately pass through every portion of the space an infinite number of times. In fact, if the initial distribution of points is properly chosen, then, with the exception of a set of points of zero probability, the average proportion of time spent in a given region by an arbitrary point is equal to the probability associated with that region in the initial distribution. Thus the behavior of any system in the long run is the same as the behavior of any other, except for a collection of exceptional systems with special properties and with zero probability of occurrence.

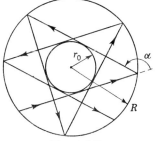

FIG. 3.5-5

Example 3.5-5. As our next example of a stationary and ergodic random process, we consider the motion of a perfectly elastic billiard ball on a frictionless circular table with perfectly elastic boundaries. We assume the diameter of the ball to be zero and its speed to be a constant v. As illustrated in Fig. 3.5-5, it is clear that upon each impact with the boundary of the table the direction of motion of the ball changes by the fixed amount α. From elementary geometry it is found that all paths are tangent to an inner circle of radius

$$r_0 = R \cos (\alpha/2)$$

and that each chord length is $2R \sin (\alpha/2)$.

For given values of r_0 and R, it is clear from the above picture that there is a unique correspondence between the direction of motion of the ball and the line along which it moves. If we define a function $x(t)$ to be the horizontal component of the position of the ball at time t, then the derivative of this function can be expressed in the form

$$\frac{dx(t)}{dt} = \begin{cases} v \cos \theta_0 & 0 < t < t_1 \\ v \cos \theta_1 & t_1 < t < t_2 \\ \cdot \cdot \cdot \cdot \cdot \cdot \cdot \cdot \cdot \cdot \cdot \cdot \cdot \cdot \\ v \cos \theta_n & t_n < t < t_{n+1} \end{cases}$$

where θ_0 represents its original direction of motion, $\theta_n = \theta_0 + n\alpha$, where t_1 is the time of the first impact with the boundary, and

$$t_n = t_1 + \frac{2(n-1)R}{v} \sin (\alpha/2)$$

is the time of the nth impact. The function $x(t)$ itself is of course the integral of the above expression for dx/dt and constitutes a set of straight-line segments, as indicated by Fig. 3.5-6.

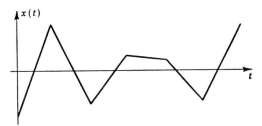

F<small>IG</small>. 3.5-6

Now let the radii r_0 and R be so chosen that α/π is an irrational number. Under these conditions $n\alpha$ can never be an integer multiple of 2π for any integer n, and consequently the ball never returns exactly to its original direction of motion. As a matter of fact it can further be shown that the directions of motion are uniformly distributed between 0 and 2π. This statement is to be interpreted in the following sense. We observe the motion of the ball for a long time $0 < t < t_N$ and let n be the number of intervals $t_k < t < t_{k+1}$ for which θ_k lies between arbitrary assigned limits $\gamma < \theta_k < \beta$. Then

$$\lim_{N \to \infty} \frac{n}{N} = \frac{\beta - \gamma}{2\pi}$$

for every such interval (γ,β) and for every value of the original direction θ_0. An equivalent statement is that if we observe the direction θ at a random time instant in the interval $0 < t < \infty$, then the random variable θ has the constant probability density

$$f(\theta) = \frac{1}{2\pi} \qquad 0 \leqq \theta < 2\pi$$

We now consider the motion of an ensemble of balls, with an initial probability distribution as yet to be assigned. For simplicity we assume that each ball moves in such a direction that its path is tangent to the same inner circle of radius r_0, and assume the motion to be in the counterclockwise direction. Associated with the ensemble of balls is a corresponding collection of functions $\{x(t)\}$ constituting a random process. If the process is to be stationary, the uniform density of directions of motion as described above suggests that the probability density for the ensemble of balls should not depend upon direction of motion but only upon the radial distance from the origin.

We therefore assume this to be the case, and write

$$f(r_1) \, dr_1 = \Pr (r_1 < r \leq r_1 + dr_1)$$

where r is the radial distance of a randomly selected ball.

To compute $f(r_1)$, we assume that in any given region precisely half the balls are moving, respectively, inward toward the center or outward away from the center. Now consider the collection of balls lying in the interval $(r_1 < r \leq r_2)$ at time t and moving in an outward direction. The probability associated with this set is $\frac{1}{2}[F(r_2) - F(r_1)]$, where

$$F(r) = \int_{r_0}^{r} f(u) \, du$$

For the process to be stationary, the time rate of change of the probability associated with this moving set of balls must be zero. Since for any of these balls

$$\frac{dr}{dt} = v \sqrt{1 - \left(\frac{r_0}{r}\right)^2}$$

we have

$$\frac{d}{dt}\left\{ \frac{1}{2}[F(r_2) - F(r_1)] \right\} = \frac{1}{2}\left[f(r_2) \frac{dr_2}{dt} - f(r_1) \frac{dr_1}{dt} \right]$$

$$= \frac{v}{2}\left[f(r_2) \sqrt{1 - \left(\frac{r_0}{r_2}\right)^2} - f(r_1) \sqrt{1 - \left(\frac{r_0}{r_1}\right)^2} \right]$$

If this expression is to vanish for all r_1 and r_2, each of the two terms must be equal to the same fixed constant. Thus

$$f(r) = \frac{c}{\sqrt{1 - \left(\frac{r_0}{r}\right)^2}} = \frac{cr}{\sqrt{r^2 - r_0^2}}$$

To find c, we note that

$$\int_{r_0}^{R} f(r) \, dr = 1$$

and obtain, upon solving for c, the expression

$$f(r) = \frac{r}{\sqrt{(r^2 - r_0^2)(R^2 - r_0^2)}}$$

We now assert that the random process $\{x(t)\}$ is both stationary and ergodic. It can readily be shown that the above process of construction of the probability density leads to a probability that is independent of translations in time. It can further be shown that for any particular ball [for any function $x(t)$] the average fraction of time spent in an arbitrary region of the plane is proportional to the integral of the probability density over that region. Thus the process possesses the ergodic property. In this case, incidentally, there are no exceptional functions for which the property fails.

The random process $\{x(t)\}$ is not the only one that is derivable from this particular model. For any function $W(x,y)$ the set of functions

$$w(t) = W[x(t),y(t)]$$

form a stationary and ergodic random process, where $x(t)$ and $y(t)$ are the rectangular cartesian coordinates of the position of the ball at time t.

In this particular example the usual situation in empirical analysis is perhaps reversed: here, it would generally be simpler to compute ensemble averages than to compute time averages on a single representative function of the ensemble. Thus, for example,

$$\lim_{T \to \infty} \frac{1}{T} \int_0^T w(t) \, dt = E[w(t)] = \frac{1}{2\pi} \int_0^{2\pi} d\theta \int_{r_0}^R f(r) W(r \cos \theta, \, r \sin \theta) \, dr$$

On the other hand, by suitable analogue-computing equipment the time average of $w(t)$ might at times be of use in evaluating the above double integral. Experiments of this general type have actually been carried out in isolated cases for which the direct numerical evaluation of a complicated integral has proved to be too tedious.

Example 3.5-6. We return again to the coin-tossing experiment discussed in Example 3.5-2. Since each function of that example consists of a "random sequence of zeros and ones," it would appear highly likely that we could equate time averages with respect to a particular function and corresponding ensemble averages. We are not in a position here to prove this statement, although it is indeed provable. Rather, we shall illustrate its significance by tracing the behavior in the $t_0 u$ plane of a single "representative" point.

All functions $f(t)$ for which u is a rational number can be shown to be periodic; thus the ergodic property is not valid for rational values of u. Since the set of all rational numbers has zero probability, this fact does not contradict our assertion that the random process $f(t)$ is ergodic. To demonstate the ergodic property, we must therefore pick a representative irrational number. For example, consider a number u whose binary expansion is

$$u = .00100 \quad 10000 \quad 11111 \quad 10110$$
$$10101 \quad 00010 \quad 00100 \quad 00101$$
$$10100 \quad 01100 \quad 00100 \quad 01101 \; \cdots$$

The corresponding function $f(t)$ is formed, according to the construction process of Example 3.5-2, by writing alternate digits of u to the right and left of the origin. We indicate the result schematically by the array

$$11000 \quad 01000 \quad 11000 \quad 00000$$
$$01111 \quad 00100 \mid 01000 \quad 11101$$
$$11101 \quad 01000 \quad 11010 \quad 01010$$

Here the vertical bar indicates the origin in time and the tabulated numbers represent the values taken on by $f(t)$ over successive unit intervals before and after $t = 0$. Thus

$$f(t) = \begin{cases} 0 & 0 < t \leqq 1 \\ 1 & 1 < t \leqq 2 \\ 0 & 2 < t \leqq 5 \\ 1 & 5 < t \leqq 8 \\ \cdots\cdots\cdots\cdots\cdots \\ 1 & -9 < t \leqq -5 \\ 0 & -5 < t \leqq -3 \\ 1 & -3 < t \leqq -2 \\ 0 & -2 < t \leqq 0 \end{cases}$$

Now starting with $t_0 = 0$ and u as given ($= u_0$), corresponding to point A in Fig. 3.5-7, we translate $f(t)$ by the amount τ. For $0 \leqq \tau < 1$, the result in the t_0u plane is an upward motion of the point representing $f(t)$, taking place along the line

$$u = u_0 = 0.14$$

When τ reaches the value of unity (point B), however, the array representing $f(t)$ is shifted to the right by one full unit, and we obtain

$$\cdots 0011110010 \mid 0010001110 \cdots$$

From this shifted array we form a new value u_1 given by

$$u_1 = .00011 \quad 00001 \quad 01111 \quad 11000 \cdots$$

Converting to decimal notation, we find

$$u_1 = 0.09$$

Thus in the t_0u plane the point representing $f(t - \tau)$ moves from point $B(t_0 = 1, u = 0.14)$ to the point $C(t_0 = 0, u = 0.09)$, as indicated by the dotted arrow.

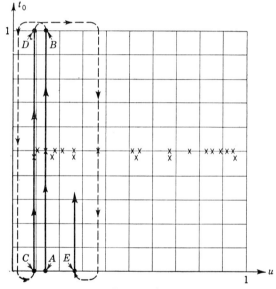

Fig. 3.5-7

Continuing the translation, we again move upward along the line $u = 0.09$, as τ changes from 1 to 2. When $\tau = 2$, we again have a jump, as indicated, from point $D(t_0 = 1, u = 0.09)$ to the point $E(t_0 = 0, u = u_2 = 0.26)$. In this manner we generate a sequence of lines in the t_0u plane. The approximate u coordinates of the lines corresponding to values of τ in the interval $(-10 < \tau < 10)$ are indicated by crosses in the figure. It is seen that the distribution of these values is roughly uniform over the interval $(0 \leqq u < 1)$; in fact, the degree of uniformity is just about what one would expect from a random selection of points.

Now let us consider any random variable $V[f]$ associated with the set of functions $f(t)$. Corresponding to each such function there is a point in the (t_0, u) plane; consequently V may be considered as an ordinary function of t_0 and u, and

$$E[V] = \int_0^1 dt_0 \int_0^1 V(t_0, u) \, du$$

The time average of V for a particular function $f(t)$ is obtained by averaging V along a path consisting of a family of lines in the (t_0, u) plane, as indicated in Fig. 3.5-7. The implication of the ergodic property is, in effect, that these lines are distributed over the square with a uniform average density in the limit, and that the limiting average of V along this family of lines is the same as its integral over the square.

We conclude the discussion of the ergodic property with one simple but important result. A time-invariant filter may be defined as a device such that any translation of its input alters the output only by an equal translation. Thus a linear or nonlinear system with constant coefficients possesses the property of time-invariance. Now let $\{x(t)\}$ be a stationary and ergodic random process considered as the input to such a device, and let $\{y(t)\}$ be the corresponding output. We assert that $\{y(t)\}$ is also a stationary and ergodic random process.

For proof we first note that the probability associated with any set of output functions $\{y(t)\}$ is equal to the probability associated with the corresponding set of inputs $\{x(t)\}$. The latter probability is unaltered by translation of the functions $\{x(t)\}$, however, since $\{x(t)\}$ is postulated to be stationary. Hence the probability of the set of functions $\{y(t)\}$ is also unaltered by translation, and $\{y(t)\}$ is thus a stationary random process. To establish the ergodic property, let $V[y]$ be any random variable associated with y. Since any function $y(t)$ is determined by the corresponding function $x(t)$, the quantity $V[y]$ is also a random variable $V_1[x]$ associated with x. Since the random process $\{x(t)\}$ is ergodic, the time and ensemble averages of $V_1[x]$ are almost always identical. Hence the same property is true for $V[y]$.

The importance of this result lies in the following fact. If we can establish that a given random process $\{x(t)\}$ is stationary and ergodic, then it follows that all random processes $\{y(t)\}$ derivable from it by time-invariant filtering are also stationary and ergodic. In particular we apply this result in Chap. 4 to show that all random processes thus derived from the shot effect or from the general stationary Gaussian random process are of necessity themselves stationary and ergodic.

3.6   Power Spectral Density

In analyzing the effect of a filter on a periodic signal input, it is common to decompose the signal into its harmonic components, which are the terms in the Fourier series expansion of the signal. The action of the filter on each harmonic component is then determined and the results superimposed.   If the signal is not periodic it cannot of course be decomposed into discrete harmonic components with nonzero amplitudes; however, if it has a Fourier transform it then has a so-called continuous frequency spectrum, given in terms of the transform, which can be treated mathematically much like a spectrum of harmonics.   The techniques of Fourier analysis can also be applied profitably to stationary random processes; in this section we give these notions a precise significance and develop the basic relations to be used in such an application.

To begin with, let a periodic voltage $e_i(t)$ be applied to a linear time-invariant filter possessing a frequency-response function $Y(j\omega)$.   Let $e_i(t)$ be represented by the Fourier series

$$e_i(t) = \sum_{k=0}^{\infty} a_k \cos(k\omega_0 t + \alpha_k) \tag{3.6-1}$$

where ω_0 is the fundamental frequency.   Then the output voltage is

$$e_o(t) = \sum_{k=0}^{\infty} b_k \cos(k\omega_0 t + \beta_k) \tag{3.6-2}$$

where $b_k = |Y(jk\omega_0)|a_k$.   The phase shift $\beta_k - \alpha_k$ is also determined by $Y(jk\omega_0)$, of course, but we are not immediately concerned with this fact.

If there is a resistor of resistance R across the output terminals of the filter, the instantaneous power dissipated in the resistor is

$$P = \frac{1}{R} e_o(t)^2 = \frac{1}{R}\left[\sum_{k=0}^{\infty} b_k \cos(k\omega_0 t + \beta_k)\right]^2$$

Correspondingly, the average dissipated power P_{av} is obtained by averaging P over one full period, giving

$$P_{\mathrm{av}} = \frac{1}{RT_0} \int_0^{T_0} \left[\sum_{k=0}^{\infty} b_k \cos(k\omega_0 t + \beta_k)\right]^2 dt$$

$$= \frac{1}{2R} \sum_{k=0}^{\infty} b_k^2$$

$$= \frac{1}{2R} \sum_{k=0}^{\infty} |Y(jk\omega_0)|^2 a_k^2 \tag{3.6-3}$$

where the period T_0 is given by $T_0 = 2\pi/\omega_0$.

If now the filter were very sharply selective, so that

$$|Y(j\omega)| = \begin{cases} 1 & m\omega_0 \leq \omega \leq n\omega_0 \\ 0 & \omega < m\omega_0;\ \omega > n\omega_0 \end{cases} \tag{3.6-4}$$

we would have

$$P_{av} = \frac{1}{2R} \sum_{k=m}^{n} a_k^2 \qquad (3.6\text{-}5)$$

It is thus natural to say that the expression (3.6-5) is the average power transmitted by the signal $e_i(t)$ to a resistor R in a particular frequency range, i.e., the range $(m\omega_0 \leqq \omega \leqq n\omega_0)$. If $Y(j\omega) = 1$ for all values of ω, the voltage $e_i(t)$ is then applied directly across the resistance R, and the average power associated with the input $e_i(t)$ is seen to be

$$\frac{1}{RT_0} \int_0^{T_0} e_i(t)^2 \, dt = \frac{1}{2R} \sum_{k=0}^{\infty} a_k^2 \qquad [(3.6\text{-}6)$$

A comparison with (3.6-5) shows that by the relation (3.6-6) we have in effect decomposed the average power of $e_i(t)$ into a sum of separate contributions from the various frequencies involved. This is accomplished in such manner that the average power associated with any particular set of frequencies is given directly by the sum of the corresponding terms from (3.6-6).

We have here a situation that is analogous to that of a discrete probability distribution. Associated with each of a discrete set of frequencies $k\omega_0$ is a certain positive power $a_k^2/2R$. We could define a power spectral density as the quantity

$$\frac{1}{2R} \sum_{k=0}^{\infty} a_k^2 \delta(\omega - k\omega_0)$$

by direct analogy with Eq. (2.7-21) for the probability density in the discrete case. Then the power associated with a particular interval of frequencies is seen to be given by the integral of the power spectral density over that frequency interval. In general, our interest is centered about nonperiodic cases involving a continuous power spectral density rather than one that is discrete in nature. For such cases, the Fourier integral plays much the same role as the Fourier series in the above application.

Before considering the extension of these notions, we wish to free ourselves from the obligation of continual reference to a specific physical model of the problem. In the case just considered the average power depends not only upon properties of the voltage $e_i(t)$ but also upon the particular value selected for the resistance R. If instead of a voltage input to the filter we were to have considered a corresponding current $I(t)$, then the corresponding power would have been associated with the quantity I^2R. In either case the power is proportional to the square of the function [$e_i(t)$ or $I(t)$] with which we are dealing, with a constant of proportionality that depends on the particular application. A similar situation prevails in the fields of optics and acoustics, in which the power transmitted by an electromagnetic or acoustic oscillation is proportional to the squared amplitude of the oscillation. In our following work we should prefer not to have to keep track of the appropriate factors of proportionality, and we therefore adopt a generalized definition of what we mean by the term "power".

There is still another important reason for wishing to generalize our terminology. In many applications we shall apply the concept of spectral density to physical situations in which it is difficult to assign a power in the ordinary physical sense; e.g., it may be desirable to study the power spectral density of a function $A(t)$ that is an angle. Now we could of course meet this situation by dropping the term power from our vocabulary in these applications. However, as we shall see below, there are cases in which we shall wish to consider an energy spectral density as well as a power spectral density, and it is important to maintain the distinction between these concepts. In addition, the use of the physical terminology is often convenient in serving to give an intuitive significance to these ideas. We therefore introduce the following definitions.

Definition. For an arbitrary real-valued function of time $x(t)$, we call the quantity $x(t)^2$ the *instantaneous power* associated with $x(t)$. The total *energy* associated with this function is the integral

$$\int_{-\infty}^{\infty} x(t)^2 \, dt \tag{3.6-7}$$

when this integral converges. The *average power* of $x(t)$ is the quantity

$$\lim_{T \to \infty} \frac{1}{2T} \int_{-T}^{T} x(t)^2 \, dt \tag{3.6-8}$$

when this limit exists.

As the next step we wish to consider the energy spectral density for an arbitrary function $x(t)$ for which the integral (3.6-7) is finite. Let $a(\omega)$ be the Fourier transform of $x(t)$, given by

$$a(\omega) = \frac{1}{\sqrt{2\pi}} \int_{-\infty}^{\infty} x(t)e^{-j\omega t} \, dt \tag{3.6-9}$$

Then $x(t)$ in turn is given in terms of $a(\omega)$ by

$$x(t) = \frac{1}{\sqrt{2\pi}} \int_{-\infty}^{\infty} a(\omega)e^{j\omega t} \, d\omega \tag{3.6-10}$$

Also by the Parseval formula for Fourier transforms,

$$\int_{-\infty}^{\infty} x(t)^2 \, dt = \int_{-\infty}^{\infty} |a(\omega)|^2 \, d\omega \tag{3.6-11}$$

The function $a(\omega)$ is generally a complex-valued quantity; thus, from (3.6-9),

$$a(\omega) = \frac{1}{\sqrt{2\pi}} \int_{-\infty}^{\infty} x(t) \cos \omega t \, dt - j \frac{1}{\sqrt{2\pi}} \int_{-\infty}^{\infty} x(t) \sin \omega t \, dt \tag{3.6-12}$$

Denoting the complex conjugate of $a(\omega)$ by the symbol $a(\omega)^*$, we have

$$a(\omega)^* = a(-\omega) \tag{3.6-13}$$

The quantity $|a(\omega)|^2$ can be written, by means of (3.6-13), in the form

$$|a(\omega)|^2 = a(\omega)a(\omega)^* = a(\omega)a(-\omega) \tag{3.6-14}$$

If we replace ω by $-\omega$ in this expression, the value of the expression is obviously unaltered. Thus the quantity $|a(\omega)|^2$ is an even function of ω. This fact permits us to rewrite Eq. (3.6-11) entirely in terms of positive frequencies, in the form

$$\int_{-\infty}^{\infty} x(t)^2 \, dt = 2 \int_{0}^{\infty} |a(\omega)|^2 \, d\omega \tag{3.6-15}$$

Definition. The quantity

$$E(\omega,x) = 2|a(\omega)|^2$$
$$= \frac{1}{\pi} \left| \int_{-\infty}^{\infty} x(t)e^{-j\omega t} \, dt \right|^2 \tag{3.6-16}$$

is called the *energy spectral density* of the function $x(t)$.

To justify this definition, we first observe by (3.6-15) that the total energy of x is equal to $\int_{0}^{\infty} E(\omega,x) \, d\omega$. In addition, as in the case of the Fourier series, we may let $x(t)$ be the input to an ideal bandpass filter with a frequency response $Y(j\omega)$ satisfying

$$|Y(j\omega)| = \begin{cases} 1 & 0 \leq \omega_1 \leq \omega \leq \omega_2 \\ 0 & \omega < \omega_1; \, \omega > \omega_2 \end{cases} \tag{3.6-17}$$

Denoting the filter output by $y(t)$ and its Fourier transform by $b(\omega)$, we have

$$b(\omega) = \frac{1}{\sqrt{2\pi}} \int_{-\infty}^{\infty} y(t)e^{-j\omega t} \, dt$$

and also

$$b(\omega) = Y(j\omega)a(\omega) \tag{3.6-18}$$

The total energy of the filter output is that portion of the energy of x which is associated with the frequency band ($\omega_1 \leq \omega \leq \omega_2$), and is given by

$$\int_{-\infty}^{\infty} y(t)^2 \, dt = 2 \int_{0}^{\infty} |b(\omega)|^2 \, d\omega$$

$$= 2 \int_{0}^{\infty} |Y(j\omega)|^2 |a(\omega)|^2 \, d\omega$$

$$= 2 \int_{\omega_1}^{\omega_2} |a(\omega)|^2 \, d\omega$$

$$= \int_{\omega_1}^{\omega_2} E(\omega, x) \, d\omega \qquad (3.6\text{-}19)$$

by virtue of (3.6-17) and (3.6-18). Thus the energy of $x(t)$ associated with the arbitrary frequency band ($\omega_1 \leq \omega \leq \omega_2$) is given by the integral of $E(\omega, x)$ over this interval of frequencies. Our assignment of the term *energy spectral density* to this quantity is therefore justified.

Turning now to the case in which the total energy of $x(t)$ is infinite, we suppose that $x(t)$ possesses a finite average power; i.e., that the limit (3.6-8) is finite. Since the integrated square of $x(t)$ is infinite, we can no longer define a Fourier transform $a(\omega)$ since the integral (3.6-9) will not converge in general. To overcome this difficulty, we first consider the average power associated with a large but finite time interval ($-T < t < T$), then compute a corresponding power spectral density, and finally let T approach infinity.

Let $x(t)$ be given, and let a new function $x_T(t)$ be defined by

$$x_T(t) = \begin{cases} x(t) & |t| \leq T \\ 0 & |t| > T \end{cases} \qquad (3.6\text{-}20)$$

In the limit as T becomes infinite, the function $x_T(t)$ becomes equal to $x(t)$; however, $x_T(t)$ possesses the advantage of having only a finite total energy for finite values of T. This energy is given by

$$\int_{-\infty}^{\infty} x_T(t)^2 \, dt = \int_{-T}^{T} x_T(t)^2 \, dt = \int_{-T}^{T} x(t)^2 \, dt \qquad (3.6\text{-}21)$$

If we seek to define an average power associated with $x(t)$ over the finite interval ($-T \leq t \leq T$), it is natural to divide the expression (3.6-21) by the interval length $2T$; in fact our definition (3.6-8) is precisely the limit of such an expression. We now write

$$a_T(\omega) = \frac{1}{\sqrt{2\pi}} \int_{-\infty}^{\infty} x_T(t) e^{-j\omega t} \, dt$$

$$= \frac{1}{\sqrt{2\pi}} \int_{-T}^{T} x(t) e^{-j\omega t} \, dt \qquad (3.6\text{-}22)$$

The energy spectral density of $x_T(t)$ is given by

$$E(\omega, x_T) = 2|a_T(\omega)|^2$$

Since

$$\frac{1}{2T} \int_{-T}^{T} x(t)^2 \, dt = \int_{-\infty}^{\infty} \left[\frac{x_T(t)}{\sqrt{2T}} \right]^2 dt$$

it is natural to consider the quantity

$$E\left(\omega, \frac{x_T}{\sqrt{2T}}\right) = 2\left|\frac{a_T(\omega)}{\sqrt{2T}}\right|^2 = \frac{|a_T(\omega)|^2}{T} \tag{3.6-23}$$

as representing the spectral density associated with the average power in x over the finite interval. In the limiting case, we therefore introduce the following definition.

Definition. The quantity

$$\begin{aligned} G(\omega,x) &= \lim_{T\to\infty} \frac{|a_T(\omega)|^2}{T} \\ &= \lim_{T\to\infty} \frac{1}{T}\left|\frac{1}{\sqrt{2\pi}}\int_{-T}^{T} x(t)e^{-i\omega t}\,dt\right|^2 \end{aligned} \tag{3.6-24}$$

is called the *power spectral density* of the function $x(t)$, whenever the indicated limit exists.

It follows without difficulty from the case of the energy spectral density that

$$\lim_{T\to\infty} \frac{1}{2T}\int_{-T}^{T} x(t)^2\,dt = \int_0^{\infty} G(\omega,x)\,d\omega \tag{3.6-25}$$

It further follows that if $x(t)$ is introduced as an input to the ideal band-pass filter specified by (3.6-17), the average power in the output is

$$\int_{\omega_1}^{\omega_2} G(\omega,x)\,d\omega$$

The power spectral density is an even function of ω. It is also obvious, but nonetheless worth noting explicitly, that both the energy and power spectral densities are real-valued and nonnegative functions.

It is also worthwhile to remark that the (energy or power) spectral density of a function $x(t)$ is invariant under a translation of the function by an arbitrary amount τ. Consider, for example, the energy spectral density of $x(t - \tau)$. Since

$$\frac{1}{\sqrt{2\pi}}\int_{-\infty}^{\infty} x(t-\tau)e^{-i\omega t}\,dt = e^{-i\omega\tau}a(\omega)$$

where $a(\omega)$ is given by (3.6-9), we have

$$\begin{aligned} E[\omega,x(t-\tau)] &= 2|e^{-i\omega\tau}a(\omega)|^2 = 2|a(\omega)|^2 \\ &= E[\omega,x(t)] \end{aligned} \tag{3.6-26}$$

for all values of τ. A similar relation follows at once for the power spectral density.

Up to this point of the discussion we have applied the notion of spectral density exclusively to individual functions of time. For most of our work, however, we shall wish to apply this concept to random processes. We therefore introduce the following rather obvious definition.

Definition. The *power* (*or energy*) *spectral density* of a *random process* $\{x(t)\}$ is defined to be the mathematical expectation of the spectral densities of the individual functions comprising the process. Denoting the spectral densities for the process by $G_{xx}(\omega)$ or $E_{xx}(\omega)$, we have

$$G_{xx}(\omega) = \overline{G(\omega,x)}$$
$$E_{xx}(\omega) = \overline{E(\omega,x)}$$
(3.6-27)

For the most part we shall be concerned with the notion of the power spectral density of a random process only when the process is stationary. Since the spectral density of a function or set of functions is unaltered by an arbitrary translation, evidently any calculations based upon spectral densities can lead only to types of results that are themselves independent of translations. In the process of formation of the spectrum of a function, we have in effect lost track of the origin on the time axis. The type of information recoverable from spectral-density analysis therefore relates mainly to time-average properties of a random process. In the usual nonstationary problem, however, we are generally interested in analyzing the properties of a random process in the vicinity of some well-defined time instant. Since this type of information cannot be derived from a knowledge of the spectral density, we generally do not find it profitable to utilize the spectrum for nonstationary problems.

On the other hand, for a stationary random process the individual functions do not generally possess a finite integrated square over the infinite time interval. Consequently, the total energy for a stationary process is infinite and the energy spectral density does not exist. We thus employ the energy spectrum only in a limited class of nonstationary situations. Of the two concepts, that of the power spectral density appears to be by far the more useful. In the remainder of the text we therefore shall use the terms *spectral density* or *spectrum* to mean the power spectral density, unless we explicitly note that the energy spectral density is intended.

Example 3.6-1. As an illustration of the calculation of the energy spectral density of a function, we consider the situation depicted in Fig. 3.6-1. A point P is moving at a constant speed v along the straight line L. A line is drawn from an arbitrary origin O to the point P; it is desired to compute the angular velocity $W(t)$ of this line and the energy spectral density of $W(t)$.

Let R be the distance from O to P, and R_m the minimum passing distance of P from O. Measuring time t from the instant at which P passes the point P_m, we have

$$W(t) = \frac{v \sin \theta}{R} = \frac{vR_m}{R^2} = \frac{vR_m}{R_m^2 + v^2t^2}$$

To compute the energy spectrum, we note that since $W(t)$ is an even function

$$a(\omega) = \frac{1}{\sqrt{2\pi}} \int_{-\infty}^{\infty} \frac{vR_m}{R_m^2 + v^2t^2} e^{-j\omega t} \, dt$$

$$= \frac{1}{\sqrt{2\pi}} \int_{-\infty}^{\infty} \frac{vR_m}{R_m^2 + v^2t^2} \cos \omega t \, dt$$

$$= \sqrt{\frac{\pi}{2}} \exp\left(-\frac{R_m}{v} |\omega|\right)$$

Thus by (3.6-16) the energy spectral density is

$$E[\omega, W(t)] = \pi \exp\left(-\frac{2R_m}{v} |\omega|\right)$$

We now consider an ensemble of such motions, corresponding to different values of R_m, for a fixed value of the speed v. Assuming the random variable R_m to be uni-

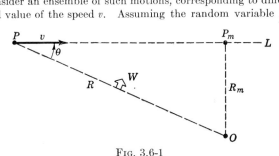

FIG. 3.6-1

formly distributed over some interval $0 \leqq R_m \leqq R'_m$, we have

$$E_{WW}(\omega) = \frac{1}{R'_m} \int_0^{R'_m} \pi \exp\left(-\frac{2R_m}{v} |\omega|\right) dR_m$$

$$= \frac{\pi v}{2R'_m |\omega|} \left[1 - \exp\left(-\frac{2R'_m}{v} |\omega|\right)\right]$$

as the energy spectral density for this random process.

Example 3.6-2. As a second illustration we now compute the power spectral density of the random step function considered in Example 3.5-2 and elsewhere. To avoid some slight algebraic complications, we pick $t_0 = 0$, $T = N + \frac{1}{2}$, and integrate over the unsymmetric range $(-N < t < N + 1)$ to obtain, by a slight modification of (3.6-22),

$$a_T(\omega) = \frac{1}{\sqrt{2\pi}} \int_{-N}^{N+1} f(t)e^{-j\omega t} \, dt$$

$$= \frac{1}{\sqrt{2\pi}} \sum_{n=-N}^{N} \int_n^{n+1} f(t)e^{-j\omega t} \, dt$$

$$= \frac{1}{\sqrt{2\pi}} \sum_{n=-N}^{N} f_n \int_n^{n+1} e^{-j\omega t} \, dt$$

$$= \frac{1 - e^{-j\omega}}{j\omega \sqrt{2\pi}} \sum_{n=-N}^{N} f_n e^{-j\omega n}$$

Multiplication of this quantity by its complex conjugate gives, after division by T,

$$\frac{|a_T(\omega)|^2}{T} = \frac{2(1 - \cos \omega)}{(2N + 1)\pi\omega^2} \sum_{m=-N}^{N} f_m e^{-j\omega m} \sum_{n=-N}^{N} f_n e^{j\omega n}$$

$$= \frac{2(1 - \cos \omega)}{(2N + 1)\pi\omega^2} \sum_{m=-N}^{N} \sum_{n=-N}^{N} f_m f_n e^{-j\omega(m-n)}$$

We are not able to compute the limit of this expression directly for any particular nontrivial function $f(t)$; however, we may determine the power spectral density of the random process $\{f(t)\}$ by forming the mathematical expectation of this quantity and subsequently letting N become infinite. We note that

$$\overline{f_m f_n} = \overline{f_m} \times \overline{f_n} = \tfrac{1}{4} \qquad \text{if } m \neq n$$

$$\overline{f_m f_n} = \overline{f_m^2} = \tfrac{1}{2} \qquad \text{if } m = n$$

We may summarize this pair of relations by writing

$$\overline{f_m f_n} = \tfrac{1}{4}(1 + \delta_{mn})$$

where $\delta_{mn} = 1$ if $m = n$ and zero otherwise. Then

$$E\left[\frac{|a_T(\omega)|^2}{T}\right] = \frac{2(1 - \cos \omega)}{(2N + 1)\pi\omega^2} \sum_{m=-N}^{N} \sum_{n=-N}^{N} \overline{f_m f_n} e^{-j\omega(m-n)}$$

and we have

$$\sum_{m=-N}^{N} \sum_{n=-N}^{N} \overline{f_m f_n} e^{-j\omega(m-n)}$$

$$= \tfrac{1}{4} \sum_{m=-N}^{N} \sum_{n=-N}^{N} \delta_{mn} e^{-j\omega(m-n)} + \tfrac{1}{4} \sum_{m=-N}^{N} \sum_{n=-N}^{N} e^{-j\omega(m-n)}$$

$$= \frac{2N + 1}{4} + \frac{1}{4} \left(\sum_{m=-N}^{N} e^{-j\omega m} \right)\left(\sum_{n=-N}^{N} e^{j\omega n} \right)$$

$$= \frac{2N + 1}{4} + \frac{1}{4} \left[\frac{\sin\left(\dfrac{2N + 1}{2}\omega\right)}{\sin(\omega/2)} \right]^2$$

Here, use is made of the standard formula (derivable by considering the indicated sums as elementary geometric series)

$$\sum_{n=-N}^{N} e^{-j\omega n} = \frac{\sin\left(\dfrac{2N + 1}{2}\omega\right)}{\sin(\omega/2)}$$

The expression for the approximate spectral density then becomes, by a slight rearrangement,

$$E\left[\frac{|a_T(\omega)|^2}{T}\right] = \frac{1 - \cos \omega}{2\pi\omega^2} + \frac{1 - \cos \omega}{4\sin^2(\omega/2)} \left[\frac{2}{(2N + 1)\pi} \frac{\sin^2\left(\dfrac{2N + 1}{2}\omega\right)}{\omega^2} \right]$$

In the limit as N approaches infinity, the first term in this expression remains unaltered. To obtain the limit for the second term, we note that

$$\frac{2}{(2N+1)\pi} \frac{\sin^2\left(\dfrac{2N+1}{2}\omega\right)}{\omega^2} \geq 0 \qquad -\infty < \omega < \infty$$

and that

$$\lim_{N\to\infty} \frac{2}{(2N+1)\pi} \frac{\sin^2\left(\dfrac{2N+1}{2}\omega\right)}{\omega^2} = 0 \qquad \omega \neq 0$$

On the other hand, for all $N \geq 0$,

$$\int_{-\infty}^{\infty}\left[\frac{2}{(2N+1)\pi} \frac{\sin^2\left(\dfrac{2N+1}{2}\omega\right)}{\omega^2}\right] d\omega = \frac{1}{\pi}\int_{-\infty}^{\infty}\frac{\sin^2 x}{x^2}\,dx = 1$$

Comparing these results with the relations (2.7-15) to (2.7-17) used in defining a delta function (with $\epsilon = 1/N$), we see that we are justified in writing

$$\lim_{N\to\infty} \frac{2}{(2N+1)\pi} \frac{\sin^2\left(\dfrac{2N+1}{2}\omega\right)}{\omega^2} = \delta(\omega)$$

We therefore obtain for the power spectral density

$$G_{ff}(\omega) = \frac{1-\cos\omega}{2\pi\omega^2} + \frac{1-\cos\omega}{4\sin^2(\omega/2)}\delta(\omega)$$

This expression may be simplified slightly by noting that the coefficient of $\delta(\omega)$ may be replaced by any other continuous quantity having the same value for $\omega = 0$, since $\delta(\omega) = 0$ for $\omega \neq 0$. In particular, since

$$\lim_{\omega\to 0}\frac{1-\cos\omega}{4\sin^2(\omega/2)} = \frac{1}{2}$$

we may simply write $\frac{1}{2}$ as the required coefficient, to obtain as the final expression

$$G_{ff}(\omega) = \frac{1-\cos\omega}{2\pi\omega^2} + \frac{1}{2}\delta(\omega)$$

The presence of the delta-function term indicates a positive amount of power associated with the discrete frequency $\omega = 0$; that is, a d-c component. The latter, for any one of the functions $f(t)$, is its time average. According to the ergodic property, however, this time average is almost always equal to the ensemble average:

$$\lim_{T\to\infty}\frac{1}{2T}\int_{-T}^{T}f(t)\,dt = E[f(t)] = \frac{1}{2}$$

and the corresponding power is $(\frac{1}{2})^2 = \frac{1}{4}$. The discrepancy between this value and the coefficient of $\delta(\omega)$ is readily explained. Since

$$\frac{1}{2}\int_{-\infty}^{\infty}G(\omega,x)\,d\omega = \lim_{T\to\infty}\int_{-\infty}^{\infty}\frac{|a_T(\omega)|^2}{2T}\,d\omega$$

$$= \lim_{T\to\infty}\frac{1}{2T}\int_{-T}^{T}x(t)^2\,dt$$

for any function $x(t)$, we see that the average power of x can be represented by one-half of the integral of its spectrum from $-\infty$ to $+\infty$. Now we have also stated, in

(3.6-25), that the average power is obtainable by integrating the spectrum itself from 0 to $+\infty$, basing our argument on the fact that G is an even function of ω. However, if G contains a delta-function term at $\omega = 0$, we must define what we mean by the integral with zero as the lower limit of integration. If we write

$$G(\omega,x) = a\delta(\omega) + G_1(\omega,x)$$

where G_1 is continuous at $\omega = 0$, then the correct value of the average power is

$$\frac{1}{2}\int_{-\infty}^{\infty} G(\omega,x)\, d\omega = \frac{a}{2} + \frac{1}{2}\int_{-\infty}^{\infty} G_1(\omega,x)\, d\omega$$

$$= \frac{a}{2} + \int_{0}^{\infty} G_1(\omega,x)\, d\omega$$

Thus if a power spectral density calculated according to Eq. (3.6-24) gives rise to a term in $\delta(\omega)$, we must agree that the coefficient of this term is to be multiplied by $\frac{1}{2}$ in using Eq. (3.6-25) or the corresponding relation for the spectrum of a random process. With this understanding we may check our present result by noting that

$$\frac{1}{2}\int_{-\infty}^{\infty}\left[\frac{1-\cos\omega}{2\pi\omega^2} + \frac{1}{2}\delta(\omega)\right] d\omega = \int_{-\infty}^{\infty}\left[\frac{1-\cos\omega}{4\pi\omega^2} + \frac{1}{4}\delta(\omega)\right] d\omega$$

$$= \frac{1}{4} + \frac{1}{2\pi}\int_{0}^{\infty}\frac{1-\cos\omega}{\omega^2}\, d\omega = \frac{1}{2}$$

which is the same as $\overline{f(t)^2}$. In particular we may now assign the correct power of $\frac{1}{4}$ to the d-c term.

The delta-function term appearing in the expression for the spectral density in this example arises from the fact that a nonzero amount of power is concentrated at zero frequency. A term $\delta(\omega - \omega_0)$ will occur, in general, whenever a nonzero amount of power is associated with a particular frequency ω_0. The difficulties arising in connection with these delta-function terms may be avoided by forming a new random process from which all periodic components have been subtracted. Thus, in this example, if we had anticipated that the random process involved had a mean value of $\frac{1}{2}$, the computation would have been considerably simplified by dealing with the function $f(t) - \frac{1}{2}$ instead of with $f(t)$ directly. In particular we would have found that

$$\overline{(f_m - \frac{1}{2})(f_n - \frac{1}{2})} = \frac{1}{4}\delta_{mn}$$

so that

$$E\left[\frac{|a_T(\omega)|^2}{T}\right] = \frac{2(1-\cos\omega)}{(2N+1)\pi\omega^2}\sum_{m=-N}^{N}\sum_{n=-N}^{N}\overline{(f_m - \frac{1}{2})(f_n - \frac{1}{2})}e^{-j\omega(m-n)}$$

$$= \frac{2(1-\cos\omega)}{(2N+1)\pi\omega^2}\frac{(2N+1)}{4} = \frac{1-\cos\omega}{2\pi\omega^2}$$

is obtained as the spectral density of the random step function with zero mean value which agrees with the original result with the delta-function term missing.

In many cases a simpler computation of the spectral density of a random process can be accomplished by forming the Fourier transform of the correlation function, according to relations established below, rather than by a direct appeal to the basic definition, as was done in the example just considered. In particular, it is left as an exercise (cf. Prob. 3-5 at the end of the chapter) to show that the spectrum for the random step function can be derived in this way. Since for a random process containing periodic components the correlation function itself contains periodic components (cf. Example 3.5-3), in computing the spectrum by this means it is necessary only to recognize that the Fourier transform of a constant or a sine wave is a delta function according to the conventions which we have adopted.

We now wish to consider the relations between power spectral density and the autocorrelation function. Although we are interested primarily in random processes, it is convenient again, as previously, to consider first a single function $x(t)$. Let us suppose that $x(t)$ is a function such that $a_T(\omega)$ and $G(\omega,x)$, as defined by (3.6-22) and (3.6-24), both exist, together with the function

$$\psi(\tau) = \lim_{T \to \infty} \frac{1}{2T} \int_{-T}^{T} x(t)x(t+\tau)\,dt \qquad (3.6\text{-}28)$$

We refrain from calling $\psi(\tau)$ the autocorrelation function or from denoting it by $\phi(\tau)$ since we are not yet dealing with a random process. Even for a random process the function $\psi(\tau)$ can exist without being equal to the autocorrelation function if the ergodic property is not valid.

We denote by $\psi_T(\tau)$ the function

$$\psi_T(\tau) = \frac{1}{2T} \int_{-\infty}^{\infty} x_T(t)x_T(t+\tau)\,dt \qquad (3.6\text{-}29)$$

and note that

$$\lim_{T \to \infty} \psi_T(\tau) = \psi(\tau) \qquad (3.6\text{-}30)$$

We now compute the Fourier transform of $\psi(\tau)$ using (3.6-28) to (3.6-30) to obtain, after rearrangement of the order of operations and a subsequent change in the variable of integration,

$$\frac{1}{\pi} \int_{-\infty}^{\infty} \psi(\tau)e^{-j\omega\tau}\,d\tau = \lim_{T \to \infty} \frac{1}{\pi} \int_{-\infty}^{\infty} \psi_T(\tau)e^{-j\omega\tau}\,d\tau$$

$$= \lim_{T \to \infty} \frac{1}{2\pi T} \int_{-\infty}^{\infty} e^{-j\omega\tau}\,d\tau \int_{-\infty}^{\infty} x_T(t)x_T(t+\tau)\,dt$$

$$= \lim_{T \to \infty} \frac{1}{2\pi T} \int_{-\infty}^{\infty} dt \int_{-\infty}^{\infty} [x_T(t)e^{j\omega t}][x_T(t+\tau)e^{-j\omega(t+\tau)}]\,d\tau$$

$$= \lim_{T \to \infty} \frac{1}{2\pi T} \int_{-\infty}^{\infty} x_T(t)e^{j\omega t}\,dt \int_{-\infty}^{\infty} x_T(t_1)e^{-j\omega t_1}\,dt_1$$

$$= \lim_{T \to \infty} \frac{a_T(\omega)^* a_T(\omega)}{T} = G(\omega,x)$$

Thus, in summary,

$$G(\omega,x) = \frac{1}{\pi} \int_{-\infty}^{\infty} \psi(\tau)e^{-j\omega\tau}\, d\tau \qquad (3.6\text{-}31)$$

for any $x(t)$ for which the required limits exist.

If, now, $x(t)$ belongs to a suitable random process, we have

$$G_{xx}(\omega) = \overline{G(\omega,x)} = \frac{1}{\pi} \int_{-\infty}^{\infty} \overline{\psi(\tau)}e^{-j\omega\tau}\, d\tau \qquad (3.6\text{-}32)$$

where

$$\overline{\psi(\tau)} = E\left[\lim_{T\to\infty} \frac{1}{2T} \int_{-T}^{T} x(t)x(t+\tau)\, dt\,\right]$$

$$= \lim_{T\to\infty} \frac{1}{2T} \int_{-T}^{T} \overline{x(t)x(t+\tau)}\, dt$$

$$= \lim_{T\to\infty} \frac{1}{2T} \int_{-T}^{T} \phi_{xx}(t,\, t+\tau)\, dt \qquad (3.6\text{-}33)$$

Thus for any random process, stationary or not, we have

$$G_{xx}(\omega) = \frac{1}{\pi} \int_{-\infty}^{\infty} e^{-j\omega\tau}\, d\tau\left[\lim_{T\to\infty} \frac{1}{2T} \int_{-T}^{T} \phi_{xx}(t,\, t+\tau)\, dt\right] \qquad (3.6\text{-}34)$$

under appropriate assumptions concerning the existence of the various limits used.

As discussed previously, our interest in the power spectral density is centered largely about the case in which the random process is stationary. In this case $\phi_{xx}(t,\, t+\tau)$ depends only upon τ, and we have

$$\lim_{T\to\infty} \frac{1}{2T} \int_{-T}^{T} \phi_{xx}(t,\, t+\tau)\, dt = \lim_{T\to\infty} \frac{1}{2T} \int_{-T}^{T} \phi_{xx}(\tau)\, dt = \phi_{xx}(\tau) \qquad (3.6\text{-}35)$$

Thus

$$G_{xx}(\omega) = \frac{1}{\pi} \int_{-\infty}^{\infty} \phi_{xx}(\tau)e^{-j\omega\tau}\, d\tau \qquad (3.6\text{-}36)$$

The relation (3.6-36) represents the case that is the most commonly used; our derivation of the relation (3.6-34) as an intermediate result is aimed at showing that the spectral density can legitimately be derived from the correlation function even in the nonstationary case. In the event that the random process $\{x(t)\}$ is not only stationary but also ergodic, our derivation can be somewhat simplified since the function $\psi(\tau)$ can be identified with the correlation function. In particular, almost all functions $x(t)$ possess the same $\psi(\tau)$ and $G(\omega,x)$; thus the step from (3.6-31) to (3.6-36) is immediate in the ergodic case.

Since $\phi_{xx}(\tau)$ is an even function, Eq. (3.6-36) may be written in the equivalent form

$$G_{xx}(\omega) = \frac{2}{\pi} \int_{0}^{\infty} \phi_{xx}(\tau)\, \cos\omega\tau\, d\tau \qquad (3.6\text{-}37)$$

Also we have, by inversion of the Fourier transform, the pair of relations

$$\phi_{xx}(\tau) = \frac{1}{2} \int_{-\infty}^{\infty} G_{xx}(\omega) e^{j\omega\tau} \, d\omega$$

$$= \int_{0}^{\infty} G_{xx}(\omega) \cos \omega\tau \, d\omega \tag{3.6-38}$$

The latter form of this equation is of course subject to the remarks made previously concerning a possible term $\delta(\omega)$.

Equations (3.6-34) and (3.6-36) have some importance largely because they show the extension of a property of ergodic stationary processes to a somewhat wider class. The determination of power spectral density is important if it is desired to know the effect of a filter on the random process. The calculation of power spectral density as the Fourier transform of the autocorrelation function is a practical technique which is certainly justified if the process is ergodic; Eq. (3.6-36) indicates that the validity of such a calculation need not rest entirely on the supposed ergodicity. Since usually it is extremely difficult to determine whether a random process which represents a physical problem is ergodic or not, this knowledge is encouraging.

We now consider the notion of the cross-power spectral density associated with two functions $x(t)$ and $y(t)$, in relation to the spectrum of their sum $z(t) = x(t) + y(t)$. Let

$$a_T(\omega) = \frac{1}{\sqrt{2\pi}} \int_{-T}^{T} x(t) e^{-j\omega t} \, dt$$

$$b_T(\omega) = \frac{1}{\sqrt{2\pi}} \int_{-T}^{T} y(t) e^{j\omega t} \, dt \tag{3.6-39}$$

$$c_T(\omega) = \frac{1}{\sqrt{2\pi}} \int_{-T}^{T} z(t) e^{-j\omega t} \, dt$$

Then

$$c_T(\omega) = a_T(\omega) + b_T(\omega) \tag{3.6-40}$$

and

$$\frac{|c_T(\omega)|^2}{T} = \frac{1}{T} [a_T(\omega) + b_T(\omega)][a_T(\omega)^* + b_T(\omega)^*]$$

$$= \frac{|a_T(\omega)|^2}{T} + \frac{a_T(\omega)b_T(\omega)^*}{T} + \frac{a_T(\omega)^*b_T(\omega)}{T} + \frac{|b_T(\omega)|^2}{T} \tag{3.6-41}$$

Upon passage to the limit, we find

$$G(\omega,z) = G(\omega,x) + G(\omega; y,x) + G(\omega; x,y) + G(\omega,y) \tag{3.6-42}$$

in which the quantities $G(\omega,x)$, $G(\omega,y)$, and $G(\omega,z)$ are the respective power spectral densities of x, y, and z, and

$$G(\omega; y,x) = \lim_{T\to\infty} \frac{a_T(\omega)b_T(\omega)^*}{T}$$

$$G(\omega; x,y) = \lim_{T\to\infty} \frac{a_T(\omega)^*b_T(\omega)}{T} \tag{3.6-43}$$

The latter quantities are defined to be the *cross-power spectral densities* of x and y. The cross spectra are generally complex-valued functions of ω. It is readily seen that

$$G(\omega; x,y)^* = G(\omega; y,x) \tag{3.6-44}$$

so that the sum of the two cross spectral densities is a real-valued function. Also by relations of the type of (3.6-13),

$$G(-\omega; x,y) = G(\omega; x,y)^* \tag{3.6-45}$$

and

$$G(-\omega; y,x) = G(\omega; y,x)^* \tag{3.6-46}$$

so that these quantities are not even functions of ω, in general.

The cross-power spectral densities of two random processes are defined to be ensemble averages of the respective cross spectral densities of the pairs of individual functions. Thus

$$\begin{aligned} G_{xy}(\omega) &= \overline{G(\omega; x,y)} \\ G_{yx}(\omega) &= \overline{G(\omega; y,x)} \end{aligned} \tag{3.6-47}$$

Relations between the cross spectral densities and the cross-correlation functions can be established without difficulty by methods that essentially duplicate the derivation of Eqs. (3.6-31), (3.6-34), and (3.6-36). The results may be summarized as follows. Let

$$\psi_{xy}(\tau) = \lim_{T \to \infty} \frac{1}{2T} \int_{-T}^{T} x(t)y(t + \tau) \, dt \tag{3.6-48}$$

Then

$$G(\omega; x,y) = \frac{1}{\pi} \int_{-\infty}^{\infty} \psi_{xy}(\tau)e^{-j\omega\tau} \, d\tau \tag{3.6-49}$$

For a pair of random processes $\{x(t)\}$ and $\{y(t)\}$,

$$G_{xy}(\omega) = \frac{1}{\pi} \int_{-\infty}^{\infty} e^{-j\omega\tau} \, d\tau \left[\lim_{T \to \infty} \frac{1}{2T} \int_{-T}^{T} \phi_{xy}(t, t + \tau) \, dt \right] \tag{3.6-50}$$

In particular if the processes $\{x(t)\}$ and $\{y(t)\}$ are both stationary,

$$G_{xy}(\omega) = \frac{1}{\pi} \int_{-\infty}^{\infty} \phi_{xy}(\tau)e^{-j\omega\tau} \, d\tau \tag{3.6-51}$$

The cross-correlation function can of course be derived from the cross-power spectral density by inversion of the Fourier transform (3.6-51), to give

$$\phi_{xy}(\tau) = \frac{1}{2} \int_{-\infty}^{\infty} G_{xy}(\omega)e^{j\omega\tau} \, d\omega \tag{3.6-52}$$

Relations similar to (3.6-37) and the second form of (3.6-38), involving cosine transforms, cannot be written in the present case, however, since the functions involved are generally not even.

The principal application of the concept of cross spectral densities is in consideration of the spectrum of a sum of two or more random processes. To be specific, the spectrum of the sum is given by the sum of all spectral densities and cross spectral densities that can be formed from the terms of the sum. The required relation is essentially equivalent to that of (3.4-14) for the correlation function of a sum, and can be readily derived from it. In particular, if the random processes have zero cross-correlation functions, the spectral density of the sum is simply the sum of the corresponding spectra.

3.7 Further Examples of Random Processes

In this section we wish to illustrate some of the ideas and techniques developed in this chapter and in Chap. 2 by analyzing properties of a random step function of a somewhat more complicated type than that considered previously. By a suitable limiting process, we also arrive at the notion of a *white noise*, referred to frequently in later chapters.

To begin with, we compute the first and second distribution functions, frequency functions, and the correlation function for a random step function defined as follows. A sequence of points is distributed at random, independently and with uniform average density λ, along the time axis. (For a more careful analysis of this concept, see Sec. 2.11). Let a random step function $x(t)$ assume the constant value a_n over the nth such interval

$$x(t) = a_n \qquad t'_n < t < t'_{n+1}; \quad -\infty < n < \infty \qquad (3.7\text{-}1)$$

where the points t'_n are the points of subdivision, labeled in order, starting with some arbitrary one of these points. We postulate that the values a_n form a set of mutually independent random variables, each of which possesses the same distribution function $F(a)$ and frequency function $f(a)$.

$$\Pr\,(a_n \leqq a) = F(a) \qquad -\infty < n < \infty \qquad (3.7\text{-}2)$$

To begin with, the distribution function for $X_1 = x(t_1)$ is identical with that of a_n (where n is the number associated with the interval in which t_1 lies):

$$F_1(x_1,t_1) = \Pr\,[x(t_1) \leqq x_1] = \Pr\,(a_n \leqq x_1) = F(x_1)$$

In particular, $F_1(x_1,t_1)$ is independent of t_1. Correspondingly we have

$$f_1(x_1,t_1) = f(x_1)$$

To compute the second distribution function, let A be the event that the points t_1 and t_2 lie in the same interval; i.e., for some value n,

$$t'_n < t_1 < t'_{n+1} \qquad t'_n < t_2 < t'_{n+1}$$

Then by (2.5-11)

$$F_2(x_1, t_1; x_2, t_2)\dot{} = \Pr\left[x(t_1) \leq x_1; x(t_2) \leq x_2\right]$$
$$= P(A) \Pr\left[x(t_1) \leq x_1; x(t_2) \leq x_2 \mid A\right]$$
$$+ P(A^*) \Pr\left[x(t_1) \leq x_1; x(t_2) \leq x_2 \mid A^*\right] \quad (3.7\text{-}3)$$

Now if t_1 and t_2 lie in different intervals, the random variables $x(t_1)$ and $x(t_2)$ are independent. Thus

$$\Pr\left[x(t_1) \leq x_1; x(t_2) \leq x_2 \mid A^*\right] = \Pr\left[x(t_1) \leq x_1 \mid A^*\right] \Pr\left[x(t_2) \leq x_2 \mid A^*\right]$$

The event $x(t_1) \leq x_1$ and the event A^* are independent; therefore,

$$\Pr\left[x(t_1) \leq x_1 \mid A^*\right] = \Pr\left[x(t_1) \leq x_1\right] = F(x_1)$$

with a similar expression holding for $\Pr\left[x(t_2) \leq x_2 \mid A^*\right]$. We thus find

$$\Pr\left[x(t_1) \leq x_1; x(t_2) \leq x_2 \mid A^*\right] = F(x_1)F(x_2) \quad (3.7\text{-}4)$$

To compute the first term in (3.7-3), we observe that by virtue of the hypothesis A, t_1 and t_2 lie in the same interval, and thus $x(t_1) = x(t_2)$. It follows that for both inequalities $x(t_1) \leq x_1$ and $x(t_2) \leq x_2$ to be valid, it is necessary and sufficient that $x(t_1) \leq \min (x_1, x_2)$ to hold, where $\min (x_1, x_2)$ denotes the smaller one of the quantities x_1 or x_2.   The event that this condition is satisfied is independent of the event A; therefore,

$$\Pr\left[x(t_1) \leq x_1; x(t_2) \leq x_2 \mid A\right] = \Pr\left[x(t_1) \leq \min (x_1, x_2) \mid A\right]$$
$$= \Pr\left[x(t_1) \leq \min (x_1, x_2)\right]$$
$$= F[\min (x_1, x_2)] \quad (3.7\text{-}5)$$

To complete the evaluation of (3.7-3), we require values for $P(A)$ and $P(A^*)$.   Now the event A, that t_1 and t_2 lie in the same interval, is equivalent to the event that exactly no point of subdivision lies in the interval between t_1 and t_2.   In Sec. 2.11 this probability was computed to be $\exp(-\lambda|t_2 - t_1|)$.   Therefore

$$\begin{aligned} P(A) &= e^{-\lambda|t_2-t_1|} \\ P(A^*) &= 1 - e^{-\lambda|t_2-t_1|} \end{aligned} \quad (3.7\text{-}6)$$

Substitution from (3.7-4), (3.7-5), and (3.7-6) into (3.7-3) gives

$$F_2(x_1,t_1; x_2,t_2) = e^{-\lambda|t_2-t_1|}F[\min (x_1,x_2)] + (1 - e^{-\lambda|t_2-t_1|})F(x_1)F(x_2) \quad (3.7\text{-}7)$$

To compute the corresponding frequency function from this relation, we first consider the case in which $x_1 < x_2$.   Then

$$F_2(x_1,t_1; x_2,t_2) = e^{-\lambda|t_2-t_1|}F(x_1)$$
$$+ (1 - e^{-\lambda|t_2-t_1|})F(x_1)F(x_2) \quad x_1 < x_2 \quad (3.7\text{-}8)$$

Thus, forming the second partial derivative by (3.3-9)

$$f_2(x_1,t_1; x_2,t_2) = (1 - e^{-\lambda|t_2-t_1|})f(x_1)f(x_2) \quad (3.7\text{-}9)$$

For $x_1 > x_2$ the right-hand member of Eq. (3.7-8) must be modified by replacing $F(x_1)$ in the first term with $F(x_2)$; subsequent partial differentiation again leads to (3.7-9). The result as it stands, however, is not entirely correct. Along points of the line in the (x_1,x_2) plane described by the equation $x_1 = x_2$, the function $F[\min (x_1,x_2)]$ does not possess the second partial derivative required by (3.3-9), and special considerations must be employed.

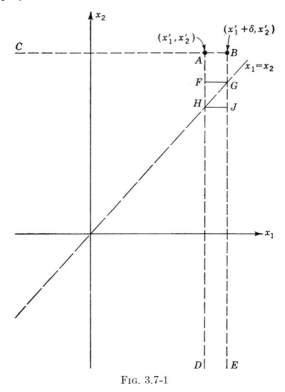

Fig. 3.7-1

For the sake of a physical picture, we invoke the mass analogy considered previously. Let the function $F[\min (x_1,x_2)]$ represent the distribution of a mass in the (x_1,x_2) plane. Specifically, for an arbitrary point $A = (x_1',x_2')$, as shown in Fig. 3.7-1, the total mass in the infinite rectangle CAD below and to the left of the point A is defined to be the quantity $F[\min (x_1',x_2')]$. For the case shown in the figure, $x_1' \leqq x_2'$ and

$$F[\min (x_1',x_2')] = F(x_1')$$

is the value of the mass in question. Considering a new point

$$B = (x_1' + \delta,\ x_2')$$

as shown (with $\delta < x_2' - x_1'$), we have

$$F[\min (x_1, x_2) \text{ at } B] = F[\min (x_1' + \delta, x_2')]$$
$$= F(x_1' + \delta)$$

as the mass in the rectangle CBE. The mass in the vertical strip $DABE$ is therefore the difference of these expressions, or

$$F(x_1' + \delta) - F(x_1')$$

Now the above argument depends only on the property that $x_1 \leqq x_2$ for each of the points A and B considered; thus the mass in the strip $DFGE$ is also given by $F(x_1' + \delta) - F(x_1')$. On the other hand, a computation of the mass in the strip $DHJE$ gives a value

$$F[\min (x_1, x_2) \text{ at } J] - F[\min (x_1, x_2) \text{ at } H]$$
$$= F[\min (x_1' + \delta, x_1')] - F[\min (x_1', x_1')]$$
$$= F(x_1') - F(x_1') = 0$$

It follows that the total mass within the strip $DABE$ is isolated within the small square $FGJH$. Allowing the end of the strip (line AB) to move upward indefinitely, we find that the total mass between the lines $x_1 = x_1'$ and $x_1 = x_1' + \delta$ is contained in the square $FGJH$. If we now partition the whole plane into an infinite sequence of such vertical strips, and allow the spacing δ to approach zero, we see that the total mass in the plane is concentrated on the diagonal line $x_1 = x_2$. Thus the distribution function $F[\min (x_1, x_2)]$ represents the distribution of a mass along this diagonal line. The total amount of mass involved is readily found by setting $x_1 = x_2$ and subsequently letting their common value become infinite. Since $F(\infty) = 1$, the total mass is unity. Also, it can be seen without great difficulty that the distribution of mass along the line is such that its projection on the x_1 axis would be describable by the density function $f(x_1)$.

Returning to (3.7-9) we correct this formula by addition of a singular term.

$$f_2(x_1, t_1; x_2, t_2) = e^{-\lambda|t_2 - t_1|} s(x_1, x_2) + (1 - e^{-\lambda|t_2 - t_1|}) f(x_1) f(x_2) \quad (3.7\text{-}10)$$

Here $s(x_1, x_2)$ represents the (singular) density function corresponding to the distribution of one unit mass (probability) along the line, as discussed.

To compute the correlation function of $x(t)$, we first employ the double integral expression (3.3-17). As an alternate derivation, we subsequently perform a simple and independent calculation of the correlation function by using the notion of conditional expectation.

From (3.3-17) and (3.7-10) we have, formally,

$$\phi_{xx}(t_1, t_2) = e^{-\lambda|t_2 - t_1|} \int_{-\infty}^{\infty} dx_1 \int_{-\infty}^{\infty} dx_2\, x_1 x_2 s(x_1, x_2)$$
$$+ [1 - e^{-\lambda|t_2 - t_1|}] \int_{-\infty}^{\infty} dx_1 \int_{-\infty}^{\infty} dx_2\, x_1 x_2 f(x_1) f(x_2) \quad (3.7\text{-}11)$$

Considering the second double integral expression first, we obtain

$$\int_{-\infty}^{\infty} dx_1 \int_{-\infty}^{\infty} dx_2 \, x_1 x_2 f(x_1) f(x_2)$$

$$= \left[\int_{-\infty}^{\infty} x_1 f(x_1) \, dx_1 \right]\left[\int_{-\infty}^{\infty} x_2 f(x_2) \, dx_2 \right]$$

$$= \left[\int_{-\infty}^{\infty} af(a) \, da \right]^2 = \bar{a}^2 \qquad (3.7\text{-}12)$$

where $\bar{a} = \int_{-\infty}^{\infty} af(a) \, da$.

To compute the first double integral term in (3.7-11), we return to our interpretation of the singular density function $s(x_1,x_2)$. If we regard this integral as analogous to the calculation of the product of inertia of the mass distribution in question, we see that we must multiply each differential element of mass dm by the product $x_1 x_2$ of its coordinates and sum over all mass elements. The mass element in the strip between x_1 and $x_1 + dx_1$ is

$$dm = f(x_1) \, dx_1$$

and the corresponding coordinate product (recalling that the mass is concentrated on the line $x_1 = x_2$) is x_1^2. Thus

$$\int_{-\infty}^{\infty} dx_1 \int_{-\infty}^{\infty} dx_2 \, x_1 x_2 s(x_1,x_2) = \int_{-\infty}^{\infty} x_1^2 f(x_1) \, dx_1$$

$$= \int_{-\infty}^{\infty} a^2 f(a) \, da = \overline{a^2} \qquad (3.7\text{-}13)$$

The substitution of expressions (3.7-12) and (3.7-13) into (3.7-11) then yields the simple result

$$\phi_{xx}(t_1,t_2) = \overline{a^2} e^{-\lambda|t_2 - t_1|} + \bar{a}^2[1 - e^{-\lambda|t_2 - t_1|}] \qquad (3.7\text{-}14)$$

To derive (3.7-14) by an alternate method, we use the concept of conditional expectation discussed in Sec. 2.8. We have, by (2.8-26),

$$\phi_{xx}(t_1,t_2) = E[x(t_1)x(t_2)]$$

$$= P(A)E[x(t_1)x(t_2) \mid A] + P(A^*)E[x(t_1)x(t_2) \mid A^*] \qquad (3.7\text{-}15)$$

where the event A is that defined earlier in this section. If t_1 and t_2 lie in distinct intervals (hypothesis A^*), then $x(t_1)$ and $x(t_2)$ are independent. Thus

$$E[x(t_1)x(t_2) \mid A^*] = E[x(t_1)]E[x(t_2)] = \bar{a}^2$$

However, if t_1 and t_2 lie in the same interval (hypothesis A), then

$$x(t_1) = x(t_2)$$

and

$$E[x(t_1)x(t_2) \mid A] = E[x(t_1)^2] = \overline{a^2}$$

Substituting these values into (3.7-15), together with the expressions for $P(A)$ and $P(A^*)$, we again have Eq. (3.7-14) as the result. Clearly either of the two techniques used here could be employed to compute the general moment $\alpha_{ik} = E[x(t_1)^i x(t_2)^k]$.

The physical nature of the random process under study is quite evidently independent of any choice of time origin; the process is therefore stationary. Supporting evidence for this statement is found in the fact that the correlation function (3.7-14) depends upon t_1 and t_2 only through their difference $\tau = t_2 - t_1$. Thus we may write

$$\phi_{xx}(\tau) = \overline{a^2}e^{-\lambda|\tau|} + \bar{a}^2(1 - e^{-\lambda|\tau|}) \tag{3.7-16}$$

Intuition would also suggest that the random process $\{x(t)\}$ is ergodic; a demonstration of this property would require a somewhat more careful and precise treatment than that given above, however.

To develop further properties of the random step function, we compute the power spectral density of the random process $\{x(t)\}$. From Eqs. (3.6-36) and (3.7-16), we have

$$\begin{aligned}
G_{xx}(\omega) &= \frac{1}{\pi} \int_{-\infty}^{\infty} \phi_{xx}(\tau)e^{-j\omega\tau}\,d\tau \\
&= \frac{1}{\pi}(\overline{a^2} - \bar{a}^2) \int_{-\infty}^{\infty} e^{-\lambda|\tau|}e^{-j\omega\tau}\,d\tau + \frac{1}{\pi}\bar{a}^2 \int_{-\infty}^{\infty} e^{-j\omega\tau}\,d\tau \\
&= \frac{2}{\pi}(\overline{a^2} - \bar{a}^2)\frac{\lambda}{\lambda^2 + \omega^2} + 2\bar{a}^2\delta(\omega)
\end{aligned} \tag{3.7-17}$$

The delta-function term in this relation is calculated by use of Eq. (2.9-9). Its coefficient is to be interpreted in the manner discussed in Example 3.6-2, and indicates an average d-c power of amount $\bar{a}^2$. The remaining term is proportional to the variance of a; the total power contributed by this term is precisely this variance, as is seen from the relation

$$\frac{1}{2}\int_{-\infty}^{\infty}\left[\frac{2}{\pi}(\overline{a^2} - \bar{a}^2)\frac{\lambda}{\lambda^2 + \omega^2}\right]d\omega = \overline{a^2} - \bar{a}^2 \tag{3.7-18}$$

An interesting limiting case of the random process studied here is that in which the frequency λ of the points of discontinuity tends toward infinity and simultaneously the size of the steps becomes infinite. To remove the d-c term from our calculations, we henceforth assume that

$$\bar{a} = 0 \tag{3.7-19}$$

Then (3.7-17) becomes

$$G_{xx}(\omega) = \frac{2\lambda\overline{a^2}}{\pi(\lambda^2 + \omega^2)} \tag{3.7-20}$$

For large values of λ and $\overline{a^2}$, the above expression is approximately the constant $2\overline{a^2}/\pi\lambda$, except for very large values of ω. If λ and $\overline{a^2}$ are to approach infinity in a way that retains the notion of spectral density as a useful one, the quantity $2\overline{a^2}/\pi\lambda$ must remain finite. To normalize the problem, we therefore assume that

$$\frac{2\overline{a^2}}{\pi\lambda} = 1 \tag{3.7-21}$$

The expression (3.7-20) then becomes

$$G_{xx}(\omega) = \frac{\lambda^2}{\lambda^2 + \omega^2} \tag{3.7-22}$$

If we now allow λ to become infinite, we obtain the simple expression

$$G_{xx}(\omega) = 1 \tag{3.7-23}$$

A random process $\{x(t)\}$ possessing a constant power spectral density is henceforth referred to as a *white noise*. The physical origin of this term is in the concept of white light: a light that possesses all frequencies or wavelengths in equal amount. The concept of a white noise is one that recurs frequently in the remaining chapters of the book. In particular, we often find it convenient to assume that a given random process can be generated by passing a white noise through a suitable filter.

The physical model of white noise as developed above may be visualized as a collection of small random impulses, occurring at a high rate of frequency. If each separate step is regarded as an impulse, then the strength of an "average impulse" (i.e., its magnitude times its duration) is of the general order of magnitude of the rms pulse height $\sqrt{\overline{a^2}}$ times the average duration $1/\lambda$. Since $\sqrt{\overline{a^2}}$ is proportional to $\sqrt{\lambda}$, it is seen that the strength of the impulses tends toward zero as λ becomes infinite. Considered in this light, the mathematical model of white noise is seen to resemble physical phenomena such as the impact of a stream of electrons on the anode of a vacuum tube or the random impacts of particles studied in the Brownian motion problem (Example 2.12-3 and Example 3.3-3). More generally, we may regard as white noise any signal made up of the superposition of a very large number of independent random effects of very brief duration.

The notion of white noise is developed above by passage to the limit from the random process consisting of steps of random amplitude and duration. The precise random process used as a starting point is relatively unimportant, however. To see this, let $\{y(t)\}$ be any stationary process for which

$$\overline{y(t)} = 0 \qquad G_{yy}(0) > 0 \tag{3.7-24}$$

For $\lambda > 1$, the random process

$$z(t,\lambda) = \sqrt{\lambda}\, y(\lambda t) \tag{3.7-25}$$

is basically the same as y, except that its time scale is multiplied by the factor λ and its amplitude is increased. The correlation function of z is

$$\phi_{zz}(\tau) = \lambda\phi_{yy}(\lambda\tau) \tag{3.7-26}$$

and its spectral density is given by

$$
\begin{aligned}
G_{zz}(\omega) &= \frac{2}{\pi} \int_0^\infty \phi_{zz}(\tau) \cos \omega\tau \, d\tau \\
&= \frac{2\lambda}{\pi} \int_0^\infty \phi_{yy}(\lambda\tau) \cos \omega\tau \, d\tau \\
&= \frac{2}{\pi} \int_0^\infty \phi_{yy}(\tau_1) \cos \left(\frac{\omega}{\lambda} \tau_1\right) d\tau_1 \\
&= G_{yy}\left(\frac{\omega}{\lambda}\right)
\end{aligned} \tag{3.7-27}
$$

As λ increases toward infinity, we have

$$\lim_{\lambda \to \infty} G_{zz}(\omega) = G_{yy}(0) \tag{3.7-28}$$

for any frequency ω. Thus, in the limiting case, a white noise results. The term *white noise* is not of course confined exclusively to the case of an infinitely dense collection of infinitesmal impulses; any random process possessing a constant spectral density is a white noise. In particular, it is shown at the end of Sec. 4.1 that a random sequence of impulses with a finite average frequency of occurrence and a finite pulse strength is a white noise.

In a strict sense, white noise is a physically unrealizable phenomenon since it is a random process possessing an infinite average power. To see this, it is only necessary to note that the average power is

$$\int_0^\infty G(\omega) \, d\omega = G(0) \int_0^\infty d\omega$$

In spite of this fact, it is a useful concept both for certain theoretical purposes and as a practical approximation to noise of a very broad bandwidth. In many problems a noise spectrum may be known to be substantially constant over the frequency band of interest in the problem. When this is true, the use of a constant spectral density for all values of frequency often simplifies formal mathematical calculation without introducing any significant inaccuracy in the end result.

The correlation function for white noise is readily obtained by taking the Fourier transform of its spectral density. By (3.7-23), (3.6-38), and (2.9-9) we have

$$\phi_{xx}(\tau) = \frac{1}{2} \int_{-\infty}^\infty e^{i\omega\tau} \, d\omega = \pi\delta(\tau) \tag{3.7-29}$$

The same result is readily obtained in the limit from the correlation function (3.7-16). Writing $\bar{a} = 0$, $\overline{a^2} = \lambda\pi/2$, we have for finite λ

$$\phi_{xx}(\tau) = \frac{\lambda\pi}{2} e^{-\lambda|\tau|} \tag{3.7-30}$$

Since for all positive values of λ

$$\int_{-\infty}^{\infty} \phi_{xx}(\tau) \, d\tau = \pi \tag{3.7-31}$$

and since

$$\lim_{\lambda \to \infty} \phi_{xx}(\tau) = 0 \qquad \tau \neq 0 \tag{3.7-32}$$

we see that the conditions (2.7-15) to (2.7-17) are satisfied for $\frac{1}{\pi} \phi_{xx}(\tau)$ to approach the delta function $\delta(\tau)$ in the limit.

Example 3.7-1. In Example 3.3-3, the correlation function of the Brownian motion random process was found to be

$$\phi_{xx}(t_1,t_2) = a^2 \min (t_1,t_2)$$

The random process $\{x(t)\}$ under study in that example was in effect the time integral of a white noise. Writing

$$x(t) = \int_0^t y(\tau) \, d\tau$$

we show that the correlation function of y is a delta function.

Since $y(t)$ is the derivative of $x(t)$, from (3.4-13) we have

$$\phi_{yy}(t_1,t_2) = \frac{\partial^2}{\partial t_1 \, \partial t_2} \phi_{xx}(t_1,t_2)$$

$$= a^2 \frac{\partial^2}{\partial t_1 \, \partial t_2} [\min (t_1,t_2)]$$

Now

$$\min (t_1,t_2) = \begin{cases} t_2 & t_2 < t_1 \\ t_1 & t_2 > t_1 \end{cases}$$

Therefore

$$\frac{\partial}{\partial t_2} \min (t_1,t_2) = \begin{cases} 1 & t_2 < t_1 \\ 0 & t_2 > t_1 \end{cases}$$

Considered as a function of t_1, this quantity is a step function that changes its value from zero to unity as t_1 increases from a value less than t_2 to one greater than t_2. Since the derivative of a step function is a delta function, we have

$$\frac{\partial^2}{\partial t_1 \, \partial t_2} \min (t_1,t_2) = \delta(t_1 - t_2)$$

giving

$$\phi_{yy}(t_1,t_2) = a^2\delta(t_1 - t_2)$$

as the desired result.

PROBLEMS

3-1. Let A be a normally distributed random variable with standard deviation σ and zero mean value. Let θ be a second random variable, statistically independent of A, with a probability density $f(\theta)$ given by

$$f(\theta) = \frac{1}{2\pi} \qquad 0 \leq \theta \leq 2\pi$$

Calculate the correlation function of the random process consisting of the functions

$$x(t) = A \cos (\omega t + \theta)$$

where ω is a fixed constant.

3-2. Let $\{x(t)\}$ represent an arbitrary random process, and let

$$y(t) = \int_0^t x(\tau) \, d\tau$$

Derive an expression for the autocorrelation function for $\{y(t)\}$ in terms of the autocorrelation function for $\{x(t)\}$.

3-3. Let $x(t)$ be a member of an arbitrary nonstationary random process. A very elementary linear predictor for $x(t)$ may be formed as follows. Let $t_1 < t_2 < t_3$, and let

$$y = ax(t_1) + bx(t_2)$$

The problem is to choose a and b so that y in some statistical sense approximates the quantity $x(t_3)$. To do this, let the prediction error ϵ be defined by

$$\epsilon = y - x(t_3) = ax(t_1) + bx(t_2) - x(t_3)$$

We define the optimum predictor to be that which makes the mean-squared prediction error, that is, $E[\epsilon^2]$, as small as possible. Calculate the numbers a and b, which give this optimum predictor, in terms of the correlation function of x.

3-4. A predictor of a somewhat more refined type than that considered above is one for which the predicted value y at time t is given by a linear extrapolation based on the values of x and its derivative at the instant t. Analytically,

$$y(t) = x(t) + T \frac{dx(t)}{dt}$$

where T is the time interval of prediction. Letting the error be defined by

$$\epsilon(t) = y(t) - x(t + T)$$

compute $E[\epsilon(t)^2]$ in terms of the correlation function for x.

3-5. Compute the correlation function and spectral density for the stationary random process considered in Example 3.5-2.

3-6. In the situation considered in Prob. 3-1, let ω also be a random variable, independent of A and θ, and taking on only positive values. Show that the spectral density of the random process $\{x(t)\}$ is proportional to the probability frequency function for the random variable ω.

3-7. A random process $\{x(t)\}$ consists of three functions of time each occurring with equal probability as shown in the accompanying figure. Calculate the following statistical parameters: $\overline{x(2)}$, $\overline{x(6)}$, $F_1(x,2)$, $F_1(x,6)$, $F_2(x_1,2; x_2,6)$, $\phi_{xx}(2,6)$.

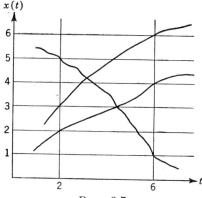

PROB. 3-7

3-8. Consider two stationary random processes whose correlation functions are expressed as follows

$$\phi_{xx}(\tau) = Ae^{-a|\tau|}$$
$$\phi_{yy}(\tau) = Ae^{-a|\tau|} \cos b\tau$$

Show that the spectral densities $G_{xx}(\omega)$ and $G_{yy}(\omega)$ are each rational functions of ω^2.

3-9. Let $\{x(t)\}$ be a stationary random process. Then by considering the expression

$$E[\{x(t) \pm x(t + \tau)\}^2]$$

show that

$$|\phi_{xx}(\tau)| \le \phi_{xx}(0)$$

In a similar way show that

$$2|\phi_{xy}(\tau)| \le \phi_{xx}(0) + \phi_{yy}(0)$$

where $\{y(t)\}$ is also a stationary random process.

3-10. Compute the autocorrelation function for a random process consisting of an infinite train of triangular pulses. All the time functions are identical except for phase which is a random variable uniformly distributed over the interval $(0,P)$. Assume the period P is not less than $2a$, where a is the duration of a single pulse.

Note that the autocorrelation function is periodic with the same period as the original time functions. Show that this property is true in general. That is, if a random process has any periodic components, the correlation function will have

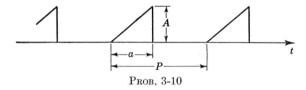

PROB. 3-10

periodic components of the same period. All phase relationships in the original time functions are lost during the process of autocorrelation. From an alternate point of view one may say that functions having the same harmonic content but differing in phase will have the same correlation function.

3-11. A random process is composed of identical time functions, each consisting of an infinite train of rectangular pulses of height B and width a occurring with a period P. Assuming that the phase is a random variable uniformly distributed over the interval $(0,P)$, compute the cross-correlation function for this random process and the one of Prob. 3-10.

3-12. A random process $\{x(t)\}$ is defined as follows:

$$x(t) = u_n \qquad (t_0 + n)\Delta < t \le (t_0 + n + 1)\Delta \qquad n = 0, \pm 1, \pm 2, \cdots$$

where t_0 is a random variable uniformly distributed over the interval $(0,\Delta)$ and $\{u_n\}$ is a sequence of mutually independent random variables which assume either of the two values $\pm \sqrt{A/2\Delta}$ with equal probability. Compute the autocorrelation function and spectral density of $\{x(t)\}$. Show that in the limit as Δ approaches zero the correlation function tends to a delta function and the spectral density tends to a constant. Here we have a physical representation of a white noise consisting of an infinitely dense sequence of impulses of infinite amplitude and zero strength.

CHAPTER 4

THE SHOT EFFECT AND
GAUSSIAN RANDOM PROCESSES

4.1 The Shot Effect

As our first detailed study of a random process, we consider the shot effect, which affords a mathematical description of the voltage fluctuations that might be expected in the output of a vacuum-tube circuit. A linear electric circuit is assumed to receive a number of impulses at randomly occurring times and of random magnitudes. Let $W(t,\tau)$ be the output response of the circuit at time t to a unit impulse applied at time τ. We shall assume that $W(t,\tau)$ is essentially zero when the absolute difference between t and τ exceeds some fixed number T_1 (that is, $|t - \tau| > T_1$), which is a reasonable assumption for most physical circuits.[1] The circuit is allowed to have time-varying parameters, so that generally $W(t,\tau)$ depends independently upon both t and τ and not simply upon their difference.

We assume that the times of occurrence of the impulses are distributed at random and independently over the time axis with a constant average density v in the manner discussed in Sec. 2.11. Letting a_k be the magnitude of the kth impulse and t_k its time of occurrence, the random process $\{V(t)\}$ to be studied is expressed by a series of the form

$$V(t) = \Sigma a_k W(t,t_k) \tag{4.1-1}$$

The coefficients a_k are assumed to form a set of random variables that are mutually independent and also independent of the numbers t_k. They are further assumed to possess the same probability density function $f(a)$. The series (4.1-1) contains an infinite number of terms, and for computational purposes it is somewhat simpler to consider a corresponding finite sum. We therefore fix upon a large but finite interval $(-T < t < T)$, where $T \gg T_1$, and define the event E_n to be the occurrence of exactly n of the points t_k within the interval in question. For

---

[1] It is also true, for physical circuits, that $W(t,\tau) = 0$ whenever $\tau > t$. We shall not make this assumption at this stage, however, since much of our calculation is valid under more general conditions.

convenience, we label these from $k = 1$ to $k = n$, and write

$$-T < t_k < T \qquad k = 1, 2, \ldots, n \qquad (4.1\text{-}2)$$

If t is now constrained to lie within a subinterval

$$-T + T_1 < t < T - T_1 \qquad (4.1\text{-}3)$$

then by a previous assumption the effect at time t of any impulse occurring outside the interval $(-T,T)$ can be neglected. Under hypothesis E_n we thus may write

$$V(t) = \sum_{k=1}^{n} a_k W(t,t_k) \qquad (4.1\text{-}4)$$

To compute statistical parameters associated with the random process $\{V(t)\}$, our general procedure is as follows. We first compute a conditional expectation of the sought-for quantity under hypothesis E_n. Now under this hypothesis we have to consider the $2n$ mutually independent variables $(t_1, \ldots, t_n; a_1, \ldots, a_n)$. Each of the a's possesses the density function $f(a)$; also, each of the numbers t_k is uniformly distributed over the interval (4.1-2). Thus we have to deal with a finite set of random variables with a reasonably simple joint distribution. Following the calculation of the conditional expectation, for $n = 0, 1, 2, \ldots$, we may employ Eq. (2.8-26) to obtain the desired final results, utilizing the fact that $P(E_n)$ is given by the Poisson distribution.

1. *The Mean Value of* $V(t)$. To obtain the mean value of $V(t)$, we first use Eq. (2.8-26) to obtain

$$E[V(t)] = \sum_{n=0}^{\infty} P(E_n)E[V(t) \mid E_n] \qquad (4.1\text{-}5)$$

Now under hypothesis E_n, $V(t)$ is given by (4.1-4), and

$$E[V(t) \mid E_n] = \sum_{k=1}^{n} E[a_k W(t,t_k) \mid E_n] \qquad (4.1\text{-}6)$$

Examining a typical term of this sum, since a_k and t_k are independent and since t_k is uniformly distributed over the interval $(-T,T)$,

$$E[a_k W(t,t_k) \mid E_n] = \frac{1}{2T} \int_{-\infty}^{\infty} af(a)\, da \int_{-T}^{T} W(t,t_k)\, dt_k$$

$$= \frac{\bar{a}}{2T} \int_{-T}^{T} W(t,\tau)\, d\tau$$

$$= \frac{\bar{a}}{2T} \int_{-\infty}^{\infty} W(t,\tau)\, d\tau \qquad (4.1\text{-}7)$$

In the last line of this relation, use is made of the approximation that $W(t,\tau) = 0$ when t lies inside the interval (4.1-3) and τ lies outside of $(-T,T)$.

Since the sum (4.1-6) contains n identical terms of the form (4.1-7), we have

$$E[V(t) \mid E_n] = \frac{n\bar{a}}{2T} \int_{-\infty}^{\infty} W(t,\tau)\, d\tau \qquad (4.1\text{-}8)$$

By the Poisson distribution, however,

$$P(E_n) = \frac{(2vT)^n}{n!} e^{-2vT} \qquad (4.1\text{-}9)$$

Combining these results in Eq. (4.1-5), we then obtain

$$\begin{aligned}
E[V(t)] &= \sum_{n=0}^{\infty} \left[\frac{(2vT)^n}{n!} e^{-2vT} \frac{n\bar{a}}{2T} \int_{-\infty}^{\infty} W(t,\tau)\, d\tau \right] \\
&= \left[\frac{\bar{a}e^{-2vT}}{2T} \int_{-\infty}^{\infty} W(t,\tau)\, d\tau \right] \sum_{n=0}^{\infty} \frac{n(2vT)^n}{n!} \\
&= \left[\frac{\bar{a}e^{-2vT}}{2T} \int_{-\infty}^{\infty} W(t,\tau)\, d\tau \right] (2vT)e^{2vT} \\
&= v\bar{a} \int_{-\infty}^{\infty} W(t,\tau)\, d\tau \qquad (4.1\text{-}10)
\end{aligned}$$

as our final result.

A generally similar approach can be used to compute the mean-squared value and higher moments of $V(t)$. Rather than follow this procedure directly we prefer first to calculate the characteristic function and frequency function for $V(t)$, and to derive the general moments from this result.

2. The Characteristic Function of $V(t)$. The computation of the characteristic function $\phi(u)$ for the random process $V(t)$ follows essentially the same procedure as used for the mean value. We have

$$\begin{aligned}
\phi(u) &= E[e^{juV(t)}] \\
&= \sum_{n=0}^{\infty} P(E_n)E[e^{juV(t)} \mid E_n] \\
&= \sum_{n=0}^{\infty} P(E_n)E\left[\exp\left\{ ju \sum_{k=1}^{n} a_k W(t,t_k) \right\} \mid E_n \right] \\
&= \sum_{n=0}^{\infty} P(E_n)\{E[\exp\{jua_k W(t,t_k)\} \mid E_n]\}^n \qquad (4.1\text{-}11)
\end{aligned}$$

where in the last line k is any single integer corresponding to an impulse lying in the interval $(-T,T)$. The last step in this calculation follows from the fact that the random variables $a_k W(t,t_k)$ for $k = 1, 2, \ldots, n$ are independent and identically distributed. Examining a typical term, we have

$$E[\exp\{jua_k W(t,t_k)\} \mid E_n]$$

$$= \frac{1}{2T} \int_{-\infty}^{\infty} f(a)\, da \int_{-T}^{T} \exp[juaW(t,\tau)]\, d\tau$$

$$= 1 + \frac{1}{2T} \int_{-\infty}^{\infty} f(a)\, da \int_{-T}^{T} \{\exp[juaW(t,\tau)] - 1\}\, d\tau$$

$$= 1 + \frac{1}{2T} \int_{-\infty}^{\infty} f(a)\, da \int_{-\infty}^{\infty} \{\exp[juaW(t,\tau)] - 1\}\, d\tau \quad (4.1\text{-}12)$$

In passing to the last line of (4.1-12), we have used the fact that

$$\exp[juaW(t,\tau)] = 1$$

for $|\tau| > T$ and t in the interval (4.1-3), since by hypothesis $W(t,\tau)$ is itself negligibly small. Denoting the quantity (4.1-12) temporarily by $1 + \alpha$, we have, from (4.1-9) and (4.1-11),

$$\phi(u) = \sum_{n=0}^{\infty} \frac{(2vT)^n}{n!} e^{-2vT}(1 + \alpha)^n$$

$$= \exp(2vT\alpha)$$

$$= \exp\left\{v \int_{-\infty}^{\infty} f(a)\, da \int_{-\infty}^{\infty} [e^{juaW(t,\tau)} - 1]\, d\tau\right\} \quad (4.1\text{-}13)$$

To compute the moments of $V(t)$ from the above expression for its characteristic function, we take the logarithm of both sides of (4.1-13), expand the exponential appearing in the integrand in a power series in ju, and interchange the order of integration and summation to obtain

$$\log \phi(u) = \sum_{n=1}^{\infty} \frac{(ju)^n}{n!} v\bar{a}^n \int_{-\infty}^{\infty} W(t,\tau)^n\, dt \quad (4.1\text{-}14)$$

Comparing this expression with Eq. (2.9-14), we see that

$$\lambda_n(t) = v\bar{a}^n \int_{-\infty}^{\infty} W(t,\tau)^n\, d\tau \quad (4.1\text{-}15)$$

from which the moments $\alpha_n(t)$ follow immediately by applying the equations in (2.9-15). In particular we may check our previous calculation for the mean value of $V(t)$ by taking $n = 1$.

The first probability density function for this random process may be found by taking the Fourier transform of the characteristic function as expressed by Eq. (2.9-7). We could also derive the second and higher probability densities by a more complicated application of the ideas used

above.   However, the results would be too cumbersome for direct applications.   Instead we shall content ourselves with a derivation of the
correlation function of $V(t)$.

3. *The Correlation Function of* $V(t)$.   Proceeding essentially as before,
we have

$$\phi_{VV}(t_1',t_2') = E[V(t_1')V(t_2')]$$

$$= \sum_{n=0}^{\infty} P(E_n)E[V(t_1')V(t_2') \mid E_n]$$

$$= \sum_{n=0}^{\infty} P(E_n) \sum_{i=1}^{n} \sum_{k=1}^{n} E[a_i a_k W(t_1',t_i)W(t_2',t_k) \mid E_n] \quad (4.1\text{-}16)$$

For those terms in the double sum in which i and k are different, the
random variables $a_i W(t_1',t_i)$ and $a_k W(t_2',t_j)$ are statistically independent,
so that

$$E[a_i a_k W(t_1',t_i)W(t_2',t_k) \mid E_n]$$

$$= \frac{\bar{a}^2}{4T^2} \int_{-\infty}^{\infty} \int_{-\infty}^{\infty} W(t_1',\tau_1)W(t_2',\tau_2) \, d\tau_1 \, d\tau_2 \quad i \neq k \quad (4.1\text{-}17)$$

For terms in which $i = k$ we have

$$E[a_k^2 W(t_1',t_k)W(t_2',t_k) \mid E_n] = \frac{\overline{a^2}}{2T} \int_{-T}^{T} W(t_1',t_k)W(t_2',t_k) \, dt_k$$

$$\simeq \frac{\overline{a^2}}{2T} \int_{-\infty}^{\infty} W(t_1',\tau)W(t_2',\tau) \, d\tau \quad (4.1\text{-}18)$$

Extending the range of integration is valid since t_1' and t_2' are both confined to the interval defined by (4.1-3) and the integrand in Eq. (4.1-18)
is essentially zero beyond the range of integration used.

There are a total of $n^2 - n$ nonzero terms of the form (4.1-17) and n
terms of the form (4.1-18) so that

$$E[V(t_1')V(t_2') \mid E_n] = \frac{(n^2-n)\bar{a}^2}{4T^2} \int_{-\infty}^{\infty} \int_{-\infty}^{\infty} W(t_1',\tau_1)W(t_2',\tau_2) \, d\tau_1 \, d\tau_2$$

$$+ \frac{n\overline{a^2}}{2T} \int_{-\infty}^{\infty} W(t_1',\tau)W(t_2',\tau) \, d\tau \quad (4.1\text{-}19)$$

Multiplying by $P(E_n)$ and summing, we obtain from Eq. (4.1-16)

$$\phi_{VV}(t_1',t_2') = v\overline{a^2} \int_{-\infty}^{\infty} W(t_1',\tau)W(t_2',\tau) \, d\tau$$

$$+ (v\bar{a})^2 \int_{-\infty}^{\infty} \int_{-\infty}^{\infty} W(t_1',\tau_1)W(t_2',\tau_2) \, d\tau_1 \, d\tau_2$$

$$= v\overline{a^2} \int_{-\infty}^{\infty} W(t_1',\tau)W(t_2',\tau) \, d\tau + \overline{V(t_1')}\,\overline{V(t_2')} \quad (4.1\text{-}20)$$

so that the correlation function of $V(t)$ is quite simply expressed in terms of the filter response characteristics.

For the special case in which the electric circuit contains only constant parameters, the statistical properties that we have calculated for the shot effect take a simpler form. The weighting function $W(t,\tau)$ becomes $W(t - \tau)$ so that the average of $V(t)$ from Eq. (4.1-10) becomes

$$E[V(t)] = \overline{va} \int_{-\infty}^{\infty} W(\tau) \, d\tau \qquad (4.1\text{-}21)$$

Similarly, the expression for the semi-invariants (4.1-15) becomes

$$\lambda_n = \overline{va^n} \int_{-\infty}^{\infty} [W(\tau)]^n \, d\tau \qquad (4.1\text{-}22)$$

and the correlation function (4.1-20) may be reduced to

$$\phi_{VV}(t) = \overline{va^2} \int_{-\infty}^{\infty} W(\tau) W(\tau + t) \, d\tau + \left[\overline{va} \int_{-\infty}^{\infty} W(\tau) \, d\tau \right]^2$$
$$= \overline{va^2} \int_{-\infty}^{\infty} W(\tau) W(\tau + t) \, d\tau + \bar{V}^2 \qquad (4.1\text{-}23)$$

Thus, for this case we see that the correlation function does not depend directly on t_1' and t_2' but only on the difference $t = t_2' - t_1'$. Furthermore, the statistical parameters computed from the characteristic function were also independent of the time origin. Therefore, apart from our rather strong intuitive feelings that the random process as described is indeed stationary, we have a considerable amount of analytical verification of this fact.

As a final calculation we shall compute the power spectral density of $V(t)$ for the stationary case.

4. *The Power Spectral Density of $V(t)$.* The spectral density of $V(t)$ is obtained by substituting the expression for the correlation function, Eq. (4.1-23), into Eq. (3.6-36) to obtain

$$G(\omega) = \frac{1}{\pi} \int_{-\infty}^{\infty} \bar{V}^2 e^{-j\omega t} \, dt$$
$$+ \frac{1}{\pi} \int_{-\infty}^{\infty} \left[\overline{va^2} \int_{-\infty}^{\infty} W(t) W(t + \tau) \, dt \right] e^{-j\omega\tau} \, d\tau \qquad (4.1\text{-}24)$$

The first term in this relation may be evaluated using Eq. (2.9-9),[1] while the second is simplified by a change of variable. Thus

$$G(\omega) = 2\bar{V}^2 \delta(\omega) + \frac{\overline{va^2}}{\pi} \int_{-\infty}^{\infty} e^{j\omega t} W(t) \, dt \int_{-\infty}^{\infty} e^{-j\omega u} W(u) \, du$$
$$= 2\bar{V}^2 \delta(\omega) + \frac{\overline{va^2}}{\pi} \left| \int_{-\infty}^{\infty} W(t) e^{-j\omega t} \, dt \right|^2 \qquad (4.1\text{-}25)$$

[1] See Example 3.6-2 for a discussion of the coefficient of the delta-function term.

For the special case in which the electric circuit responding to the random impulses is a first-order filter with time constant T, the output correlation function and spectral density may be readily evaluated. In this case

$$W(t) = \begin{cases} \dfrac{1}{T} e^{-t/T} & t \geqq 0 \\ 0 & t < 0 \end{cases} \qquad (4.1\text{-}26)$$

Then Eq. (4.1-23) becomes

$$\phi_{VV}(\tau) = \overline{va^2} \int_0^\infty \frac{1}{T} e^{-t/T} \frac{1}{T} e^{-(t+\tau)/T}\, dt$$
$$+ \left(v\bar{a} \int_0^\infty \frac{1}{T} e^{-t/T}\, dt \right)^2 \qquad \text{for } \tau \geqq 0 \quad (4.1\text{-}27)$$

and $$\phi_{VV}(\tau) = \overline{va^2} \int_{-\tau}^\infty \frac{1}{T} e^{-t/T} \frac{1}{T} e^{-(t+\tau)/T}\, dt$$
$$+ \left(v\bar{a} \int_0^\infty \frac{1}{T} e^{-t/T}\, dt \right)^2 \qquad \text{for } \tau \leqq 0 \quad (4.1\text{-}28)$$

Therefore $$\phi_{VV}(\tau) = \begin{cases} \dfrac{\overline{va^2}}{2T} e^{-\tau/T} + (v\bar{a})^2 & \tau \geqq 0 \\[2mm] \dfrac{\overline{va^2}}{2T} e^{\tau/T} + (v\bar{a})^2 & \tau \leqq 0 \end{cases}$$

or simply

$$\phi_{VV}(\tau) = \frac{\overline{va^2}}{2T} e^{-|\tau|/T} + (v\bar{a})^2 \qquad (4.1\text{-}29)$$

Similarly, for the spectral density, we obtain, from Eq. (4.1-25),

$$G(\omega) = 2(v\bar{a})^2 \delta(\omega) + \frac{\overline{va^2}}{\pi} \left| \int_0^\infty \frac{1}{T} e^{-t/T} e^{-i\omega t}\, dt \right|^2$$
$$= 2(v\bar{a})^2 \delta(\omega) + \frac{\overline{va^2}}{\pi} \left| \frac{1}{1 + j\omega T} \right|^2$$
$$= 2(v\bar{a})^2 \delta(\omega) + \frac{\overline{va^2}}{\pi} \frac{1}{1 + \omega^2 T^2} \qquad (4.1\text{-}30)$$

We note that, except for the delta-function term which vanishes when $\bar{a} = 0$, the spectral density just calculated has the same form as that derived for the random step function in Sec. 3.7. This illustrates the fact, also borne out by Prob. 5-7, that two random processes can possess the same spectral density but still be generally dissimilar in their other properties.

If we further specialize to the case for which T approaches zero, we see, from Eqs. (4.1-26) and (2.7-18), that

$$\lim_{T \to 0} W(t) = \delta(t) \tag{4.1-31}$$

Since a filter with weighting function $\delta(t)$ simply passes its input signal without modification, we may obtain the correlation function and spectral density for the pure (i.e., unfiltered) shot effect by letting T approach zero in Eqs. (4.1-29) and (4.1-30). The result is simply

$$\phi_{VV}(\tau) = \overline{va^2}\delta(\tau) + (v\bar{a})^2 \tag{4.1-32}$$

$$G(\omega) = 2(v\bar{a})^2\delta(\omega) + \frac{\overline{va^2}}{\pi} \tag{4.1-33}$$

In practice the average value of $V(t)$ is often zero which, from Eq. (4.1-21), implies that $\bar{a} = 0$, so that finally

$$\phi_{VV}(\tau) = \overline{va^2}\delta(\tau) \tag{4.1-34}$$

$$G(\omega) = \frac{\overline{va^2}}{\pi} \tag{4.1-35}$$

It is clear from this result that pure shot effect is not physically realizable. This follows since $G(\omega)$ is a constant independent of the frequency ω and hence pure shot effect must contain infinite power. The pure shot effect is therefore a white noise, as discussed in Sec. 3.7. In that section, a white noise is derived as an infinitely dense collection of infinitesmal impulses. Here, the density is finite and the pulse amplitudes are different from zero. On the other hand, if, for the shot effect, we let the density v become infinite while the strength of the individual pulses tends to zero in such a way that

$$\overline{va^2} = \mu \tag{4.1-36}$$

remains constant, there results a random process all of whose probability density functions are normal. Such a random process is called Gaussian and is discussed in detail in the following section.

To show that this limiting case of the shot effect is a Gaussian random process let us consider the joint characteristic function for $V(t_1)$, $V(t_2)$, . . . , $V(t_n)$. The derivation is entirely similar to the one used to obtain Eq. (4.1-14). The result is simply

$$\log \phi(u_1, u_2, \ldots, u_n) = \sum_{k=1}^{\infty} \frac{\overline{va^k}}{k!} \int_{-\infty}^{\infty} \left[j \sum_{i=1}^{n} u_i W(t_i, \tau) \right]^k d\tau \tag{4.1-37}$$

Suppose now that the average value of $V(t)$ is zero, that is $\bar{a} = 0$, and consider the limiting process described above. Since $\overline{a^2}$ is of the order of $1/v$, we must have $\overline{va^k}$ tending to zero for all $k > 2$. Thus, Eq. (4.1-37) becomes in the limit

$$\log \phi(u_1, u_2, \ldots, u_n) = -\frac{\mu}{2} \int_{-\infty}^{\infty} \left[\sum_{i=1}^{n} u_i W(t_i, \tau) \right]^2 d\tau$$

$$= -\frac{\mu}{2} \int_{-\infty}^{\infty} \sum_{i=1}^{n} \sum_{k=1}^{n} u_i u_k W(t_i, \tau) W(t_k, \tau) \, d\tau \quad (4.1\text{-}38)$$

Using Eq. (4.1-20), we have, finally,

$$\log \phi(u_1, u_2, \ldots, u_n) = -\frac{1}{2} \sum_{i=1}^{n} \sum_{k=1}^{n} u_i u_k \phi_{VV}(t_i, t_k) \quad (4.1\text{-}39)$$

Comparing this result with Eq. (2.13-16), we see that the joint distribution of the random variables $V(t_1)$, $V(t_2)$, $\ldots$, $V(t_n)$ is indeed an n-dimensional normal distribution.

We have already seen that the pure shot effect is a white noise and now have shown that in a limiting sense the filtered shot effect is a Gaussian random process. Thus, we have a physical model of a Gaussian random process as a linearly filtered white noise.

4.2 The Gaussian Random Process

A random process $\{x(t)\}$ is said to be Gaussian if for every n and every set $(t_1, t_2, \ldots, t_n)$, its nth probability density function is normal in the variables $x_1, x_2, \ldots, x_n$. From Eq. (2.13-31) this implies that

$$f_n(x_1, t_1; x_2, t_2; \ldots; x_n, t_n)$$

$$= \frac{1}{(2\pi)^{n/2} \sqrt{|M|}} \exp\left(-\frac{1}{2} \sum_{i=1}^{n} \sum_{k=1}^{n} m_{ik}^{-1} x_i x_k \right) \quad (4.2\text{-}1)$$

The quantity $|M|$ is the determinant of the moment matrix

$$M = \begin{Vmatrix} m_{11} & m_{12} & \ldots & m_{1n} \\ m_{21} & m_{22} & \ldots & m_{2n} \\ \cdot & \cdot & \cdot & \cdot & \cdot & \cdot & \cdot \\ m_{n1} & m_{n2} & \ldots & m_{nn} \end{Vmatrix} \quad (4.2\text{-}2)$$

whose elements are the second moments m_{ik} and are defined by

$$m_{ik} = E[x_i x_k] = E[x(t_i) x(t_k)] = \phi_{xx}(t_i, t_k) = \phi_{ik} \quad (4.2\text{-}3)$$

The quantities m_{ik}^{-1} are the elements of the inverse of the moment matrix and are obtained as solutions of the n^2 equations

$$\sum_{s=1}^{n} m_{is} m_{sk}^{-1} = \begin{cases} 0 & \text{for } i \neq k \\ 1 & \text{for } i = k \end{cases} \quad (4.2\text{-}4)$$

The characteristic function corresponding to the distribution given by Eq. (4.2-1) is obtained from Eq. (2.13-16) and may be expressed as

$$E\left[\exp\left(j\sum_{i=1}^{n}x_is_i\right)\right] = \exp\left(-\frac{1}{2}\sum_{i=1}^{n}\sum_{k=1}^{n}m_{ik}s_is_k\right) \qquad (4.2\text{-}5)$$

The Gaussian random process is important because of the special fact that all statistical properties can be determined from a knowledge of the correlation function. Thus, in order to establish the stationary property for a Gaussian random process, it is sufficient to show that the correlation function is a function of only a single variable. Under normal circumstances the determination of even the second probability density of an experimentally observed random process is an almost impossible numerical task. Therefore, many mathematical advantages accrue if it is known, or may be safely assumed, that the given random process is Gaussian.

As we have seen the Gaussian random process occurs as an idealization of many natural phenomena associated with the superposition of large numbers of small effects. Thus, Gaussian noise or random processes related to it are to be expected in all electronic devices. Since the filtered shot effect is a Gaussian random process, we may use arguments analogous to those of Sec. 3.5 to establish the plausibility of the ergodic property for stationary Gaussian noise. Therefore, in the absence of any conflicting information we often find it convenient to assume a given stationary Gaussian process is also ergodic.

As a particular example of Eq. (4.2-1) we form the second probability density function. Equation (4.2-4) may be written as

$$\phi_{11}m_{11}^{-1} + \phi_{12}m_{21}^{-1} = 1$$
$$\phi_{21}m_{11}^{-1} + \phi_{22}m_{21}^{-1} = 0$$
$$\phi_{21}m_{12}^{-1} + \phi_{22}m_{22}^{-1} = 1$$
$$\phi_{11}m_{12}^{-1} + \phi_{12}m_{22}^{-1} = 0$$

from which we obtain

$$m_{11}^{-1} = \frac{\phi_{22}}{D} \qquad m_{21}^{-1} = m_{12}^{-1} = -\frac{\phi_{21}}{D} = -\frac{\phi_{12}}{D} \qquad m_{22}^{-1} = \frac{\phi_{11}}{D}$$

where
$$D = \phi_{11}\phi_{22} - \phi_{12}^2$$

Therefore, Eq. (4.2-1) becomes

$$f_2(x_1,t_1; x_2,t_2)$$
$$= \frac{1}{2\pi\sqrt{\phi_{11}\phi_{22} - \phi_{12}^2}}\exp\left(-\frac{\phi_{22}x_1^2 - 2\phi_{12}x_1x_2 + \phi_{11}x_2^2}{2(\phi_{11}\phi_{22} - \phi_{12}^2)}\right) \qquad (4.2\text{-}6)$$

Another important property enjoyed by the Gaussian random process is that it remains Gaussian after passing through a linear filter. That is, if $x(t)$ belongs to a Gaussian random process and if $W(t,\tau)$ is the unit impulse response function of a linear filter, then the response $y(t)$ of this filter to the input $x(t)$, also belongs to a Gaussian random process, where

$$y(t) = \int_{-\infty}^{t} W(t,\tau)x(\tau)\, d\tau \qquad (4.2\text{-}7)$$

To prove this theorem, we apply a technique developed in Sec. 2.13. Since $\{x(t)\}$ is Gaussian, the random variables $x(\tau_i)$ for $i = 1, 2, \ldots$ are normally distributed. The input-output relation expressed by Eq. (4.2-7) is simply a limiting form of the following sum

$$y(t_k) \cong \sum_{i} W(t_k,\tau_i)x(\tau_i)(\Delta\tau)_i \qquad (4.2\text{-}8)$$

Thus, according to the theorem associated with Eq. (2.13-32), if we identify $W(t_k,\tau_i)(\Delta\tau)_i$ with C_{ki}, we may deduce that since the random variables $y(t_k)$ are linear combinations of the quantities $x(\tau_i)$, they are also normally distributed. Hence, by definition, $\{y(t)\}$ is a Gaussian random process.

It is also of interest to note that by a slight generalization of this argument, if

$$y_i(t) = \int_{-\infty}^{t} W_i(t,\tau)x(\tau)\, d\tau$$

for $i = 1, 2, \ldots, n$ then the random variables $y_i(t)$ possess a joint normal distribution.

The Fourier series representation of a Gaussian random process is frequently used in the literature. Let $x(t)$ belong to a stationary Gaussian random process. Over an interval $(0 < t < T)$ the function $x(t)$ may be expressed in terms of the Fourier series

$$x(t) = \frac{a_0}{2} + \sum_{n=1}^{\infty} (a_n \cos n\omega t + b_n \sin n\omega t) \qquad (4.2\text{-}9)$$

where

$$a_n = \frac{2}{T} \int_{0}^{T} x(t) \cos n\omega t\, dt \qquad (4.2\text{-}10)$$

$$b_n = \frac{2}{T} \int_{0}^{T} x(t) \sin n\omega t\, dt \qquad (4.2\text{-}11)$$

and

$$\omega = \frac{2\pi}{T} \qquad (4.2\text{-}12)$$

Let us define two functions $C_n(t)$ and $S_n(t)$ by

$$C_n(t) = \begin{cases} \dfrac{2}{T} \cos n\omega t & \text{for } 0 \leq t \leq T \\ 0 & \text{otherwise} \end{cases} \qquad (4.2\text{-}13)$$

and
$$S_n(t) = \begin{cases} -\dfrac{2}{T} \sin n\omega t & \text{for } 0 \leqq t \leqq T \\ 0 & \text{otherwise} \end{cases} \tag{4.2-14}$$

Thus, Eqs. (4.2-10) and (4.2-11) may be expressed in the form

$$a_n = \int_0^T C_n(T - \tau)x(\tau)\, d\tau \tag{4.2-15}$$

$$b_n = \int_0^T S_n(T - \tau)x(\tau)\, d\tau \tag{4.2-16}$$

Hence the quantities a_n and b_n may be regarded as responses of linear filters at time T with $x(t)$ as input. Therefore, a_n and b_n are normally distributed random variables and the joint distribution of $(a_0, a_1, b_1, a_2, b_2, \ldots)$ is also normal.

In addition we may show that for sufficiently large values of T, the variables $(a_0, a_1, b_1, a_2, b_2, \ldots)$ are independent. Since these variables are normally distributed, this conclusion will follow if we can show that they are uncorrelated. For this purpose, let us first compute the average $\overline{a_i a_k}$.

From Eq. (4.2-15) we have

$$a_i a_k = \int_0^T C_i(T - \tau_1)\, d\tau_1 \int_0^T C_k(T - \tau_2)x(\tau_1)x(\tau_2)\, d\tau_2 \tag{4.2-17}$$

Taking the average of this result, we obtain

$$\overline{a_i a_k} = \int_0^T C_i(T - \tau_1)\, d\tau_1 \int_0^T C_k(T - \tau_2)\phi_{xx}(\tau_1,\tau_2)\, d\tau_2 \tag{4.2-18}$$

Now since $x(t)$ belongs to a stationary random process, we have

$$\phi_{xx}(\tau_1,\tau_2) = \phi_{xx}(\tau_2 - \tau_1) = \phi_{xx}(\tau) \tag{4.2-19}$$

so that

$$\begin{aligned}
\overline{a_i a_k} &= \int_0^T C_i(T - \tau_1)\, d\tau_1 \int_0^T C_k(T - \tau_2)\phi_{xx}(\tau_1 - \tau_2)\, d\tau_2 \\
&= \int_0^T C_i(t)\, dt \int_{-t}^{T-t} C_k(t + \tau)\phi_{xx}(\tau)\, d\tau \\
&= \int_0^T C_i(t)\, dt \int_{-T}^{T} C_k(t + \tau)\phi_{xx}(\tau)\, d\tau \\
&= \int_{-T}^{T} \phi_{xx}(\tau)\, d\tau \int_0^T C_i(t)C_k(t + \tau)\, dt
\end{aligned} \tag{4.2-20}$$

Hence a_i and a_k with $i \neq k$ will be uncorrelated if we can show that

$$\int_0^T C_i(t)C_k(t + \tau)\, dt$$

vanishes. As a matter of fact all that we will be able to show is that under certain circumstances a_i and a_k are only slightly correlated for large T and that their correlation coefficient tends to zero as T approaches infinity.

For $\tau \geqq 0$ we have, using Eq. (4.2-13),

$$\int_0^T C_i(t)C_k(t + \tau) \, dt = \frac{4}{T^2} \int_0^{T-\tau} \cos i\omega t \cos k\omega(t + \tau) \, dt \quad (4.2\text{-}21)$$

By the orthogonality properties of the trigonometric functions we have

$$\frac{4}{T^2} \int_0^T \cos i\omega t \cos k\omega(t + \tau) \, dt = \begin{cases} \dfrac{2}{T} \cos k\omega\tau & \text{for } i = k \\ 0 & \text{for } i \neq k \end{cases} \quad (4.2\text{-}22)$$

Also
$$\left| \frac{4}{T^2} \int_{T-\tau}^T \cos i\omega t \cos k\omega(t + \tau) \, dt \right| \leq \frac{4\tau}{T^2} \quad (4.2\text{-}23)$$

Therefore, since

$$\int_0^{T-\tau} = \int_0^T - \int_{T-\tau}^T$$

we obtain

$$\int_0^T C_i(t)C_k(t + \tau) \, dt = \begin{cases} \dfrac{2}{T} \cos k\omega\tau + O\left(\dfrac{\tau}{T^2}\right) & \text{for } i = k \\ O\left(\dfrac{\tau}{T^2}\right) & \text{for } i \neq k \end{cases} \quad (4.2\text{-}24)$$

Hence for $i \neq k$ we have, from Eq. (4.2-18),

$$|\overline{a_i a_k}| \leq \frac{8}{T^2} \left| \int_0^T \tau\phi_{xx}(\tau) \, d\tau \right| \quad (4.2\text{-}25)$$

so that a_i and a_k are, indeed, independent in the limit, provided that $\int_0^\infty \tau\phi_{xx}(\tau) \, d\tau$ is finite.

For the case in which $i = k$, we may write

$$\overline{a_k^2} = \frac{2}{T} \int_{-T}^T \phi_{xx}(\tau) \cos k\omega\tau \, d\tau + O\left(\frac{1}{T^2}\right) \quad (4.2\text{-}26)$$

using Eqs. (4.2-20) and (4.2-24). Here we have again assumed that $\int_0^\infty \tau\phi_{xx}(\tau) \, d\tau$ is finite. Thus, the correlation coefficient ρ of a_i and a_k defined as

$$\rho = \frac{\overline{a_i a_k}}{\sqrt{\overline{a_i^2}} \sqrt{\overline{a_k^2}}} = O\left(\frac{1}{T}\right) \quad (4.2\text{-}27)$$

tends to zero with increasing T, as asserted.

A similar argument can be used to show that the correlation coefficient of b_i and b_k and that of a_i and b_k both tend to zero as T approaches infinity.

As an additional result, we can relate the quantities $\overline{a_k^2}$ and $\overline{b_k^2}$ to the spectral density $G_{xx}(\omega)$ of the random process $\{x(t)\}$. From Eq. (4.2-26) we see that for large T we have

$$\overline{a_k^2} = \frac{2\pi}{T} G_{xx}(k\omega) + O\left(\frac{1}{T^2}\right) \tag{4.2-28}$$

and a similar calculation also gives

$$\overline{b_k^2} = \frac{2\pi}{T} G_{xx}(k\omega) + O\left(\frac{1}{T^2}\right) \tag{4.2-29}$$

Writing

$$\omega_k = k\frac{2\pi}{T} = k\omega \tag{4.2-30}$$

and

$$\Delta\omega = \omega_{k+1} - \omega_k = \frac{2\pi}{T} \tag{4.2-31}$$

we have

$$\overline{a_k^2} = \overline{b_k^2} \cong G_{xx}(\omega_k)\,\Delta\omega \tag{4.2-32}$$

for large values of T.

Since the average power associated with a specific pair of terms $a_k \cos \omega_k t + b_k \sin \omega_k t$ is given by $\frac{1}{2}(a_k^2 + b_k^2)$, we see that the relation (4.2-32) associates with the frequency ω_k an average power equal to the average power in $x(t)$ lying between ω_k and ω_{k+1}. In other words, since T is large and $\Delta\omega$ is small, our Fourier series representation in effect replaces the continuous spectrum $G_{xx}(\omega)$ by a very finely subdivided discrete spectrum, associating with each frequency ω_k an average power equal to the average power in the continuous spectrum lying between ω_k and ω_{k+1}. The concept of a random process composed of a large number of discrete harmonic oscillations, independent in amplitude and phase, is often quite convenient from the standpoint of visualizing the nature of a particular operation. [Independence in phase is implied by the independence of the cosine and sine coefficients (a_k,b_k).]

4.3   The Empirical Determination of Correlation Functions

As an example of practical significance which illustrates an application of the ideas presented in Sec. 4.2 we consider the problem of determining the correlation function of a stationary random process from empirical data. More specifically, we wish to study the length of data required in order to ensure that an empirically determined autocorrelation function is a reasonably accurate approximation to the true autocorrelation. In order to formulate an answer to the problem posed, we assume that

$x(t)$ belongs to a stationary, ergodic, and Gaussian random process. Strictly speaking, our results are limited to the Gaussian case; however, they certainly can be used as a guide in other cases.

Let

$$V(\tau) = \frac{1}{T} \int_0^T x(t)x(t + \tau) \, dt \qquad (4.3\text{-}1)$$

The approximate correlation function $V(\tau)$ is a random variable, since it depends upon the particular function $x(t)$ chosen from the ensemble. We seek to determine the mean value of $V(\tau)$ over the ensemble, and the standard deviation of $V(\tau)$ with respect to this mean.

The mean value of $V(\tau)$ is given by

$$E[V(\tau)] = \frac{1}{T} \int_0^T E[x(t)x(t + \tau)] \, dt$$
$$= \frac{1}{T} \int_0^T \phi(\tau) \, dt = \phi(\tau) \qquad (4.3\text{-}2)$$

Thus the average of $V(\tau)$ over a large number of trials is the correlation function $\phi(\tau)$, as one might expect.

To compute the variance of $V(\tau)$, which we denote by $\sigma(\tau)^2$, we have

$$\sigma(\tau)^2 = E[\{V(\tau) - \phi(\tau)\}^2] = E[V(\tau)^2] - \phi(\tau)^2$$
$$= \frac{1}{T^2} \int_0^T dt_1 \int_0^T dt_2 \, E[x(t_1)x(t_2)x(t_1 + \tau)x(t_2 + \tau)] - \phi(\tau)^2 \qquad (4.3\text{-}3)$$

To evaluate $E[x(t_1)x(t_2)x(t_1 + \tau)x(t_2 + \tau)]$ we observe that the random variables

$$
\begin{aligned}
X_1 &= x(t_1) \\
X_2 &= x(t_2) \\
X_3 &= x(t_1 + \tau) \\
X_4 &= x(t_2 + \tau)
\end{aligned}
\qquad (4.3\text{-}4)
$$

possess a joint normal distribution. By the procedure outlined at the end of Sec. 2.13, we find

$$E[X_1 X_2 X_3 X_4] = m_{12}m_{34} + m_{13}m_{24} + m_{14}m_{23} \qquad (4.3\text{-}5)$$

where

$$
\begin{aligned}
m_{12} &= E[x(t_1)x(t_2)] = \phi(t_2 - t_1) \\
m_{13} &= E[x(t_1)x(t_1 + \tau)] = \phi(\tau) \\
m_{14} &= E[x(t_1)x(t_2 + \tau)] = \phi(t_2 - t_1 + \tau) \\
m_{23} &= E[x(t_2)x(t_1 + \tau)] = \phi(t_1 - t_2 + \tau) \\
m_{24} &= E[x(t_2)x(t_2 + \tau)] = \phi(\tau) \\
m_{34} &= E[x(t_1 + \tau)x(t_2 + \tau)] = \phi(t_2 - t_1)
\end{aligned}
\qquad (4.3\text{-}6)
$$

Equation (4.3-3) then becomes

$$\sigma(\tau)^2 = \frac{1}{T^2} \int_0^T dt_1 \int_0^T dt_2 \left[\phi(t_2 - t_1)^2 + \phi(t_2 - t_1 + \tau)\phi(t_1 - t_2 + \tau)\right]$$

$$= \frac{1}{T^2} \int_0^T dt_1 \int_{-t_1}^{T-t_1} \left[\phi(t)^2 + \phi(t + \tau)\phi(-t + \tau)\right] dt \tag{4.3-7}$$

The integrand in this expression is an even function of t which we shall denote by $f(t)$. The region of integration is shown in Fig. 4.3-1.

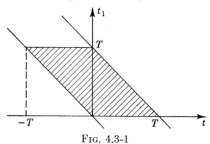

FIG. 4.3-1

By changing the order of integration, Eq. (4.3-7) becomes

$$\int_0^T dt_1 \int_{-t_1}^{T-t_1} f(t)\, dt = \int_0^T f(t)\, dt \int_0^{T-t} dt_1 + \int_{-T}^0 f(t)\, dt \int_{-t}^T dt_1$$

$$= \int_0^T (T - t)f(t)\, dt + \int_{-T}^0 (T + t)f(t)\, dt$$

$$= 2 \int_0^T (T - t)f(t)\, dt \tag{4.3-8}$$

The last step in this computation follows from the fact that $f(t) = f(-t)$. Hence, Eq. (4.3-7) may be written finally as

$$\sigma(\tau)^2 = \frac{2}{T} \int_0^T \left(1 - \frac{t}{T}\right)\left[\phi(t)^2 + \phi(t + \tau)\phi(-t + \tau)\right] dt \tag{4.3-9}$$

Results up to this point have been expressed in terms of exact equalities, depending only upon the Gaussian character of $x(t)$. However in practical cases, the integral of Eq. (4.3-9) may be quite difficult to evaluate. An upper bound for $\sigma(\tau)^2$, which will turn out to be considerably more manageable and independent of τ, may be obtained in the following way.

$$\sigma(\tau)^2 \leq \frac{2}{T} \int_0^T \left|1 - \frac{t}{T}\right| \left|\phi(t)^2 + \phi(t + \tau)\phi(-t + \tau)\right| dt$$

$$\leq \frac{2}{T} \int_0^T \phi(t)^2\, dt + \frac{1}{T} \int_{-T}^T \left|\phi(t + \tau)\phi(-t + \tau)\right| dt \tag{4.3-10}$$

A bound on this second integral is obtained using the Schwarz inequality.[1]

[1] For any two functions $f(t)$ and $g(t)$,

$$\left|\int_a^b f(t)g(t)\, dt\right|^2 \leq \int_a^b f(t)^2\, dt \int_a^b g(t)^2\, dt$$

Thus

$$\int_{-T}^{T} |\phi(t+\tau)\phi(-t+\tau)| \, dt \leq \sqrt{\int_{-T}^{T} \phi(t+\tau)^2 \, dt \int_{-T}^{T} \phi(-t+\tau)^2 \, dt}$$

$$(4.3\text{-}11)$$

Let us suppose that $\int_{0}^{\infty} \phi(t)^2 \, dt$ is finite. Then the right side of (4.3-11) is bounded by $2 \int_{0}^{\infty} \phi(t)^2 \, dt$ and the inequality (4.3-10) becomes simply

$$\sigma(\tau)^2 \leq \frac{4}{T} \int_{0}^{\infty} \phi(t)^2 \, dt \qquad (4.3\text{-}12)$$

By way of illustration, let $x(t)$ be obtained by passing a white noise through a simple filter with a response $(1 + T_1 j\omega)^{-1}$, giving a spectral density of the form

$$G_{xx}(\omega) = \frac{2T_1}{\pi} \frac{1}{1 + T_1^2 \omega^2} \qquad (4.3\text{-}13)$$

and a correlation function

$$\phi_{xx}(\tau) = e^{-|\tau|/T_1} \qquad (4.3\text{-}14)$$

We have, by (4.3-12),

$$\sigma^2 \leq \frac{4}{T} \int_{0}^{\infty} e^{-2t/T_1} \, dt = \frac{2T_1}{T}$$

Thus, for example, for 10 per cent dispersion in results ($\sigma = 0.1$) we should require a length of data T equal to 200 times the filter time constant. Stated in another way, if ω_c is the break point of the filter and T_c is the associated period,

$$\omega_c = \frac{1}{T_1} \qquad T_c = \frac{2\pi}{\omega_c}$$

then

$$\sigma^2 = \frac{T_c}{\pi T}$$

Hence, for $\sigma = 0.1$, we should take

$$T = \frac{100}{\pi} T_c \cong 30 T_c$$

4.4   Correlation Function of the Output of Simple Nonlinear Devices

Consider a simple nonlinear device for which the output $w(t)$ is a fixed function of the input $z(t)$ as indicated by

$$w(t) = F[z(t)] \qquad (4.4\text{-}1)$$

Assuming the input $z(t)$ to consist of the sum of a preassigned function $y(t)$ and a Gaussian random process $\{x(t)\}$ with known statistical characteristics, it is required to calculate the correlation function of w. Common examples of this type of situation include the square-law device

$$F(z) = z^2 \qquad (4.4\text{-}2)$$

the rectifier

$$F(z) = |z| \tag{4.4-3}$$

and a linear device with saturation (i.e., limiter)

$$F(z) = \begin{cases} -a & z < -a \\ z & |z| < a \\ +a & z > a \end{cases} \tag{4.4-4}$$

Since $\{x(t)\}$ is a Gaussian random process, its first probability density function, as obtained from Eq. (4.2-1), is given by

$$f_1(x_1,t_1) = \frac{1}{\sqrt{2\pi\phi_0}} e^{-x^2/2\phi_0} \tag{4.4-5}$$

where

$$\phi_0 = \phi_{xx}(t_1,t_1) \tag{4.4-6}$$

Then the average value of

$$w(t_1) = F[x(t_1) + y(t_1)] \tag{4.4-7}$$

is computed from

$$E[w(t_1)] = \overline{w(t_1)} = \frac{1}{\sqrt{2\pi\phi_0}} \int_{-\infty}^{\infty} F[x + y(t_1)]e^{-x^2/2\phi_0}\, dx \tag{4.4-8}$$

since $y(t_1)$ is a fixed function.

It is noted that in general $\overline{w(t_1)} \neq F[y(t_1)]$. For the case in which F possesses a continuous second derivative and in which the mean-squared value of $x(t)$ is small, $w(t)$ may be found approximately by writing

$$F[x + y(t)] \cong F[y(t)] + xF'[y(t)] + \frac{x^2}{2} F''[y(t)] \tag{4.4-9}$$

Substitution of this expression into (4.4-8) gives

$$\overline{w(t_1)} \cong F[y(t_1)] \frac{1}{\sqrt{2\pi\phi_0}} \int_{-\infty}^{\infty} e^{-x^2/2\phi_0}\, dx + F'[y(t_1)] \frac{1}{\sqrt{2\pi\phi_0}} \int_{-\infty}^{\infty} xe^{-x^2/2\phi_0}\, dx$$
$$+ \frac{1}{2} F''[y(t_1)] \frac{1}{\sqrt{2\pi\phi_0}} \int_{-\infty}^{\infty} x^2 e^{-x^2/2\phi_0}\, dx$$
$$= F[y(t_1)] + \tfrac{1}{2}\phi_0 F''[y(t_1)] \tag{4.4-10}$$

The change in the mean value of the output caused by the presence of the random process $\{x(t)\}$ is thus approximately

$$\overline{w(t)} - F[y(t)] = \tfrac{1}{2}\phi_{xx}(t,t)F''[y(t)] \tag{4.4-11}$$

The correlation function of the output $\phi_{ww}(t_1,t_2)$ is computed as the average value of the product of the two random variables

$$w(t_1) = F[x(t_1) + y(t_1)] \tag{4.4-12}$$

and

$$w(t_2) = F[x(t_2) + y(t_2)] \tag{4.4-13}$$

Writing $x_1 = x(t_1)$, $x_2 = x(t_2)$, the second probability density function of x is given by (4.2-3) and (4.2-6). Again, since y is a fixed function, we compute $\phi_{ww}(t_1,t_2)$ by forming the average with respect to x_1 and x_2 according to the relation

$$\phi_{ww}(t_1,t_2) = E[w(t_1)w(t_2)]$$

$$= \frac{1}{2\pi \sqrt{\phi_{11}\phi_{22} - \phi_{12}^2}}$$

$$\times \int_{-\infty}^{\infty} dx_1 \int_{-\infty}^{\infty} dx_2 \, F[x_1 + y(t_1)]F[x_2 + y(t_2)]$$

$$\times \exp\left[-\frac{1}{2(\phi_{11}\phi_{22} - \phi_{12}^2)}(\phi_{22}x_1^2 - 2\phi_{12}x_1x_2 + \phi_{11}x_2^2)\right] \quad (4.4\text{-}14)$$

In general the evaluation of integrals of the form (4.4-14) by purely analytical means is quite difficult, although a few important cases have been carried out. By analogue or numerical techniques the evaluation is entirely feasible although fairly tedious. To simplify the calculation, it is convenient first to employ a change of variables to reduce the exponent in the integrand to a standardized form. Writing

$$u_1 = \sqrt{\frac{\phi_{22}}{2(\phi_{11}\phi_{22} - \phi_{12}^2)}} \, x_1 \quad (4.4\text{-}15)$$

$$u_2 = \sqrt{\frac{\phi_{11}}{2(\phi_{11}\phi_{22} - \phi_{12}^2)}} \, x_2 \quad (4.4\text{-}16)$$

and
$$c^2 = \frac{\phi_{12}^2}{\phi_{11}\phi_{22}} \quad (4.4\text{-}17)$$

we find

$$\phi_{ww}(t_1,t_2) = \frac{\sqrt{1 - c^2}}{\pi} \int_{-\infty}^{\infty} du_1 \int_{-\infty}^{\infty} du_2 \, e^{-(u_1^2 - 2cu_1u_2 + u_2^2)}$$

$$\times F[u_1\sqrt{2\phi_{11}(1 - c^2)} + y(t_1)]F[u_2\sqrt{2\phi_{22}(1 - c^2)} + y(t_2)] \quad (4.4\text{-}18)$$

Since $c^2 \leq 1$, we may write, for later convenience,

$$c = -\cos\alpha \quad (4.4\text{-}19)$$

where α is an angle between 0 and π.

1. *The Rectifier with* $y(t) = 0$. With $F(z)$ defined by Eq. (4.4-3) and with only the random process $\{x(t)\}$ considered, we have from, Eq. (4.4-18),

$$\phi_{ww}(t_1,t_2) = \frac{2}{\pi} \sqrt{\phi_{11}\phi_{22}} (1 - c^2)^{3/2} \int_{-\infty}^{\infty} du_1 \int_{-\infty}^{\infty} du_2 \, |u_1u_2|$$

$$\times e^{-(u_1^2 - 2cu_1u_2 + u_2^2)} \quad (4.4\text{-}20)$$

Evaluating the double integral over each of the four quadrants separately, we readily find

$$\int_{-\infty}^{\infty} du_1 \int_{-\infty}^{\infty} du_2 \, |u_1 u_2| e^{-(u_1{}^2 - 2cu_1u_2 + u_2{}^2)}$$
$$= 2 \int_0^{\infty} du_1 \int_0^{\infty} du_2 \, u_1 u_2 e^{-(u_1{}^2 - 2cu_1u_2 + u_2{}^2)}$$
$$+ 2 \int_0^{\infty} du_1 \int_0^{\infty} du_2 \, u_1 u_2 e^{-(u_1{}^2 + 2cu_1u_2 + u_2{}^2)}$$

Expressions for integrals of this form are derived in Appendix A. Using the notation of the Appendix we have

$$\phi_{ww}(t_1, t_2) = \frac{4}{\pi} \sqrt{\phi_{11}\phi_{22}} \, (1 - c^2)^{3/2}[I_{11}(\alpha) + I_{11}(\pi - \alpha)] \quad (4.4\text{-}21)$$

From Eq. (A-14), we obtain

$$I_{11}(\alpha) + I_{11}(\pi - \alpha) = \frac{\csc^2 \alpha}{4} (2 - 2\alpha \cot \alpha + \pi \cot \alpha) \quad (4.4\text{-}22)$$

and the substitution of Eq. (4.4-19) gives

$$\phi_{ww}(t_1, t_2) = \frac{2}{\pi} \sqrt{\phi_{11}\phi_{22}} \left[\sqrt{1 - c^2} + c \cos^{-1}(-c) - \frac{\pi}{2} c \right]$$
$$= \frac{2}{\pi} \left\{ \sqrt{\phi_{xx}(t_1, t^1)\phi_{xx}(t_2, t_2) - \phi_{xx}(t_1, t_2)^2} \right.$$
$$\left. + \phi_{xx}(t_1, t_2) \cos^{-1}\left[-\frac{\phi_{xx}(t_1, t_2)}{\sqrt{\phi_{xx}(t_1, t_1)\phi_{xx}(t_2, t_2)}} \right] - \frac{\pi}{2} \phi_{xx}(t_1, t_2) \right\} \quad (4.4\text{-}23)$$

If $\{x(t)\}$ is a stationary Gaussian process, this result is further simplified to give

$$\phi_{ww}(\tau) = \frac{2}{\pi} \left\{ \sqrt{\phi_{xx}(0)^2 - \phi_{xx}(\tau)^2} \right.$$
$$\left. + \phi_{xx}(\tau) \cos^{-1}\left[-\frac{\phi_{xx}(\tau)}{\phi_{xx}(0)} \right] - \frac{\pi}{2} \phi_{xx}(\tau) \right\} \quad (4.4\text{-}24)$$

From Eq. (4.4-8) we also have

$$\overline{w(t)} = \frac{1}{\sqrt{2\pi\phi_0}} \int_{-\infty}^{\infty} |x| e^{-x^2/2\phi_0} \, dx$$
$$= \sqrt{\frac{\pi}{2} \phi_0} = \sqrt{\frac{\pi}{2}} \, (\text{rms}) x(t) \quad (4.4\text{-}25)$$

Hence for a stationary Gaussian process, the d-c portion of the rectifier output is a direct measure of the rms input.

2. *The Square-law Device.* When $F(z)$ is defined by Eq. (4.4-2) and $y(t) = 0$, the analysis is similar to that given above. We obtain

$$\phi_{ww}(t_1, t_2) = \frac{8}{\pi} \phi_{11}\phi_{22}(1 - c^2)^{3/2}[I_{22}(\alpha) + I_{22}(\pi - \alpha)]$$
$$= \phi_{11}\phi_{22}(1 + 2c^2)$$
$$= \phi_{xx}(t_1, t_1)\phi_{xx}(t_2, t_2) + 2\phi_{xx}(t_1, t_2)^2 \quad (4.4\text{-}26)$$

For $y(t) \neq 0$, the problem is somewhat complicated algebraically but can be treated by a straightforward application of the same ideas. From (4.4-18) we have

$$\phi_{ww}(t_1,t_2) = \frac{\sqrt{1-c^2}}{\pi} \int_{-\infty}^{\infty} du_1 \int_{-\infty}^{\infty} du_2 \, e^{-(u_1{}^2 - 2cu_1u_2 + u_2{}^2)}$$
$$\times \{[2\phi_{11}(1-c^2)u_1^2 + 2y_1\sqrt{2\phi_{11}(1-c^2)}\,u_1 + y_1^2]$$
$$\times [2\phi_{22}(1-c^2)u_2^2 + 2y_2\sqrt{2\phi_{22}(1-c^2)}\,u_2 + y_2^2]\} \quad (4.4\text{-}27)$$

where $y_1 = y(t_1)$, $y_2 = y(t_2)$. Taking into account the relation

$$\int_{-\infty}^{\infty} du_1 \int_{-\infty}^{\infty} du_2 \, u_1^m u_2^n e^{-(u_1{}^2 - 2cu_1u_2 + u_2{}^2)} = 0 \qquad m+n \text{ odd} \quad (4.4\text{-}28)$$

we find

$$\phi_{ww}(t_1,t_2) = \frac{\sqrt{1-c^2}}{\pi} \int_{-\infty}^{\infty} du_1 \int_{-\infty}^{\infty} du_2 \, e^{-(u_1{}^2 - 2cu_1u_2 - {}_2{}^2)}$$
$$\times [4\phi_{11}\phi_{22}(1-c^2)^2 u_1^2 u_2^2 + 2\phi_{11}(1-c^2)y_2^2 u_1^2$$
$$+ 2\phi_{22}(1-c^2)y_1^2 u_2^2 + 8(1-c^2)\sqrt{\phi_{11}\phi_{22}}\,y_1 y_2 u_1 u_2 + y_1^2 y_2^2]$$
$$= 2\frac{\sqrt{1-c^2}}{\pi} \{4\phi_{11}\phi_{22}(1-c^2)^2[I_{22}(\alpha) + I_{22}(\pi - \alpha)]$$
$$+ 2\phi_{11}(1-c^2)y_2^2[I_{02}(\alpha) + I_{02}(\pi - \alpha)]$$
$$+ 2\phi_{22}(1-c^2)y_1^2[I_{02}(\alpha) + I_{02}(\pi - \alpha)]$$
$$+ 8(1-c^2)\sqrt{\phi_{11}\phi_{22}}\,y_1 y_2[I_{11}(\alpha) - I_{11}(\pi - \alpha)]$$
$$+ y_1^2 y_2^2[I_{00}(\alpha) + I_{00}(\pi - \alpha)]\} \quad (4.4\text{-}29)$$

No attempt is made here to carry this process further analytically; clearly the result is adaptable to numerical computation.

3. *The Limiter with $y(t) = 0$.* The case for which $F(z)$ is defined by Eq. (4.4-4) cannot be readily treated by the method used in the previous examples. We resort instead to a rather interesting technique which is applicable to a wide variety of problems.

The function $F(z)$, as defined in (4.4-4), may be expressed in analytical form as

$$F(z) = \frac{2}{\pi} \int_0^{\infty} \sin zu \, \sin au \, \frac{du}{u^2} \quad (4.4\text{-}30)$$

(This expression is found in standard tables of integrals.) With $y(t) = 0$ we compute the correlation function of the output of the limiter as

$$\phi_{ww}(t_1,t_2) = E[F\{x(t_1)\}F\{x(t_2)\}]$$
$$= \frac{4}{\pi^2} \int_0^{\infty}\int_0^{\infty} E[\sin x_1 u \, \sin x_2 v]\frac{\sin au \, \sin av}{u^2 v^2} \, du \, dv \quad (4.4\text{-}31)$$

Now

$$E[\sin x_1 u \sin x_2 v] = E\left[\frac{e^{jux_1} - e^{-jux_1}}{2j} \frac{e^{jvx_2} - e^{-jvx_2}}{2j}\right]$$

$$= \frac{1}{4} E[e^{j(ux_1 - vx_2)} + e^{j(vx_2 - ux_1)} - e^{j(ux_1 + vx_2)} - e^{-j(ux_1 + vx_2)}]$$

$$= \frac{1}{2} e^{-(\phi_{11}u^2 - 2\phi_{12}uv + \phi_{22}v^2)/2} - \frac{1}{2} e^{-(\phi_{11}u^2 + 2\phi_{12}uv + \phi_{22}v^2)/2}$$

$$= e^{-(\phi_{11}u^2 + \phi_{22}v^2)/2} \frac{e^{\phi_{12}uv} - e^{-\phi_{12}uv}}{2}$$

$$= e^{-(\phi_{11}u^2 + \phi_{22}v^2)/2} \sinh \phi_{12}uv \qquad (4.4\text{-}32)$$

Substituting (4.4-32) into (4.4-31), there results

$$\phi_{ww}(t_1, t_2)$$

$$= \frac{4}{\pi^2} \int_0^\infty \int_0^\infty e^{-(\phi_{11}u^2 + \phi_{22}v^2)/2} \sinh \phi_{12}uv \frac{\sin au \sin av}{u^2 v^2} \, du \, dv \qquad (4.4\text{-}33)$$

In order to carry the computation further, we use the expansion

$$\sinh \phi_{12}uv = \sum_{n=0}^\infty \frac{(\phi_{12}uv)^{2n+1}}{(2n+1)!} \qquad (4.4\text{-}34)$$

in Eq. (4.4-33) and interchange the order of summation and integration to obtain

$$\phi_{ww}(t_1, t_2) = \frac{4}{\pi^2} \sum_{n=0}^\infty \frac{\phi_{12}^{2n+1}}{(2n+1)!} \int_0^\infty u^{2n-1} e^{-\phi_{11}u^2/2} \sin au \, du$$

$$\times \int_0^\infty v^{2n-1} e^{-\phi_{22}v^2/2} \sin av \, dv$$

$$= \sum_{n=0}^\infty \frac{\phi_{12}^{2n+1}}{(2n+1)!} h_n(\phi_{11}) h_n(\phi_{22}) \qquad (4.4\text{-}35)$$

where

$$h_n(\phi) = \frac{2}{\pi} \int_0^\infty u^{2n-1} e^{-\phi u^2/2} \sin au \, du \qquad (4.4\text{-}36)$$

To evaluate this integral, we use a standard table of integrals to obtain

$$\int_0^\infty e^{-\phi u^2/2} \cos au \, du = \sqrt{\frac{\pi}{2\phi}} e^{-a^2/2\phi} \qquad (4.4\text{-}37)$$

Then

$$h_0(\phi) = \sqrt{\frac{2}{\pi\phi}} \int_0^a e^{-\alpha^2/2\phi} \, d\alpha \qquad (4.4\text{-}38)$$

and

$$h_n(\phi) = (-1)^n \sqrt{\frac{2}{\pi\phi}} \frac{d^{2n-1}}{da^{2n-1}} e^{-a^2/2\phi} \qquad n = 1, 2, \ldots \qquad (4.4\text{-}39)$$

The quantities $h_n(\phi)$ may be expressed in terms of the Hermite polynomials which are defined by

$$H_n(s) = (-1)^n e^{s^2} \frac{d^n e^{-s^2}}{ds^n} \tag{4.4-40}$$

Taking $s = a/\sqrt{2\phi}$, we obtain

$$h_n(\phi) = (-1)^{n-1} \frac{2}{\sqrt{\pi}} (2\phi)^{-n} e^{-a^2/2\phi} H_{2n-1}\left(\frac{a}{\sqrt{2\phi}}\right) \qquad n = 1, 2, \ldots \tag{4.4-41}$$

Substituting Eqs. (4.4-38) and (4.4-41) into Eq. (4.4-35), there results

$$\phi_{ww}(t_1,t_2) = \frac{2}{\pi} \rho \int_0^a e^{-\alpha^2/2\phi_{11}} \, d\alpha \int_0^a e^{-\alpha^2/2\phi_{22}} \, d\alpha + \frac{4}{\pi} \phi_{12} e^{-a^2(1/\phi_{11}+1/\phi_{22})/2}$$

$$\times \sum_{n=1}^{\infty} \frac{(\rho/2)^{2n}}{(2n+1)!} H_{2n-1}\left(\frac{a}{\sqrt{2\phi_{11}}}\right) H_{2n-1}\left(\frac{a}{\sqrt{2\phi_{22}}}\right) \tag{4.4-42}$$

where ρ is the correlation coefficient defined by

$$\rho = \frac{\phi_{12}}{\sqrt{\phi_{11}\phi_{22}}} \tag{4.4-43}$$

If we allow a to become infinite, then in the limit the function $F(z)$ is linear and we would expect such a device to pass the signal unchanged; i.e., the correlation function of the output should equal the correlation function of the input. To verify that the expression for the output correlation function has these properties, we observe that

$$\lim_{a \to \infty} \phi_{ww}(t_1,t_2) = \frac{2}{\pi} \rho \int_0^{\infty} e^{-\alpha^2/2\phi_{11}} \, d\alpha \int_0^{\infty} e^{-\alpha^2/2\phi_{22}} \, d\alpha$$

$$= \frac{2}{\pi} \rho \sqrt{\frac{\pi\phi_{11}}{2}} \sqrt{\frac{\pi\phi_{22}}{2}} = \phi_{12} = \phi_{xx}(t_1,t_2) \tag{4.4-44}$$

The special case in which the input noise has stationary characteristics is treated in detail in Appendix B. In Appendix B the function $\phi_{ww}(\tau)/\phi_0$ is tabulated for values of $\rho(\tau)$ and $a/\sqrt{\phi_0}$.

The method of analysis used above may be applied, in general, to any system for which the function $F(z)$ may be expressed as

$$F(z) = \int_{-\infty}^{\infty} q(u)e^{izu} \, du \tag{4.4-45}$$

The procedure is as follows.

With $z(t) = x(t) + y(t)$, the output correlation function of the non-linear device defined by Eq. (4.4-45) is obtained as

$$\phi_{ww}(t_1,t_2) = E[F(x_1 + y_1)F(x_2 + y_2)]$$

$$= \int_{-\infty}^{\infty} du \int_{-\infty}^{\infty} dv \, q(u)q(v)e^{j(y_1u+y_2v)} E[e^{j(x_1u+x_2v)}]$$

$$= \int_{-\infty}^{\infty} du \int_{-\infty}^{\infty} dv \, q(u)q(v)e^{j(y_1u+y_2v)} e^{-(\phi_{11}u^2+2\phi_{12}uv+\phi_{22}v^2)/2} \tag{4.4-46}$$

This is the basic formula from which we may proceed in any particular case.

The case for which

$$F(z) = \cos z \tag{4.4-47}$$

may be treated in a somewhat similar manner. For if we write

$$F(z) = \frac{e^{jz} + e^{-jz}}{2} \tag{4.4-48}$$

the output correlation function is simply

$$\phi_{ww}(t_1,t_2) = \tfrac{1}{4}E[(e^{j(x_1+y_1)} + e^{-j(x_1+y_1)})(e^{j(x_2+y_2)} + e^{-j(x_2+y_2)})]$$
$$= \tfrac{1}{2}e^{-(\phi_{11}+\phi_{22})/2}[e^{-\phi_{12}} \cos{(y_1 + y_2)} + e^{\phi_{12}} \cos{(y_1 - y_2)}] \tag{4.4-49}$$

This method is of course applicable for any system for which

$$F(z) = \sum_{n=-\infty}^{\infty} a_n e^{jnz} \tag{4.4-50}$$

Equation (4.4-50) is the series analogue of Eq. (4.4-45). The usefulness of this approach lies in the fact that simple trigonometric series can often give reasonable numerical approximations to functions for which a precise analysis of the type carried out above would be most difficult. The results must of course be interpreted with due regard for the regions in which they are valid.

By way of illustration, let

$$F(z) = \sum_{n=1}^{\infty} a_n \sin n\omega z \tag{4.4-51}$$

and assume $y(t) = 0$. Then

$$E[F\{x(t_1)\}F\{x(t_2)\}] = \sum_{m=1}^{\infty} \sum_{n=1}^{\infty} a_m a_n E[\sin m\omega x(t_1) \sin n\omega x(t_2)]$$

Noting that

$$\sin m\omega x_1 \sin n\omega x_2 = -\tfrac{1}{4}(e^{j(m\omega x_1+n\omega x_2)} - e^{j(m\omega x_1-n\omega x_2)}$$
$$- e^{j(-m\omega x_1+n\omega x_2)} + e^{j(-m\omega x_1-n\omega x_2)})$$

we find

$$E[\sin m\omega x_1 \sin n\omega x_2] = e^{-\omega^2(m^2\phi_{11}+n^2\phi_{22})/2} \sinh \omega^2 mn\phi_{12}$$

Thus

$$\phi_{ww}(t_1,t_2) = \sum_{m=1}^{\infty} \sum_{n=1}^{\infty} a_m a_n \exp\left[-\frac{\omega^2(m^2\phi_{11} + n^2\phi_{22})}{2}\right] \sinh \omega^2 mn\phi_{12}$$

$$\tag{4.4-52}$$

4. *An Approximate Limiter.* In the light of the above discussion we reconsider the limiter problem. The function

$$F(z) = \frac{a}{32}\left(38 \sin \frac{z}{2a} + 7 \sin \frac{3z}{2a} + \sin \frac{5z}{2a}\right) \qquad (4.4\text{-}53)$$

is shown in Fig. 4.4-1. It is of course an odd periodic function with a period of $4\pi a$. Over the interval $-4a < z < 4a$ it behaves as an approximate limiter, with a gradual rather than abrupt transition to the limiting

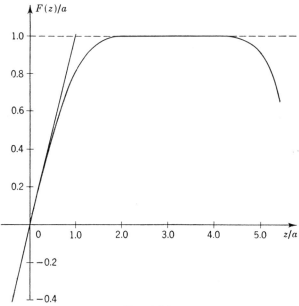

FIG. 4.4-1

value. For many physical limiting devices this gradual transition is more typical than the sharp transition shown by the limiter previously studied. The limiter described by Eq. (4.4-53) thus has an independent interest. Because of the periodicity of (4.4-53), this expression can be used to study the limiter only when ϕ_0 is reasonably small. Tables I and II of Appendix B give numerical values of $\phi_{ww}(\tau)/\phi_{xx}(0)$ for the two limiters studied.

4.5 Analysis of an Automatic Tracking System

Let us consider the following problem in the design of an automatic radar tracking system. In simplified form, the problem may be presented as follows. We are required to construct a servo system which is to follow one of several typical signals $y_1(t), \ldots, y_n(t)$, in the presence of a superimposed interference $\{x(t)\}$ which we postulate to be a

Gaussian random process.   Letting $z(t)$ be the servo output, we say that we have "lost the target" whenever the difference $z(t) - y(t)$ exceeds a preassigned (constant or variable) bound $a(t)$.   Our problem is to compute the average number of "losses" over a designated time interval $(t_1 \leqq t \leqq t_2)$, as a performance index of the system.   We do this in the hope that by trial-and-error adjustments in the servo parameters we can minimize this performance index.   We postulate the servo to be linear.

In terms of a block diagram, the problem may be represented by Fig. 4.5-1.   The tracking error $\epsilon(t)$ is the quantity which primarily determines

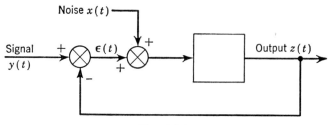

FIG. 4.5-1

the fact that we have lost the target; we require that

$$-a(t) < \epsilon(t) < a(t) \tag{4.5-1}$$

for tracking to continue.

By virtue of the assumed linearity of the system, we can represent $\epsilon(t)$ as the sum of two terms arising from the independent action of the signal and noise.   Let $\epsilon_d(t)$ be the dynamic lag in tracking the signal in the absence of noise and $\epsilon_n(t)$ the value of ϵ arising from noise by itself.   Then

$$\epsilon(t) = \epsilon_d(t) + \epsilon_n(t) \tag{4.5-2}$$

and the inequalities (4.5-1) may be written in the form

$$-a(t) - \epsilon_d(t) < \epsilon_n(t) < a(t) - \epsilon_d(t) \tag{4.5-3}$$

We suppose in the following that, for a specified tracking system and signal, the dynamic lag can be computed satisfactorily by simulation or other appropriate means.   Since our concern here is primarily with the statistical aspects of the problem, we therefore rewrite (4.5-3) in the form

$$-a_1(t) < \epsilon_n(t) < a_2(t) \tag{4.5-4}$$

where $a_1(t)$ and $a_2(t)$ are regarded as known functions.   Further, since the system is linear and the noise $\{x(t)\}$ is Gaussian, it follows that $\{\epsilon_n(t)\}$ is a Gaussian random process.   By techniques to be discussed in Chaps. 5 and 6, we can readily compute the correlation function of ϵ_n from a knowledge of the correlation function of $x(t)$ and the response characteristics of a linear system.   For present purposes we therefore make the additional assumption that the correlation function of ϵ_n is known. For typographical reasons, we write

$$w(t) = \epsilon_n(t) \tag{4.5-5}$$

in all subsequent calculations.

By means of these somewhat arbitrary steps, we have reduced the problem to the following form: We are given a Gaussian random process $\{w(t)\}$ with a known correlation function, together with two known functions $a_1(t)$ and $a_2(t)$. Over a specified time interval $t_1 \leqq t \leqq t_2$, we say that the target is "lost" at time t whenever either

$$\begin{aligned} w(t) &= -a_1(t) \\ w'(t) &\leqq -a_1'(t) \end{aligned} \tag{4.5-6}$$

or

$$\begin{aligned} w(t) &= a_2(t) \\ w'(t) &\geqq a_2'(t) \end{aligned} \tag{4.5-7}$$

The conditions on the derivatives of w, a_1, and a_2 ensure that we count only those crossings by w of the curves $-a_1$ and a_2 in which w is passing from the inside to the outside of the interval

$$-a_1(t) < w(t) < a_2(t) \tag{4.5-8}$$

We then define the performance index of the system to be the average number of such losses occurring in the interval $t_1 \leqq t \leqq t_2$.

In many respects this performance index is unrealistic; in fact, the only positive claim that can be made is that it may be somewhat more realistic than other performance indices related to mean-squared errors. In the first place, there is no sharply defined physical boundary corresponding to our function $a(t)$ of (4.5-1). In the second place, a physical radar is quite nonlinear in its behavior for large tracking errors, and it is precisely this region in which our interest is centered. Finally, in computing the expected or average number of losses in a stated time interval, we are ignoring the fact that there is relatively little likelihood of regaining the target after the first loss. A more realistic performance index would be the "probability that one or more losses (in the above sense) would occur in the stated time interval." Unfortunately, existing techniques do not seem to permit this computation. In spite of these objections, however, the expected number of losses still provides a reasonable design criterion if used with a certain amount of engineering judgment.

To compute the expectation of losses, let an arbitrary point t_0 be designated, and let

$$p_1(t_0)\, dt = \text{Pr } [w(t) = -a_1(t); w'(t) \leqq -a_1'(t); t_0 \leqq t \leqq t_0 + dt] \tag{4.5-9}$$
$$p_2(t_0)\, dt = \text{Pr } [w(t) = a_2(t); w'(t) \geqq a_2'(t); t_0 \leqq t \leqq t_0 + dt] \tag{4.5-10}$$

Denoting by $N(t_1,t_2)$ the number of losses incurred during the time interval $t_1 \leq t \leq t_2$, we have

$$\overline{N(t_1,t_2)} = \int_{t_1}^{t_2} [p_1(t) + p_2(t)] \, dt \qquad (4.5\text{-}11)$$

In order to calculate $p_1(t)$ and $p_2(t)$, let

$$u(t) = w'(t) = \frac{dw(t)}{dt} \qquad (4.5\text{-}12)$$

and let the joint probability distribution of $w(t_1)$ and $u(t_2)$ be specified by the density function $f(w,t_1; u,t_2)$. Considering first the calculation of p_2, let u_0 be an arbitrary number such that $u_0 > a_2'(t)$. The function $w(t)$ will cross $a_2(t)$ with slope u_0 in the interval $t_0 \leq t \leq t_0 + dt$ if and only if

$$a_2(t_0) - [u_0 - a_2'(t_0)] \, dt \leq w(t_0) \leq a_2(t_0) \qquad (4.5\text{-}13)$$

as may be seen from Fig. 4.5-2.

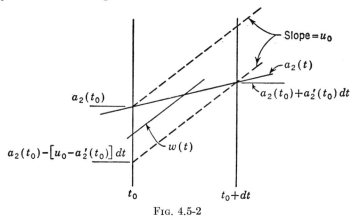

$$\text{Slope} = u_0$$
$$a_2(t)$$
$$a_2(t_0)$$
$$a_2(t_0) + a_2'(t_0)\, dt$$
$$a_2(t_0) - [u_0 - a_2'(t_0)]\, dt$$
$$w(t)$$
$$t_0 \qquad t_0 + dt$$

Fig. 4.5-2

In terms of the joint density function, we have[1]

$$\Pr \{a_2(t_0) - [u_0 - a_2'(t_0)] \, dt \leq w(t_0) \leq a_2(t_0); \; u_0 \leq u(t_0) \leq u_0 + du\}$$
$$= f[a_2(t_0), t_0; u_0, t_0][u_0 - a_2'(t_0)] \, dt \, du \quad (4.5\text{-}14)$$

This quantity, however, is precisely the probability of a crossing with a slope lying between u_0 and $u_0 + du$. The probability of a crossing with any slope whatever in excess of $a_2'(t_0)$ is then given by

$$dt \int_{a_2'(t_0)}^{\infty} f[a_2(t_0), t_0; u, t_0][u - a_2'(t_0)] \, du$$

[1] Observe that

$$\Pr (x - \Delta x \leq X \leq x) = \int_{x - \Delta x}^{x} f(u) \, du \cong f(x) \, \Delta x$$

Since $p_2(t_0)\, dt$ is by definition equal to this same probability, we find

$$p_2(t) = \int_{a_2'(t)}^{\infty} f[a_2(t),t;\, u,t][u - a_2'(t)]\, du \qquad (4.5\text{-}15)$$

A similar calculation gives

$$p_1(t) = -\int_{-\infty}^{-a_1'(t)} f[-a_1(t),t;\, u,t][u + a_1'(t)]\, du \qquad (4.5\text{-}16)$$

We thus find

$$\overline{N(t_1,t_2)} = \int_{t_1}^{t_2}\left[\int_{a_2'}^{\infty} f(a_2,t;\, u,t)(u - a_2')\, du\right.$$
$$\left. -\int_{-\infty}^{-a_1'} f(-a_1,t;\, u,t)(u + a_1')\, du\right] dt \qquad (4.5\text{-}17)$$

To relate this expression explicitly to the correlation function of $w(t)$, we compute the joint density function $f(w,t_1;\, u,t_2)$. Since the process is Gaussian, w and u possess a joint normal distribution with zero mean. From Eq. (4.2-6) it follows that

$$f(w,t_1;\, u,t_2) = \frac{1}{2\pi q}\exp\left\{-\frac{1}{2q^2}[\phi_{ww}(t_1,t_1)u^2 - 2\phi_{wu}(t_1,t_2)wu + \phi_{uu}(t_2,t_2)w^2]\right\}$$
$$(4.5\text{-}18)$$

where
$$q^2 = \phi_{ww}(t_1,t_1)\phi_{uu}(t_2,t_2) - \phi_{wu}(t_2,t_2)^2 \qquad (4.5\text{-}19)$$

In Example 3.4-1 it was shown that

$$\phi_{wu}(t_1,t_2) = \frac{\partial}{\partial t_2}\phi_{ww}(t_1,t_2) \qquad (4.5\text{-}20)$$

$$\phi_{uu}(t_1,t_2) = \frac{\partial^2}{\partial t_1\,\partial t_2}\phi_{ww}(t_1,t_2) \qquad (4.5\text{-}21)$$

so that all correlation functions are expressible in terms of $\phi_{ww}(t_1,t_2)$ and its partial derivatives. To simplify further calculations, we let

$$A(t) = \phi_{ww}(t,t) \qquad (4.5\text{-}22)$$
$$B(t) = \phi_{wu}(t,t) \qquad (4.5\text{-}23)$$
$$C(t) = \phi_{uu}(t,t) \qquad (4.5\text{-}24)$$

Then
$$f(a_2,t;\, u,t) = \frac{1}{2\pi q}\exp\left(-\frac{Ca_2^2 - 2Ba_2u + Au^2}{2q^2}\right) \qquad (4.5\text{-}25)$$

and
$$f(-a_1,t;\, u,t) = \frac{1}{2\pi q}\exp\left(-\frac{Ca_1^2 + 2Ba_1u + Au^2}{2q^2}\right) \qquad (4.5\text{-}26)$$

where
$$q^2 = AC - B^2 \qquad (4.5\text{-}27)$$

By some tedious but reasonably direct algebraic manipulations, we find

$$\int_{a_2'}^{\infty} (u - a_2')f(a_2,t;\, u,t)\, du$$
$$= \frac{\sqrt{AC - B^2}}{\pi A}e^{-a_2^2/2A}F\left[\frac{Ba_2 - Aa_2'}{\sqrt{2A(AC - B^2)}}\right] \qquad (4.5\text{-}28)$$

and $\quad -\displaystyle\int_{-\infty}^{-a_1'} (u + a_1')f(-a_1,t;\, u,t)\, du$

$$= \frac{\sqrt{AC - B^2}}{\pi A} e^{-a_1^2/2A} F\left[\frac{Ba_1 - Aa_1'}{\sqrt{2A(AC - B^2)}}\right] \quad (4.5\text{-}29)$$

where $\qquad F(x) = \displaystyle\int_0^\infty z e^{-(z-x)^2}\, dz \qquad (4.5\text{-}30)$

Thus the expectation of the number of losses may be expressed, from (4.5-17), in the form

$$\overline{N(t_1,t_2)} = \int_{t_1}^{t_2} \left\{ e^{-a_1^2/2A} F\left[\frac{Ba_1 - Aa_1'}{\sqrt{2A(AC - B^2)}}\right] \right.$$
$$\left. + e^{-a_2^2/2A} F\left[\frac{Ba_2 - Aa_2'}{\sqrt{2A(AC - B^2)}}\right] \right\} \frac{\sqrt{AC - B^2}}{\pi A}\, dt \quad (4.5\text{-}31)$$

where A, B, C, a_1, a_2, a_1', and a_2' are functions of time that can be calculated.

The evaluation of this expression for the nonstationary case wherein A, B, and C are variable is a task that would be difficult but possible in isolated cases. For the stationary case, however, considerable simplification is possible. Since

$$\phi_{ww}(t_1,t_2) = \phi_{ww}(t_2 - t_1) \quad (4.5\text{-}32)$$

we find, from (4.5-22) to (4.5-24),

$$A = \phi_{ww}(0) = \phi_0 \quad (4.5\text{-}33)$$
$$B = \phi_{ww}'(0) = 0 \quad (4.5\text{-}34)$$
$$C = -\phi_{ww}''(0) = -\phi_2 \quad (4.5\text{-}35)$$

The second of these relations follows from the fact that $\phi_{ww}(\tau)$ is an even function; also we have $\phi_2 < 0$ so that $AC = -\phi_0\phi_2 > 0$. We then find

$$\overline{N(t_1,t_2)} = \frac{1}{\pi}\sqrt{-\frac{\phi_2}{\phi_0}} \int_{t_1}^{t_2} \left[e^{-a_1^2/2\phi_0} F\left(\frac{-a_1'}{\sqrt{-2\phi_2}}\right) \right.$$
$$\left. + e^{-a_2^2/2\phi_0} F\left(\frac{-a_2'}{\sqrt{-2\phi_2}}\right) \right] dt \quad (4.5\text{-}36)$$

In this form, assuming knowledge of ϕ_0 and ϕ_2, an evaluation of the integral itself might be made as a simultaneous part of the tests for dynamic lag used in determining $a_1(t)$ and $a_2(t)$. It would thus be entirely practical to carry out a relatively extensive exploration of design parameters by this means, provided that the assumption of a stationary random process could be justified.

CHAPTER 5

ANALYSIS OF THE EFFECTS OF TIME-INVARIANT LINEAR SYSTEMS ON STATIONARY RANDOM PROCESSES

5.1 Filtering and Prediction

In the present chapter we give a detailed study of the application of methods of statistical analysis to a specific class of problems in automatic control. The general problem considered is that of the statistical behavior of the output of a linear time-invariant control system or filter in relation to the statistical properties of one or more random processes that may enter it as inputs. In particular, we wish to present methods for the calculation of a useful performance index for a system that gives a quantitative measure of the degree to which it is regarded as satisfactory. Applications are given to the problems of smoothing unwanted random roughness in data and also to the prediction of a future value of a random signal. Before becoming more specific, however, we wish to discuss prediction and filtering problems in a general way.

A task which both communications and control systems often must perform is to separate as well as possible a desired signal input from an extraneous signal input. Thus if $s(t)$ is a time-varying signal representing the useful information fed into a device and $q_i(t) = s(t) + n(t)$ is the total input signal, we may ask that the device yield $s(t)$ as an output. Under these circumstances we usually call $n(t)$ the *interference* or *noise* input, although it may or may not have a random character. The process described is often called *smoothing* because in many instances $n(t)$ has higher frequency components than $s(t)$, and the removal of $n(t)$ actually amounts to smoothing the graph of the signal. A classical example of this is the effect of audiofrequency filters on a rectified, modulated radio wave.

An apparently dissimilar but actually closely related task is that of predicting a future value of an input signal. Thus, if $s(t)$ is known for past values of time, we require the device to yield $s(t + \tau)$, with $\tau > 0$, as an output at time t. Such a device is a *predictor*. A more general problem comprises both smoothing and prediction; that is, the determination from $s(t) + n(t)$ of a future value, $s(t + \tau)$, for $\tau \geqq 0$.

Any filter or servomechanism transforms a set of input functions, $q_i^{(1)}(t), \ldots, q_i^{(n)}(t)$ into a set of output functions, $q_o^{(1)}(t), \ldots, q_o^{(m)}(t)$. Thus the servomechanism may be represented mathematically as an operator P (which we shall call its performance operator) which carries a set of n real-valued functions of time into a set of m real-valued functions of time. If in particular there is a single input and a single output, we may write

$$P[q_i(t)] = q_o(t) \qquad (5.1\text{-}1)$$

If P is to be an ideal smoothing and predicting operator, we have

$$P[s(t) + n(t)] = s(t + \tau) \qquad \tau \geqq 0 \qquad (5.1\text{-}2)$$

The over-all problem of designing systems to perform smoothing and prediction may conveniently be considered in two parts. First, there is the question of determining according to some criterion what the best smoothing and prediction can be and what the optimum performance operator is. Second, there is the question of realizing the desired performance operator in a workable device. These considerations are obviously not independent, but here we are especially concerned with the first.

There are certain ideas basic to any prediction and smoothing theory which need to be discussed before we become specific. We give a brief consideration of some of these in the remainder of this section. First, however, we state some simple, hypothetical smoothing and prediction problems in an effort to give a rough orientation.

1. Let $s(t)$ be known to be an analytic function, and let $n(t) = 0$. Then by the fact that an analytic function is determined uniquely by its behavior on any interval, $s(t + \tau)$ can be predicted perfectly, at least in an ideal sense.

2. Let $s(t)$ be white noise, $n(t) = 0$. Then, since white noise is completely independent of its past history, $s(t + \tau)$ cannot be predicted at all.

3. Let $s(t)$ be the distance of an airplane flying a straight-line course from a fixed observation point at time t; let $n(t) = 0$. Then since the airplane cannot accelerate at more than some fixed rate because of physical limitations, we may characterize $s(t)$ as a function with bounded second derivative. One prediction for $s(t + \tau)$ could be made on the hypothesis that the velocity is held constant. Whether or not this is the "best" prediction is obviously a meaningless question in view of the limited information given. At least, however, it might give a mean for the possible values of $s(t + \tau)$.

4. Let $s(t)$ be an audio signal and $n(t)$ be 60-cycle hum. We ask to find $s(t)$ from $s(t) + n(t)$. Since an infinitesimal amount of the audio signal power will be at exactly 60 cycles, the best "smoother" would be

an ideal filter with infinite transfer impedance to 60 cycles and zero transfer impedance to all other frequencies. This is unrealizable, but a filter
with an impedance characteristic sharply peaked at 60 cycles would be
satisfactory.

5. Let $s(t)$ be a radar-range signal, and suppose that the only interference is due to resistor noise and shot effect in the receiver. Then,
since $s(t)$ is a relatively slowly varying signal whereas $n(t)$ has a more or
less uniform frequency spectrum up to quite high frequencies, a conventional low-pass filter will eliminate much of $n(t)$ without disturbing $s(t)$.

6. Let $s(t)$ be any analytic function and $n(t)$ be any analytic function.
Then it is clearly impossible to separate $s(t)$ from $s(t) + n(t)$ at all.

In the light of such examples as these and from our intuition we can
write two fundamental principles of predicting and smoothing, which we
shall take to be axiomatic. First, no separation of $s(t)$ from $s(t) + n(t)$
is possible unless $s(t)$ and $n(t)$ have known distinguishing properties.
Second, no prediction of $s(t)$ into the future can be made unless it has some
known property which relates its past and future, at least in some statistical sense.

Let us consider first the pure prediction problem. Suppose a device
with performance operator P is intended to yield a value of $s(t_0 + \tau)$
from a knowledge of a signal $s(t)$ for all $t \leq t_0$. How could we test its
operation? The obvious experiment would be to operate the device
several times with representative input signals $s(t)$ and compute some
kind of mean or average error. It is significant that we never want such
a device to respond properly just to one signal (for then the device would
impart no information) but rather to any one of a family (probably
infinite) of signals. Clearly we can imagine cases in which two or more
signals $s(t)$ belonging to the family agree for $t \leq t_0$ but do not agree at
$t = t_0 + \tau$. Then, perfect prediction is not possible for every trial of the
experiment. Under such circumstances what do we mean by a best
prediction operator?

One consistent point of view is to regard the possible signals $s(t)$ as
being elements of a random process (ideally, with a known set of distributions) and call the best performance operator P that operator which
minimizes the average of a suitably chosen function of the prediction
error

$$\epsilon = P[s(t)] - s(t + \tau) \tag{5.1-3}$$

Thus, for example, we might define a performance index for the predictor
to be one of the quantities $\bar{\epsilon}$, $\overline{\epsilon^2}$, or $\overline{|\epsilon|}$. The first of these is generally not
appropriate, for when ϵ itself is averaged, positive and negative errors
tend to cancel even though for any particular t the magnitude of the error
may be quite large. The second and third of these do not have this

defect, and the mean-squared error in particular is commonly used because it lends itself conveniently to mathematical analysis.

For the fire-control problem in which $s(t + \tau)$ may be taken as the position of the target at time $t + \tau$ (or at least one coordinate of position) and $P[s(t)]$ the position of the shell at time $t + \tau$, the mean-squared error has the serious defect that it weighs bad misses much more heavily than near misses, which is obviously unrealistic. An alternate possibility for the performance index is the quantity $E[F(\epsilon)]$, where

$$F(\epsilon) = \begin{cases} 0 & \text{if } |\epsilon| < a \\ 1 & \text{if } |\epsilon| \geq a \end{cases} \tag{5.1-4}$$

Since $E[F(\epsilon)] = \Pr(|\epsilon| \geq a)$, it is clear that this measure of error is at least physically appropriate to the fire-control problem, although apparently too difficult to handle mathematically.

The fire-control situation suggests that the above types of performance index, in some cases at least, somewhat oversimplify the real problem. The objective of a fire-control system is to destroy a designated target, by the direction of fire by guns or other weapons. In the usual case, more than one projectile is launched, and any one of these may achieve the intended effect. If the performance index is taken to be the probability that the objective of the system is achieved, then its evaluation evidently involves consideration of the random error in more than one projectile. In the case of n shots fired in sequence, at times $t_1, t_2, \ldots, t_n$, a possible performance index might be

$$\Pr(|\epsilon(t_j)| \leq a \text{ for one or more values of } j) \qquad j = 1, 2, \ldots, n \tag{5.1-5}$$

An alternate, and somewhat more manageable, performance index would be the quantity

$$\sum_{j=1}^{n} \overline{\epsilon(t_j)^2} \tag{5.1-6}$$

Consideration of Example 2.6-2 suggests that these two indices are in no sense equivalent; in the two cases examined in the example cited, the mean-squared errors were identical and yet the quantity (5.1-5) took on two significantly different values.

In spite of these facts, limitations of mathematical technique considerably restrict the types of performance index that can be used practically. As a result, the mean-squared error is used almost exclusively in the analysis which follows, even though it is recognized as possessing serious limitations for some types of applications. Portions of the theory considered in Chap. 8 permit use of other criteria, in principle at least; however, a nontrivial case has as yet to be solved by the indicated methods.

The same general considerations apply to the problems of pure smoothing and combined smoothing and prediction if we regard $s(t)$ and $n(t)$ as belonging to random processes with known joint properties. Thus in general we wish to find that performance operator P which causes the expectation $E[F(\epsilon)]$ to be a minimum, where

$$\epsilon = P[s(t) + n(t)] - s(t + \tau) \tag{5.1-7}$$

and where $F(\epsilon)$ is a suitably defined function such as ϵ^2, $|\epsilon|$, or the function (5.1-4).

For the case in which the random process cannot be assumed stationary there exists no complete, rigorous prediction theory. There are partial theories and techniques, however, and some of these are discussed in Chaps. 6 and 8. If the random process can be taken to be stationary and ergodic then the expectation can be calculated as a time average instead of as an ensemble average. In particular, the Wiener theory of prediction calls for a minimization of

$$\lim_{T \to \infty} \frac{1}{2T} \int_{-T}^{T} \{s(t + \tau) - P[s(t) + n(t)]\}^2 \, dt \tag{5.1-8}$$

by a choice of P from a specified class of operators. If P is a linear operator, then (5.1-8) can be expressed entirely in terms of autocorrelation and cross-correlation functions. These may be regarded as the invariants of the random process which make the smoothing and prediction possible. We consider in the remainder of this chapter a class of prediction and smoothing problems in which the predicting or smoothing servomechanism is a linear time-invariant filter; the signal and noise are members of a stationary random process so that the correlation functions and spectral densities are invariants; and the criterion of error is the mean-squared value of an error signal.

It is generally harder to design a system to perform a given function in the best possible way than it is to analyze the performance of an existing system. Certain prediction techniques, notably the Wiener theory considered in Chap. 7, give a direct specification of an optimum realizable performance operator, which is then to be realized by the synthesis of a filter or servomechanism according to existing techniques. Even after the performance operator is specified the remaining job may be difficult.

In certain cases where a straightforward synthesis is impossible or is too unwieldy, the design may have to be carried out by the common engineering procedure of first making an experienced guess and then analyzing the effects of parameter changes and minor modifications. Well-organized analysis procedures and the use of machine calculations obviously extend the applicability of such methods. Thus we shall be partly concerned with material which treats really only analysis of existing systems. In particular, this chapter and the next relate almost exclusively to the analytic rather than the synthetic approach.

5.2 The Response Characteristics of Linear Systems

Let a system receive as an input a quantity $x(t)$ and produce as output a corresponding quantity $y(t)$. The system is said to be *linear*, provided that for every pair of inputs $[x_1(t), x_2(t)]$ and corresponding outputs $[y_1(t), y_2(t)]$, the input $ax_1(t) + bx_2(t)$ produces as output $ay_1(t) + by_2(t)$, where a and b are arbitrary constants. For a linear system it is thus possible to superimpose the effects produced by any number of inputs.

Passive electrical networks are usually very nearly linear (although not, of course, if they contain saturated iron-core inductors, crystal rectifiers, etc.). Networks with electronic amplifiers may operate under approximately linear conditions. Servomechanisms using hydraulic elements are likely to be appreciably nonlinear. If the parameters of a linear system are constants, then the system can generally be handled by the methods of network analysis. However, if the parameters vary with time (not with signal amplitude), then the system is still linear but its analysis is more difficult.

Most of our efforts are confined to the analysis of linear control systems or filters because at present there exist no mathematical techniques giving more than fragmentary information about nonlinear systems. For this reason most prediction and filtering theories aim, from the beginning, at finding the best possible linear operation. Another restriction that we impose on the class of admissible performance operators is that they be physically realizable. Since any physical system can respond only to inputs which it has already received in the past or present, not every operator characterizes a constructable servomechanism.

In this section we shall discuss two common methods of representing the response characteristics of linear systems, i.e., the weighting function and the transfer function. The first of these is based on an analysis of the response in the time domain and the second in the frequency domain. The two methods will be seen to be equivalent, each having its own merits for particular classes of problem.

Considering, first, the response in the time domain let a unit impulse be applied as the input to a linear system at time τ where the system is understood to be at rest prior to time τ. The output $W(t,\tau)$ depends upon time t and also upon the time τ at which the impulse is applied. The function $W(t,\tau)$ is called the *unit-impulse-response* or *weighting function* for the system. For a system describable in terms of linear ordinary differential equations with constant coefficients, or, in general, for a system with response characteristics that are independent of time of application of the input, the unit impulse response depends only upon the interval between application of the impulse and observation of the output. In other words, for such a system

$$W(t,\tau) = W(t - \tau) \tag{5.2-1}$$

More generally, however, the weighting function depends directly upon both t and τ.

The primary usefulness of the weighting function lies in the fact that it permits a convenient representation of the system output to be made in terms of the corresponding input. The input function $x(t)$ may be approximated by a set of rectangles, as shown in Fig. 5.2-1. An input which has the value $x(\tau)$ over an infinitesimal interval of length $\Delta\tau$ and is zero elsewhere may be regarded as an impulse of magnitude $x(\tau)\,\Delta\tau$.

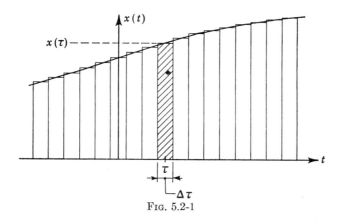

FIG. 5.2-1

The corresponding system output at time t is given by $W(t,\tau)x(\tau)\,\Delta\tau$. The actual input $x(t)$ may be regarded as being composed of a sum of functions of this type so that the general output $y(t)$ is obtained as a sum or integral of $W(t,\tau)x(\tau)\,\Delta\tau$. Thus

$$y(t) = P[x(t)] = \int_{-\infty}^{t} W(t,\tau)x(\tau)\,d\tau \tag{5.2-2}$$

The upper limit of integration indicates that only those values of $x(\tau)$ for which $\tau \leq t$ are significant in determining $y(t)$. For physically realizable systems, $W(t,\tau)$ is always zero for $t < \tau$; otherwise the system would produce an effect in advance of the corresponding cause. Therefore, the upper limit of integration may be replaced by infinity whenever convenient. The choice of negative infinity as the lower limit of integration implies that, in general, all past values of the input may influence the present value of the output.

In the special case of a constant coefficient system, Eq. (5.2-2) assumes the form of a convolution integral

$$y(t) = \int_{-\infty}^{t} W(t - \tau)x(\tau) \, d\tau \tag{5.2-3}$$

This relationship may also be written

$$y(t) = \int_{0}^{\infty} W(\tau)x(t - \tau) \, d\tau \tag{5.2-4}$$

by a change of variable. The value of y at time t is thus seen to be composed of a weighted sum (or integral) of values of x observed τ time units in the past. It is this relation which has been responsible for the name *weighting function*.

Example 5.2-1. The weighting function for the system describable by the first-order differential equation

$$T(t) \frac{dy}{dt} + y = x$$

is given by

$$W(t,\tau) = \begin{cases} \dfrac{1}{T(\tau)} \exp\left[-\int_{\tau}^{t} \dfrac{dr}{T(r)} \right] & \text{for } t > \tau \\ 0 & \text{for } t < \tau \end{cases}$$

For the case in which $T(t)$ is a constant T the weighting function reduces to

$$W(t - \tau) = \begin{cases} \dfrac{1}{T} \exp\left[-\dfrac{t - \tau}{T} \right] & \text{for } t > \tau \\ 0 & \text{for } t < \tau \end{cases}$$

and thus depends upon t and τ only through their difference.

Example 5.2-2. The weighting function for the system describable by the second-order differential equation

$$\frac{d^2 y}{dt^2} + t \frac{dy}{dt} + y = x$$

is given by

$$W(t,\tau) = \begin{cases} e^{-t^2/2} \displaystyle\int_{\tau}^{t} e^{r^2/2} \, dr & \text{for } \tau < t \\ 0 & \text{for } t < \tau \end{cases}$$

For the case in which the coefficient of dy/dt is a constant equal to 2, the weighting function becomes

$$W(t,\tau) = \begin{cases} (t - \tau)e^{-(t-\tau)} & \text{for } \tau < t \\ 0 & \text{for } \tau > t \end{cases}$$

For systems describable by differential equations of the form

$$a_0(t) \frac{d^n y}{dt^n} + a_1(t) \frac{d^{n-1} y}{dt^{n-1}} + \cdots + a_n(t)y = x \tag{5.2-5}$$

or, in a more compact notation,

$$L_t y = x \tag{5.2-6}$$

the weighting function $W(t,\tau)$ may be given either of the following equivalent interpretations: (1) for fixed τ, $W(t,\tau)$ is the solution of the equation

$$L_t W(t,\tau) = \delta(t - \tau) \tag{5.2-7}$$

for all values of t, with $W(t,\tau) = 0$ for $t < \tau$; (2) for fixed τ, $W(t,\tau)$ is the solution of the homogeneous equation

$$L_t W(t,\tau) = 0 \tag{5.2-8}$$

for all $t > \tau$, which, together with its first $n - 2$ derivatives, vanishes for $t = \tau$ but whose $(n - 1)$st derivative has the value $1/a_0(\tau)$ for $t = \tau + 0$. Equation (5.2-8) is obviously satisfied identically for $t < \tau$ for then the weighting function $W(t,\tau)$ is identically zero. Hence, we see that for fixed τ, $W(t,\tau)$ is a continuous function of t with $n - 2$ continuous derivatives. The $(n - 1)$st derivative is continuous for all t except for $t = \tau$ where it experiences a finite jump discontinuity of magnitude $1/a_0(\tau)$. (One may readily verify that the weighting functions in the two examples considered above satisfy both of the above conditions.) Thus, we may think of the weighting function as being the response of a system to a unit impulse or, equivalently, as being the solution of a homogeneous equation which satisfies certain initial conditions.

The equivalence of these two interpretations of the weighting function may be readily visualized physically by means of an analogue-computer[1] block diagram. Equation (5.2-5) may be simulated by solving for the highest derivative to obtain

$$\frac{d^n y}{dt^n} = \frac{x(t)}{a_0(t)} - \frac{a_1(t)}{a_0(t)} \frac{d^{n-1} y}{dt^{n-1}} - \cdots - \frac{a_n(t)}{a_0(t)} y \tag{5.2-9}$$

Clearly, it will require n integrators to complete the simulation, one of which will have as input the right-hand side of Eq. (5.2-9) and an output equal to $-d^{n-1}y/dt^{n-1}$. This single integrator is shown in Fig. 5.2-2.

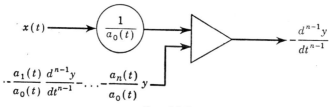

FIG. 5.2-2

Now if $x(t)$ is the unit impulse $\delta(t - \tau)$, it will appear at the input to the integrator as $\delta(t - \tau)/a_0(t)$. As soon as the pulse occurs (at time $t = \tau$), it will be integrated and immediately appear as a step function

[1] A general discussion of analogue computers is given in Appendix C.

of magnitude $1/a_0(\tau)$ on the output of the integrator at time $t = \tau$. This voltage, suddenly applied to the output of the integrator at time $t = \tau$, is entirely equivalent to an initial condition placed on this integrator at $t = \tau$ and zero initial conditions on all other integrators. Therefore, the impulse response of the system may be obtained by solving the homogeneous equation with an appropriate initial condition on the $(n - 1)$st derivative.

We may now verify explicitly that the integral (5.2-2) is the solution of the differential equation (5.2-5) by direct substitution. Using our first interpretation of the weighting function as the response to a unit impulse, we differentiate Eq. (5.2-2) with the upper limit infinite[1] to obtain

$$\frac{d^k y}{dt^k} = \int_{-\infty}^{\infty} \frac{\partial^k W(t,\tau)}{\partial t^k} x(\tau)\, d\tau \qquad k = 0, 1, \ldots, n \qquad (5.2\text{-}10)$$

Multiplying (5.2-10) by $a_{n-k}(t)$ and summing on k yields

$$L_t y = \int_{-\infty}^{\infty} L_t[W(t,\tau)]x(\tau)\, d\tau$$
$$= \int_{-\infty}^{\infty} \delta(t - \tau)x(\tau)\, d\tau = x(t) \qquad (5.2\text{-}11)$$

in agreement with (5.2-6).

Using the second interpretation of the weighting function as the solution of the homogeneous equation satisfying certain conditions at $t = \tau$, we proceed in a similar manner to compute the derivatives of Eq. (5.2-2). Thus

$$\frac{dy}{dt} = \int_{-\infty}^{t} \frac{\partial W(t,\tau)}{\partial t} x(\tau)\, d\tau + W(t,\tau)x(\tau)\bigg|_{\tau = t - 0} \qquad (5.2\text{-}12)$$

The second term vanishes because of the conditions imposed on $W(t,\tau)$ at $t = \tau$. Similarly, we establish

$$\frac{d^k y}{dt^k} = \int_{-\infty}^{t} \frac{\partial^k W(t,\tau)}{\partial t^k} x(\tau)\, d\tau \qquad k = 0, 1, \ldots, n - 1 \qquad (5.2\text{-}13)$$

For the nth derivative we have

$$\frac{d^n y}{dt^n} = \int_{-\infty}^{t} \frac{\partial^n W(t,\tau)}{\partial t^n} x(\tau)\, d\tau + \frac{\partial^{n-1} W(t,\tau)}{\partial t^{n-1}} x(\tau)\bigg|_{\tau = t - 0}$$
$$= \int_{-\infty}^{t} \frac{\partial^n W(t,\tau)}{\partial t^n} x(\tau)\, d\tau + \frac{x(t)}{a(t)} \qquad (5.2\text{-}14)$$

Again multiplying $y(t)$ and each of its derivatives by the appropriate coefficient, adding the results, and remembering that $W(t,\tau)$ is a solution

[1] Since $W(t,\tau) = 0$ for $\tau > t$, the contribution to the integral is zero for $t < \tau < \infty$.

of the homogeneous equation (5.2-8), we obtain directly the desired verification.

Systems which are activated at some finite time instant, say $t = 0$, must be treated somewhat differently. Let the input-output relation be represented by the differential equation (5.2-5). In addition to the forced response, an arbitrary transient exists which is determined by the values of y and its first $n - 1$ derivatives just prior to the instant $t = 0$. This transient may be expressed in the form[1]

$$y(0-)Y_0(t) + y'(0-)Y_1(t) + \cdots + y^{(n-1)}(0-)Y_{n-1}(t)$$

where the function $Y_k(t)$ is the solution of the homogeneous equation

$$a_0(t)\frac{d^n Y_k}{dt^n} + a_1(t)\frac{d^{n-1}Y_k}{dt^{n-1}} + \cdots + a_n(t)Y_k = 0 \qquad (5.2\text{-}15)$$

which satisfies the conditions

$$Y_k^{(m)}(0) = \begin{cases} 0 & \text{for } m \neq k \\ 1 & \text{for } m = k \end{cases} \qquad (5.2\text{-}16)$$

The general solution of Eq. (5.2-5) is then given by

$$y(t) = y(0-)Y_0(t) + \cdots + y^{(n-1)}(0-)Y_{n-1}(t) + \int_{0-}^{t} W(t,\tau)x(\tau)\,d\tau \qquad (5.2\text{-}17)$$

It is not clear that a relation of this form is satisfied except when the input and output are related by a differential equation.

A similar relation, often more conveniently applied in practice, arises when the system in question consists of a collection of interconnected integrators. Let these be labeled 1 to n, and let c_k be the initial condition on integrator k. The system output may then be expressed in the form

$$y(t) = c_1 u_1(t) + \cdots + c_n u_n(t) + \int_0^t W(t,\tau)x(\tau)\,d\tau \qquad (5.2\text{-}18)$$

where the function $u_k(t)$ is the system output for the special case in which the input $x(t)$ is zero and the initial condition is unity for integrator k and is zero for all other integrators.

The ideas developed thus far are not limited to cases involving only one system input and output. For a general linear system with inputs $x_1(t), x_2(t), \ldots, x_m(t)$ and outputs $y_1(t), y_2(t), \ldots, y_n(t)$ an equation of the following form may be written:

$$y_i(t) = \sum_{k=1}^{m} \int_{-\infty}^{t} W_{ik}(t,\tau)x_k(\tau)\,d\tau \qquad i = 1, 2, \ldots, n \qquad (5.2\text{-}19)$$

[1] The notation $y(0-)$ is to be interpreted as follows:

$$y(0-) = \lim_{\epsilon \to 0} y(0 - \epsilon)$$

The general weighting function $W_{ik}(t,\tau)$ in this relation is defined as the value of the ith output at time t obtained in response to a unit impulse applied at the kth input at time τ, with all other inputs identically equal to zero. An example of such a general system would be one satisfying the following set of simultaneous linear differential equations.

$$\frac{dy_i}{dt} = \sum_{k=1}^{n} a_{ik}(t) y_k(t) + x_i(t) \qquad i = 1, 2, \ldots, n \qquad (5.2\text{-}20)$$

The set of equations (5.2-20) may be considered as describing the performance of a system consisting of a collection of n interconnected integrators. If $x_i(t)$ and $y_i(t)$ are the respective input and output of the ith integrator, the relationship (5.2-19) holds with $m = n$. Assume now that the input to the ith integrator is a unit impulse $\delta(t - \tau)$ and that all other inputs are zero. The pulse will be integrated and immediately appear as a unit step function on the output of the ith integrator at time $t = \tau$. The other integrators will maintain a zero output the instant after the pulse is applied. Therefore, from the definition of $W_{ik}(t,\tau)$, we see that

$$W_{ik}(t,t) = \begin{cases} 0 & \text{for } i \neq k \\ 1 & \text{for } i = k \end{cases} \qquad (5.2\text{-}21)$$

In some of our work it will be convenient to consider a matrix of weighting functions

$$\mathbf{W}(t,\tau) = ||W_{ik}(t,\tau)|| \qquad (5.2\text{-}22)$$

As a matter of fact, for the system of equations (5.2–20), it is shown in Appendix F that $\mathbf{W}(t,\tau)$, as a function of t for fixed τ, is the matrix solution of the set of homogeneous equations

$$\frac{dW_{ik}(t,\tau)}{dt} = \sum_{j=1}^{n} a_{ij}(t) W_{jk}(t,\tau) \qquad (5.2\text{-}23)$$

satisfying the condition that $\mathbf{W}(t,t)$ is the identity matrix.

Most of the results developed in connection with Eq. (5.2-5) hold equally well when the forcing function x is replaced by

$$M_t x = b_0(t) \frac{d^m x}{dt^m} + b_1(t) \frac{d^{m-1} x}{dt^{m-1}} + \cdots + b_m(t) x \qquad (5.2\text{-}24)$$

where $m \leq n$. If we denote the weighting function of such a system by $W_1(t,\tau)$, we have

$$L_t W_1(t,\tau) = M_t \delta(t - \tau) \qquad (5.2\text{-}25)$$

for all values of t and for fixed τ. The solution of the equation

$$L_t y = M_t x \qquad (5.2\text{-}26)$$

may then be expressed in terms of $W_1(t,\tau)$ as

$$y(t) = \int_{-\infty}^{\infty} W_1(t,\tau) x(\tau)\, d\tau \qquad (5.2\text{-}27)$$

Also, by replacing $x(\tau)$ in Eq. (5.2-2) by the more general forcing function (5.2-24), we obtain

$$y(t) = \int_{-\infty}^{\infty} W(t,\tau) \left[b_0(\tau) \frac{d^m x}{d\tau^m} + \cdots + b_m(\tau) x(\tau) \right] d\tau \qquad (5.2\text{-}28)$$

This expression for $y(t)$ may be reduced to the form of Eq. (5.2-27) by applying successive integration by parts. The desired relationship is then

$$W_1(t,\tau) = b_m(\tau) W(t,\tau) - \frac{\partial}{\partial \tau}[b_{m-1}(\tau) W(t,\tau)]$$

$$+ \cdots + (-1)^m \frac{\partial^m}{\partial \tau^m}[b_0(\tau) W(t,\tau)]$$

$$= M_\tau^* W(t,\tau) \qquad (5.2\text{-}29)$$

The operator M_τ^* is called the adjoint of the operator M_t.

Example 5.2-3. We now illustrate these ideas for the constant-coefficient system described in Example 5.2-1.

1. The output of this system when the input is $x(t) = \sin t$ is obtained from Eq. (5.2-2). Thus,

$$y(t) = \int_{-\infty}^{t} \frac{1}{T} e^{-(t-\tau)/T} \sin \tau\, d\tau$$

$$= \frac{1}{T} e^{-t/T} \int_{-\infty}^{t} e^{\tau/T} \sin \tau\, d\tau$$

$$= \frac{T}{1 + T^2} \left(\frac{1}{T} \sin t - \cos t \right)$$

One may readily verify that this is the solution of the equation

$$T \frac{dy}{dt} + y = \sin t$$

2. If the system is unexcited prior to time $t = 0$ at which time the input $x(t) = \sin t$ is suddenly applied, and if the response $y(t)$ has the value y_0 just prior to the application of the input, the response is obtained from Eq. (5.2-17). The transient response is found from Eq. (5.2-15) subject to the conditions imposed by (5.2-16). In our case we must solve

$$T \frac{dY_0}{dt} + Y_0 = 0$$

subject to the condition that $Y_0(0) = 1$ and the solution is readily found to be

$$Y_0(t) = e^{-t/T}$$

Therefore, the over-all response of the system is given by

$$y(t) = y_0 Y_0(t) + \int_0^t \frac{1}{T} e^{-(t-\tau)/T} \sin \tau \, d\tau$$

$$= y_0 e^{-t/T} + \frac{T}{1 + T^2} \left(\frac{1}{T} \sin t - \cos t + e^{-t/T} \right)$$

Clearly, this solution satisfies all the required conditions.

3. If the forcing function has the form given by Eq. (5.2-24), where, in particular, $m = 1$, $b_0(t) = e^{-t/T}$, $b_1(t) = 1$, and $x(t) = \sin t$, the weighting function is obtained from Eq. (5.2-29). Thus

$$W_1(t,\tau) = W(t,\tau) - \frac{\partial}{\partial \tau} [e^{-\tau/T} W(t,\tau)]$$

$$= W(t,\tau) + \frac{1}{T} e^{-\tau/T} W(t,\tau) - e^{-\tau/T} \frac{\partial}{\partial \tau} W(t,\tau)$$

The derivative of $W(t,\tau)$ with respect to τ is obtained in the following manner. For $\tau < t$ we have

$$\frac{\partial}{\partial \tau} W(t,\tau) = \frac{1}{T^2} e^{-(t-\tau)/T} \qquad \tau < t$$

while for $\tau > t$ this derivative is zero, since W itself is identically zero in this region. At $\tau = t$ the function $W(t,\tau)$ experiences a jump of magnitude $-1/T$ so that the derivative at that point gives rise to a delta function of magnitude $-1/T$ or simply $-\delta(t - \tau)/T$. Thus

$$W_1(t,\tau) = W(t,\tau) \left(1 + \frac{1}{T} e^{-\tau/T} \right) + \frac{1}{T} e^{-\tau/T} \delta(t - \tau) - \frac{1}{T^2} e^{-t/T}$$

$$= \frac{1}{T} e^{-\tau/T} \delta(t - \tau) + \frac{1}{T} e^{-(t-\tau)/T} \qquad \text{for } t > \tau$$

and
$$W_1(t,\tau) = 0 \qquad \text{for } t < \tau$$

Therefore
$$y(t) = \int_{-\infty}^{\infty} W_1(t,\tau) \sin \tau \, d\tau$$

$$= \frac{T}{1 + T^2} \left(\frac{1}{T} \sin t - \cos t + \frac{1}{T} e^{-t/T} \sin t \right)$$

It is easy to verify that this is the solution of the equation

$$T \frac{dy}{dt} + y = e^{-t/T} \frac{d}{dt} \sin t + \sin t$$

$$= e^{-t/T} \cos t + \sin t$$

and could have been obtained by evaluating

$$y(t) = \int_{-\infty}^{t} \frac{1}{T} e^{-(t-\tau)/T} (e^{-\tau/T} \cos \tau + \sin \tau) \, d\tau$$

directly, as indicated by Eq. (5.2-28).

Under certain conditions an nth-order system describable by a differential equation of the form of (5.2-26) may be replaced by a system of n first-order equations in which no derivatives of the forcing function $x(t)$ occur. To see this, consider the differential equation

$$\frac{d^n y}{dt^n} + a_1(t) \frac{d^{n-1}y}{dt^{n-1}} + \cdots + a_n(t)y$$

$$= b_0(t) \frac{d^n x}{dt^n} + b_1(t) \frac{d^{n-1}x}{dt^{n-1}} + \cdots + b_n(t)x \quad (5.2\text{-}30)$$

There is no loss in generality to assume the coefficient of the highest-order derivative of y to be unity. Any of the other coefficients on either side may be zero. Then, if the remaining coefficients possess a sufficient number of derivatives, Eq. (5.2-30) is equivalent to the following system of n first-order equations.

$$y = y_1 + F_0(t)x$$

$$\frac{dy_1}{dt} = y_2 + F_1(t)x$$

$$\cdots \cdots \cdots \cdots \cdots \cdots \cdots \cdots \cdots \cdots \quad (5.2\text{-}31)$$

$$\frac{dy_{n-1}}{dt} = y_n + F_{n-1}(t)x$$

$$\frac{dy_n}{dt} = -a_1(t)y_n - a_2(t)y_{n-1} - \cdots - a_n(t)y_1 + F_n(t)x$$

The functions $F_k(t)$ are combinations of the coefficients $a_i(t)$ and $b_j(t)$, which may be determined by successively eliminating $y_1, y_2, \ldots, y_n$ from Eqs. (5.2-31) and requiring that the resulting nth-order differential equation be identical with Eq. (5.2-30). By this method we obtain

$$\sum_{k=0}^{n} \sum_{j=0}^{n-k} a_{n-k-j}(t) \frac{d^j}{dt^j}[F_k(t)x(t)] = \sum_{r=0}^{n} b_{n-r}(t) \frac{d^r x}{dt^r} \quad (5.2\text{-}32)$$

as an identity in $x(t)$ and its derivatives. Since

$$\frac{d^j}{dt^j} F_k(t)x(t) = \sum_{r=0}^{j} \binom{j}{r} \frac{d^{j-r}F_k}{dt^{j-r}} \frac{d^r x}{dt^r} \quad (5.2\text{-}33)$$

we have

$$\sum_{k=0}^{n} \sum_{j=0}^{n-k} \sum_{r=0}^{j} \binom{j}{r} a_{n-k-j} \frac{d^{j-r}F_k}{dt^{j-r}} \frac{d^r x}{dt^r} = \sum_{r=0}^{n} b_{n-r} \frac{d^r x}{dt^r} \quad (5.2\text{-}34)$$

If we now permute the order of summation as indicated by

$$\sum_{k=0}^{n} \sum_{j=0}^{n-k} \sum_{r=0}^{j} = \sum_{k=0}^{n} \sum_{r=0}^{n-k} \sum_{j=r}^{n-k} = \sum_{r=0}^{n} \sum_{k=0}^{n-r} \sum_{j=r}^{n-k}$$

we obtain

$$\sum_{r=0}^{n} \sum_{k=0}^{n-r} \sum_{j=r}^{n-k} \binom{j}{r} a_{n-k-j} \frac{d^{j-r}F_k}{dt^{j-r}} \frac{d^r x}{dt^r} = \sum_{r=0}^{n} b_{n-r} \frac{d^r x}{dt^r} \quad (5.2\text{-}35)$$

By equating the coefficients of $d^r x/dt^r$ and making a change in indices, we have

$$b_i(t) = \sum_{k=0}^{i} \sum_{s=0}^{i-k} \binom{n+s-i}{n-i} a_{i-k-s}(t) \frac{d^s F_k}{dt^s} \qquad i = 1, 2, \ldots, n \quad (5.2\text{-}36)$$

Or, alternately,

$$F_0(t) = b_0(t)$$

$$F_i(t) = b_i(t) - \sum_{k=0}^{i-1} \sum_{s=0}^{i-k} \binom{n+s-i}{n-i} a_{i-k-s}(t) \frac{d^s F_k}{dt^s} \qquad (5.2\text{-}37)$$

In this final form we have a recurrence formula from which $F_i(t)$ is determined in terms of $F_0, F_1, \ldots, F_{i-1}$. For example, if $n = 2$, we obtain

$$F_1(t) = b_1 - a_1 F_0 - 2a_0 \frac{dF_0}{dt} = b_1 - a_1 b_0 - 2 \frac{db_0}{dt}$$

$$F_2(t) = b_2 - a_2 F_0 - a_1 \frac{dF_0}{dt} - a_0 \frac{d^2 F_0}{dt^2} - a_1 F_1 - a_0 \frac{dF_1}{dt}$$

$$= b_2 - a_2 b_0 + a_1 \left(2 \frac{db_0}{dt} - b_1 + a_1 b_0 \right) + b_0 \frac{da_1}{dt} + 2 \frac{d^2 b_0}{dt^2}$$

In practice, the task of finding an analytic expression for the weighting function for any particular problem is quite formidable even in the constant-coefficient case. For the variable-coefficient case this procedure is, for all practical purposes, impossible except for very special cases. Thus, we are forced to rely on the analogue computer as a means of obtaining the kinds of solutions we desire.

For the remainder of our discussion on linear systems, we wish to distinguish between stable and nonstable systems. A system is said to be stable if and only if every bounded input gives rise to a bounded output. It can be shown that a necessary and sufficient condition for a linear system to be stable is that

$$\int_{-\infty}^{\infty} |W(t,\tau)| \, d\tau < \text{constant} < \infty \qquad \text{for all } t \qquad (5.2\text{-}38)$$

Although the weighting function completely determines the response characteristics of a linear system, a characterization which is often used for stable constant-coefficient systems is the frequency-response function, i.e., the response of the system to a sinusoidal input. Using complex notation, we take the input of the system as

$$x(t) = e^{j\omega t} \qquad (5.2\text{-}39)$$

The output is then obtained from Eq. (5.2-4) and is given by

$$y(t) = \int_0^\infty W(\tau)e^{j\omega(t-\tau)} \, d\tau$$
$$= e^{j\omega t} \int_0^\infty W(\tau)e^{-j\omega\tau} \, d\tau \tag{5.2-40}$$

Thus, it is seen that the output of the system differs from the input only by a constant complex factor.

$$Y(j\omega) = \int_0^\infty W(\tau)e^{-j\omega\tau} \, d\tau \tag{5.2-41}$$

The quantity $Y(j\omega)$ is called the *frequency-response function.*

Example 5.2-4. For the constant-coefficient first-order system discussed in Example 5.2-1 we have, from Eq. (5.2-41),

$$Y(j\omega) = \frac{1}{T} \int_0^\infty e^{-\tau/T} e^{-j\omega\tau} \, d\tau$$
$$= \frac{1}{1 + j\omega T} = \frac{1}{\sqrt{1 + (\omega T)^2}} \, e^{-j \tan^{-1} \omega T}$$

Thus, for an input of the form given by Eq. (5.2-39), the output amplitude is

$$[1 + (\omega T)^2]^{-\frac{1}{2}}$$

and the phase is $\omega t - \tan^{-1} \omega T$.

A generalization of Eq. (5.2-41) is obtained by computing the Laplace transform of $W(t)$ rather than the Fourier transform. Thus, we have

$$Y(p) = \int_0^\infty W(t)e^{-pt} \, dt \tag{5.2-42}$$

where p is a complex constant. $Y(p)$ is called the *transfer function* of the system. The transfer function for the constant-coefficient system corresponding to Eq. (5.2-26) is given by

$$Y(p) = \frac{b_0 p^m + b_1 p^{m-1} + \cdots + b_m}{a_0 p^n + a_1 p^{n-1} + \cdots + a_n} \tag{5.2-43}$$

The condition for stability of this system is that the denominator polynomial have all roots with negative real parts.

It is possible to generalize the notion of frequency response function to include the variable-coefficient linear system. For such a system we define $Y(j\omega,t)$ in such a way that $Y(j\omega,t)e^{j\omega t}$ is the response of the system to an input $e^{j\omega t}$. When the $j\omega$ is replaced by a complex constant p, we have $Y(p,t)$ as the generalized transfer function.

As in the constant-coefficient case, the transfer function is related to the weighting function. Since by definition

$$Y(p,t)e^{pt} = \int_{-\infty}^t W(t,\tau)e^{p\tau} \, d\tau$$

we have

$$Y(p,t) = \int_{-\infty}^{t} W(t,\tau)e^{-p(t-\tau)} \, d\tau \tag{5.2-44}$$

An equivalent relation is

$$Y(p, t) = \int_{0}^{\infty} W(t, t - \tau)e^{-p\tau} \, d\tau \tag{5.2-45}$$

A useful property of the transfer function is contained in the following property. The transfer function of the series combination of two constant-coefficient linear systems is the product of the individual transfer functions. A somewhat analogous relation exists for the generalized transfer function, but is not so simple as in the constant-coefficient case.

5.3 Input-output Relations for Correlation Functions and Spectral Densities

For the remainder of this chapter, we restrict our attention to the analysis of the response of linear time-invariant systems having one or more stationary random processes as inputs. Correlation functions and power spectral densities are the basic tools in this study. In particular, we now wish to establish relations between the correlation functions of the various system inputs and the correlation function of the output, together with corresponding relations between input and output spectral densities.

To begin with, we consider the case of a system with a single input random process $\{x(t)\}$ and output $\{y(t)\}$. Letting $W(t)$ denote the weighting function for the system,

$$\begin{aligned} y(t) &= \int_{-\infty}^{t} W(t - \tau)x(\tau) \, d\tau \\ &= \int_{0}^{\infty} W(\tau)x(t - \tau) \, d\tau \end{aligned} \tag{5.3-1}$$

To form the correlation function of y, we first replace t and τ in the above relation by (t_1,τ_1) and (t_2,τ_2), respectively, to obtain the two equations

$$\begin{aligned} y(t_1) &= \int_{0}^{\infty} W(\tau_1)x(t_1 - \tau_1) \, d\tau_1 \\ y(t_2) &= \int_{0}^{\infty} W(\tau_2)x(t_2 - \tau_2) \, d\tau_2 \end{aligned} \tag{5.3-2}$$

Thus

$$y(t_1)y(t_2) = \int_{0}^{\infty} W(\tau_1)x(t_1 - \tau_1) \, d\tau_1 \int_{0}^{\infty} W(\tau_2)x(t_2 - \tau_2) \, d\tau_2 \tag{5.3-3}$$

Although the above expression is derived as the product of two integrals, we may equally well regard it as a double integral. The quantity $x(t_1 - \tau_1)$ may then be moved under the second integral, giving

$$y(t_1)y(t_2) = \int_{0}^{\infty} W(\tau_1) \, d\tau_1 \int_{0}^{\infty} W(\tau_2)x(t_1 - \tau_1)x(t_2 - \tau_2) \, d\tau_2 \tag{5.3-4}$$

We now may compute the mathematical expectation of both sides of this equation, averaging under the integral sign in the right-hand member. Noting that the random processes $\{x\}$ and $\{y\}$ are stationary, we have

$$
\begin{aligned}
E[y(t_1)y(t_2)] &= \phi_{yy}(t_2 - t_1) \\
E[x(t_1 - \tau_1)x(t_2 - \tau_2)] &= \phi_{xx}(t_2 - t_1 - \tau_2 + \tau_1)
\end{aligned}
\tag{5.3-5}
$$

Thus, from (5.3-4),

$$
\phi_{yy}(\tau) = \int_0^\infty W(\tau_1)\, d\tau_1 \int_0^\infty W(\tau_2)\phi_{xx}(\tau - \tau_2 + \tau_1)\, d\tau_2 \tag{5.3-6}
$$

where we have replaced $t_2 - t_1$ by τ for simplicity.

Relationships of the type of (5.3-6) form the starting point for a considerable portion of our subsequent analysis. In effect, this equation gives us a way of relating certain statistical characteristics of the output of a system to the statistical characteristics of the input and the response properties of the system itself. In particular, we may determine the mean-squared value of the output by setting τ equal to zero in (5.3-6). Thus

$$
\overline{y^2} = \phi_{yy}(0) = \int_0^\infty W(\tau_1)\, d\tau_1 \int_0^\infty W(\tau_2)\phi_{xx}(\tau_1 - \tau_2)\, d\tau_2 \tag{5.3-7}
$$

If the system in question is a filter and the input $x(t)$ an unwanted interference or noise, we have in the mean-squared output an immediate index of the success of the filter in smoothing the noise.

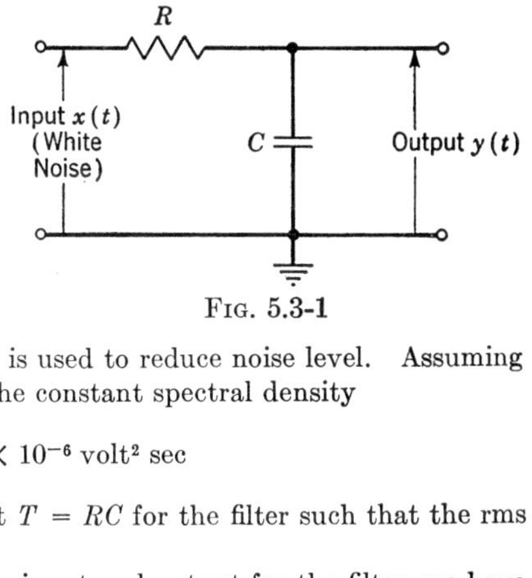

FIG. 5.3-1

Example 5.3-1. In a certain stage of a vacuum-tube amplifier a simple one-stage RC filter of the form indicated in Fig. 5.3-1 is used to reduce noise level. Assuming the input to consist of a white noise, with the constant spectral density

$$
G(\omega) = G_0 = 2 \times 10^{-6} \text{ volt}^2 \text{ sec}
$$

we wish to find the minimum time constant $T = RC$ for the filter such that the rms filter output does not exceed 50 millivolts.

Letting $x(t)$ and $y(t)$ denote the respective input and output for the filter, we have

$$
\phi_{xx}(\tau) = \pi G_0 \delta(\tau)
$$

Substitution of this value into the right-hand integral of (5.3-7) gives

$$
\int_0^\infty W(\tau_2)\phi_{xx}(\tau_1 - \tau_2)\, d\tau_2 = \pi G_0 \int_0^\infty W(\tau_2)\delta(\tau_1 - \tau_2)\, d\tau_2 = \pi G_0 W(\tau_1)
$$

Thus
$$
\overline{y^2} = \pi G_0 \int_0^\infty W(\tau_1)^2\, d\tau_1 = \frac{\pi G_0}{T^2} \int_0^\infty e^{-2\tau_1/T} d\tau_1 = \frac{\pi G_0}{2T}
$$

If the rms output is to be 50 millivolts, then $\overline{y^2} = 25 \times 10^{-4}$ volt^2, giving

$$T = \frac{\pi G_0}{2\overline{y^2}} = \frac{\pi(2 \times 10^{-6} \text{ volt}^2 \text{ sec})}{2(25 \times 10^{-4} \text{ volt}^2)}$$
$$= 0.00126 \text{ sec}$$

Clearly any smaller value of T will give a larger rms output; thus the above value represents the desired minimum.

From the relation (5.3-6) between the input and output correlation functions for a linear time-invariant system we may readily derive a relation between input and output spectral densities. By (3.6-36) the spectral density $G_{yy}(\omega)$ is given as the Fourier transform of $\phi_{yy}(\tau)$. Using Eq. (5.3-6), by means of an interchange of order of integration and a subsequent change of variable, we obtain

$$
\begin{aligned}
G_{yy}(\omega) &= \frac{1}{\pi} \int_{-\infty}^{\infty} \phi_{yy}(\tau) e^{-j\omega\tau} \, d\tau \\
&= \frac{1}{\pi} \int_{-\infty}^{\infty} e^{-j\omega\tau} \, d\tau \int_{0}^{\infty} W(\tau_1) \, d\tau_1 \int_{0}^{\infty} W(\tau_2) \phi_{xx}(\tau - \tau_2 + \tau_1) \, d\tau_2 \\
&= \frac{1}{\pi} \int_{0}^{\infty} W(\tau_1) \, d\tau_1 \int_{0}^{\infty} W(\tau_2) \, d\tau_2 \int_{-\infty}^{\infty} \phi_{xx}(\tau - \tau_2 + \tau_1) e^{-j\omega\tau} \, d\tau \\
&= \frac{1}{\pi} \int_{0}^{\infty} W(\tau_1) e^{j\omega\tau_1} \, d\tau_1 \int_{0}^{\infty} W(\tau_2) e^{-j\omega\tau_2} \, d\tau_2 \\
&\qquad\qquad\qquad \times \int_{-\infty}^{\infty} \phi_{xx}(\tau - \tau_2 + \tau_1) e^{-j\omega(\tau-\tau_2+\tau_1)} \, d\tau \\
&= \int_{0}^{\infty} W(\tau_1) e^{j\omega\tau_1} \, d\tau_1 \int_{0}^{\infty} W(\tau_2) e^{-j\omega\tau_2} \, d\tau_2 \\
&\qquad\qquad\qquad\qquad \times \frac{1}{\pi} \int_{-\infty}^{\infty} \phi_{xx}(t) e^{-j\omega t} \, dt \quad (5.3\text{-}8)
\end{aligned}
$$

In the last form of this equation, each variable of integration occurs only under one integral sign; thus the triple integral can be represented as the product of three single integrals. We have

$$\frac{1}{\pi} \int_{-\infty}^{\infty} \phi_{xx}(t) e^{-j\omega t} \, dt = G_{xx}(\omega) \qquad (5.3\text{-}9)$$

and, by (5.2-41),

$$\int_{0}^{\infty} W(\tau_2) e^{-j\omega\tau_2} \, d\tau_2 = Y(j\omega) \qquad (5.3\text{-}10)$$

Also, since the weighting function takes on only real values, the remaining integral is found to be the complex conjugate of the frequency response function

$$\int_{0}^{\infty} W(\tau_1) e^{j\omega\tau_1} \, d\tau_1 = Y(j\omega)^* \qquad (5.3\text{-}11)$$

Thus, in summary,

$$G_{yy}(\omega) = Y(j\omega)^*Y(j\omega)G_{xx}(\omega)$$
$$= |Y(j\omega)|^2 G_{xx}(\omega) \qquad (5.3\text{-}12)$$

The simple manner by which the input and output spectral densities are related, for a time-invariant system, is one of the main reasons why the concept of spectral density is so useful. We have already used a special form of Eq. (5.3-12), for an ideal bandpass filter, in our initial discussion of spectral density in Sec. 3.6. Since the mean-squared value of the system output $y(t)$ is given by the integral of its spectral density, it is often easy to see by inspection the effect on the output of altering the parameters of the system transfer function. It is also frequently much easier to compute the mean-squared output from the single integral

$$\overline{y^2} = \int_0^\infty G_{yy}(\omega)\,d\omega$$
$$= \int_0^\infty |Y(j\omega)|^2 G_{xx}(\omega)\,d\omega \qquad (5.3\text{-}13)$$

than from the double integral (5.3-7).

Example 5.3-2. To illustrate the application of (5.3-13), we reexamine the problem posed in Example 5.3-1. Since the input spectral density is

$$G_{xx}(\omega) = G_0$$

and the filter transfer function is

$$Y(j\omega) = \frac{1}{1 + Tj\omega}$$

we have

$$\overline{y^2} = \int_0^\infty \left|\frac{1}{1 + Tj\omega}\right|^2 G_0\,d\omega = G_0 \int_0^\infty \frac{d\omega}{1 + T^2\omega^2} = \frac{\pi G_0}{2T}$$

as before.

Example 5.3-3. A voltage $f(t)$, given by the random step function studied in Example 3.6-2 is introduced as input to the high-pass filter shown in Fig. 5.3-2. To

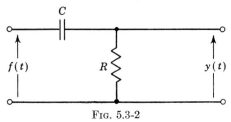

FIG. 5.3-2

compute the mean-squared output $\overline{y^2}$, we note that

$$G_{ff}(\omega) = \frac{1 - \cos \omega}{2\pi\omega^2} + \frac{1}{2}\delta(\omega)$$

by a previous calculation, and that the filter transfer function is

$$Y(j\omega) = \frac{Tj\omega}{1 + Tj\omega}$$

where $T = RC$. Thus

$$G_{yy}(\omega) = |Y(j\omega)|^2 G_{ff}(\omega) = \frac{T^2\omega^2}{1 + T^2\omega^2} \frac{1 - \cos \omega}{2\pi\omega^2} + \frac{T^2\omega^2}{2(1 + T^2\omega^2)} \delta(\omega)$$

The second term in this expression can make no contribution to the mean-squared value of y, since the coefficient of $\delta(\omega)$ is a function that is zero when $\omega = 0$. Physically this amounts to saying that, since the filter in question will not pass direct current, the contribution to the output power from the d-c component of the input must be zero. Thus the output spectral density may be written in the simpler form

$$G_{yy}(\omega) = \frac{T^2}{2\pi} \frac{1 - \cos \omega}{1 + T^2\omega^2}$$

and

$$\overline{y^2} = \frac{T^2}{2\pi} \int_0^\infty \frac{1 - \cos \omega}{1 + T^2\omega^2} \, d\omega = \frac{T}{4} (1 - e^{-1/T})$$

Pursuing this example somewhat further, we consider the limiting case as T approaches infinity. The filter of Fig. 5.3-2 will then pass all frequencies except direct current, and consistent with this we find as the limiting form of the output spectrum

$$G_{yy}(\omega) = \frac{1 - \cos \omega}{2\pi\omega^2}$$

Also

$$\overline{y^2} = \frac{1}{4}$$

The output random process $\{y(t)\}$ is now the same as $\{f(t)\}$, except that the average value $\frac{1}{2}$ has been subtracted; thus $y(t)$ is a random step function taking on the values $\pm \frac{1}{2}$ rather than zero and unity.

We now consider the random process $\{z(t)\}$ derived by integrating the limiting random process $\{y(t)\}$. Since the frequency-response function for an ideal integrator is $(j\omega)^{-1}$, by a formal operation we find

$$G_{zz}(\omega) = \left| \frac{1}{j\omega} \right|^2 G_{yy}(\omega) = \frac{1 - \cos \omega}{2\pi\omega^4}$$

Since

$$\int_0^\infty \frac{1 - \cos \omega}{\omega^4} \, d\omega = +\infty$$

we conclude that z does not possess a finite mean-squared value. Inasmuch as the random process $\{y(t)\}$ possesses a zero mean value, this conclusion may be somewhat surprising.

To explain this apparent discrepancy, let us consider the (nonstationary) random process $\{z_1(t)\}$ defined by

$$z_1(t) = \int_0^t y(\tau) \, d\tau$$

The function $y(t)$ takes on the values $\pm \frac{1}{2}$ at random over successive unit time intervals where, for convenience, we assume that these intervals start at the origin and that t is some positive integer n. Then

$$z_1(n) = \sum_{k=1}^n y_k$$

where y_k is the value of $y(t)$ over the kth such interval.

The random variable $z_1(n)$ is the sum of n independent random variables y_k, each of which can take on the two values $+\frac{1}{2}$ and $-\frac{1}{2}$ with equal probability. The quantity $2z_1(n)$ is thus distributed according to the binomial distribution discussed in Sec. 2.10. Applying the results of Example 2.8-4, we find

$$\overline{z_1(n)} = 0 \qquad \overline{z_1(n)^2} = \frac{n}{4}$$

Thus, in spite of the fact that the mean value of $z_1(n)$ is zero, its mean-squared value tends toward infinity with n. If we attempt to generate the random process $\{z(t)\}$ by integrating $\{y(t)\}$ starting at some finite time instant, the resulting integral grows without limit and does not approach a stationary random process even in a statistical sense.

This general result can also be seen in another way. We have

$$\overline{z_1(t)^2} = \int_0^t d\tau_1 \int_0^t \phi_{yy}(\tau_2 - \tau_1) \, d\tau_2$$

As t becomes very large, for most values of τ_1 in the range $0 < \tau_1 < t$, the quantity $\int_0^t \phi_{yy}(\tau_2 - \tau_1) \, d\tau_2$ can be approximated by $\int_{-\infty}^{\infty} \phi_{yy}(\tau) \, d\tau$. Thus for large enough t

$$\overline{z_1(t)^2} \cong \int_0^t d\tau_1 \int_{-\infty}^{\infty} \phi_{yy}(\tau) \, d\tau = t \int_{-\infty}^{\infty} \phi_{yy}(\tau) \, d\tau$$

Thus for any random process $\{y(t)\}$, the integral $\{z_1(t)\}$ will tend toward infinity in a statistical sense as t becomes large unless the integral of $\phi_{yy}(\tau)$ vanishes. However, since

$$G_{yy}(0) = \frac{1}{\pi} \int_{-\infty}^{\infty} \phi_{yy}(\tau) \, d\tau$$

this condition is equivalent to the vanishing of the spectrum of y at the origin. If $G_{yy}(\omega)$ is an even analytic function, however, the condition $G_{yy}(0) = 0$ is precisely that required to make $G_{yy}(\omega)/\omega^2$ an integrable function and therefore to give

$$z(t) = \int y(t) \, dt$$

a finite mean-squared value.

In many problems it is required to compute the cross-spectral density between the input and output of a linear time-invariant system. We shall now derive a relation similar to Eq. (5.3-12) by which we may express this cross-spectral density in terms of the spectral density of the input and the transfer function of the system.

Let $x(t)$ be the input of a system whose weighting function is $W(t)$. Then the output $y(t)$ is given by Eq. (5.3-1). The cross-correlation function between $x(t)$ and $y(t)$ is obtained from

$$\phi_{xy}(\tau) = \overline{x(t)y(t + \tau)} = \int_0^{\infty} W(\tau_1)\overline{x(t)x(t + \tau - \tau_1)} \, d\tau_1$$

$$= \int_0^{\infty} W(\tau_1)\phi_{xx}(\tau - \tau_1) \, d\tau_1 \qquad\qquad (5.3\text{-}14)$$

By Eq. (3.6-51) the cross-spectral density $G_{xy}(\omega)$ is given as the Fourier transform of $\phi_{xy}(\tau)$. Thus

$$
\begin{aligned}
G_{xy}(\omega) &= \frac{1}{\pi} \int_{-\infty}^{\infty} \phi_{xy}(\tau) e^{-j\omega\tau} \, d\tau \\
&= \frac{1}{\pi} \int_{0}^{\infty} W(\tau_1) e^{-j\omega\tau_1} \, d\tau_1 \int_{-\infty}^{\infty} \phi_{xx}(\tau - \tau_1) e^{-j\omega(\tau-\tau_1)} \, d\tau \\
&= \frac{1}{\pi} \int_{0}^{\infty} W(\tau_1) e^{-j\omega\tau_1} \, d\tau_1 \int_{-\infty}^{\infty} \phi_{xx}(t) e^{-j\omega t} \, dt \\
&= Y(j\omega) G_{xx}(\omega)
\end{aligned}
\tag{5.3-15}
$$

using Eqs. (5.3-9) and (5.3-10).

Considerations up to this point have been restricted to the case of the filtering of a single stationary random process. The extension to the case in which more than one random process is involved is fairly direct, although slightly complicated algebraically. Let the system receive as inputs the quantities $x_1(t)$, $x_2(t)$, . . . , $x_n(t)$. Assuming in general that the action of the system on each input is different, there will be a corresponding set of weighting functions $W_1(t)$, $W_2(t)$, . . . , $W_n(t)$. The system output $y(t)$ may then be expressed in the form

$$
y(t) = \sum_{k=1}^{n} \int_{0}^{\infty} W_k(\tau) x_k(t - \tau) \, d\tau
\tag{5.3-16}
$$

Following the same general procedure as was used in Eqs. (5.3-4) to (5.3-6), we express the product $y(t_1)y(t_2)$ in the form of a double sum

$$
\begin{aligned}
y(t_1)y(t_2) = \sum_{m=1}^{n} \sum_{k=1}^{n} \int_{0}^{\infty} W_m(\tau_1) \, d\tau_1 \\
\times \int_{0}^{\infty} W_k(\tau_2) x_m(t_1 - \tau_1) x_k(t_2 - \tau_2) \, d\tau_2
\end{aligned}
\tag{5.3-17}
$$

If we now average both sides of this equation with respect to the ensemble of possible inputs x_1, . . . , x_n, replace $t_2 - t_1$ by τ as before, and write

$$
\phi_{mk}(\tau) = E[x_m(t) x_k(t + \tau)]
\tag{5.3-18}
$$

for the cross-correlation function for x_m and x_k, we find

$$
\phi_{yy}(\tau) = \sum_{m=1}^{n} \sum_{k=1}^{n} \int_{0}^{\infty} W_m(\tau_1) \, d\tau_1 \int_{0}^{\infty} W_k(\tau_2) \phi_{mk}(\tau - \tau_2 + \tau_1) \, d\tau_2
\tag{5.3-19}
$$

To compute the spectral density of y, we compute the Fourier transform of the above expression as in Eq. (5.3-8).

$$G_{yy}(\omega) = \frac{1}{\pi} \int_{-\infty}^{\infty} \phi_{yy}(\tau) e^{-j\omega\tau} \, d\tau$$

$$= \frac{1}{\pi} \sum_{m=1}^{n} \sum_{k=1}^{n} \int_{0}^{\infty} W_m(\tau_1) \, d\tau_1 \int_{0}^{\infty} W_k(\tau_2) \, d\tau_2$$

$$\times \int_{-\infty}^{\infty} \phi_{mk}(\tau - \tau_2 + \tau_1) e^{-j\omega\tau} \, d\tau$$

$$= \frac{1}{\pi} \sum_{m=1}^{n} \sum_{k=1}^{n} \int_{0}^{\infty} W_m(\tau_1) e^{j\omega\tau_1} \, d\tau_1 \int_{0}^{\infty} W_k(\tau_2) e^{-j\omega\tau_2} \, d\tau_2$$

$$\times \int_{-\infty}^{\infty} \phi_{mk}(\tau - \tau_2 + \tau_1) e^{-j\omega(\tau-\tau_2+\tau_1)} \, d\tau$$

$$= \sum_{m=1}^{n} \sum_{k=1}^{n} Y_m(j\omega)^* Y_k(j\omega) G_{mk}(\omega) \tag{5.3-20}$$

5.4 A General Class of Filtering and Prediction Problems

In the remainder of this chapter and in Chap. 7 we consider a class of prediction and smoothing problems having the following general characteristics.

1. The predicting or smoothing system is linear and time-invariant.

2. The signal and noise are members of stationary random processes so that the correlation functions are invariant with respect to a time origin.

3. The error criterion is the mean-squared value of an error signal.

The basic theory of optimum design founded on these hypotheses is due to Wiener and is treated in Chap. 7.

Although we speak of smoothing and prediction theory, we may just as well consider a more general class of operations. We might, for example, wish that the system smooth and differentiate or predict and differentiate. In general, we shall consider any linear operation that can be accomplished by the integral

$$\int_{-\infty}^{\infty} W_I(\tau) q(t - \tau) \, d\tau$$

Here $W_I(\tau)$ is used to denote the weighting function of an ideal system that accomplishes perfectly the desired task, so that we need not impose any requirements as to the physical realizability of $W_I(\tau)$. For example, we shall speak of the "ideal predictor" as a hypothetical device that gives a perfect prediction at time t of the future value of the signal at time $t + T$.

We allow $W_I(\tau)$ to include δ functions or derivatives of a δ function. Furthermore, we do not require that the signal and noise enter the system in the same way. Hence the weighting function $W_s(t)$ that relates the signal $s(t)$ to the output $q_o(t)$ may be different from the weighting function $W_n(t)$ that relates the noise $n(t)$ to the output $q_o(t)$. A diagram of the general problem is given in Fig. 5.4-1.

The part of the diagram below the dotted line represents the actual system while the part above the dotted line represents the hypothetical ideal system together with a comparator for generating the error signal. We determine $W_I(t)$ from the specified performance requirements of the system. For example, if the system is required to estimate the future value of the signal $s(t)$, then we must take $W_I(t) = \delta(t + T)$. Having fixed $W_I(t)$, the problem is then to determine $W_s(t)$ and $W_n(t)$ so as to minimize $\overline{\epsilon^2}$. Of course, $W_n(t)$ is never independent of $W_s(t)$, for then

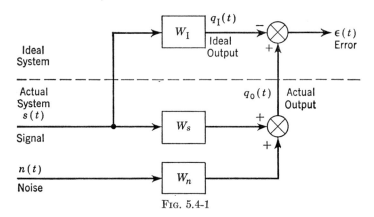

FIG. 5.4-1

the noise could be completely eliminated from the system by taking $W_n(t) = 0$.

While it might appear that the usefulness of the block diagram in Fig. 5.4-1 is confined to problems of filtering, as contrasted with feedback control systems, actually this is not the case. The weighting functions W_s and W_n are the responses of an arbitrary linear time-invariant system to unit impulses of signal and noise, respectively. Thus Fig. 5.4-1 includes feedback systems as well as filters. It will be seen in Example 5.4-2 that one can often cast other related problems into the same general form. In the example cited, these notions are applied to a feedback system with no signal input and two noise inputs entering at different points of the loop.

Example 5.4-1. To illustrate how a typical problem may be cast in the above form, let us consider the system shown in Fig. 5.4-2, representing a radar tracking system. Here $s(t)$ represents the signal which the radar is called upon to follow. The quantity $n_1(t)$ is radar noise due to fading and related effects, and $n_2(t)$ represents an output disturbance such as would be caused by wind torques acting on the radar dish. It is desired that $q_o(t)$ shall be equal to the signal portion of the input.

The quantities P_1 and P_2 are the performance operators of two time-invariant linear systems. The ideal operator P_I is unity and $W_I(t) = \delta(t)$ since it is desired that $q_o(t) = s(t)$.

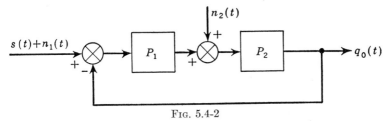

FIG. 5.4-2

The output may be expressed in terms of the inputs in the following manner:

$$q_o(t) = P_2\{P_1[s(t) + n_1(t) - q_o(t)] + n_2(t)\}$$
$$= P_2P_1[s(t) + n_1(t)] - P_2P_1[q_o(t)] + P_2[n_2(t)] \qquad (5.4\text{-}1)$$

Solving for $q_o(t)$, we obtain

$$q_o(t) = \frac{P_2P_1}{1 + P_2P_1}[s(t)] + \frac{P_2P_1}{1 + P_2P_1}[n_1(t)] + \frac{P_2}{1 + P_2P_1}[n_2(t)] \qquad (5.4\text{-}2)$$

Thus, we see that this particular system may be put in the general form indicated in Fig. 5.4-1. The result is shown in Fig. 5.4-3. The problem is then to determine the performance functions P_1 and P_2 so as to minimize $\overline{\epsilon^2}$.

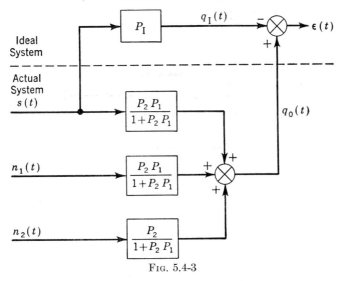

FIG. 5.4-3

Example 5.4-2. Let us consider again the system discussed in Example 5.4-1. Suppose further that the portion of the system described by P_2 is fixed and incapable of alteration. For example, P_1 could represent a servo amplifier and filter, and P_2 could represent the servo motor, gear train, and radar dish itself. Furthermore, let us neglect the signal portion of the input $s(t)$. The problem is then to determine P_1 so as to minimize the mean-squared output of the system. The effect will be to determine the system with a given configuration which will filter the noise without regard for its effect upon the signal. The practical significance of this procedure would be to obtain an estimate of the best possible filtering that could be performed on the noise. With this accomplished, one could then determine what effect this system would have upon the signal itself. At this point the system parameters could be adjusted to arrive at a compromise between optimum filtering and ideal system performance.

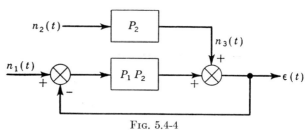

Fig. 5.4-4

Under the conditions imposed above we may replace the system shown in Fig. 5.4-2 by the equivalent system of Fig. 5.4-4. The error $\epsilon(t)$ may be expressed in terms of the two components of noise $n_1(t)$ and $n_2(t)$ as follows.

$$\epsilon(t) = P_1 P_2[n_1(t) - \epsilon(t)] + n_3(t) \tag{5.4-3}$$

Solving for $\epsilon(t)$, we obtain

$$\epsilon(t) = \frac{P_1 P_2}{1 + P_1 P_2}[n_1(t)] + \frac{1}{1 + P_1 P_2}[n_3(t)] \tag{5.4-4}$$

We can now show how this problem is equivalent to a more conventional type of filtering problem. Consider the system shown in Fig. 5.4-5. The input-output rela-

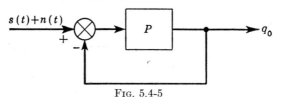

Fig. 5.4-5

tion takes the form

$$q_o(t) = P[s(t) + n(t) - q_o(t)] \tag{5.4-5}$$

or

$$q_o(t) = \frac{P}{1 + P}[s(t) + n(t)] \tag{5.4-6}$$

Defining

$$\epsilon(t) = q_o(t) - s(t) \tag{5.4-7}$$

we have

$$\epsilon(t) = -\frac{1}{1 + P}[s(t)] + \frac{P}{1 + P}[n(t)] \tag{5.4-8}$$

Comparing Eqs. (5.4-4) and (5.4-8), we see that our original problem of choosing P_1 so as to minimize the effects of the noise inputs to the system is equivalent to the simple feedback filtering problem of Fig. 5.4-5 if we identify the negative of the signal with $n_3(t)$ and the noise with $n_1(t)$, and identify P with $P_1 P_2$.

For the general system shown in Fig. 5.4-1 we shall now obtain expressions for the autocorrelation function and the spectral density of $\epsilon(t)$ in terms of the correlation functions and spectral densities of the inputs together with the ideal and actual system performance functions.   Let $\phi_{ss}(\tau)$, $\phi_{nn}(\tau)$, and $\phi_{\epsilon\epsilon}(\tau)$ be the autocorrelation functions of $s(t)$, $n(t)$, and $\epsilon(t)$, respectively.   Let $\phi_{sn}(\tau)$ be the cross-correlation function of $s(t)$ and $n(t)$.   Similarly, let $G(\omega)$ with the same subscript arrangement denote the corresponding power spectral densities.   Let $Y_I(j\omega)$, $Y_s(j\omega)$, and $Y_n(j\omega)$ be the transfer functions corresponding to W_I, W_s, and W_n, respectively. Then we have

$$\epsilon(t) = \int_{-\infty}^{\infty} W_s(\tau)s(t-\tau)\,d\tau + \int_{-\infty}^{\infty} W_n(\tau)n(t-\tau)\,d\tau$$
$$- \int_{-\infty}^{\infty} W_I(\tau)s(t-\tau)\,d\tau \quad (5.4\text{-}9)$$

or $$\epsilon(t) = \int_{-\infty}^{\infty} W_1(\tau)s(t-\tau)\,d\tau + \int_{-\infty}^{\infty} W_n(\tau)n(t-\tau)\,d\tau \quad (5.4\text{-}10)$$

where we have defined

$$W_1(\tau) = W_s(\tau) - W_I(\tau) \quad (5.4\text{-}11)$$

We use doubly infinite limits in the integration because $W_I(\tau)$ need not vanish for negative values of τ.

The correlation function for $\epsilon(t)$ is obtained by

$$\begin{aligned}
\phi_{\epsilon\epsilon}(\tau) &= \overline{\epsilon(t)\epsilon(t+\tau)} \\
&= \int_{-\infty}^{\infty}\int_{-\infty}^{\infty} W_1(\tau_1)W_1(\tau_2)\phi_{ss}(\tau+\tau_1-\tau_2)\,d\tau_1\,d\tau_2 \\
&\quad + \int_{-\infty}^{\infty}\int_{-\infty}^{\infty} W_1(\tau_1)W_n(\tau_2)\phi_{sn}(\tau+\tau_1-\tau_2)\,d\tau_1\,d\tau_2 \\
&\quad + \int_{-\infty}^{\infty}\int_{-\infty}^{\infty} W_n(\tau_1)W_1(\tau_2)\phi_{ns}(\tau+\tau_1-\tau_2)\,d\tau_1\,d\tau_2 \\
&\quad + \int_{-\infty}^{\infty}\int_{-\infty}^{\infty} W_n(\tau_1)W_n(\tau_2)\phi_{nn}(\tau+\tau_1-\tau_2)\,d\tau_1\,d\tau_2 \quad (5.4\text{-}12)
\end{aligned}$$

The details of this computation are omitted since they are the same as those used in Sec. 5.3 to derive Eq. (5.3-19).

To obtain a relationship between the input and output spectral densities, we take the Fourier transform of Eq. (5.4-12).   Following the procedure used to derive Eq. (5.3-20), we have

$$\begin{aligned}
G_{\epsilon\epsilon}(\omega) &= \frac{1}{\pi}\int_{-\infty}^{\infty} \phi_{\epsilon\epsilon}(\tau)e^{-j\omega\tau}\,d\tau \\
&= |Y_1(j\omega)|^2 G_{ss}(\omega) + Y_1(j\omega)^* Y_n(j\omega)G_{sn}(\omega) \\
&\quad + Y_1(j\omega)Y_n(j\omega)^* G_{ns}(\omega) + |Y_n(j\omega)|^2 G_{nn}(\omega) \quad (5.4\text{-}13)
\end{aligned}$$

Equations (5.4-12) and (5.4-13) may form the starting point for the analysis of many time-invariant linear systems possessing stationary random inputs.   We list below for ready reference the common forms of the ideal prediction and smoothing weighting and transfer functions.

Quantity system is required to estimate—	Weighting function, $W_I(t)$	Transfer function, $Y_I(j\omega)$
Present value of $s(t)$..........................	$\delta(t)$	1
Present value of $\dot{s}(t)$.......................	$\dot{\delta}(t)$	$j\omega$
Present value of $\ddot{s}(t)$.......................	$\ddot{\delta}(t)$	$(j\omega)^2$
Future value of $s(t) = s(t+T)$.............	$\delta(t+T)$	$e^{j\omega T}$
Past value of $s(t) = s(t-T)$...............	$\delta(t-T)$	$e^{-j\omega T}$

Example 5.4-3.   We consider here the specific problem of separating a random signal $s(t)$ from a noise $n(t)$.   For simplicity, we assume the signal and noise to be uncorrelated, so that

$$G_{sn}(\omega) = G_{ns}(\omega) = 0$$

The signal is taken to be a low-frequency random process with

$$G_{ss}(\omega) = \frac{a}{w_s^2 + \omega^2}$$

and the noise spectrum is assumed to be of the form

$$G_{nn}(\omega) = \frac{b}{\omega_n^2 + \omega^2}$$

where $\omega_n \gg \omega_s$.   We further assume the filter to be a first-order system, possessing a transfer function

$$Y_s(j\omega) = \frac{1}{1 + Tj\omega}$$

Since the desired action is simple filtering, we have

$$Y_I(j\omega) = 1$$

Thus

$$Y_1(j\omega) = Y_s(j\omega) - Y_I(j\omega)$$

$$= \frac{1}{1 + Tj\omega} - 1 = -\frac{Tj\omega}{1 + Tj\omega}$$

Also

$$Y_n(j\omega) = Y_s(j\omega) = \frac{1}{1 + Tj\omega}$$

Substitution of these expressions into Eq. (5.4-13) gives for the error spectral density

$$G_{\epsilon\epsilon}(\omega) = \left| -\frac{Tj\omega}{1 + Tj\omega} \right|^2 \left(\frac{a}{\omega_s^2 + \omega^2} \right) + \left| \frac{1}{1 + Tj\omega} \right|^2 \left(\frac{b}{\omega_n^2 + \omega^2} \right)$$

$$= \frac{aT^2\omega^2}{(1 + T^2\omega^2)(\omega_s^2 + \omega^2)} + \frac{b}{(1 + T^2\omega^2)(\omega_n^2 + \omega^2)}$$

The mean-squared error is therefore given by

$$\overline{\epsilon^2} = aT^2 \int_0^\infty \frac{\omega^2 \, d\omega}{(1 + T^2\omega^2)(\omega_s^2 + \omega^2)} + b \int_0^\infty \frac{d\omega}{(1 + T^2\omega^2)(\omega_n^2 + \omega^2)} \qquad (5.4\text{-}14)$$

The above integrals can be evaluated by partial fraction expansions of the integrands or by the techniques of the next section. However, a certain amount of information can be obtained from this expression by inspection. The first integral in (5.4-14) arises from an expression of the form

$$\int_0^\infty |Y_s(j\omega) - 1|^2 G_{ss}(\omega)\, d\omega \tag{5.4-15}$$

It is seen that if $Y_s(j\omega)$ is approximately unity for the range of signal frequencies, then the integral is small. This, however, is true for small values of the time constant T, and we note that the first term in (5.4-14) is approximately proportional to T when T is small. Physically, the expression (5.4-15) represents the contribution to $\overline{\epsilon^2}$ arising from distortion of the signal.

The second term in (5.4-14) is a special case of the integral

$$\int_0^\infty |Y_s(j\omega)|^2 G_{nn}(\omega)\, d\omega \tag{5.4-16}$$

If $Y_s(j\omega)$ is small for those frequencies at which the noise is important, then (5.4-16) is small. In the example this is true if T is large, corresponding to a heavy damping of the noise. The selection of an optimum value for T thus requires a compromise between the two terms of (5.4-14), and is achieved quantitatively by finding that value of T for which $\overline{\epsilon^2}$ is minimized.

5.5   The Analytical Computation of the Mean-squared Error

In Sec. 5.4 an expression was derived for the spectral density of the error by which a certain class of systems deviated from their ideal performance. The mean-squared value of this error can be obtained from

$$\overline{\epsilon^2} = \int_0^\infty G_{\epsilon\epsilon}(\omega)\, d\omega = \tfrac{1}{2} \int_{-\infty}^\infty G_{\epsilon\epsilon}(\omega)\, d\omega \tag{5.5-1}$$

Therefore, to solve the problem proposed in Sec. 5.4, we should minimize the integral of Eq. (5.5-1) by an appropriate choice of $Y_1(j\omega)$ and $Y_n(j\omega)$. This cannot be done until the constraining relation between $Y_1(j\omega)$ and $Y_n(j\omega)$ is established. Even then the problem might be a very difficult one. For the particular case in which

$$Y_n(j\omega) = Y_s(j\omega) = 1 + Y_1(j\omega)$$

a direct minimization can be accomplished by the original Wiener theory. This method is treated in detail in Chap. 7. For the present we shall leave Eq. (5.4-13) in its general form and seek merely an efficient analytical procedure for the calculation of $\overline{\epsilon^2}$.

The method that we shall use applies to lumped-parameter systems when each of the spectral densities $G_{ss}(\omega)$, $G_{sn}(\omega)$, and $G_{nn}(\omega)$ is a rational function of ω. If these spectra are known nonrational functions, or if they are only known empirically, they must be approximated by rational functions before this method can be used. The discussion of a technique by which this may be accomplished is given in Appendix D.

With the various input spectral densities satisfying the above condition we wish to reduce the necessary integrals to a certain standard form defined below and evaluated in Appendix E. As the first step we consider the term $|Y_1(j\omega)|^2 G_{ss}(\omega)$.

The power spectral density is a real-valued, even, nonnegative function of ω for real values of ω. In the present discussion we are also assuming it to be a rational function, so that it is expressible as the ratio of two polynomials in ω, with real coefficients and with only even powers of ω present.

The roots of a polynomial with real coefficients are either real or occur in complex conjugate pairs. If in addition the polynomial is an even function, for every root ω_k there is a corresponding root $-\omega_k$. Therefore, pure real and pure imaginary roots occur in pairs as $(u_k, -u_k)$ and $(jv_k, -jv_k)$, respectively, while complex roots occur in sets of four $(\omega_k, \omega_k^*, -\omega_k, -\omega_k^*)$ placed symmetrically with respect to both real and imaginary axes.

If we now write

$$G_{ss}(\omega) = \frac{A(\omega)}{B(\omega)} \tag{5.5-2}$$

where A and B are two such polynomials, then $B(\omega)$ can have no real roots; otherwise, $G_{ss}(\omega)$ would contain a pole on the real axis, and would not possess a finite integral. It is of course understood that any common factors in $A(\omega)$ and $B(\omega)$ are deleted. Since $G_{ss}(\omega) \geq 0$ for all real values of ω, it also follows that the value of $A(\omega)$ cannot change sign. Thus any real root which $A(\omega)$ may possess must be a multiple root of even order.

From the above discussion, $B(\omega)$ may be expressed in the factored form

$$B(\omega) = c \prod_k (\omega - \omega_k)(\omega - \omega_k^*)(\omega + \omega_k)(\omega + \omega_k^*)$$

$$\times \prod_m (\omega - jv_m)(\omega + jv_m) \tag{5.5-3}$$

We specify that ω_k, $-\omega_k^*$, and jv_m all lie in the upper half plane and define

$$Q(\omega) = \sqrt{c} \prod_k (\omega - \omega_k)(\omega + \omega_k^*) \prod_m (\omega - jv_m) \tag{5.5-4}$$

Then $B(\omega)$ can be expressed in the factored form

$$B(\omega) = \pm Q(\omega)Q(-\omega) \tag{5.5-5}$$

As a result of this discussion, we have shown that $G_{ss}(\omega)$ can be written as

$$G_{ss}(\omega) = \pm \frac{A(\omega)}{Q(\omega)Q(-\omega)}$$

$$= \frac{P(\omega)}{Q(\omega)Q(-\omega)} \qquad (5.5\text{-}6)$$

where $P(\omega)$ = a polynomial in ω^2 with real coefficients

$Q(\omega)$ = a polynomial whose roots all lie in the upper half plane and are symmetrically placed with respect to the imaginary axis

Now let us observe that a transfer function of a stable lumped-parameter system is a rational function of the complex variable $p = j\omega$ with real coefficients so that its zeros and poles are symmetrically placed about the real axis. Furthermore, this transfer function has no poles in the right half plane. It will be convenient here to consider the transfer function $Y(j\omega)$ as a rational function of ω instead of $j\omega$. To emphasize this we define a new function $\tilde{Y}(\omega)$ as

$$\tilde{Y}(\omega) = Y(j\omega)$$

The poles and zeros of $\tilde{Y}(\omega)$ are rotated $90°$ clockwise from those of $Y(j\omega)$ so that they are symmetric with respect to the imaginary axis. Furthermore, $\tilde{Y}(\omega)$ has no poles in the lower half of the ω plane.

From the above discussion we may conclude that for real values of ω

$$|Y_1(j\omega)|^2 = |\tilde{Y}_1(\omega)|^2 = \tilde{Y}_1(\omega)\tilde{Y}_1(\omega)^*$$

is a rational function of ω^2. The poles and zeros of this rational function are distributed symmetrically about the real and imaginary axis.[1] Thus, the term $|Y_1(j\omega)|^2 G_{ss}(\omega)$ has the same properties as $G_{ss}(\omega)$, and we may write

$$|Y_1(j\omega)|^2 G_{ss}(\omega) = \frac{g_n(\omega)}{h_n(\omega)h_n(-\omega)} \qquad (5.5\text{-}7)$$

where
$$h_n(\omega) = a_0\omega^n + a_1\omega^{n-1} + \cdots + a_n \qquad (5.5\text{-}8)$$
$$g_n(\omega) = b_0\omega^{2n-2} + b_1\omega^{2n-4} + \cdots + b_{n-1} \qquad (5.5\text{-}9)$$

and the roots of $h_n(\omega)$ all lie in the upper half plane. We note that the degree of $g_n(\omega)$ must be at least two less than the degree of $h_n(\omega)h_n(-\omega)$ in order that the integral from $-\infty$ to $+\infty$ of Eq. (5.5-7) exist.

The same argument used above applies also to the term $|Y_n(j\omega)|^2 G_{nn}(\omega)$.

---

[1] Note, however, that $Y_1(j\omega)$ may not be physically realizable if the idealized operator involves prediction. In this case the discussion must be modified (cf. Example 5.5-3).

Having disposed of the first and fourth terms of Eq. (5.4-13), let us now consider the rational function composed of the sum of the two remaining terms

$$Y_1(j\omega)^*Y_n(j\omega)G_{sn}(\omega) + Y_1(j\omega)Y_n(j\omega)^*G_{ns}(\omega)$$
$$= \tilde{Y}_1(\omega)^*\tilde{Y}_n(\omega)G_{sn}(\omega) + \tilde{Y}_1(\omega)\tilde{Y}_n(\omega)^*G_{ns}(\omega) \quad (5.5\text{-}10)$$

Since $G_{ns}(\omega) = G_{sn}(\omega)^*$ for real ω, it is clear that the two terms of Eq. (5.5-10) are complex conjugates. Hence, their sum is a real function for real values of ω. Furthermore, we observe that since

$$G_{sn}(-\omega^*) = \frac{1}{\pi} \int_{-\infty}^{\infty} \phi_{sn}(\tau)e^{j\omega^*\tau}\, d\tau$$

we have

$$G_{sn}(-\omega^*)^* = \frac{1}{\pi} \int_{-\infty}^{\infty} \phi_{sn}(\tau)e^{-j\omega\tau}\, d\tau = G_{sn}(\omega) \quad (5.5\text{-}11)$$

Thus, the zeros and poles of $G_{sn}(\omega)$ are symmetrically placed about the imaginary axis. The same remark applies to $G_{ns}(\omega)$. In addition, since

$$G_{sn}(\omega) = \frac{1}{\pi} \int_{-\infty}^{\infty} \phi_{sn}(\tau)e^{-j\omega\tau}\, d\tau = \frac{1}{\pi} \int_{-\infty}^{\infty} \phi_{ns}(-\tau)e^{j\omega(-\tau)}\, d\tau$$
$$= \frac{1}{\pi} \int_{-\infty}^{\infty} \phi_{ns}(\tau)e^{j\omega\tau}\, d\tau = G_{ns}(\omega^*)^* \quad (5.5\text{-}12)$$

it follows that the zeros and poles of $G_{sn}(\omega)$ are the complex conjugates of those of $G_{ns}(\omega)$. Thus, the zeros and poles of the function

$$\tilde{Y}_1(\omega)^*\tilde{Y}_n(\omega)G_{sn}(\omega) + \tilde{Y}_1(\omega)\tilde{Y}_n(\omega)^*G_{ns}(\omega)$$

are located symmetrically about both the real and imaginary axis. Hence, this function satisfies all the requirements necessary to be expressible in the form

$$\frac{g_n(\omega)}{h_n(\omega)h_n(-\omega)}$$

where g_n and h_n are of the form given in Eqs. (5.5-8) and (5.5-9).

From the above discussion we may now conclude that the problem of evaluating the integral of Eq. (5.5-1) is equivalent to evaluating integrals of the form

$$\int_{-\infty}^{\infty} \frac{g_n(\omega)}{h_n(\omega)h_n(-\omega)}\, d\omega$$

The evaluation of this integral is given in Appendix E.

Example 5.5-1. The position of a target moving in a straight line is denoted by $x(t)$. A simple predictor determines its position at time T seconds later according to the formula

$$x_p(t) = x(t) + Tv(t) \quad (5.5\text{-}13)$$

The velocity $v(t)$ is determined by supplying the observed positional information to a differentiating network whose transfer function is given by

$$Y(p) = \frac{p}{1 + T_0 p} \qquad (5.5\text{-}14)$$

Due to random inaccuracies the observed position of the target differs from the true position by an amount $n(t)$. If this difference, i.e., the noise, belongs to a stationary random process with a spectral density given by

$$G_{nn}(\omega) = \frac{A}{\omega^2 + a^2} \qquad (5.5\text{-}15)$$

and if it is assumed that the signal and noise are uncorrelated, the problem is to determine the mean-squared output of the prediction system due to the presence of the noise alone.

Let $\epsilon(t)$ be the output of the predictor when $n(t)$ is the only input. Let $N(t)$ be the output of the differentiating network when $n(t)$ is the input. Then from Eq. (5.5-13) we have

$$\epsilon(t) = n(t) + TN(t) \qquad (5.5\text{-}16)$$

The relation between the input and output correlation functions is then

$$\phi_{\epsilon\epsilon}(\tau) = \overline{\epsilon(t)\epsilon(t + \tau)}$$
$$= \phi_{nn}(\tau) + T[\phi_{nN}(\tau) + \phi_{Nn}(\tau)] + T^2\phi_{NN}(\tau) \qquad (5.5\text{-}17)$$

Taking the Fourier transform leads to a corresponding relation between the input and output spectral densities.

$$G_{\epsilon\epsilon}(\omega) = G_{nn}(\omega) + T[G_{nN}(\omega) + G_{Nn}(\omega)] + T^2 G_{NN}(\omega) \qquad (5.5\text{-}18)$$

According to the procedure described in Sec. 5.3 we obtain the following values for the input spectral densities.

$$G_{nn}(\omega) = \frac{A}{\omega^2 + a^2} \qquad (5.5\text{-}19)$$

$$G_{Nn}(\omega) = \frac{A}{\omega^2 + a^2} \frac{j\omega}{1 + j\omega T_0} = G_{nN}(\omega)^* \qquad (5.5\text{-}20)$$

$$G_{NN}(\omega) = \frac{A}{\omega^2 + a^2} \left| \frac{j\omega}{1 + j\omega T_0} \right|^2 \qquad (5.5\text{-}21)$$

Using these values, Eq. (5.5-18) becomes

$$G_{\epsilon\epsilon}(\omega) = \frac{A}{\omega^2 + a^2} \left[1 + T \frac{2\omega^2 T_0}{1 + \omega^2 T_0^2} + T^2 \frac{\omega^2}{1 + \omega^2 T_0^2} \right] \qquad (5.5\text{-}22)$$

The mean-squared error is then computed according to Eq. (5.5-1).

Since
$$\int_{-\infty}^{\infty} \frac{d\omega}{\omega^2 + a^2} = \frac{\pi}{2a} \qquad (5.5\text{-}23)$$

we need only concern ourselves with the following integral

$$J = \int_{-\infty}^{\infty} \frac{\omega^2}{(\omega^2 + a^2)(1 + \omega^2 T_0^2)} d\omega \qquad (5.5\text{-}24)$$

which is of the form discussed in Appendix E if we write

$$h_2(\omega) = -T_0\omega^2 + j(1 + aT_0)\omega + a$$
$$g_2(\omega) = \omega^2$$

Comparing with Eqs. (E-2) and (E-3), we see that

$$
\begin{aligned}
a_0 &= -T_0 & b_0 &= 1 \\
a_1 &= j(1 + aT_0) & b_1 &= 0 \\
a_2 &= a
\end{aligned}
$$

According to Eqs. (E-1) and (E-15) we see that our integral J is given by

$$J = 2\pi j I_2 = 2\pi j \frac{(-1)^{2+1} N_2}{2a_0 \; D_2} = -\frac{\pi j}{a_0} \frac{N_2}{D_2} \tag{5.5-25}$$

The denominator determinant D_2 is

$$D_2 = \begin{vmatrix} d_{11} & d_{12} \\ d_{21} & d_{22} \end{vmatrix} = \begin{vmatrix} a_1 & a_0 \\ a_3 & a_2 \end{vmatrix} = \begin{vmatrix} a_1 & a_0 \\ 0 & a_2 \end{vmatrix} \tag{5.5-26}$$

according to Eq. (E-16). The numerator determinant N_2 is found from D_2 by replacing the elements of the first column of D_2 by b_0 and b_1. Thus

$$N_2 = \begin{vmatrix} b_0 & a_0 \\ b_1 & a_2 \end{vmatrix} \tag{5.5-27}$$

In our particular case

$$
\begin{aligned}
D_2 &= a_1 a_2 = ja(1 + aT_0) \\
N_2 &= b_0 a_2 - b_1 a_0 = a
\end{aligned}
$$

so that substitution into Eq. (5.5-25) yields

$$J = \frac{-\pi j}{-T_0} \frac{a}{ja(1 + aT_0)} = \frac{\pi}{T_0(1 + aT_0)}$$

Finally, by combining our results, we obtain for the mean-squared error

$$
\begin{aligned}
\overline{\epsilon^2} &= \frac{\pi A}{4a} + \frac{J}{2}(2T_0 TA + AT^2) \\
&= \frac{\pi A}{2}\left(\frac{1}{2a} + \frac{2T_0 T + T^2}{T_0(1 + aT_0)}\right)
\end{aligned} \tag{5.5-28}
$$

Example 5.5-2. A servo follow-up system consisting of a filter and a motor is shown in Fig. 5.5-1. The input $s(t)$ is a modulated sine wave of random phase and amplitude, that is,

$$s(t) = x(t)\sin(\omega_0 t + \phi) \tag{5.5-29}$$

The phase angle ϕ is a random variable uniformly distributed over the interval $(0,2\pi)$ and is independent of the amplitude. The amplitude $x(t)$ belongs to a stationary random process and has a correlation function given by

$$\phi_{xx}(\tau) = Ae^{-a|\tau|} \tag{5.5-30}$$

The transfer functions for the filter and motor are as indicated in the figure. The problem is to compute the mean-squared error by which the motor fails to follow the input signal.

First, we must compute the correlation function of the signal $s(t)$.   We have

$$\phi_{ss}(\tau) = \overline{s(t)s(t+\tau)}$$
$$= \overline{x(t)x(t+\tau) \sin (\omega_0 t + \phi) \sin [\omega_0(t+\tau) + \phi]}$$
$$= \phi_{xx}(\tau) \overline{\sin (\omega_0 t + \phi) \sin [\omega_0(t+\tau) + \phi]} \qquad (5.5\text{-}31)$$

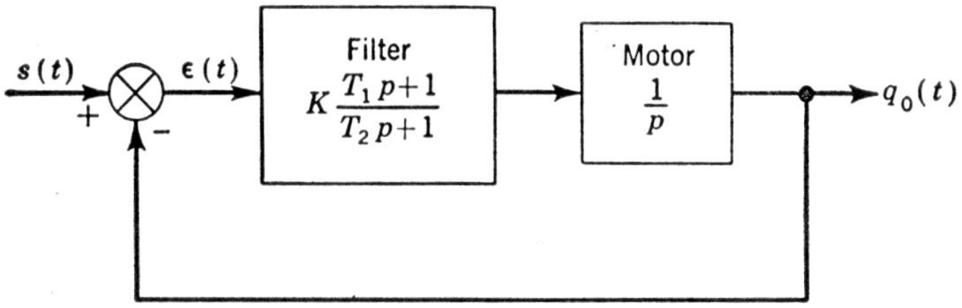

FIG. 5.5-1

because of the assumed independence in amplitude and phase.   Since ϕ is a uniformly distributed random variable, the second factor in Eq. (5.5-31) is equivalent to the following integral:

$$\frac{1}{2\pi} \int_0^{2\pi} \sin (\omega_0 t + \phi) \sin [\omega_0(t+\tau) + \phi] \, d\phi = \tfrac{1}{2} \cos \omega_0 \tau$$

Thus
$$\phi_{ss}(\tau) = \tfrac{1}{2} A e^{-a|\tau|} \cos \omega_0 \tau \qquad (5.5\text{-}32)$$

and the corresponding spectral density is obtained by

$$G_{ss}(\omega) = \frac{2}{\pi} \int_0^\infty \phi_{ss}(\tau) \cos \omega\tau \, d\tau$$
$$= \frac{Aa}{\pi} \frac{a^2 + \omega_0^2 + \omega^2}{\omega^4 + 2(a^2 - \omega_0^2)\omega^2 + (a^2 + \omega_0^2)^2} \qquad (5.5\text{-}33)$$

The transfer function for the system of Fig. 5.5-1 regarding $s(t)$ as input and $\epsilon(t)$ as output is easily seen to be

$$Y(p) = \frac{\dfrac{K}{p} \dfrac{T_1 p + 1}{T_2 p + 1}}{1 + \dfrac{K}{p} \dfrac{T_1 p + 1}{T_2 p + 1}}$$
$$= K \frac{T_1 p + 1}{T_2 p^2 + (KT_1 + 1)p + K} \qquad (5.5\text{-}34)$$

The spectral density of $\epsilon(t)$ is then found from

$$G_{\epsilon\epsilon}(\omega) = |Y(j\omega)|^2 G_{ss}(\omega) \qquad (5.5\text{-}35)$$

so that the mean-squared error is obtained as indicated in Eq. (5.5-1).   Thus, we have

$$\overline{\epsilon^2} = \frac{AaK^2}{\pi} \int_{-\infty}^\infty \frac{g_4(\omega)}{h_4(\omega)h_4(-\omega)} \, d\omega \qquad (5.5\text{-}36)$$

where
$$g_4(\omega) = T_1^2 \omega^4 + [T_1^2(a^2 + \omega_0^2) + 1]\omega^2 + (a^2 + \omega_0^2) \qquad (5.5\text{-}37)$$
$$h_4(\omega) = [T_2(j\omega)^2 + (KT_1 + 1)j\omega + K][(j\omega)^2 + 2aj\omega + (a^2 + \omega_0^2)]$$
$$= T_2\omega^4 - j(KT_1 + 1 + 2aT_2)\omega^3$$
$$\quad - [K + 2a(KT_1 + 1) + T_2(a^2 + \omega_0^2)]\omega^2$$
$$\quad + j[2aK + (KT_1 + 1)(a^2 + \omega_0^2)]\omega + K(a^2 + \omega_0^2) \qquad (5.5\text{-}38)$$

By a comparison with Eqs. (E-2) and (E-3) we see that

$$a_0 = T_2$$
$$a_1 = -j(KT_1 + 1 + 2aT_2)$$
$$a_2 = -[K + 2a(KT_1 + 1) + T_2(a^2 + \omega_0^2)]$$
$$a_3 = j[2aK + (KT_1 + 1)(a^2 + \omega_0^2)]$$
$$a_4 = K(a^2 + \omega_0^2)$$
$$b_0 = 0 \qquad b_2 = T_1^2(a^2 + \omega_0^2) + 1$$
$$b_1 = T_1^2 \qquad b_3 = a^2 + \omega_0^2$$

Comparing Eqs. (5.5-36) and (E-1), we see that

$$\overline{\epsilon^2} = 2jAaK^2I_4 \tag{5.5-39}$$

and from Eq. (E-15)

$$\overline{\epsilon^2} = \frac{(-1)^{4+1}}{2a_0} 2jAaK^2 \frac{N_4}{D_4} \tag{5.5-40}$$

The denominator determinant is formed as described by Eq. (E-16)

$$D_4 = \begin{vmatrix} a_1 & a_0 & 0 & 0 \\ a_3 & a_2 & a_1 & a_0 \\ 0 & a_4 & a_3 & a_2 \\ 0 & 0 & 0 & a_4 \end{vmatrix}$$
$$= a_1a_2a_3a_4 - a_0a_3^2a_4 - a_1^2a_4^2 \tag{5.5-41}$$

The numerator determinant is given by

$$N_4 = \begin{vmatrix} 0 & a_0 & 0 & 0 \\ T_1^2 & a_2 & a_1 & a_0 \\ T_1^2(a^2 + \omega_0^2) + 1 & a_4 & a_3 & a_2 \\ (a^2 + \omega_0^2) & 0 & 0 & a_4 \end{vmatrix}$$
$$= (a^2 + \omega_0^2)(a_0^2a_3 - a_0a_1a_2 + a_0a_1a_4T_1^2) - a_0a_3a_4T_1^2 + a_0a_1a_4 \tag{5.5-42}$$

Finally, we have

$$\overline{\epsilon^2} = AaK^2j \frac{(a^2 + \omega_0^2)(a_0a_3 - a_1a_2 + a_1a_4T_1^2) - a_3a_4T_1^2 + a_1a_4}{a_1^2a_4^2 + a_0a_3^2a_4 - a_1a_2a_3a_4} \tag{5.5-43}$$

where the various constants are defined above.

The integration formula derived in Appendix E cannot be applied when the performance of the ideal system is prescribed to be a pure prediction. From the table of Sec. 5.4 we see that the transfer function for an ideal predictor is

$$Y_I(j\omega) = e^{j\omega T} \tag{5.5-44}$$

When an integrand contains exponential factors of this form, then other methods must be used for evaluating the relevant integrals. For example, one might use a table of definite integrals or the Cauchy residue theorem of complex variable theory.

Example 5.5-3. In Sec. 7.2 it is shown that the optimum linear predictor for a signal $s(t)$ whose spectral density is

$$G_{ss}(\omega) = \frac{1}{1 + \omega^2} \qquad (5.5\text{-}45)$$

is given by

$$Y_s(j\omega) = e^{-T} \qquad (5.5\text{-}46)$$

where T is the amount by which the output of the predictor is to lead the input. From Eq. (5.4-13) we have

$$\begin{aligned}
G_{\epsilon\epsilon}(\omega) &= |e^{-T} - e^{j\omega T}|^2 \frac{1}{1 + \omega^2} \\
&= \frac{1 + e^{-2T} - 2e^{-T} \cos \omega T}{1 + \omega^2} \qquad (5.5\text{-}47)
\end{aligned}$$

Then the mean-squared error, found by integrating this equation, is

$$\overline{\epsilon^2} = \frac{\pi}{2}(1 - e^{-2T}) \qquad (5.5\text{-}48)$$

The ideas developed so far may be used to optimize the parameters in an existing or proposed system. After first obtaining an expression for the mean-squared error in terms of the parameters of the system, the optimum parameter values may be determined, using ordinary minimizing techniques of the calculus.

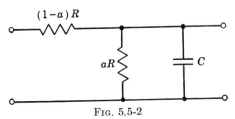

FIG. 5.5-2

Example 5.5-4. It is desired to design a voltage divider and filter combination of the form shown in Fig. 5.5-2. The desired portion of the input is a pure sine wave

$$s(t) = \sin \omega_0 t \qquad (5.5\text{-}49)$$

while the noise portion is white noise with a spectrum given by

$$G_{nn}(\omega) = A \qquad (5.5\text{-}50)$$

The system is required to attenuate the signal portion by the amount a and do the best possible filtering of the noise. Thus, we are to select the time constant

$$T = RC \qquad (5.5\text{-}51)$$

so that the mean-squared error will be a minimum.

The transfer function of the system is easily found to be

$$Y_s(p) = Y_n(p) = \frac{aR}{R + a(1 - a)R^2 Cp} = \frac{a}{1 + a(1 - a)Tp} \qquad (5.5\text{-}52)$$

From the conditions imposed on the system performance the ideal transfer function is simply

$$Y_I(p) = a \tag{5.5-53}$$

Thus
$$Y_1(p) = Y_s(p) - Y_I(p) = -\frac{a^2(1 - a)Tp}{1 + a(1 - a)Tp} \tag{5.5-54}$$

The spectral density of the signal portion of the input is found by direct application of the definition given in Eq. (3.6-24). We obtain

$$G(\omega) = \lim_{T \to \infty} \frac{1}{T} \left| \frac{1}{\sqrt{2\pi}} \int_{-T}^{T} e^{-j\omega t} \sin \omega_0 t \, dt \right|^2$$

$$= \frac{1}{2\pi} \lim_{T \to \infty} \frac{1}{T} \left| \frac{\sin (\omega_0 - \omega)T}{\omega_0 - \omega} + \frac{\sin (\omega_0 + \omega)T}{\omega_0 + \omega} \right|^2 \tag{5.5-55}$$

Since $G(\omega)$ is an even function of ω, we need consider only positive values of ω. If $\omega \neq \omega_0$, it is clear from Eq. (5.5-55) that $G(\omega) = 0$. On the other hand if we let $\omega \to \omega_0$ before allowing T to become infinite, we see that $G(\omega_0) = \infty$. Furthermore,

$$\int_0^\infty G(\omega) \, d\omega = \frac{1}{2\pi} \lim_{T \to \infty} \frac{1}{T} \left[\int_0^\infty \frac{\sin^2 (\omega_0 - \omega)T}{(\omega_0 - \omega)^2} \, d\omega \right.$$

$$+ 2 \int_0^\infty \frac{\sin (\omega_0 - \omega)T}{\omega_0 - \omega} \frac{\sin (\omega_0 + \omega)T}{\omega_0 + \omega} \, d\omega$$

$$\left. + \int_0^\infty \frac{\sin^2 (\omega_0 + \omega)T}{(\omega_0 + \omega)^2} \, d\omega \right]$$

$$= \frac{1}{2\pi} \lim_{T \to \infty} \frac{1}{T} \left[T \int_{-\infty}^{\omega_0 T} \frac{\sin^2 x}{x^2} \, dx \right.$$

$$\left. + 2T \int_{\omega_0 T}^\infty \frac{\sin (2\omega_0 T - x)}{2\omega_0 T - x} \frac{\sin x}{x} \, dx + T \int_{\omega_0 T}^\infty \frac{\sin^2 x}{x^2} \, dx \right] \tag{5.5-56}$$

The first and third of these integrals may be combined. Clearly, the second tends to zero with increasing T. The result is

$$\int_0^\infty G(\omega) \, dw = \frac{1}{2\pi} \int_{-\infty}^\infty \frac{\sin^2 x}{x^2} \, dx = \frac{1}{2} \tag{5.5-57}$$

Therefore, from the definition of the δ function we may write

$$G(\omega) = \tfrac{1}{2}\delta(\omega - \omega_0) \tag{5.5-58}$$

The computations leading to Eq. (5.5-58) should be compared with those of Example 3.6-2.

With the completion of these preliminaries we may return to the basic problem. The spectral density of the error in performance of the voltage divider is obtained from Eq. (5.4-13) with the result

$$G_{\epsilon\epsilon}(\omega) = \frac{1}{2} \frac{a^4(1 - a)^2 T^2 \omega^2}{1 + a^2(1 - a)^2 T^2 \omega^2} \delta(\omega - \omega_0) + \frac{a^2}{1 + a^2(1 - a)^2 T^2 \omega^2} A \tag{5.5-59}$$

Integrating this expression from zero to infinity yields

$$\overline{\epsilon^2} = \frac{1}{2} \left[\frac{a^4(1 - a)^2 T^2 \omega_0^2}{1 + a^2(1 - a)^2 T^2 \omega_0^2} + \frac{\pi a A}{(1 - a)T} \right] \tag{5.5-60}$$

If ω_0 is zero, that is, if the signal is direct current, the mean-squared error may be reduced by increasing the time constant T. In other cases the value of T yielding a minimum mean-squared error is found by setting the derivative of Eq. (5.5-60) equal to zero.   The result is

$$2a^3(1 - a)^3\omega_0^2 T^3 = \pi A[1 + a^2(1 - a)^2\omega_0^2 T^2]^2 \tag{5.5-61}$$

This equation yields two positive real roots, provided that A is small enough.   Since $\overline{\epsilon^2}$ is a continuous differentiable function of T which becomes infinite as $T \to 0$ and approaches $a^2/2$ as $T \to \infty$, it is clear that the smaller of these two roots gives the value of T_0 that actually does provide the desired solution of the problem.

We shall close this section by showing how a general stationary random process possessing a rational spectrum (or, alternatively, one that can be approximated by a rational spectrum) can be generated from white noise. In the discussion accompanying Eq. (5.5-2) it was shown that a rational spectral density $G(\omega)$ may be factored in the form

$$G(\omega) = H_1(\omega)H_2(\omega) \tag{5.5-62}$$

where $H_1(\omega)$ and $H_2(\omega)$ satisfy the following conditions:
1. $H_1(\omega)$ is a function which is bounded and analytic in the lower half plane.   Its poles and zeros lie in the upper half plane and coincide with the poles and zeros of $G(\omega)$ there.
2. $H_2(\omega)$ has complementary properties.
3. For real values of ω,

$$H_2(\omega) = H_1(\omega)^* \tag{5.5-63}$$

Thus, for real values of ω, we have

$$G(\omega) = H_1(\omega)H_1(\omega)^* = |H_1(\omega)|^2 \tag{5.5-64}$$

We observe that $H_1(\omega)$ possesses all the properties required of a transfer function for a stable time-invariant linear system.

Consider now a white noise possessing a correlation function and spectral density given by

$$\phi_{nn}(\tau) = \delta(\tau) \qquad G_{nn}(\omega) = \frac{1}{\pi} \tag{5.5-65}$$

If this white noise is passed through a filter with transfer function $Y(j\omega)$, the spectrum of the output is obtained by

$$G(\omega) = \frac{|Y(j\omega)|^2}{\pi} \tag{5.5-66}$$

By comparing Eqs. (5.5-66) and (5.5-64) we may make the following observation.   A random process having the spectrum $G(\omega)$ may be generated by passing a white noise whose spectrum is given by Eq. (5.5-65) through a filter whose transfer function is defined by

$$\tilde{Y}(\omega) = Y(j\omega) = \sqrt{\pi}\, H_1(\omega) \tag{5.5-67}$$

Henceforth, we shall refer to such a filter as a *shaping filter*.

Example 5.5-5. By way of illustration we shall construct a shaping filter for the spectrum

$$G(\omega) = \frac{1 + a^2\omega^2}{(1 + b^2\omega^2)(1 + c^2\omega^2)}$$

The two functions

$$H_1(\omega) = \frac{1 + aj\omega}{(1 + bj\omega)(1 + cj\omega)}$$

$$H_2(\omega) = \frac{1 - aj\omega}{(1 - bj\omega)(1 - cj\omega)}$$

are readily seen to possess the required properties. The transfer function of the appropriate shaping filter is then

$$Y(p) = \sqrt{\pi}\, \frac{1 + ap}{(1 + bp)(1 + cp)}$$

Example 5.5-6. To construct a shaping filter for a random process whose correlation function is given by

$$\phi(\tau) = A e^{-c|\tau|}$$

we first obtain the corresponding spectral density from

$$G(w) = \frac{2}{\pi} \int_0^\infty A e^{-c\tau} \cos \omega\tau\, d\tau = \frac{2}{\pi}\frac{Ac}{c^2 + \omega^2}$$

Hence

$$Y(j\omega) = \sqrt{\pi}\, H_1(\omega) = \sqrt{2Ac}\, \frac{1}{c + j\omega}$$

5.6 Analogue Computation Techniques

Having completed a detailed discussion of the various analytical techniques available for analyzing linear constant-coefficient systems with stationary random inputs, we shall now consider several simulator methods which can often be used to advantage where analytical methods become too burdensome to carry through in practice. The various methods to be discussed have relative advantages and disadvantages so that the particular choice of method to be used depends upon the nature of the problem, the amount of simulator equipment available, the number of times the calculation is to be made, and other similar factors.

Consider a linear constant-coefficient system with a single stationary random input $x(t)$ and output $y(t)$. If we let $W(t)$ denote the weighting function of the system, then we have, from Sec. 5.3, the following relation existing between the input and output correlation functions.

$$\phi_{yy}(\tau) = \int_0^\infty W(\tau_1)\, d\tau_1 \int_0^\infty W(\tau_2) \phi_{xx}(\tau - \tau_2 + \tau_1)\, d\tau_2 \qquad (5.6\text{-}1)$$

All our simulator techniques will depend upon an appropriate physical interpretation of the meaning of this relationship.

Method I. The first method to be discussed provides a practical technique for obtaining in graphical form the output correlation function of the system from an empirically determined input correlation function.

Let us make the following change of variable in Eq. (5.6-1)

$$\tau + \tau_1 = -t \qquad (5.6-2)$$

so that we have

$$\phi_{yy}(\tau) = \int_{-\infty}^{-\tau} W(-\tau - t) \, dt \int_{0}^{\infty} W(\tau_2)\phi_{xx}(-t - \tau_2) \, d\tau_2 \qquad (5.6-3)$$

Since $\phi_{yy}(\tau)$ is an even function of τ so that $\phi_{yy}(\tau) = \phi_{yy}(-\tau)$, we may rewrite Eq. (5.6-3) to give

$$\phi_{yy}(\tau) = \int_{-\infty}^{\tau} W(\tau - t) \, dt \int_{0}^{\infty} W(\tau_2)\phi_{xx}(-t - \tau_2) \, d\tau_2 \qquad (5.6-4)$$

For the purpose of physical interpretation of this relationship it is convenient to write Eq. (5.6-4) as two equations in the following manner.

$$z(t) = \int_{0}^{\infty} W(\tau_2)\phi_{xx}(t - \tau_2) \, d\tau_2 \qquad (5.6-5)$$

$$\phi_{yy}(\tau) = \int_{-\infty}^{\tau} W(\tau - t)z(-t) \, dt \qquad (5.6-6)$$

Equation (5.6-5) shows that $z(t)$ is the response of the system in question at time t when the input to the system is the forcing function $\phi_{xx}(t)$. Then from Eq. (5.6-6) we see that $\phi_{yy}(\tau)$ is the response of the system at time τ when the input is the forcing function $z(-\tau)$. Thus we have the following procedure for obtaining $\phi_{yy}(\tau)$ from $\phi_{xx}(\tau)$ using simulator equipment:

1. The particular system to be studied is simulated using analogue equipment.

2. $\phi_{xx}(t)$ is fed into this system and the output $z(t)$ is recorded.[1]

3. This output is then used as an input and the direction of the time drive is reversed. The input, which is now $z(-t)$, is then fed into the original system and the output is again recorded. The result will be a graph of the output correlation function $\phi_{yy}(t)$. In particular the value of this output at $t = 0$ will be the mean-squared response of the system with $x(t)$ as input. This procedure is indicated schematically in Fig. 5.6-1.

Method II. The second method to be considered provides a means of obtaining a value of $\phi_{yy}(t)$ for any prescribed value of t by means of a single simulator test.

We introduce the following change of variable in Eq. (5.6-1)

$$\tau + \tau_1 = t \qquad (5.6-7)$$

so that we have

$$\phi_{yy}(\tau) = \int_{\tau}^{\infty} W(t - \tau) \, dt \int_{0}^{\infty} W(\tau_2)\phi_{xx}(t - \tau_2) \, d\tau_2 \qquad (5.6-8)$$

[1] Note that $\phi_{xx}(t)$ must be used for both negative and positive values of t.

Again, for the purpose of physical interpretation, let us write Eq. (5.6-8) as two equations as follows.

$$z(t) = \int_0^\infty W(\tau_2)\phi_{xx}(t - \tau_2)\, d\tau_2 \tag{5.6-9}$$

$$\phi_{yy}(\tau) = \int_\tau^\infty W(t - \tau)z(t)\, dt = \int_{-\infty}^\infty W(t - \tau)z(t)\, dt \tag{5.6-10}$$

The interval of integration may be extended to minus infinity in Eq. (5.6-10) since $W(t)$ is zero for negative values of the argument.

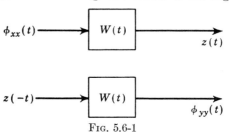

FIG. 5.6-1

As before, $z(t)$ is the response of the system at time t when the input to the system is the forcing function $\phi_{xx}(t)$. $W(t - \tau)$ is, of course, the response of the system at time t due to a unit impulse input initiated at time τ. We may now describe a procedure for obtaining $\phi_{yy}(\tau)$ for a fixed value of τ from $\phi_{xx}(t)$ using simulator equipment:

1. Two identical simulations of the particular system to be studied are made using analogue equipment.

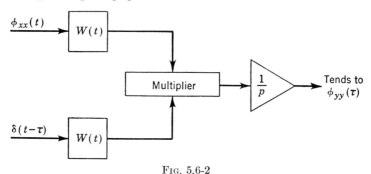

FIG. 5.6-2

2. $\phi_{xx}(t)$ is fed into one of these systems and τ seconds after time $t = 0$ is reached a unit impulse is applied to the input of the other system.

3. The outputs of these two systems are multiplied together and the product integrated. The output of this integrator approaches $\phi_{yy}(\tau)$ asymptotically as t tends to infinity. This procedure is illustrated schematically in Fig. 5.6-2.

Method III. In applying the third method it will be assumed that the input spectrum of $x(t)$ can be approximated by a rational function and the necessary factorization carried out, as discussed in Sec. 5.5, so that an appropriate shaping filter can be found. If the system under discussion is preceded by this shaping filter, then a white noise input to the over-all system will produce the same output $y(t)$ as is produced by $x(t)$ for the original system. Let us denote the weighting function of these two systems in cascade by $W_1(t)$. Since the correlation function of white noise is simply

$$\phi_{nn}(\tau) = \delta(\tau) \tag{5.6-11}$$

Eq. (5.6-1) becomes

$$\phi_{yy}(\tau) = \int_0^\infty W_1(\tau_1)\, d\tau_1 \int_0^\infty W_1(\tau_2)\delta(\tau - \tau_2 + \tau_1)\, d\tau_2$$
$$= \int_0^\infty W_1(\tau_1)W_1(\tau + \tau_1)\, d\tau_1 \tag{5.6-12}$$

For the special case in which $\tau = 0$ we have

$$\overline{\epsilon^2} = \int_0^\infty W_1(\tau)^2\, d\tau \tag{5.6-13}$$

The simulator technique for obtaining $\overline{\epsilon^2}$ is illustrated in Fig. 5.6-3.

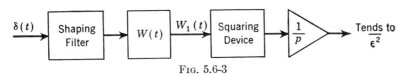

FIG. 5.6-3

When τ is not zero, we may compute $\phi_{yy}(\tau)$ for a fixed value of τ in the following manner. Let us make a change of variable in Eq. (5.6-12) given by

$$\tau + \tau_1 = t \tag{5.6-14}$$

so that we obtain

$$\phi_{yy}(\tau) = \int_\tau^\infty W_1(t - \tau)W(t)\, dt = \int_0^\infty W_1(t - \tau)W(t)\, dt \tag{5.6-15}$$

Here again the interval of integration may be extended in Eq. (5.6-15) since $W(t)$ is zero for negative values of the argument. We may now describe a procedure for obtaining $\phi_{yy}(\tau)$, using simulator equipment:

1. Two identical simulations of the original system cascaded with the shaping filter are made.

2. To one of these is applied a unit impulse and τ seconds later the other is excited by a unit impulse.

3. The outputs of these two systems are multiplied together and the product integrated. The output of this integrator approaches $\phi_{yy}(\tau)$

asymptotically as t tends to infinity. This procedure is shown schematically in Fig. 5.6-4.

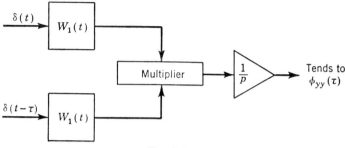

FIG. 5.6-4

PROBLEMS

5-1. In the two-stage RC network shown below, with input voltage E_i and output E_o, for each stage $R = 1$ megohm and $C = 1$ microfarad. Assuming the output impedance to be infinite, calculate the weighting function for the network (*a*) under the assumption that the switch S is always closed; (*b*) under the assumption that the switch S is open before the instant $t = 0$ and closed thereafter.

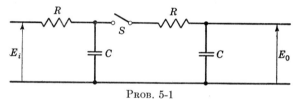

PROB. 5-1

5-2. For the network shown below, with infinite output impedance, show how this system could be simulated using only standard analogue integrators, amplifiers, and potentiometers.

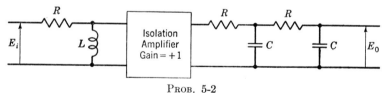

PROB. 5-2

5-3. Two time-invariant linear systems, with respective weighting functions $W_1(t)$ and $W_2(t)$, are connected in series as shown below. Show that the weighting function of the series combination is given by a convolution integral.

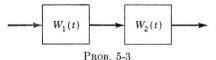

PROB. 5-3

5-4. For the network in Prob. 5-1, with the switch S always closed, a white noise is introduced as input. Compute the output spectral density and the rms output for an input spectral density $G(\omega) = G_0 = 0.2$ volt² sec.

5-5. It is desired to generate physically a stationary random process with the auto-correlation function

$$\phi(\tau) = 2.4e^{-4|\tau|} \cos 2\tau \text{ volts}^2$$

starting with a white noise possessing a spectral density $G_0 = 3$ volts² sec.

a. Find the transfer function of the linear time-invariant system required.

b. Construct a block diagram to achieve this result using analogue equipment.

5-6. A first-order filter, possessing the transfer function

$$Y(p) = \frac{1}{1 + Tp}$$

is to be used to remove white noise $n(t)$ from a voltage signal $s(t)$ given by the random step function of Example 3.6-2. Assuming that the signal and noise are uncorrelated, that the rms signal is 1 volt, and that $G_{nn}(\omega) = 0.2$ volts² sec, determine the optimum filter time constant T to minimize the mean-squared output error.

5-7. A hypothetical simulator block diagram is shown below, in which A is an inverting amplifier, I is an integrator, and D is an ideal unit time delay; that is, a device for which the output at time t is the same as the input at time $t - 1$, for all t. Show that if white noise is introduced as the input to this system, the output spectral density is of the same form as that for the random step function (Example 3.6-2) with the d-c component removed.

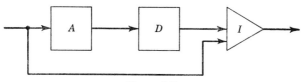

PROB. 5-7

5-8. The simple RC filter shown in the accompanying figure has as input a stationary random process $\{x(t)\}$ with correlation function

$$\phi_{xx}(\tau) = Ae^{-c|\tau|}$$

Compute the output correlation function $\phi_{yy}(\tau)$ directly from the correlation function of the input and the weighting function of the filter. Compute the output spectral density directly from the spectral density of the input and the transfer function of the filter. Show by a calculation that for this case the correlation function $\phi_{yy}(\tau)$ and the spectral density $G_{yy}(\omega)$ are Fourier transforms of each other.

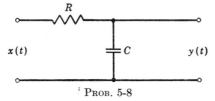

PROB. 5-8

5-9. A simple proportional control servo is shown on page 224. The input consists of a stationary random signal with correlation function

$$\phi_{ss}(\tau) = Ae^{-c|\tau|}$$

together with a superimposed white noise which is statistically independent of the signal. Compute the mean-squared error by which the servo output fails to follow the input.

Assuming now that cT and c/K are small compared with unity, find the optimum value of K to minimize the mean-squared error. Show that for large values of the motor time constant T, the minimum mean-squared error is proportional to T. In addition show that for small T, the minimum mean-squared error is largely independent of T.

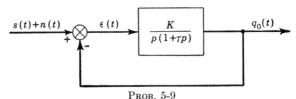

PROB. 5-9

5-10. A proportional control servo with tachometer feedback is shown in the accompanying figure. Assuming that the input is the same as for Prob. 5-9, compute the mean-squared error by which the servo output fails to follow the input. By letting the amplifier and tachometer gains K_1 and K_2 become infinite in such a way that K_1/K_2 remains constant, show that the mean-squared error is independent of the motor time constant T_1. Compute the mean-squared error for this limiting case.

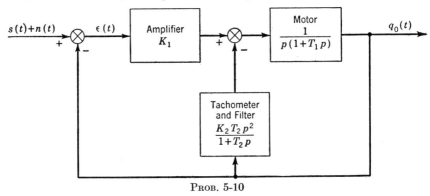

PROB. 5-10

5-11. The first-order filter whose transfer function is given by

$$Y(p) = \frac{1}{1 + Tp}$$

is used to remove a noise $\{n(t)\}$ with spectral density

$$G_{nn}(\omega) = \frac{(29)^2\omega^2}{(\omega^2 + 3\omega_0^2)^2 + 16\omega_0^4}$$

from a signal $\{s(t)\}$ with spectrum

$$G_{ss}(\omega) = \frac{54}{\omega^2 + \omega_0^2}$$

Assuming the signal and noise to be uncorrelated, show that the optimum filter time constant to minimize the mean-squared output error is given by

$$T = \frac{2}{\omega_0}$$

Compute the minimum mean-squared error obtainable with this filter.

CHAPTER 6

MEAN-SQUARED ERROR ANALYSIS
FOR NONSTATIONARY PROBLEMS

6.1 General Integral Formulas for Mean-squared Errors

An extensive body of mathematical techniques has been developed in the literature for the analysis of the response of linear constant-coefficient control systems to stationary random processes as inputs. For non-stationary inputs or variable-coefficient systems, no corresponding theory exists, even though problems of this nature arise quite often in practice. The material presented in this chapter treats the techniques available for the analysis of the mean-squared errors in the response of linear systems to random processes, under conditions in which the statistics of the problem vary with time.

The methods presented are heavily dependent upon analogue computation, and are far less elegant mathematically than those of Chap. 7. Furthermore, they are analytic rather than synthetic; the primary question treated is the study of the response of a prescribed linear system rather than the direct synthesis of an optimum system for an assigned task. The main value of these procedures lies in the fact that they permit practical study of problems that are not amenable to treatment by the more conventional techniques.

A problem can fall into the nonstationary category for two distinct reasons. In the first place, the response characteristics of the system under study may vary with time. In a guided-missile problem, for example, the system parameters may be variable functions of the range from the missile to its target. It is noted that a switch may often be considered as a special case of a variable coefficient (namely, a coefficient that is zero over one time interval and unity over another). Thus we have occasion to study as a special case problems in which a system, involving constant coefficients and stationary random processes as inputs, is studied during a period of transient behavior just after it is turned on. The second important reason for study of nonstationary problems is that the input data to a system may itself be nonstationary. In an automatic radar tracking system, for example, the random radar interference may

225

\

be expected to depend in both amplitude and frequency on the range of the target.

For simplicity, let us first consider a linear time-varying system having a single input and output. Assume that the system receives a random input $x(t)$ defined over $-\infty < t < \infty$ and let $\epsilon(t)$ denote the corresponding inaccuracy or error which $x(t)$ produces. Then if $W(t,\tau)$ represents the inaccuracy produced at time t by a unit impulse in x at time τ we have

$$\epsilon(t) = \int_{-\infty}^{t} W(t,\tau)x(\tau) \, d\tau \tag{6.1-1}$$

To calculate the correlation function for $\epsilon(t)$, we proceed as before by writing

$$\epsilon(t_1)\epsilon(t_2) = \int_{-\infty}^{t_1} W(t_1,\tau_1) \, d\tau_1 \int_{-\infty}^{t_2} W(t_2,\tau_2)x(\tau_1)x(\tau_2) \, d\tau_2 \tag{6.1-2}$$

Averaging both sides of this equation over the ensemble of inputs $x(t)$, and assuming that the averaging process can be carried out under the integral sign, we have

$$\phi_{\epsilon\epsilon}(t_1,t_2) = \int_{-\infty}^{t_1} W(t_1,\tau_1) \, d\tau_1 \int_{-\infty}^{t_2} W(t_2,\tau_2)\phi_{xx}(\tau_1,\tau_2) \, d\tau_2 \tag{6.1-3}$$

The significance of Eq. (6.1-3) lies in the fact that it permits the error correlation function to be calculated directly from the input correlation function and the system performance characteristics, without requiring detailed knowledge of the input functions $x(t)$. This property is particularly important in those cases in which the input correlation function is deduced from theoretical considerations; however, it represents a time-saving device even when empirical data is used.

As noted previously, the mean-squared value of a random process is derivable from its correlation function. Setting $t_1 = t_2 = t$ in (6.1-3) the rms inaccuracy is

$$(\text{rms})\epsilon(t) = \left[\int_{-\infty}^{t} W(t,\tau_1) \, d\tau_1 \int_{-\infty}^{t} W(t,\tau_2)\phi_{xx}(\tau_1,\tau_2) \, d\tau_2 \right]^{\frac{1}{2}} \tag{6.1-4}$$

Passing to a more general case, let the system receive a number of inputs $x_1(t), \ldots, x_n(t)$, and let $\epsilon(t)$ be represented by the relation

$$\epsilon(t) = \sum_{k=1}^{n} \int_{-\infty}^{t} W_k(t,\tau)x_k(\tau) \, d\tau \tag{6.1-5}$$

Proceeding as before, $\epsilon(t_1)\epsilon(t_2)$ may be represented in terms of a double sum of double integrals according to the formula

$$\epsilon(t_1)\epsilon(t_2) = \sum_{j=1}^{n} \sum_{k=1}^{n} \int_{-\infty}^{t_1} W_j(t_1,\tau_1) \, d\tau_1 \int_{-\infty}^{t_2} W_k(t_2,\tau_2)x_j(\tau_1)x_k(\tau_2) \, d\tau_2 \tag{6.1-6}$$

Averaging both sides of this relation over the ensemble of all possible combinations of inputs, we find

$$\phi_{\epsilon\epsilon}(t_1,t_2) = \sum_{j=1}^{n} \sum_{k=1}^{n} \int_{-\infty}^{t_1} W_j(t_1,\tau_1) \, d\tau_1 \int_{-\infty}^{t_2} W_k(t_2,\tau_2) \phi_{x_j x_k}(\tau_1,\tau_2) \, d\tau_2 \quad (6.1\text{-}7)$$

In the particular case in which the functions $x_1, x_2, \ldots, x_n$ are statistically independent with zero mean value, the terms for which $j \neq k$ are zero and we obtain

$$\phi_{\epsilon\epsilon}(t_1,t_2) = \sum_{k=1}^{n} \int_{-\infty}^{t_1} W_k(t_1,\tau_1) \, d\tau_1 \int_{-\infty}^{t_2} W_k(t_2,\tau_2) \phi_{x_k x_k}(\tau_1,\tau_2) \, d\tau_2 \quad (6.1\text{-}8)$$

In this case, setting $t_1 = t_2 = t$ the net mean-squared error is seen to consist of a sum of n terms, each of which is itself the mean-squared error which would arise from one of the inputs acting in the absence of the others. This additive property of mean-squared values is quite convenient in those cases where the assumptions of statistical independence and zero mean are justified. As before, the rms error is obtained as the square root of the mean-squared error.

As the final case to be considered, let the system be one which is activated at $t = 0$, with random initial conditions and a random forcing function. Taking Eq. (5.2-18) as a model, with $y(t)$ replaced by $\epsilon(t)$,

$$\overline{\epsilon(t_1)\epsilon(t_2)} = \sum_{j=1}^{n} \sum_{k=1}^{n} u_j(t_1)u_k(t_2)\overline{c_j c_k}$$

$$+ \sum_{j=1}^{n} u_j(t_1) \int_{0}^{t_2} W(t_2,\tau)\overline{c_j x(\tau)} \, d\tau$$

$$+ \sum_{j=1}^{n} u_j(t_2) \int_{0}^{t_1} W(t_1,\tau)\overline{c_j x(\tau)} \, d\tau$$

$$+ \int_{0}^{t_1} W(t_1,\tau_1) \, d\tau_1 \int_{0}^{t_2} W(t_2,\tau_2)\overline{x(\tau_1)x(\tau_2)} \, d\tau_2 \quad (6.1\text{-}9)$$

Here, the proper ensemble over which the averaging is to occur is the collection of all possible combinations of initial conditions and forcing functions.

In the special case in which the initial conditions are statistically independent of the forcing function and of each other, and further possess zero mean values, the mean-squared error is given by the simplified relation

$$\overline{\epsilon(t)^2} = \sum_{k=1}^{n} \overline{c_k^2}u_k(t)^2 + \int_{0}^{t} W(t,\tau_1) \, d\tau_1 \int_{0}^{t} W(t,\tau_2)\phi_{xx}(\tau_1,\tau_2) \, d\tau_2 \quad (6.1\text{-}10)$$

In addition to certain transient terms, the mean-squared error formulas developed above involve single or double integrals of one of the following forms:

$$J_1(t) = \int^t W(t,\tau)\overline{cx(\tau)}\, d\tau \qquad (6.1\text{-}11)$$

$$J_2(t_1,t_2) = \int^{t_1} W_1(t_1,\tau_1)\, d\tau_1 \int^{t_2} W_2(t_2,\tau_2)\phi(\tau_1,\tau_2)\, d\tau_2 \qquad (6.1\text{-}12)$$

The lower limits of integration may be zero, minus infinity, or some other suitable value in these relations; the correlation function in (6.1-12) may or may not be a cross correlation; the weighting functions may or may not be the same.

A direct approach to the calculation of these integrals would perhaps involve the determination of the appropriate weighting functions by analysis, simulator test, or numerical methods, followed by straightforward evaluation of the integrals. For variable-coefficient systems, analytical methods would in general be out of the question. Considering the number of variables involved, numerical methods would also seem impractical for all but the simplest of problems. The main hope for extensive calculations based on these formulas would thus appear to lie in the field of simulation.

Fortunately, a reference to the physical origins of these formulas shows that evaluation by means of analogue computation is quite feasible. Considering the first equation (6.1-11), let it be supposed that the physical system under study is simulated in such manner that the input $x(t)$ and error output $\epsilon(t)$ are considered as the primary input and output. All

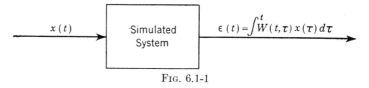

Fig. 6.1-1

other inputs are held at zero in this operation. As indicated in Fig. 6.1-1 the functions $x(t)$ and $\epsilon(t)$ are related by the formula

$$\epsilon(t) = \int^t W(t,\tau)x(\tau)\, d\tau \qquad (6.1\text{-}13)$$

no matter what the input function x may be. The particular choice $\overline{cx(t)}$ for the input, as indicated in Fig. 6.1-2, then yields as output $\int^t W(t,\tau)\overline{cx(\tau)}\, d\tau$, which is precisely the function $J_1(t)$ which we desire. In other words, the operation of the form

$$\int^t W(t,\tau)[\quad]\, d\tau \qquad (6.1\text{-}14)$$

is carried out directly by the action of the simulated system, without the need for any explicit calculation of the weighting function. Thus an integral of the form (6.1-11) may be evaluated continuously as a function of t by means of a single simulator test.

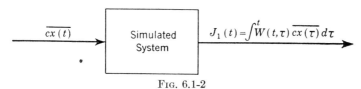

FIG. 6.1-2

The situation with respect to integrals of the form (6.1-12) is somewhat more complicated, but the general principle is the same. Let the system receive two inputs $x_1(t)$ and $x_2(t)$. The weighting functions

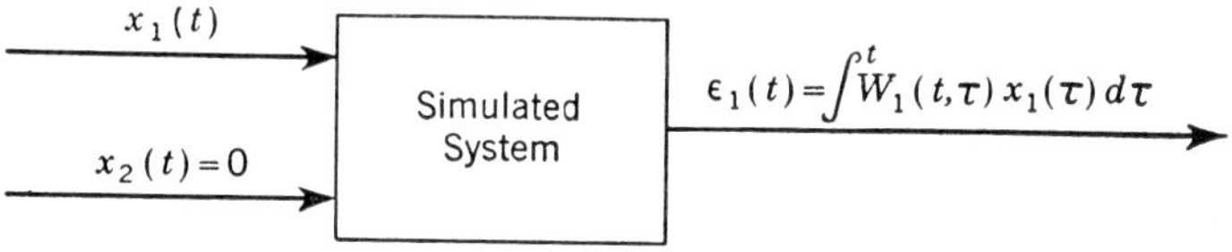

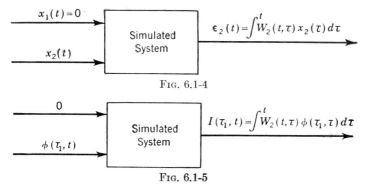

FIG. 6.1-3

$W_1(t,\tau)$ and $W_2(t,\tau)$ are defined as indicated in Figs. 6.1-3 and 6.1-4. For $x = 0$ and $x_1 \neq 0$ the error is given by

$$\epsilon_1(t) = \int^t W_1(t,\tau)x_1(\tau)\,d\tau \qquad (6.1\text{-}15)$$

whereas in the reverse situation

$$\epsilon_2(t) = \int^t W_2(t,\tau)x_2(\tau)\,d\tau \qquad (6.1\text{-}16)$$

Now let τ_1 be temporarily assigned a fixed value, and let

$$I(\tau_1,t) = \int^t W_2(t,\tau)\phi(\tau_1,\tau)\,d\tau \qquad (6.1\text{-}17)$$

A reference to Figs. 6.1-4 and 6.1-5 shows that for the selected value of

FIG. 6.1-4

FIG. 6.1-5

τ_1 the quantity $I(\tau_1,t)$ is obtained as the system output in response to $\phi(\tau_1,t)$ as input. From Eq. (6.1-12) we see that

$$J_2(t_1,t_2) = \int^{t_1} W_1(t_1,\tau_1) I(\tau_1,t_2) \, d\tau_1 \qquad (6.1\text{-}18)$$

Therefore, as the next step, a fixed value of t_2 is picked and the results $I(\tau_1,t_2)$ of numerous tests of the above type are cross-plotted against τ_1. The function $I(t,t_2)$ is thus obtained as a plot against t for the selected value of t_2. As indicated in Fig. 6.1-6, this function is then reintroduced into the system to give a plot of $J_2(t,t_2)$ as the system output. This process is then repeated for as many values of t_2 as are required.

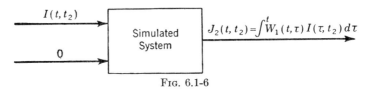

Fig. 6.1-6

The test procedure involved is obviously somewhat lengthy; in effect it requires a number of tests equal to the number of points necessary to define a smooth curve plus one subsequent test for each t_2 considered. Once the procedure is well understood and systematized, however, it is by no means prohibitively time-consuming. In particular, if it is desired only to evaluate the importance of a given source of inaccuracy in a system, without a systematic search over a range of system parameters to minimize its effect, the technique is quite practical with the use of appropriate simulator equipment.

The procedure described above is applicable to a very broad class of linear problems. In particular, it is the only method discussed here which can make direct use of empirical correlation functions without first approximating them, in some fashion, by analytic expressions. At the same time there are a number of practical nonstationary problems which do not require the degree of generality considered in this section. The remainder of this chapter is devoted to exploiting the special properties of certain classes of problems in the effort to minimize the amount of necessary computation.

6.2 Transient Statistical Analysis of a Time-invariant Linear System

Let us now consider the type of problem in which a constant-coefficient system is at rest prior to time $t = 0$, and after that time receives a stationary random process as input. In a sense, this problem may be considered as a special case of one involving variable coefficients, since it may be assumed that the input enters the system at all times, negative or positive, but is multiplied by a coefficient that is zero for $t < 0$ and unity for $t > 0$. The calculation of the mean-squared output at time t may be accomplished as a special case of the methods to be discussed in Secs. 6.4 and 6.5. In the present section we develop an alternate procedure which applies only to the constant-coefficient case.

An expression for the mean-squared error for the general variable-coefficient case in which the input random process $\{x(t)\}$ is stationary may be obtained from Eq. (6.1-3). Thus

$$\overline{\epsilon(t)^2} = \int_{-\infty}^{t} W(t,\tau_1)\, d\tau_1 \int_{-\infty}^{t} W(t,\tau_2)\phi_{xx}(\tau_2 - \tau_1)\, d\tau_2 \qquad (6.2\text{-}1)$$

In the specialized case in which $x(t)$ is a white noise, with

$$\phi_{xx}(\tau) = \delta(\tau) \qquad (6.2\text{-}2)$$

the above relation can be reduced to a single integral. Using the relation

$$\int_{-\infty}^{t} W(t,\tau_2)\delta(\tau_2 - \tau_1)\, d\tau_2 = W(t,\tau_1) \qquad (6.2\text{-}3)$$

we have

$$\overline{\epsilon(t)^2} = \int_{-\infty}^{t} W(t,\tau)^2\, d\tau \qquad (6.2\text{-}4)$$

For a general stationary random input, we may design a shaping filter with the property that a white-noise input produces the desired random

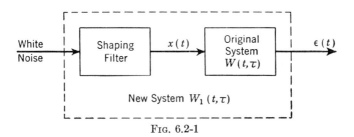

FIG. 6.2-1

output $x(t)$. (This procedure is discussed in Sec. 5.5.) Thus, our original system may be replaced by a new system, as indicated in Fig. 6.2-1. Calling the over-all weighting function $W_1(t,\tau)$, the mean-squared response of our original system to an input $x(t)$ may be found from

$$\overline{\epsilon(t)^2} = \int_{-\infty}^{t} W_1(t,\tau)^2\, d\tau \qquad (6.2\text{-}5)$$

Returning now to the specific problem defined at the beginning of this section, let us consider, for the moment, the input correlation function to be given by

$$\phi_{xx}(\tau) = e^{-c|\tau|} \qquad (6.2\text{-}6)$$

The transfer function of the appropriate shaping filter for this case is

$$Y(p) = \frac{\sqrt{2c}}{p + c} \qquad (6.2\text{-}7)$$

as was shown in Sec. 5.5. Thus, $W_1(t,\tau)$ may be obtained as the unit-impulse response of the system shown in Fig. 6.2-2.

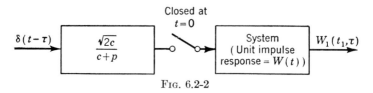

FIG. 6.2-2

To compute $W_1(t,\tau)$ in terms of $W(t,\tau)$, we first consider the case in which $\tau < 0$; that is, in which the impulse is applied before closing the switch. Writing $y(t - \tau)$ for the shaping filter output, we have

$$y(t - \tau) = \sqrt{2c}\, e^{-c(t-\tau)} \qquad t > \tau \qquad (6.2\text{-}8)$$

The function $W_1(t,\tau)$ is the system output, and is given by

$$\begin{aligned}
W_1(t,\tau) &= \int_0^t W(t - \tau_1) y(\tau_1 - \tau)\, d\tau_1 \\
&= \sqrt{2c} \int_0^t W(t - \tau_1) e^{-c(\tau_1 - \tau)}\, d\tau_1 \\
&= \sqrt{2c}\, e^{c\tau} \int_0^t W(t - \tau_1) e^{-c\tau_1}\, d\tau_1 \qquad (6.2\text{-}9)
\end{aligned}$$

for all $\tau < 0$.

For $\tau > 0$, it is the time of application of the impulse rather than the closure of the switch that starts the system in operation; thus for $\tau > 0$

$$W_1(t,\tau) = \sqrt{2c} \int_\tau^t W(t - \tau_1) e^{-c(\tau_1 - \tau)}\, d\tau_1 \qquad (6.2\text{-}10)$$

Let a function $F(t)$ be defined by

$$F(t) = \int_0^t W(t - \tau_1) e^{-c\tau_1}\, d\tau_1 \qquad (6.2\text{-}11)$$

Then from (6.2-9), for $\tau < 0$,

$$W_1(t,\tau) = \sqrt{2c}\, e^{c\tau} F(t) \qquad (6.2\text{-}12)$$

Also, for $\tau > 0$, we have, from (6.2-10),

$$\begin{aligned}
W_1(t,\tau) &= \sqrt{2c} \int_0^{t-\tau} W(t - \tau - \tau_1) e^{-c\tau_1}\, d\tau_1 \\
&= \sqrt{2c}\, F(t - \tau) \qquad (6.2\text{-}13)
\end{aligned}$$

Combining these results with (6.2-5), we have

$$\overline{\epsilon(t)^2} = \int_{-\infty}^{0} 2ce^{2c\tau}F(t)^2 \, d\tau + \int_{0}^{t} 2cF(t-\tau)^2 \, d\tau$$

$$= F(t)^2 + 2c \int_{0}^{t} F(\tau)^2 \, d\tau \qquad (6.2\text{-}14)$$

The function $F(t)$ defined by (6.2-11) is simply the output response of the system to the input which is zero for $t < 0$ and is e^{-ct} for $t > 0$. Hence in this particular case, $\overline{\epsilon(t)^2}$ may be determined continuously as a function of t by the test arrangement shown in Fig. 6.2-3. An alternate

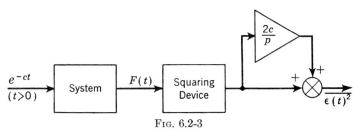

FIG. 6.2-3

and equivalent arrangement is that shown in Fig. 6.2-4. To derive this arrangement from that of the previous figure, we observe that e^{-ct} is the unit-impulse response of a filter with a transfer function $1/(c + p)$. Inserting such a filter, and subsequently interchanging the filter and the constant-coefficient system, the arrangement of Fig. 6.2-4 follows.

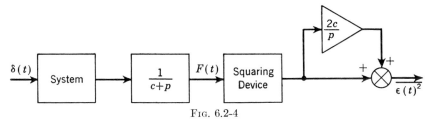

FIG. 6.2-4

The relation (6.2-14) is derived by use of physical reasoning, but can be demonstrated by entirely analytical means. Essentially this result is a statement of the integral equality

$$\int_{0}^{t} W(t - \tau_1) \, d\tau_1 \int_{0}^{t} W(t - \tau_2)e^{-c|\tau_2 - \tau_1|} \, d\tau_2$$

$$= F(t)^2 + 2c \int_{0}^{t} F(\tau)^2 \, d\tau \qquad (6.2\text{-}15)$$

with $F(t)$ given by (6.2-11).

Passing to a more general case, it follows that if $\phi_{xx}(\tau)$ is representable in the form

$$\phi_{xx}(\tau) = \sum_{k=1}^{n} A_k e^{-c_k|\tau|} \qquad (6.2\text{-}16)$$

then $\displaystyle\int_0^t W(t - \tau_1)\, d\tau_1 \int_0^t W(t - \tau_2)\phi_{xx}(\tau_2 - \tau_1)\, d\tau_2$

$$= \sum_{k=1}^{n} A_k \int_0^t W(t - \tau_1)\, d\tau_1 \int_0^t W(t - \tau_2) e^{-c_k|\tau_2 - \tau_1|}\, d\tau_2$$

$$= \sum_{k=1}^{n} A_k \left[F_k(t)^2 + 2c_k \int_0^t F_k(\tau)^2\, d\tau \right] \tag{6.2-17}$$

where $$F_k(t) = \int_0^t W(t - \tau) e^{-c_k \tau}\, d\tau \tag{6.2-18}$$

A simulator arrangement for evaluating this expression is shown in Fig. 6.2-5.

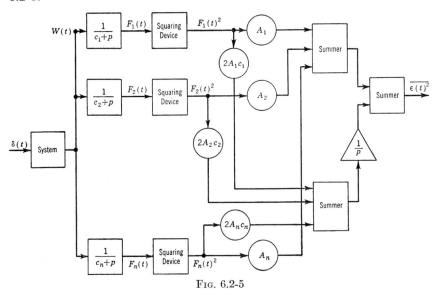

Fig. 6.2-5

As shown in Appendix D, any correlation function may be approximated by an expression of the form (6.2-16) so that this procedure may be applied generally.

6.3 Frequency Methods for Transient Analysis of Linear Systems

The response of linear systems excited from rest at time $t = 0$ may also be analyzed, using frequency-response techniques. The method to be described may be applied to variable-as well as constant-parameter linear systems. As one would expect, for problems in the frequency domain, the transfer function $Y(j\omega,t)$ replaces the weighting function $W(t,\tau)$. First, a simulator technique is described for computing $Y(j\omega,t)$ for linear systems. It is then shown how the mean-squared response of such systems to stationary random inputs may be obtained from the frequency-response function $Y(j\omega,t)$ and the input spectral density.

Ultimately, as always, we are interested in the behavior of our system when the input is a random process. It might well happen that a system operating in the steady state might display quite different frequency-response characteristics than the same system operating in the transient state. That is to say, in one mode of operation the system might be sensitive to a particular range of frequencies which would not be the case in the other mode of operation. Such a situation can be detected by comparing the transfer functions $Y(p)$ and $Y(p,t)$ for the two states. In this way all the critical frequencies of the system will be known and steps can be taken to suppress these in our random process before it appears as the input to the system.

It should be pointed out that this method is of particular value when the nature of the random input is unknown. When exact statistical characteristics of the input are known, the methods of the previous and following sections are more efficient to apply and yield more specific information with a minimum of effort.

The generalized frequency-response function $Y(j\omega,t)$ is discussed in Sec. 5.2. If we consider the linear system defined by the differential equation

$$L_t y = x(t) \tag{6.3-1}$$

then for $x(t) = e^{j\omega t}$, we have

$$y(t) = Y(j\omega,t)e^{j\omega t} \tag{6.3-2}$$

Since $Y(j\omega,t)$ is a complex function of ω and t, we may express it in polar form as follows:

$$Y(j\omega,t) = |Y(j\omega,t)|e^{j\phi(\omega,t)} \tag{6.3-3}$$

Using this form for Y, we may write the real and imaginary parts of (6.3-2) as

$$y_r(t) = |Y(j\omega,t)| \cos{(\omega t + \phi)} \tag{6.3-4}$$
$$y_i(t) = |Y(j\omega,t)| \sin{(\omega t + \phi)} \tag{6.3-5}$$

where
$$y(t) = y_r(t) + jy_i(t) \tag{6.3-6}$$

Since L_t is a linear operator, y_r and y_i are each responses of the original system for $\cos \omega t$ and $\sin \omega t$, respectively, as inputs. Thus

$$L_t y_r = \cos \omega t \tag{6.3-7}$$
$$L_t y_i = \sin \omega t \tag{6.3-8}$$

We are now in a position to describe the following simulator test procedure for computing $|Y(j\omega,t)|$:

1. Two identical simulations of the original system are made on analogue equipment.

2. The input for the first system is $\cos \omega t$ and for the second is $\sin \omega t$. The outputs will be $y_r(t)$ and $y_i(t)$, respectively.

3. These outputs are connected respectively to the x and y inputs of a plotting table so that the resulting graph will generally be a spiral-shaped curve. The radial distance from the origin to the curve at any particular time t will be $|Y(j\omega,t)|$, as indicated in Fig. 6.3-1.

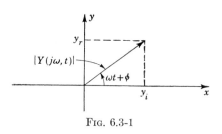

FIG. 6.3-1

4. This procedure must be repeated to obtain new graphs for each value of ω desired.

The test procedure is somewhat simplified for a constant-parameter system. For this case we need only one simulation of the system. If the input to this system is $\cos \omega t$, the output will be

$$y_r = L_t^{-1} \cos \omega t \qquad (6.3\text{-}9)$$

The quantity y_i may be expressed as

$$y_i = L_t^{-1} \sin \omega t = L_t^{-1} \int_0^t \omega \cos \omega t \, dt$$
$$= \omega \int_0^t L_t^{-1} \cos \omega t \, dt = \omega \int_0^t y_r(t) \, dt \qquad (6.3\text{-}10)$$

The interchange of operations used in deriving the above is justified since L_t is a constant-coefficient linear operator. Thus, the response $y_i(t)$ may be obtained by integrating the response $y_r(t)$, rendering a separate computation of $y_i(t)$ unnecessary.

We shall illustrate this procedure for obtaining $|Y(j\omega,t)|$ both analytically and by simulation in the following example.

Example 6.3-1. A linear constant-coefficient system described by

$$L_t y = \frac{dy}{dt} + y = x(t)$$

is at rest prior to time $t = 0$. We wish to compute analytically an expression for $|Y(j\omega,t)|$.

The solution of Eq. (6.3-7) which vanishes for $t = 0$ is easily found to be

$$y_r(t) = \frac{1}{1 + \omega^2} (\cos \omega t - e^{-t} + \omega \sin \omega t)$$

The solution of Eq. (6.3-8) is then found, using Eq. (6.3-10), to be

$$y_i(t) = \frac{1}{1 + \omega^2} (\sin \omega t + \omega e^{-t} - \omega \cos \omega t)$$

From Eqs. (6.3-4) and (6.3-5), it is seen that

$$|Y(j\omega,t)|^2 = y_r(t)^2 + y_i(t)^2$$
$$= \frac{1}{1 + \omega^2} (1 - 2e^{-t} \cos \omega t + e^{-2t})$$

Only for very simple problems is it possible to obtain an explicit expression for $|Y(j\omega,t)|$. Problems arising in practice are usually significantly more complicated so as to make analogue computation the feasible approach.   To illustrate the simulator approach, we consider this same problem.   An appropriate simulator block diagram is shown in Fig. 6.3-2.   The first part of the setup is used to generate cos ωt for input to the system.   The quantity y_r is the output and the integral of y_r gives y_i.

The solution of the problem for $\omega = 1$ is shown in Fig. 6.3-3.   The length of each of the radial lines is equal to $|Y(j\omega,t)|$.   They have been drawn in this case at 1-second intervals from $t = 0$ to $t = 12$ seconds.

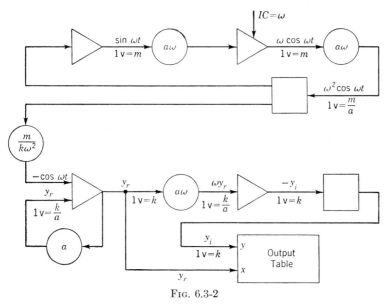

Fɪɢ. 6.3-2

There are obviously other methods of displaying the solution.   For example, one could take the square root of the sum of the squares of y_r and y_i using a servo-driven resolver operating in the polar mode to plot $|Y(j\omega,t)|$ directly as a function of time.

By a slightly more complicated procedure a direct plot of $Y(j\omega,t)$ in the complex plane with t as a parameter may be obtained.   From Eqs. (6.3-4) and (6.3-5) we have

$$|Y(j\omega,t)| \cos \phi = y_r \cos \omega t + y_i \sin \omega t \qquad (6.3\text{-}11)$$
$$|Y(j\omega,t)| \sin \phi = y_i \cos \omega t - y_r \sin \omega t \qquad (6.3\text{-}12)$$

The test procedure is the same as before except that y_r and y_i are combined as shown in Eqs. (6.3-11) and (6.3-12) and are connected respectively to the x and y inputs of the plotting table.   The plot will be similar to the one obtained before but now the angle indicated in Fig. 6.3-1 will be ϕ instead of $\omega t + \phi$.

For the numerical example considered here we find, using Eqs. (6.3-11) and (6.3-12), that

$$|Y(j\omega,t)| \cos \phi = \frac{1}{1 + \omega^2} [1 + (\omega \sin \omega t - \cos \omega t)e^{-t}]$$

$$|Y(j\omega,t)| \sin \phi = \frac{1}{1 + \omega^2} [(\omega \cos \omega t + \sin \omega t)e^{-t} - \omega]$$

Thus
$$\phi = \tan^{-1} \left(\frac{(\omega \cos \omega t + \sin \omega t)e^{-t} - \omega}{(\omega \sin \omega t - \cos \omega t)e^{-t} + 1} \right)$$

To conclude this section, we shall show how to compute the mean-squared response of a linear system from the spectral density of an input stationary random process by using the frequency-response function $Y(j\omega,t)$ of the system. From Eq. (6.1-3) the relation between the input correlation function $\phi_{xx}(t_2 - t_1)$ and the output correlation function

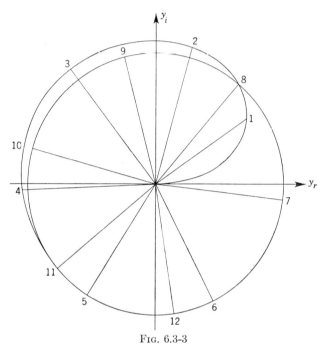

FIG. 6.3-3

$\phi_{yy}(t_1,t_2)$ for a linear system whose weighting function is $W(t,\tau)$ may be expressed as

$$\phi_{yy}(t_1,t_2) = \int_{-\infty}^{t_1} W(t_1,\tau_1)\, d\tau_1 \int_{-\infty}^{t_2} W(t_2,\tau_2)\phi_{xx}(\tau_2 - \tau_1)\, d\tau_2 \quad (6.3\text{-}13)$$

The input correlation function is related to the spectral density of the input, as seen from Eq. (3.6-38), so that

$$\phi_{xx}(t_2 - t_1) = \tfrac{1}{2}\int_{-\infty}^{\infty} G_{xx}(\omega)e^{j\omega(t_2 - t_1)}\, d\omega \quad (6.3\text{-}14)$$

Using Eq. (6.3-14), Eq. (6.3-13) may be written as

$$\phi_{yy}(t_1,t_2) = \tfrac{1}{2}\int_{-\infty}^{\infty} G_{xx}(\omega)\, d\omega \int_{-\infty}^{t_1} W(t_1,\tau_1)e^{-j\omega\tau_1}\, d\tau_1$$
$$\times \int_{-\infty}^{t_2} W(t_2,\tau_2)e^{j\omega\tau_2}\, d\tau_2 \quad (6.3\text{-}15)$$

But $$Y(j\omega,t) = \int_{-\infty}^{t} W(t,\tau)e^{-j\omega(t-\tau)}\, d\tau \quad (6.3\text{-}16)$$

as explained in Sec. 5.2, so that Eq. (6.3-15) becomes

$$\phi_{yy}(t_1,t_2) = \frac{1}{2} \int_{-\infty}^{\infty} G_{xx}(\omega) Y(j\omega,t_1)^* Y(j\omega,t_2) e^{j\omega(t_2-t_1)} \, d\omega \qquad (6.3\text{-}17)$$

Setting $t_1 = t_2 = t$, we obtain

$$\overline{y(t)^2} = \frac{1}{2} \int_{-\infty}^{\infty} G_{xx}(\omega) |Y(j\omega,t)|^2 \, d\omega \qquad (6.3\text{-}18)$$

or, since the integrand of Eq. (6.3-18) is an even function of ω, we have finally

$$\overline{y(t)^2} = \int_{0}^{\infty} G_{xx}(\omega) |Y(j\omega,t)|^2 \, d\omega \qquad (6.3\text{-}19)$$

Example 6.3-2. For the system described in Example 6.3-1 above, let us assume that the input spectral density is given by

$$G_{xx}(\omega) = \frac{1}{1 + a^2\omega^2}$$

where a is a positive constant not equal to one. Then the mean-squared response is

$$\overline{y(t)^2} = \frac{\pi}{2(1 - a^2)} (1 - e^{-2t}) - \frac{a^2}{1 - a^2} \int_{0}^{\infty} \frac{d\omega}{1 + a^2\omega^2} - 2e^{-t} \int_{0}^{\infty} \frac{\cos \omega t}{1 + a^2\omega^2} \, d\omega$$

$$+ e^{-2t} \int_{0}^{\infty} \frac{d\omega}{1 + a^2\omega^2}$$

$$= \frac{\pi}{2(1 - a^2)} (1 - e^{-2t}) - \frac{\pi a}{2(1 - a^2)} [1 - 2e^{-t}e^{-t/a} + e^{-2t}]$$

When $|Y(j\omega,t)|^2$ is not given analytically but instead is obtained from simulator tests, the procedure to calculate $\overline{y(t)^2}$ is straightforward but rather tedious. A separate simulator test is required for each value of ω when computing $|Y(j\omega,t)|$. Enough values of ω must be used so that a reasonably good approximation to the integrand of Eq. (6.3-19) is obtained. Then for each fixed value of t desired, the integral of (6.3-19) is evaluated numerically by any convenient means. The result is a set of numbers which are the mean-squared responses of the system corresponding to those values of time.

6.4 The Method of Adjoint Systems

Results derived in Sec. 6.2 show that for a general linear system with an input $x(t)$ that is stationary and possesses a rational spectrum, the mean-squared output (error) at time t can be represented by

$$\overline{\epsilon(t)^2} = \int_{-\infty}^{t} W_1(t,\tau)^2 \, d\tau \qquad (6.4\text{-}1)$$

where W_1 is the weighting function of the combination of a shaping filter in series with the original system. By direct measurement of the unit-impulse response of the combined filter and system, it is possible to obtain

$W_1(t,\tau)$ for use in this relation. If a unit impulse is introduced at time τ, the simulated system gives $W_1(t,\tau)$ as a function of t. Thus, since the variable of integration in (6.4-1) is τ, to evaluate $\overline{\epsilon(t)^2}$ for a particular value of t it would appear necessary to take a number of unit-impulse responses for various values of τ, cross-plot the results, and integrate (6.4-1) numerically.

The objective of this section is to show that this procedure is really unnecessary. By replacing the system under study by another that is closely related to it, called the *adjoint system*, it is found possible by simulator techniques to generate a weighting function continuously as a function of τ, for fixed t, rather than vice versa. Thus, it is feasible to compute an expression such as (6.4-1) by only one test, for a particular t, rather than by a family of tests. This affords a certain saving of time even when a number of values of t are to be considered. When only one t is of interest, however, the simplification is of considerable value.

The final procedures that are developed for this purpose are essentially quite simple. Unfortunately, the logical derivation of these procedures requires a fairly thorough knowledge of some topics in the theory of linear differential equations that are not customarily presented in engineering courses. For this reason, our development will be directed first at making the method plausible and a complete example will be worked out to illustrate the technique. Appendix F includes all the formal mathematics necessary to justify the method.

The notion of *reciprocity* is encountered in many physical problems in which the governing equations are linear. For example, in electric-circuit theory it is well known that a current in one loop, say loop 1, of a network caused by a voltage source in any other loop, say loop 2, of the same network is identical to the current which would be produced in loop 2 by the same voltage source in loop 1. In other words an ideal voltage source and an ideal ammeter may be interchanged without altering the reading of the instrument.

As a second example of reciprocity consider a tightly stretched string. Then a concentrated load applied at position 1 of the string produces the same deflection at position 2 as would be produced at position 1 by the same load applied at position 2.

From these two examples, and many others familiar to the reader, the notion of reciprocity may be extended heuristically to include the type of problem formulated at the beginning of this section. Thus, we are tempted to conclude that a unit impulse applied to a linear system at time τ and producing an output at time t given by $W(t,\tau)$ would be the same as the response at time τ at the input to a unit impulse applied to the output at time t. Assuming the truth of this statement and, for the moment, bypassing the question of just how such a reciprocal experiment could be carried out, let us see how the notion of reciprocity may be applied to assist in the evaluation of Eq. (6.4-1).

Let us suppose that we are interested in obtaining the mean-squared output $\overline{\epsilon(t)^2}$ of a system whose weighting function is $W(t,\tau)$ for a particular value of t, say $t = T$. Then

$$\overline{\epsilon(T)^2} = \int_{-\infty}^{T} W(T,\tau)^2 \, d\tau \tag{6.4-2}$$

The reciprocity relation would tell us that $W(T,\tau)$ could be obtained continuously as a function of τ by appling a unit impulse to the output of the system at time T and recording the response as a function of τ. The resulting quantity could then be squared and integrated, as indicated by (6.4-2), to give the desired mean-squared error.

There are two obvious difficulties which present themselves immediately. First, since time is the independent variable, the experiment described above would imply that in some sense time would have to run backwards since the time τ at which the response would be recorded occurs earlier than the time T at which the impulse would be initiated. Furthermore, since these impulse-response tests will presumably be made on some kind of simulator equipment, some technique must be found by which an impulse can be applied to the output of the simulated system.

This first difficulty may be overcome quite easily by generating all time-varying parameters in the system as if the independent variable were decreasing from T to $-\infty$ rather than increasing from $-\infty$ to T. This may be accomplished, for any such parameter $a(t)$, by starting the function table on which $a(t)$ is plotted at an initial position corresponding to the value $t = T$ and running the table in the backward direction. In other words, at the start of the test the value used for the coefficient is $a(T)$, 1 second later it is $a(T - 1)$, and so on. In effect we are introducing a mathematical change of variable $\tau = T - t_1$ in (6.4-2), in which t_1 represents the elapsed time after the start of the test in the actual simulation. The coefficient used in the test is thus $a(T - t_1)$. (Although this would appear to be a rather superficial way to overcome a difficulty that seems to be much more basic in nature, it is shown in Appendix F that this simple procedure is actually all that is required.) Since the change of variable $\tau = T - t_1$ has shifted the origin of time as well as reversed the direction of time, the unit-impulse input is applied at time $\tau = T$ or $t_1 = 0$, which corresponds to the instant of starting the simulator test.

The simulator technique by which the second difficulty is handled may be described as follows. Since any linear system may be simulated schematically by means of "integrators," "summers," and time-varying "scale-factor potentiometers," we first construct a schematic block

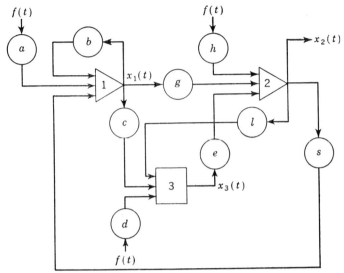

FIG. 6.4-1   Original system.

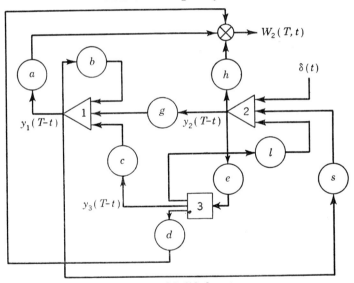

FIG. 6.4-2   Modified system.

diagram of our system, using only these three kinds of computing components. Then the simulation of the system to be used to perform the reciprocal experiment may be obtained by reversing the inputs and outputs of each of the computing components. In other words, the flow of information through each computing element is simply reversed in direction. This reversal may be effected in a formal manner by simply reversing the direction of the arrows in the diagram. Errors in simulating the modified system can be avoided by adhering to the following rules when formulating the schematic block diagram:

1. All amplifiers should be used with unit gain. Thus, the various gains or attenuations needed should be accomplished with scale-factor potentiometers without regard for whether or not such values are constant or greater or smaller than one.

2. All potentiometers should have just one input and one output.

3. The system should be so constructed as to have exactly one input and one output. This technique is illustrated in Figs. 6.4-1 and 6.4-2. The original system is shown in Fig. 6.4-1 and the modified system obtained from it is shown in Fig. 6.4-2. In this example one notes that the single input function enters the original system at three different points. In the modified system it is, therefore, necessary to introduce a summation of the corresponding three signals to produce the system output.

Example 6.4-1. As an illustration we consider the system discussed in Example 5.2-2. This system is describable by the second-order differential equation

$$L_t y \equiv \frac{d^2 y}{dt^2} + t \frac{dy}{dt} + y = x$$

and the weighting function for the system is given by

$$W(t,\tau) = \begin{cases} e^{-t^2/2} \int_\tau^t e^{r^2/2}\, dr & \text{for } \tau < t \\ 0 & \text{for } \tau > t \end{cases}$$

This system may be simulated schematically using only integrators, summers, and scale-factor pots, as shown in Fig. 6.4-3.

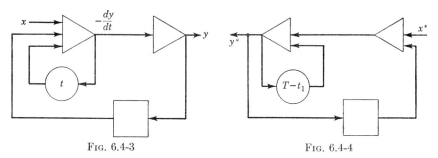

FIG. 6.4-3   FIG. 6.4-4

The modified system used for performing the reciprocal experiment is obtained from this simulation by interchanging all inputs and outputs of each of the computing elements and, in addition, replacing the variable t by $T - t_1$. Thus, the schematic diagram for the modified system is shown in Fig. 6.4-4.

The differential equation associated with the diagram of Fig. 6.4-4 is easily found to be

$$L_{t_1}^* y^* = \frac{d^2 y^*}{dt_1^2} + \frac{d}{dt_1}[(T - t_1)y^*] + y^* = x^*$$

and the corresponding weighting function is

$$W^*(t_1,\tau) = \begin{cases} e^{-(T-\tau)^2/2} \displaystyle\int_{T-t_1}^{T-\tau} e^{r^2/2}\, dr & \tau < t_1 \\ 0 & \tau > t_1 \end{cases}$$

Using the terminology of differential equations, the equation describing the performance of the modified system is the adjoint of the equation of the original system with t replaced by $T - t_1$.

Let us now compare the weighting functions for the two systems. The response of the original system at time T caused by a unit impulse initiated at time τ is given by

$$W(T,\tau) = e^{-T^2/2} \int_{\tau}^{T} e^{r^2/2}\, dr \qquad \text{for } \tau < T$$

while the response of the modified system at time t_1 caused by a unit impulse at time zero is given by

$$W^*(t_1,0) = e^{-T^2/2} \int_{T-t_1}^{T} e^{r^2/2}\, dr \qquad \text{for } 0 < t_1$$

Thus, we see that to each value of $W(T,\tau)$ for $\tau < T$ there is a correspondingly equal value of $W^*(t_1,0)$ for $t_1 = T - \tau$. That is, the collection of responses of the original system at time T caused by unit impulses initiated at all times prior to time T may be generated continuously by a single simulator test simply by recording the response of the modified system when this system is excited by a unit impulse at time $t_1 = 0$.

The relation between the mean-squared response of the original system and the weighting function of the modified system is obtained from Eq. (6.4-2). We have

$$\overline{\epsilon(T)^2} = \int_{-\infty}^{T} W(T,\,\tau)^2\, d\tau = \int_{0}^{\infty} W(T,\, T-t_1)^2\, dt_1 = \int_{0}^{\infty} W^*(t_1,\,0)^2\, dt_1 \quad (6.4\text{-}3)$$

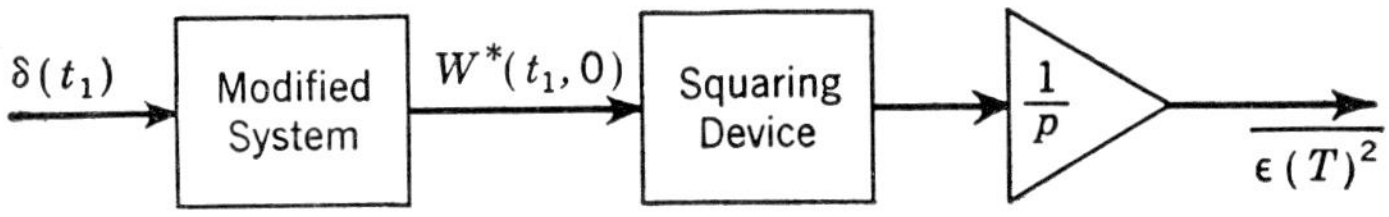

Fig. 6.4-5

Therefore $\overline{\epsilon(T)^2}$ may be obtained by a single simulator test as indicated in Fig. 6.4-5 The quantity $\overline{\epsilon(T)^2}$ is the steady value of the integrator output after the problem has been run sufficiently long so that this output has ceased to increase by any observable amount.

Example 6.4-2. For additional illustrative purposes let us consider the same problem discussed in Example 6.4-1 but including the simulator procedure and comparing the results with the straightforward approach in which a series of tests is made on the original system alone.

We first consider how one would proceed to evaluate Eq. (6.4-2) without using the adjoint method. A simulator block diagram for this problem is shown in Fig. 6.4-3. The unit-impulse input to the system is accomplished by applying an initial condition to the integrator into which the pulse is fed. The value of $W(T,0)$ is found by running the problem for T seconds beginning at $t = 0$ and observing the final output of the system. Similarly, to compute the value $W(T,\tau)$ the problem is run for $T - \tau$ seconds beginning at $t = \tau$, and the final value of the output of the system is recorded. In this way a number of values of $W(T,\tau)$ are obtained and are plotted as a function of τ. If the values of τ are chosen close enough together, a smooth curve may be

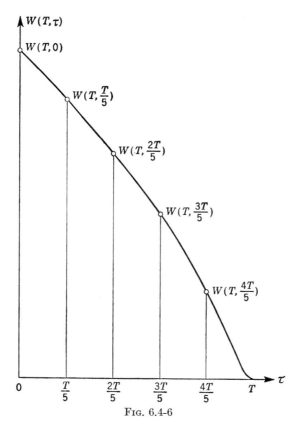

Fig. 6.4-6

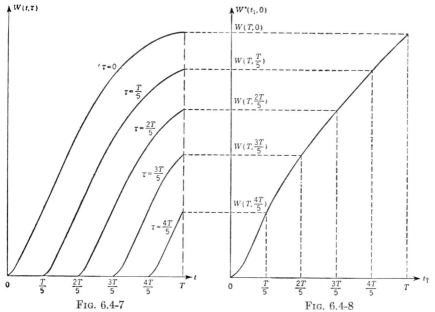

Fig. 6.4-7 Fig. 6.4-8

245

drawn to represent $W(T,\tau)$. This function may then be squared and integrated numerically to evaluate $\overline{\epsilon(T)^2}$, as expressed by Eq. (6.4-2).

The results of a number of computer runs for this problem are shown in Fig. 6.4-7. The values of τ chosen in computing $W(T,\tau)$ were taken to be 0, $T/5$, $2T/5$, $3T/5$, $4T/5$ so that the computing times for each test were, respectively, T, $4T/5$, $3T/5$, $2T/5$, $T/5$. Actually, of course, only the final values of y for each of these tests are of use to us, but the entire response over the interval from τ to T was recorded for illustrative purposes. The curve for $W(T,\tau)$ obtained from these values is shown in Fig. 6.4-6.

As we have stated previously, this curve can be generated by a single simulator test performed on the modified system. The block diagrams used for this purpose are shown in Figs. 6.4-4 and 6.4-5. Again the unit-impulse input to the modified system is accomplished by placing an initial condition on an integrator.

The result of the single simulator test performed on the modified system is shown in Fig. 6.4-8. By comparing this curve with the curves shown in Fig. 6.4-7 the direct correspondence between the values of $W^*(t_1,0)$ and the final values of $W(T,\tau)$ is seen at once. For example, we see that $W^*(2T/5, 0) = W(T, 3T/5)$. In general, we find that $W^*(T - \tau, 0) = W(T, \tau)$ or, equivalently, $W^*(t_1, 0) = W(T, T - t_1)$. Finally, we make the observation that the curves of Figs. 6.4-6 and 6.4-8 are identical except for the matter of orientation.

As discussed in Sec. 6.2 for the case in which the original system is at rest prior to time $t = 0$ and after that receives a stationary random input, we separate the system and the shaping filter by a switch which is closed at time $t = 0$ and remains closed thereafter. With this modification the over-all system is regarded as being activated by a white-noise input at all times. This switch, of course, is simply a time-varying parameter of the system which has the value one for $t > 0$ and zero for $t < 0$. In the modified system, this parameter has the value one for $T - t_1 > 0$ and zero for $T - t_1 < 0$. This implies that the switch is intially closed when performing a test on the modified system. At time $t_1 = T$ the switch is opened and remains open thereafter.

To summarize our discussion in this section, the mean-squared output at time T for a linear variable-coefficient system in response to a stationary[1] random process as an input can be calculated as follows:

1. The spectrum of the input is approximated by a rational function.

2. By factoring this rational spectrum, a shaping filter is determined such that by joining this filter to the original system a new system is formed with a white-noise input.

3. For the new system, the mean-squared output at time T is given by

$$\overline{\epsilon(T)^2} = \int_{-\infty}^{T} W_1(T, \tau)^2 \, d\tau = \int_{0}^{\infty} W_1(T, T - t_1)^2 \, dt_1$$

4. By the methods indicated in step 5 the function $W_1(T, T - t_1)$ is generated directly as a function of t_1 for $t_1 \geq 0$; the result is squared and

---

[1] It should be noted in passing that this same technique is valid for nonstationary inputs to the system, provided that a suitable time-varying shaping filter can be found.

integrated as a part of the simulation to give the mean-squared output for a fixed time T in one test.

5. To calculate $W_1(T, T - t_1)$ as a function of t_1, the adjoint of the original system plus shaping filter is simulated. As discussed above, the simulated system may be transformed into the simulated adjoint simply by reversing the flow of information through each component. In this test all variable coefficients in the system are run backwards in time, starting at the point T for which the mean-squared output is desired.

6.5   Continuous Generation of Mean-squared Errors

Using the method of adjoint systems discussed above, it is possible, for a linear time-varying system with a stationary random input, to obtain, by means of a single simulator test, the mean-squared response at some particular time T. When more than one value of T is of interest, then a separate simulator test must be performed for each. Actually, it is possible to generate $\overline{\epsilon(T)^2}$ as a continuous function of T by a somewhat different technique which will now be described. The main disadvantage of this procedure is that considerably more simulator equipment is generally required than for the method of adjoint systems. As a matter of fact, for the analysis of an nth-order system, $n(n + 1)/2$ integrators must be utilized.

In order to motivate the general discussion, let us consider first an elementary example.

Example 6.5-1.   A first-order constant-coefficient linear system described by the differential equation

$$T \frac{dy}{dt} + y = x$$

is initially at rest. At time $t = 0$, the system receives a white-noise input. The response of the system is then expressible in terms of its weighting function as

$$y(t) = \int_0^t W(t - \tau)x(\tau) \, d\tau$$

where
$$W(t - \tau) = \begin{cases} \dfrac{1}{T} \exp\left[-\dfrac{t - \tau}{T} \right] & \text{for } t > \tau \\ 0 & \text{for } t < \tau \end{cases}$$

The mean-squared value of the response is obtained from

$$\overline{y(t)^2} = \int_0^t \int_0^t W(t - \tau_1)W(t - \tau_2)\phi_{xx}(\tau_1 - \tau_2) \, d\tau_1 \, d\tau_2$$

where $\phi_{xx}(\tau_1 - \tau_2)$ is the correlation function of the input to the system. If the input is a white noise, then

$$\phi_{xx}(\tau_1 - \tau_2) = \delta(\tau_1 - \tau_2)$$

and we have

$$\overline{y(t)^2} = \int_0^t W(t - \tau)^2 \, d\tau$$

$$= \frac{1}{T^2} e^{-2t/T} \int_0^t e^{2\tau/T} \, d\tau$$

$$= \frac{1}{2T} (1 - e^{-2t/T})$$

Clearly, this last computation can be performed only when the weighting function is known explicitly, which is seldom the case. However, it is possible to find a differential equation for which $\overline{y(t)^2}$ is the solution which will avoid any computation of the weighting function.

For this purpose, we observe that

$$\frac{d}{dt} [y(t)^2] = 2y(t) \frac{dy(t)}{dt}$$

$$= \frac{2}{T} [y(t)x(t) - y(t)^2]$$

Taking the ensemble average of both sides of this equation we have

$$\frac{d\theta}{dt} + \frac{2}{T} \theta = \frac{2}{T} \overline{y(t)x(t)}$$

where, for convenience of notation, we have defined

$$\theta = \overline{y(t)^2}$$

To evaluate the right-hand side of this differential equation, we note that

$$\overline{y(t)x(t)} = \int_0^t W(t - \tau) \overline{x(t)x(\tau)} \, d\tau$$

$$= \int_0^t W(t - \tau) \delta(t - \tau) \, d\tau$$

$$= \frac{1}{2} W(0+) = \frac{1}{2T}$$

The factor $\frac{1}{2}$ arises from the fact that the δ function has its jump at the upper limit of integration. To examine this point in more detail, let us consider a random process $\{x(t)\}$ with a sharply peaked correlation function

$$\phi_{xx}(\tau) = \frac{1}{2\epsilon} e^{-|\tau|/\epsilon}$$

so that

$$\lim_{\epsilon \to 0} \phi_{xx}(\tau) = \delta(\tau)$$

Then, in the integral,

$$\overline{y(t)x(t)} = \int_0^t W(t - \tau)\phi_{xx}(t - \tau) \, d\tau$$

since $\phi_{xx}(t - \tau)$ is symmetrical about the point $\tau = t$, only one-half of the function contributes to the integral. Thus for the case at hand, we have

$$\overline{y(t)x(t)} = \frac{1}{2(\epsilon + T)} \left\{ 1 - \exp \left[-t \left(\frac{1}{T} + \frac{1}{\epsilon} \right) \right] \right\}$$

which approaches $1/2\,T$ in the limit as ϵ tends to zero.

Returning now to the original problem, we find the following differential equation which must be satisfied by $\theta = \overline{y(t)^2}$:

$$\frac{d\theta}{dt} + \frac{2}{T}\theta = \frac{1}{T^2}$$

together with the initial condition $\theta(0) = 0$. The solution is easily seen to be

$$\theta(t) = \frac{1}{2T}(1 - e^{-2t/T})$$

which is in agreement with the result obtained directly from a knowledge of the weighting function.

To extend this technique to the general case let us consider an nth-order system describable by the differential equation (5.2-30) or the equivalent set of n simultaneous first-order equations (5.2-31). We now form the following sets of equations:

$$\frac{d}{dt}(y_i y_j) = y_i \frac{dy_j}{dt} + y_j \frac{dy_i}{dt}$$
$$= y_i(y_{j+1} + F_j x) + y_j(y_{i+1} + F_i x)$$
$$i, j = 1, 2, \ldots, n-1 \quad (6.5\text{-}1)$$
$$\frac{d}{dt}(y_i y_n) = y_i(-a_1 y_n - a_2 y_{n-1} - \cdots - a_n y_1 + F_n x) + y_n(y_{i+1} + F_i x)$$
$$i = 1, 2, \ldots, n-1 \quad (6.5\text{-}2)$$
$$\frac{d}{dt}(y_n^2) = 2y_n(-a_1 y_n - a_2 y_{n-1} - \cdots - a_n y_1 + F_n x) \quad (6.5\text{-}3)$$

The procedure is now to average Eqs. (6.5-1) to (6.5-3) to obtain a system of differential equations for $\overline{y_i y_j}$. First, however, we shall compute $\overline{xy_i}$.

If the system in question is initially at rest and receives the input $x(t)$ at time $t = 0$, then, according to Eq. (5.2-19), the solution of Eqs. (5.2-31) may be written as

$$y_i(t) = \int_0^t \sum_{j=1}^n W_{ij}(t,\tau) F_j(\tau) x(\tau)\, d\tau \quad (6.5\text{-}4)$$

Multiplying by $x(t)$ and averaging, we obtain

$$\overline{x(t)y_i(t)} = \int_0^t \sum_{j=1}^n W_{ij}(t,\tau) F_j(\tau)\overline{x(t)x(\tau)}\, d\tau \quad (6.5\text{-}5)$$

Assuming now that $x(t)$ is a white noise so that

$$\overline{x(t)x(\tau)} = \delta(t - \tau) \quad (6.5\text{-}6)$$

we have, from Eq. (5.2-21),

$$\overline{x(t)y_i(t)} = \int_0^t \sum_{j=1}^n W_{ij}(t,\tau)F_j(\tau)\delta(t-\tau)\,d\tau$$

$$= \tfrac{1}{2} \sum_{j=1}^n W_{ij}(t,t)F_j(t) = \tfrac{1}{2}F_i(t) \tag{6.5-7}$$

The factor $\tfrac{1}{2}$ again occurs because the δ function has its jump at the upper limit of integration.

For convenience, we introduce the notation

$$\theta_{ij}(t) = \overline{y_i(t)y_j(t)} \tag{6.5-8}$$

so that Eqs. (6.5-1) to (6.5-3) become

$$\frac{d\theta_{ij}}{dt} = \theta_{i,j+1} + \theta_{i+1,j} + F_iF_j \qquad i, j = 1, 2, \ldots, n-1$$

$$\frac{d\theta_{in}}{dt} = \theta_{i+1,n} - a_1\theta_{in} - a_2\theta_{i,n-1} - \cdots - a_n\theta_{i,1} + F_iF_n \tag{6.5-9}$$

$$i = 1, 2, \ldots, n-1$$

$$\frac{d\theta_{nn}}{dt} = F_n^2 - 2(a_1\theta_{nn} + a_2\theta_{n,n-1} + \cdots + a_n\theta_{n,1})$$

subject to the initial conditions $\theta_{ij}(0) = 0$. Since $\theta_{ij} = \theta_{ji}$, there are $n(n+1)/2$ such equations. After obtaining the solution of Eqs. (6.5-9), the mean-squared value of y is obtained as

$$\overline{y(t)^2} = \overline{[y_1(t) + F_0(t)x(t)]^2}$$
$$= \theta_{11}(t) + F_0(t)F_1(t) + F_0(t)^2\delta(0) \tag{6.5-10}$$

The quantity $F_0(t)$ is different from zero only when the differential operator on the right-hand side of (5.2-30) is of the same order as the operator on the left-hand side. Under these circumstances, $y(t)$ contains a component of white noise and has an infinite mean-squared value. This is also seen from (6.5-10) since $\delta(0)$ is infinite. Equation (6.5-10) thus has practical significance only when $F_0(t) = 0$, in which case it takes on the simpler form

$$\overline{y(t)^2} = \theta_{11}(t) \tag{6.5-11}$$

Actually, of course, a good deal more information is obtained by using this method than by using the method of adjoint systems. The average values of the products of $y_i(t)$ and $y_j(t)$ are all generated simultaneously. However, one pays a price for all of this additional information in that the equations to be solved are, in general, much more complex than encountered in the method of adjoints.

Example 6.5-2. The system describable by the second-order differential equation

$$\frac{d^2y}{dt^2} + 2\frac{dy}{dt} + y = \frac{dx}{dt} + tx$$

is equivalent to

$$y = y_1$$

$$\frac{dy_1}{dt} = y_2 + x$$

$$\frac{dy_2}{dt} = -2y_2 - y_1 + (t - 2)x$$

so that

$$F_0 = 0 \qquad F_1 = 1 \qquad F_2 = t - 2$$

Equations (6.5-9) become simply

$$\frac{d\theta_{11}}{dt} = 2\theta_{12} + 1$$

$$\frac{d\theta_{12}}{dt} = \theta_{22} - 2\theta_{12} - \theta_{11} + t - 2$$

$$\frac{d\theta_{22}}{dt} = (t - 2)^2 - 2(2\theta_{22} + \theta_{12})$$

with

$$\theta_{11}(0) = \theta_{12}(0) = \theta_{22}(0) = 0$$

Hence

$$\overline{y(t)^2} = \theta_{11}(t) = \frac{1}{4}[(-5t^2 - 3t - 5)e^{-2t} + t^2 - 3t + 5]$$

With certain modifications this method can also be applied to systems having, as an input, a random process other than a white noise. In this case, as with the method of adjoint systems, we cascade an appropriate shaping filter and the original system, as discussed in Sec. 6.2, so that the over-all system will have a white-noise input. The procedure outlined above can now be carried through as before; however, the initial conditions to be satisfied by θ_{ij} must be appropriately modified. The method for handling the general problem is best described by means of an elementary example.

Example 6.5-3. Consider again the system analyzed in Example 6.5-1 with the exception that $x(t)$ is no longer a white noise. Instead, let $x(t)$ be a random process with correlation function given by

$$\phi_{xx}(\tau) = Ae^{-c|\tau|}$$

The transfer function for the corresponding shaping filter is derived in Example 5.5-6. We have

$$Y(j\omega) = \frac{\sqrt{2Ac}}{c + j\omega}$$

Thus, if $n(t)$ is a white noise, $x(t)$ and $n(t)$ are related by the following differential equation

$$\frac{dx}{dt} + cx = \sqrt{2Ac}\, n(t)$$

The differential equation, which describes the over-all system with a white-noise input, is found by eliminating $x(t)$ between this equation and the differential equation for the original system. There results

$$T \frac{d^2y}{dt^2} + (1 + cT) \frac{dy}{dt} + cy = \sqrt{2Ac}\, n(t)$$

Since $y(0)$ is postulated to be zero and since

$$Ty'(0) + y(0) = x(0)$$

the two initial conditions appropriate to the second-order differential equation for $y(t)$ are seen to be

$$y(0) = 0 \qquad y'(0) = \frac{x(0)}{T}$$

From a comparison with Eqs. (5.2-30) we see that

$$a_1 = \frac{1 + cT}{T} \qquad a_2 = \frac{c}{T}$$

$$b_0 = b_1 = 0 \qquad b_2 = \frac{\sqrt{2Ac}}{T}$$

Hence, from Eqs. (5.2-31) we have

$$F_0 = F_1 = 0 \qquad F_2 = \frac{\sqrt{2Ac}}{T}$$

Therefore, the equations for θ_{ij} are given by

$$\frac{d\theta_{11}}{dt} = 2\theta_{12}$$

$$\frac{d\theta_{12}}{dt} = \theta_{22} - \frac{1 + cT}{T} \theta_{12} - \frac{c}{T} \theta_{11}$$

$$\frac{d\theta_{22}}{dt} = \frac{2Ac}{T^2} - 2 \frac{(1 + cT)}{T} \theta_{22} - \frac{2c}{T} \theta_{12}$$

The corresponding initial conditions are

$$\theta_{11}(0) = \overline{y_1(0)y_1(0)} = \overline{y(0)y(0)} = 0$$
$$\theta_{12}(0) = \overline{y_1(0)y_2(0)} = \overline{y(0)y'(0)} = 0$$
$$\theta_{22}(0) = \overline{y_2(0)y_2(0)} = \overline{y'(0)y'(0)} = \frac{A}{T^2}$$

Then the solution for $\overline{y(t)^2}$ is

$$\overline{y(t)^2} = \theta_{11}(t) = A \left(\frac{1}{1 + cT} + \frac{e^{-2t/T}}{1 - cT} - \frac{2}{1 - c^2T^2} e^{-(1+cT)t/T} \right)$$

Although the examples chosen to illustrate this procedure were systems with constant parameters, the method can obviously be carried through for systems having time-varying parameters. However, in that case, it is difficult to find even a simple example that can be solved completely by analytical methods. Thus, in general, simulation equipment must be used to solve the resulting differential equations for θ_{ij}.

6.6 Optimum Design Procedure for a Class of Variable-coefficient Systems by a Method of Steepest Descents

Let us consider a linear system activated at time $t = 0$ with random initial conditions and subject to random forcing functions over the interval $0 \leq t \leq T$. We shall assume that certain of the time-varying coefficients are arbitrarily variable. It is required to find those variable coefficients which minimize the mean-squared error output $\overline{\epsilon(T)^2}$ at a chosen instant T after the time $t = 0$.

For simplicity in illustration, it is assumed that there is only one forcing function and only one initial condition to be considered, and that only one adjustable coefficient is involved. The last restriction can be

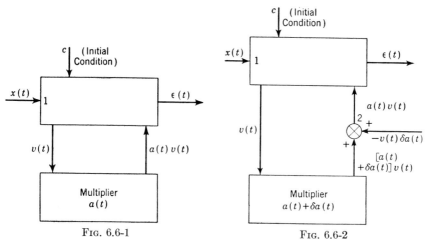

FIG. 6.6-1   FIG. 6.6-2

removed at once by applying the proposed iteration cyclically to each variable coefficient in turn. Removal of the first two restrictions complicates the detail but not the principles involved.

Let the random input to the system be denoted by $x(t)$ and the initial condition by c. Figure 6.6-1 shows the system in a schematic form in which the adjustable coefficient $a(t)$ and the variable $v(t)$ that it multiplies are shown explicitly. Then $\epsilon(t)$ may be expressed in the form

$$\epsilon(t) = cu(t) + \int_0^t W_1(t,\tau)x(\tau)\,d\tau \tag{6.6-1}$$

Here $u(t)$ represents the response of the system to a unit initial condition and $W_1(t,\tau)$ is the unit-impulse response of the system where the position 1 in the figure indicates the point of application of the input. The initial problem to be solved is the calculation of the change in $\epsilon(t)$ produced by a small change in $a(t)$.

Let $a(t)$ be altered by addition of an arbitrary small function $\delta a(t)$. If the compensating signal $-v(t)\,\delta a(t)$ is added to the multiplier output as indicated in Fig. 6.6-2, then no change whatever occurs in the remainder of the system. In particular, $\epsilon(t)$ is unaltered by this operation, and may be expressed in the form

$$\epsilon(t) = cu^{(a+\delta a)}(t) + \int_0^t W_1^{(a+\delta a)}(t,\tau)x(\tau)\,d\tau$$
$$- \int_0^t W_2^{(a+\delta a)}(t,\tau)v(\tau)\,\delta a(\tau)\,d\tau \quad (6.6\text{-}2)$$

Here again the subscripts 1 and 2 indicate the points of application of the inputs involved, the superscript $(a + \delta a)$ is used to denote the fact that the weighting functions apply to the choice $(a + \delta a)$ for the variable coefficient.

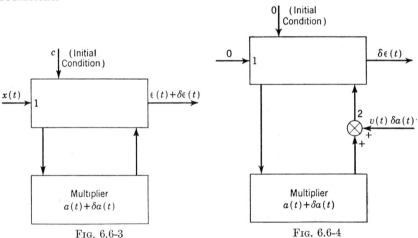

FIG. 6.6-3   FIG. 6.6-4

It is desired to compare $\epsilon(t)$ with the output $\epsilon(t) + \delta\epsilon(t)$ of the system shown in Fig. 6.6-3 in which $x(t)$ and c are unchanged, the coefficient is $a(t) + \delta a(t)$, and no compensating input is used. Reference to this figure shows that

$$\epsilon(t) + \delta\epsilon(t) = cu^{(a+\delta a)}(t) + \int_0^t W_1^{(a+\delta a)}(t,\tau)x(\tau)\,d\tau \quad (6.6\text{-}3)$$

Combination of Eqs. (6.6-2) and (6.6-3) gives

$$\delta\epsilon(t) = \int_0^t W_2^{(a+\delta a)}(t,\tau)v(\tau)\,\delta a(\tau)\,d\tau \quad (6.6\text{-}4)$$

corresponding to the test condition shown in Fig. 6.6-4. In other words, the change in $\epsilon(t)$ induced by a change $\delta a(t)$ in $a(t)$ is obtainable by a test in which $a(t)$ is replaced by $a(t) + \delta a(t)$, c and $x(t)$ are set equal to zero, and a new input $v(t)\,\delta a(t)$ is added to the multiplier output, where $v(t)$ is the original quantity (Fig. 6.6-1) which $a(t)$ multiplies.

It should be noted that these conclusions depend solely upon the linearity of the system studied, and are in no sense approximations. Now let

$$\delta W_2(t,\tau) = W_2^{(a+\delta a)}(t,\tau) - W_2^{(a)}(t,\tau) \tag{6.6-5}$$

or
$$W_2^{(a+\delta a)}(t,\tau) = W_2^{(a)}(t,\tau) + \delta W_2(t,\tau) \tag{6.6-6}$$

For sufficiently small $\delta a(t)$, the function $\delta W_2(t,\tau)$ will also be small. Thus in the relation

$$\delta\epsilon(t) = \int_0^t W_2^{(a)}(t,\tau)v(\tau)\ \delta a(\tau)\ d\tau + \int_0^t \delta W_2(t,\tau)v(\tau)\ \delta a(\tau)\ d\tau \tag{6.6-7}$$

obtained from Eq. (6.6-4) and (6.6-6), it is possible to neglect the second integral for sufficiently small $\delta a(t)$. The simplified relation

$$\delta\epsilon(t) = \int_0^t W_2^{(a)}(t,\tau)v(\tau)\ \delta a(\tau)\ d\tau \tag{6.6-8}$$

is thereby obtained.

As the next step in the calculation, the effect of a small change $\delta a(t)$ upon $\overline{\epsilon(T)^2}$ is derived. Since

$$\overline{[\epsilon(T) + \delta\epsilon(T)]^2} = \overline{\epsilon(T)^2} + 2\overline{\epsilon(T)\ \delta\epsilon(T)} + \overline{[\delta\epsilon(T)]^2} \tag{6.6-9}$$

it follows that the change $\delta[\overline{\epsilon(T)^2}]$ in $\overline{\epsilon(T)^2}$ is given to within second-order terms by

$$\begin{aligned}
\delta[\overline{\epsilon(T)^2}] &= \overline{[\epsilon(T) + \delta\epsilon(T)]^2} - \overline{\epsilon(T)^2} \\
&= 2\overline{\epsilon(T)\ \delta\epsilon(T)}
\end{aligned} \tag{6.6-10}$$

From (6.6-8)

$$\delta\epsilon(T) = \int_0^T W_2(T,\tau)v(\tau)\ \delta a(\tau)\ d\tau \tag{6.6-11}$$

Here and in subsequent calculations it is understood that all weighting functions relate to the unperturbed system with $a(t)$ as coefficient. Multiplying both sides of Eq. (6.6-11) by $\epsilon(T)$, and averaging over the ensemble of all combinations of initial conditions and forcing functions, we obtain

$$\overline{\epsilon(T)\ \delta\epsilon(T)} = \int_0^T W_2(T,\tau)\ \delta a(\tau)\overline{\epsilon(T)v(\tau)}\ d\tau \tag{6.6-12}$$

It is noted in this averaging process that $W_2(T,\tau)$ is independent of the initial conditions and forcing function, and that $\delta a(t)$ is a fixed but as yet unspecified variation in $a(t)$.

To calculate the average product of $\epsilon(T)$ and $v(t)$, it is necessary to express these quantities in terms of c and $x(t)$. From Eq. (6.6-1) with t replaced by T it is seen that

$$\epsilon(T) = cu(T) + \int_0^T W_1(T,\tau)x(\tau)\ d\tau \tag{6.6-13}$$

Considering $v(t)$ to be a second system output, it is also possible to write a relation of the form

$$v(t) = cw(t) + \int_0^t W_v(t,\tau)x(\tau)\, d\tau \rfloor \qquad (6.6\text{-}14)$$

where $w(t)$ is the transient output at v obtained by setting $c = 1$, $x(t) = 0$, and where $W_v(t,\tau)$ is the corresponding response to a unit impulse in $x(t)$. Assuming c and $x(t)$ to be statistically independent with zero mean values, the multiplication of Eqs. (6.6-13) and (6.6-14) and subsequent averaging yields

$$\overline{\epsilon(T)v(t)} = \overline{c^2}u(T)w(t)$$
$$+ \int_0^t W_v(t,\tau_1)\, d\tau_1 \int_0^T W_1(T,\tau_2)\phi_{xx}(\tau_1,\tau_2)\, d\tau_2 \qquad (6.6\text{-}15)$$

Since the derivation has been somewhat involved, a summary of progress up to this point is desirable. Let the simulated system be given, with the unperturbed coefficient $a(t)$. Let $\phi_{xx}(t_1,t_2)$ be given, as well as $\overline{c^2}$. By an appropriate combination of simulator tests of the type discussed in Sec. 6.1, the double integral in Eq. (6.6-15) may be evaluated. Since $u(t)$ and $w(t)$ represent initial condition transients observed at appropriate points of the system, a single simulator test yields the product $u(T)w(t)$. The function $\overline{\epsilon(T)v(t)}$ is thus readily calculated. Now let an arbitrary but small $\delta a(t)$ be specified. From Eqs. (6.6-10) and (6.6-12) the effect of this variation upon $\overline{\epsilon(T)^2}$ is given by

$$\delta[\overline{\epsilon(T)^2}] = 2 \int_0^T W_2(T,\tau)\, \delta a(\tau)\overline{\epsilon(T)v(\tau)}\, d\tau \qquad (6.6\text{-}16)$$

If the calculation of the change in $\overline{\epsilon(T)^2}$ corresponding to an assigned change in $a(t)$ were all that were desired, much of the preceding discussion would have been pointless. Since $\overline{\epsilon(T)^2}$ itself is calculable by the methods of Sec. 6.1, it would have been a much more direct procedure simply to change $a(t)$, calculate the new $\overline{\epsilon(T)^2}$ by the same process, and compare results. However, this approach would shed no light whatever on the question of what *kind* of change in $a(t)$ were desirable, short of trying an unlimited number of different types of change and comparing results.

To rephrase the problem somewhat, let us postulate that $a(t)$ is to be changed by a certain fixed amount, denoted by λ^2, and agree to measure the amount of change by means of the integral

$$\lambda^2 = \int_0^T [\delta a(t)]^2\, dt \qquad (6.6\text{-}17)$$

Under these conditions we seek the particular change $\delta a(t)$ which reduces the value of $\overline{\epsilon(T)^2}$ by the maximum possible amount. In other words, having specified by (6.6-17) the total amount (in a loose sense) by which

$a(t)$ is to be altered, we wish to determine the shape of the function $\delta a(t)$ which gives the best results.

Rather than derive the solution to this problem, we state it and show that it satisfies the assigned conditions. Let

$$f(t) = W_2(T,t)\overline{\epsilon(T)}v(t) \tag{6.6-18}$$

and let

$$\delta a(t) = -\lambda \left[\int_0^T f(\tau_1)^2 \, d\tau_1 \right]^{-\frac{1}{2}} f(t) \tag{6.6-19}$$

Since

$$[\delta a(t)]^2 = \frac{\lambda^2 f(t)^2}{\int_0^T f(\tau_1)^2 \, d\tau_1} \tag{6.6-20}$$

it follows at once that (6.6-17) is satisfied. Also from (6.6-16)

$$\delta[\overline{\epsilon(T)^2}] = 2 \int_0^T f(\tau) \, \delta a(\tau) \, d\tau$$

$$= -2\lambda \int_0^T f(\tau) \frac{f(\tau)}{\sqrt{\int_0^T f(\tau_1)^2 \, d\tau_1}} \, d\tau$$

$$= -2\lambda \sqrt{\int_0^T f(\tau)^2 \, d\tau} \tag{6.6-21}$$

Now let $\delta a(t)$ be chosen to be any other function $g(t)$ such that (6.6-17) is satisfied. We then have by (6.6-16) and (6.6-18)

$$\delta[\overline{\epsilon(T)^2}] = 2 \int_0^T f(\tau)g(\tau) \, d\tau \tag{6.6-22}$$

However, by the Schwarz inequality, for any two functions f and g

$$\left| \int_0^T f(t)g(t) \, dt \right| \leq \sqrt{\int_0^T f(t)^2 \, dt} \sqrt{\int_0^T g(t)^2 \, dt} \tag{6.6-23}$$

In particular

$$\int_0^T f(t)g(t) \, dt \geq - \sqrt{\int_0^T f(t)^2 \, dt} \sqrt{\int_0^T g(t)^2 \, dt} \tag{6.6-24}$$

Applying this result to (6.6-22), and noting that

$$\int_0^T g(t)^2 \, dt = \lambda^2 \tag{6.6-25}$$

we find

$$\delta[\overline{\epsilon(T)^2}] \geq -2\lambda \sqrt{\int_0^T f(t)^2 \, dt} \tag{6.6-26}$$

Thus any variation $\delta a(t) = g(t)$ satisfying (6.6-25) gives a reduction in $\overline{\epsilon(T)}^2$ which is certainly no greater than that obtained by the particular choice (6.6-19) for $\delta a(t)$. As a matter of fact, equality can exist in (6.6-23) only when $g(t)$ is proportional to $f(t)$; thus any variation $\delta a(t)$, except the one chosen, actually gives poorer results for an assigned value of λ^2.

Our results may now be formulated as a specific iteration procedure. Let $\phi_{xx}(t_1,t_2)$ and $\overline{c^2}$ be given. By some process of analysis, engineering judgment, or guesswork let a trial coefficient $a(t)$ be assigned. Using this trial function, the quantity $\overline{\epsilon(T)v(t)}$ is calculated. By a set of unit impulse tests the function $W_2(T,t)$ is also evaluated, thus giving the function $f(t)$ by (6.6-18). Selection of an arbitrary small value of λ then gives $\delta a(t)$ by (6.6-19). This variation is added to $a(t)$ to obtain a new coefficient which provides a starting point for repetition of the process.

The method of adjoint systems discussed in the previous section may be used to simplify the work needed in carrying out the steps in the iteration process outlined above. Thus, when $\{x(t)\}$ is a stationary random process, a shaping filter may be designed, as discussed in Sec. 5.5, such that a white-noise input to the filter will produce an output with the same statistical properties as $\{x(t)\}$. As before, this filter is cascaded with the system under study and separated from the system by a switch closed at time $t = 0$. If we let $W_v'(t,\tau)$ and $W_1'(t,\tau)$ be the resulting over-all weighting functions, Eq. (6.6-15) may be written as

$$\overline{\epsilon(T)v(t)} = \overline{c^2}u(T)w(t) + \int_{-\infty}^{t} W_v'(t,\tau)W_1'(T,\tau)\,d\tau \qquad (6.6\text{-}27)$$

The following simulator tests will yield all the information necessary to complete one cycle of the iteration process:

1. By the method of adjoint systems, $W_1'(T,\tau)$ may be computed as a function of τ over the interval $-\infty < \tau \leqq T$.

2. The quantity $u(T)$ is the response at T to a unit-impulse input at the proper point at time $t = 0$. Thus, $u(T)$ may be determined from the same adjoint test as above.

3. In addition, as a result of this first test, $\overline{\epsilon(T)^2}$ may be evaluated. (This quantity is needed to verify at each stage of the iteration process that the mean-squared error is actually decreasing.) $\overline{\epsilon(T)^2}$ is obtained from

$$\overline{\epsilon(T)^2} = \overline{c^2}u(T)^2 + \int_{-\infty}^{T} W_1'(T,\tau)^2\,d\tau$$
$$= \overline{c^2}u(T)^2 + \int_{0}^{\infty} W_1'^*(t,0)^2\,dt \qquad (6.6\text{-}28)$$

where $W_1'^*(t,\tau)$ is the weighting function of the over-all modified system.

4. As seen from Eq. (6.6-27) we may determine $\overline{\epsilon(T)v(t)}$ by feeding $W_1'(T,t)$ (computed according to step 1) into the input position of the shaping filter over the complete range $-\infty < t \leqq T$. At the appropriate point we also introduce $\overline{c^2}u(T)\delta(t)$ as an input. The output, observed at point (v) over the interval $0 < t \leqq T$, is $\overline{\epsilon(T)v(t)}$ as a function of t.

5. Since $\delta a(t)$ is proportional to the product of $W_2(T,t)$ and $\overline{\epsilon(T)v(t)}$, a third simulator test performed on the adjoint system will enable us to generate $W_2(T,t)$ as a function of time, multiply this result by $\overline{\epsilon(T)v(t)}$ (obtained in step 4), and add an arbitrary fraction of this product to $a(t)$ to obtain the coefficient $a(t) + \delta a(t)$ for the next step in the iteration process.

6. If it is desired, the test performed in step 5 may be used to compute the value of λ which, we recall, is the quantity used to measure the amount of change in the coefficient $a(t)$. This is easily accomplished by computing the integral of the square of the value of the $\delta a(t)$ generated in step 5.

7. If, when the iteration cycle is repeated, we find, in step 3, that our latest choice for $a(t)$ has increased the value of $\overline{\epsilon(T)^2}$, we must repeat step 5 in the previous iteration to reduce the value of $\delta a(t)$.

One element in this process is left up to the judgment of the operator, namely, the selection of the amount λ by which $a(t)$ is to be altered at each iteration. No systematic set of rules can be given for making this decision; however, the following discussion of an analogous but very much simpler problem may be of value.

Let a function $F(x,y)$ of two variables be given, for which a minimum point is sought. Let an arbitrary point (x_1,y_1) be selected and let the partial derivatives $\partial F/\partial x$ and $\partial F/\partial y$ be evaluated at (x_1,y_1). These quantities form the components of the gradient vector of $F(x,y)$. If a reduction in $F(x,y)$ is sought, it is natural to consider a change in the coordinates along the direction in which $F(x,y)$ is decreasing the most rapidly, namely, in the direction opposite to that of the gradient vector.

Let λ represent the distance in the xy plane of the step to be taken. The desired changes $(\delta x,\delta y)$ in coordinates are then given by the following two conditions:

(a) $(\delta x)^2 + (\delta y)^2 = \lambda^2$ (6.6-29)

(b) The quantities δx, δy are proportional, with reversed sign, to the derivatives $\partial F/\partial x$ and $\partial F/\partial y$, evaluated at (x_1,y_1).

The combination of these two conditions gives

$$\delta x = -\frac{\lambda}{\sqrt{\left(\frac{\partial F}{\partial x}\right)^2 + \left(\frac{\partial F}{\partial y}\right)^2}}\frac{\partial F}{\partial x} \qquad (6.6\text{-}30)$$

$$\delta y = -\frac{\lambda}{\sqrt{\left(\frac{\partial F}{\partial x}\right)^2 + \left(\frac{\partial F}{\partial y}\right)^2}}\frac{\partial F}{\partial y} \qquad (6.6\text{-}31)$$

In this relatively simple two-dimensional problem, geometric intuition provides much of the information needed in selecting suitable values for λ. If the function to be minimized is changing its character rapidly, the initial selection of too large a value for λ may cause the minimum point to be overshot, and may even produce a larger value of $F(x,y)$ than that originally prevailing. This suggests immediately that the process should be monitored by the calculation at each stage of the prevailing value of the function for which a minimum is sought. If the minimum point is overshot, it is also quite likely that the new gradient vector will be in the opposite direction from the original one, or at least will bear no close resemblance to the original. In case an overshoot is indicated by an increase in F, it is generally desirable to return to the previous iteration and pick a smaller value of λ. If the gradient vector has reversed but the value of F is reduced, it is probably best to continue the iteration, but again with a smaller λ.

On the other hand, if F is changing its character relatively slowly, it will be found that the gradient vector is also changing but little from one step to the next, and also that the successive reductions in F are approximately proportional to the lengths λ of the steps taken. In this case, an increase in length of step is obviously indicated, to save time.

In the original variational problem, we are in effect dealing with the minimization of a function $\overline{\epsilon(T)^2}$ which depends upon an infinite number of coordinates, namely, the values of $a(t)$ at each point. If this concept can be accepted, the analogy between the general minimization problem and the simplified two-dimensional problem can be fairly sharply drawn. The *distance* between two *points* $a_1(t)$ and $a_2(t)$ is given by

$$\left\{ \int_0^T [a_2(t) - a_1(t)]^2 \, dt \right\}^{1/2} \tag{6.6-32}$$

Thus the distance between $a(t)$ and the new value $a(t) + \delta a(t)$ is precisely λ, by (6.6-17). The *gradient vector* of the function $\overline{\epsilon(T)^2}$ is given by twice the function $f(t)$ of (6.6-18); it is seen from (6.6-16) and (6.6-18) that the increment in $\overline{\epsilon(T)^2}$ is given by the *scalar product* of $2f(t)$ with $\delta a(t)$. If the problem can thus be thought of in geometric terms, the interpretation of the iterative results becomes much simpler and can be used to guide the successive steps into profitable directions.

The procedure developed here is called that of *steepest descents*, and has been used to advantage in other branches of applied mathematics. Its primary usefulness lies in the fact that it provides a reasonably systematic numerical approach to many minimum-value problems where analytical methods fail. By modification of the procedures indicated in this section, it can be adapted to the solution of other problems of an analogous type; for example, the quantity $\overline{\epsilon(T)^2}$ could readily be replaced by a weighted average mean-squared error of the form $\int_0^T K(t)\overline{\epsilon(t)^2} \, dt$.

In cases involving a set of variable coefficients $a_1(t), a_2(t), \ldots, a_n(t)$, at least two possibilities are presented. On the one hand, a variation

$\delta a_1(t)$ can be computed, with $a_2, \ldots, a_n$ held fixed, followed by a variation $\delta a_2(t)$ with $a_1, a_3, \ldots, a_n$ held fixed, and so on around the cycle. On the other hand, the effects of simultaneous variations $\delta a_1, \ldots, \delta a_n$ might be studied, with

$$\int_0^T \{[\delta a_1(t)]^2 + \cdots + [\delta a_n(t)]^2\} \, dt = \lambda^2$$

The latter procedure would undoubtedly require the solution of simultaneous linear equations, and might prove impractical.

It is obvious that the procedures outlined here require considerable computational effort to be successful. On the other hand, they are not so difficult as to be impractical, as is indicated by the solution to the example studied below. In view of the intrinsic mathematical difficulty of the class of problems studied, and the potential importance of some of their applications, it is felt that the methods presented here are on the whole worthwhile. Serious attention might well be given to the adaptation of these methods to high-speed analogue or digital computation, to increase the range of their practicality.

Many interesting mathematical questions remain unanswered by the above discussion. Knowledge of the existence of an optimum coefficient and a unique minimum, together with a set of rules ensuring convergence of the iteration process, would be of considerable importance in setting up a problem of this type for automatic digital computation. In view of the singular solution obtained for the simple problem in the example to follow, this question is evidently not a trivial one mathematically.

To illustrate the practical application of the foregoing methods, the rest of this section is devoted to the detailed solution of a specific problem. Let the equation

$$\alpha(t) \frac{dy}{dt} + y = x(t)$$

define the input-output relation of a system under study over the time interval $0 \leq t \leq 1$. Let $x(t)$ be a member of a stationary random process with a correlation function given by

$$\phi(\tau) = e^{-|\tau|}$$

Let the initial value

$$y(0) = y_0$$

be random, statistically independent of $x(t)$, and such that

$$\overline{y_0^2} = 10 \qquad \bar{y}_0 = 0$$

Let the device under study be considered as a null-seeking system, so that the error $\epsilon(t)$ is identifiable with the output $y(t)$ itself. Under these conditions we seek to determine the *characteristic time* $\alpha(t)$ as a function of time in such a manner that the mean-squared output at time $t = 1$ attains a minimum value.

For convenience in subsequent calculations let us define

$$a(t) = \frac{1}{\alpha(t)}$$

so that our system equation becomes

$$\frac{dy}{dt} + a(t)y = a(t)x(t)$$

In Appendix G a formal analytical solution is obtained for this problem. From Eq. (G-29) we find that the optimum coefficient is given by

$$a(t) = \frac{5[1 + \delta(t) + \delta(t - 1)]}{u(t)}$$

where

$$u(t) = \begin{cases} 1 & t = 0 \\ 6 + 5t & 0 < t < 1 \\ 16 & t = 1 \end{cases}$$

A rigorous proof is also given that this result does in fact provide a unique optimum. Furthermore, the minimum value of $\overline{y(1)^2}$ attained with the above value of $a(t)$ is found from Eq. (G-31) to be 0.625.

In order to have a basis for estimating the net advantage gained by the use of a variable coefficient, we may compare the absolute minimum and the optimum value obtainable with a constant coefficient a. The mean-squared error calculation can be made analytically for this example in the following manner. The weighting function for the system is

$$W(t - \tau) = ae^{-a(t-\tau)}$$

when a is a constant. The value of $y(t)$ is found from Eq. (6.6-1) to be

$$y(t) = y_0 e^{-at} + a \int_0^t e^{-a(t-\tau)} x(\tau) \, d\tau$$

Then, from Eq. (6.1-10), we have

$$\overline{y(t)^2} = 10e^{-2at} + a^2 \int_0^t e^{-a(t-\tau_1)} \, d\tau_1 \int_0^t e^{-a(t-\tau_2)} e^{-|\tau_2 - \tau_1|} \, d\tau_2$$

In particular

$$\overline{y(1)^2} = 10e^{-2a} + \frac{a}{a+1} + \frac{a}{a-1} e^{-2a} - \frac{2a^2}{a^2-1} e^{-(1+a)}$$

By graphical means or otherwise one may show that this expression attains a minimum value of 0.721 for $a = 2.5$. Thus, there is a reasonable improvement obtainable through use of a variable-coefficient system in place of a time-invariant system.[1]

In order to carry out a steepest-descents procedure utilizing the method of adjoint systems, we must first design an appropriate shaping filter for the input signal. For the particular random process of this example the

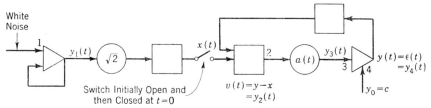

FIG. 6.6-5   Over-all system—original system and shaping filter in cascade.

transfer function of the filter may be obtained directly from Eq. (6.2-7). Thus

$$Y(p) = \frac{\sqrt{2}}{p+1}$$

A schematic simulator diagram for the original system and shaping filter in cascade is shown in Fig. 6.6-5. Using the notation of this section we observe that:

1. $W_1'(T,\tau)$ is the unit-impulse response of the over-all system with position 1 as input and position 4 as output.

2. $W_p'(t,\tau)$ is the unit-impulse response from position 1 to position 2.

3. $u(T)$ is the unit-impulse response from position 3 to position 4.

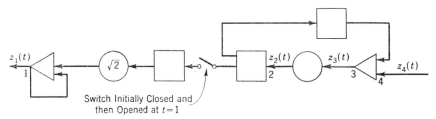

FIG. 6.6-6   Adjoint of over-all system.

We recall that if the method of adjoint systems were not available, the weighting function $W_1'(T,\tau)$ would have to be computed by a series of simulator tests, a separate test being necessary for each value of τ desired. Fortunately, as we know, $W_1'(T,\tau)$ may be obtained continuously by the use of a single simulator test performed on the adjoint system. The adjoint of the over-all system is shown schematically in Fig. 6.6-6. Thus

$$W_1'(T,\tau) = W_1'^*(T - \tau, 0)$$

[1] In all fairness it should be remarked that the numerical constants of the problem were deliberately selected so that this would be the case.

is obtained continuously as a function of $T - \tau$ by a unit-impulse-response test from position 4 to position 1 indicated on the diagram. Furthermore, $u(T)$ may be obtained from this same test since it is merely the response at time T at position 3 caused by a unit impulse initiated at time zero at position 4. In addition, using the adjoint system we may generate

$$W_2(T, t) = W_2^*(T - t, 0)$$

continuously as a function of $T - t$ by means of the same simulator test. $W_2^*(T - t, 0)$ is the response at position 3 due to a unit impulse applied at position 4. Thus, by a single unit-impulse-response test we may obtain the three quantities $W_1'(T,\tau)$, $u(T)$, and $W_2(T,t)$. Furthermore, the use of an additional integrator and squaring device permits us to obtain

$$\int_0^\infty W_1'^*(t,0)^2 \, d\tau$$

as an important by-product of this impulse test to be used in computing the mean-squared error according to Eq. (6.6-28).

To complete one cycle in the iteration process, the results obtained from the adjoint-system-response test described above are used as inputs to the original system. Thus to obtain $\overline{\epsilon(T)v(t)}$ as given by Eq. (6.6-27), we employ $W_1'(T,\tau)$ as the input at position 1 of Fig. 6.6-5 and record

$$\int_{-\infty}^t W_v'(t,\tau) W_1'(T,\tau) \, d\tau$$

as the output at position 2. Furthermore, since $w(t)$ is merely the response at time t at position 2 caused by a unit-impulse input at position 3 at time zero, the complete expression for $\overline{\epsilon(T)v(t)}$ may be obtained from a single test. That is, $W_1'(T,\tau)$ is used as input at position 1 to the overall original system. (This excitation is, of course, presumed to have been initiated at time $\tau = -\infty$.) At a time corresponding to $\tau = 0$, the switch shown in the figure is closed and simultaneously an impulse of magnitude $\overline{c^2}u(T)$ is introduced at position 3. Hence, the output observed at position 2 from the instant at which the switch is closed until a time T seconds later is the desired quantity $\overline{\epsilon(T)v(t)}$. Since $W_2(T,t)$ is obtained as a result of a test conducted on the adjoint system, we may produce $f(t)$ immediately by performing the multiplication indicated in Eq. (6.6-18). The new value of the variable coefficient $a(t) + \delta a(t)$ may be obtained by adding to $a(t)$ an arbitrary constant multiple of the negative of $f(t)$ since $\delta a(t)$ is given by Eq. (6.6-19). Finally, the value of λ corresponding to the above-mentioned arbitrary multiplicative constant may be found by simply integrating the square of $\delta a(t)$ from zero to T as indicated in Eq. (6.6-17).

The quantity λ^2 is a rough measure of the amount of change made in $a(t)$. Using the notation

$$\delta a(t) = -kf(t)$$

the value of k used in the first iteration was 12. This resulted in a value of $\lambda = 0.226$. The particular choice for k at any stage of the iteration process is arbitrary and is governed only by the experience one has obtained by the previous iteration cycles. Of course, as previously mentioned, too large a value of k may result in an increase in the mean-squared error.

Because of the inherent simplicity of this particular example it turned out to be considerably easier and more systematic to carry out the iterations in the present case by means of digital rather than analogue equipment. For the test performed on the adjoint system the following differential equations were solved numerically. (Refer to Fig. 6.6-6.)

For t in the interval $0 \le t \le 1$,

$$\frac{dz_1}{dt} = -z_1 - \sqrt{2}\, a(1 - t)z_3$$

$$\frac{dz_3}{dt} = -a(1 - t)z_3$$

$$\frac{dz_5}{dt} = z_1^2$$

The initial conditions for the variables are

$$z_1(0) = 0 \qquad z_3(0) = 1 \qquad z_5(0) = 0$$

In terms of the new notation we have

$$z_1(t) = W_1'^*(1 - t, 0)$$
$$z_3(t) = W_2^*(1 - t, 0)$$
$$z_5(t) = \int_0^t W_1'^*(t,0)^2 \, dt$$

For $t > 1$, the relevant equations are

$$\frac{dz_1}{dt} = -z_1$$

$$\frac{dz_5}{dt} = z_1^2$$

This second set of equations may be solved explicitly in terms of the final values of the variables obtained from a solution of the first set. Thus

$$z_1(t) = z_1(1)e^{-(t-1)}$$
$$z_5(\infty) = z_5(1) + \int_1^\infty z_1(1)^2 e^{-2(t-1)} \, dt$$
$$= z_5(1) + \frac{z_1(1)^2}{2}$$

and, according to Eq. (6.6-28), we have for the mean-squared error

$$\overline{\epsilon^2(1)} = 10z_3(1)^2 + z_5(1) + \frac{z_1(1)^2}{2}$$

The second part of the iteration cycle consists of a test performed on the original system. Referring to Fig. 6.6-5, we see that the following equations must be solved.

For t in the interval $-\infty < t < 0$,

$$\frac{dy_1}{dt} = -y_1 - W_1'(1,t)$$

Since $W_1'(1,t) = z_1(1 - t)$ and $y_1(-\infty) = 0$, we have

$$\frac{dy_1}{dt} + y_1 = -z_1(1)e^t$$

or

$$y_1(t) = -\frac{z_1(1)e^t}{2}$$

For t in the interval $0 \leq t \leq 1$, the equations are

$$\frac{dy_1}{dt} = -y_1 - W_1'(1,t)$$

$$\frac{dy_4}{dt} = -a(t)y_2$$

$$\frac{dy_5}{dt} = -a(t)y_5$$

together with the initial conditions

$$y_1(0) = -\frac{z_1(1)}{2} \qquad y_4(0) = 0 \qquad y_5(0) = 1$$

The quantity $\overline{\epsilon(1)v(t)}$, according to Eq. (6.6-27), is given by

$$\overline{\epsilon(1)v(t)} = 10z_3(1)y_5(t) + y_2(t)$$

where

$$y_2(t) = y_4 + \sqrt{2}\, y_1$$

Finally, from Eqs. (6.6-18) and (6.6-19), we have

$$f(t) = z_3(1 - t)\overline{\epsilon(1)v(t)}$$

and

$$\delta a(t) = -kf(t)$$

The quantity λ^2, as defined by Eq. (6.6-17), may be obtained as the final value of the solution of the differential equation

$$\frac{dy_6}{dt} = k^2 f(t)^2$$

Thus

$$y_6(1) = \lambda^2$$

Eight complete iteration cycles were carried through, reducing the mean-squared error from 0.721 to 0.658. (Recall that the optimum

variable coefficient corresponds to a mean-squared error of 0.625.)   Figure 6.6-7 contains a plot of the approximations to the optimum coefficient

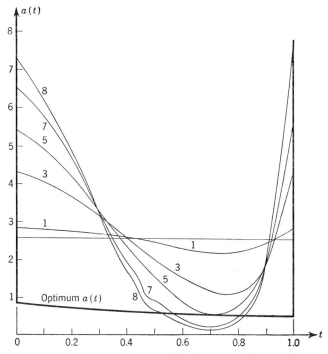

FIG. 6.6-7   Successive approximations to optimum $a(t)$.

obtained at various stages in the iteration procedure.   The values of
the resulting mean-squared errors are tabulated below.

Iteration number	$\overline{\epsilon(1)^2}$
	0.721
1	0.712
2	0.699
3	0.685
4	0.677
5	0.671
6	0.666
7	0.662
8	0.658

PROBLEMS

6-1. In an automatic radar tracking fire-control system, one component of future
target position is obtained from the relation

$$y(t) = \left[1 + \frac{T'(t)p}{1 + \tau p} \right] x(t)$$

where x and y are, respectively, the present and predicted position of the target, $T(t)$ is the time of flight of the projectile, and τ is the time constant of the differentiating filter. Assume the system is at rest prior to time $t = 0$.

Assuming $T(t) = 30 - \frac{1}{2}t$ seconds and $\tau = 1$ second show how the method of Sec. 6.1 could be used to compute the mean-squared error of this prediction over the interval $0 \leq t \leq 60$ when the input consists of radar noise only with a spectral density given by

$$G_{xx}(\omega) = \frac{200}{4 + \omega^2} \text{ yards}^2\text{-sec}$$

Include a detailed discussion of all the steps to be followed and all necessary block diagrams. Carry out analytically, as far as you find possible, the results that would be obtained at the various stages of this procedure.

6-2. Assuming a constant time of flight, $T = 15$ seconds, show how the method of Sec. 6.2 could be used to obtain information similar to that required in Prob. 6-1. Include detailed steps, block diagrams, and analytic results as before.

6-3. Show how Prob. 6-1 could be solved using the method of adjoint systems discussed in Sec. 6.4.

6-4. A second-order constant-coefficient linear system is described by the differential equation

$$\frac{d^2y}{dt^2} + 2\frac{dy}{dt} + y = x$$

The system is initially at rest and at time $t = 0$ receives a white noise with correlation function given by

$$\phi_{xx}(\tau) = \delta(\tau)$$

Show that the mean-squared response is given by

$$\overline{y(t)^2} = \frac{1}{4}[1 - (1 + 2t + 2t^2)e^{-2t}]$$

OPTIMUM LINEAR LEAST-SQUARES SMOOTHING AND PREDICTION FOR STATIONARY RANDOM PROCESSES

7.1 Formulation of the Wiener Smoothing and Prediction Problem

In the introductory section of Chap. 5 the problem of filtering and prediction was discussed from a very general point of view. We recall the statement of the basic synthesis problem for filters and predictors.

Let $s(t)$ be a time-varying signal representing the useful information fed into a device and let $q_i(t) = s(t) + n(t)$ be the total input signal. We may ask in the ideal case for that device which yields $s(t + T)$ as an output. [For the case in which $T = 0$, the device is called a *filter*. Alternatively, for $n(t) = 0$ and $T > 0$, the device is called a *predictor*. In general, however, the device sought serves the dual purpose of smoothing as well as prediction.]

We further recall that a number of considerations must be faced before a precise mathematical formulation of the synthesis problem can be made. For example, if the input signals are random, are they stationary or nonstationary in character? Again, how can we be certain that the "optimum" device has linear or nonlinear characteristics which may be approximated by physical equipment? Finally, what shall be our criterion for optimalization? That is, by what means shall we compare the performance of two devices? Any optimal design theory must contain the answer to these questions in its hypothesis.

The Wiener theory is based on four assumptions which determine the range of applicability of the results: (1) the signal $s(t)$ and noise $n(t)$ are each members of stationary random processes which have some distinguishing characteristics; (2) the device required is to perform a *linear* operation on the available information; (3) the device must be physically realizable (that is, its unit impulse response must vanish for $t < 0$); and (4) the criterion to be used in selecting the "best possible" device shall be the rms difference between the actual and desired outputs.

The performance of a linear device may be completely characterized by its unit impulse response or weighting function, as discussed in Sec. 5.2.

Denoting this weighting function by $W(t)$ (we need consider only time-invariant systems since the statistical properties of the input are assumed to be independent of time), the output of the system is simply a convolution of $s(t) + n(t)$ with $W(t)$. Thus, the difference between the desired and actual system output may be expressed as

$$\epsilon(t) = s(t + T) - \int_0^\infty [s(t - \tau) + n(t - \tau)]W(\tau)\, d\tau \qquad (7.1\text{-}1)$$

Following the discussion of Sec. 5.3, we obtain

$$\overline{\epsilon(t)^2} = \overline{s(t + T)^2} - 2\int_0^\infty [\overline{s(t + T)s(t - \tau)}$$
$$+ \overline{s(t + T)n(t - \tau)}]W(\tau)\, d\tau + \int_0^\infty W(\tau_1)\, d\tau_1$$
$$\times \int_0^\infty W(\tau_2)\overline{[s(t - \tau_1) + n(t - \tau_1)][s(t - \tau_2) + n(t - \tau_2)]}\, d\tau_2 \qquad (7.1\text{-}2)$$

According to Eq. (3.5-13) the correlation between two stationary random processes $x(t)$ and $y(t)$ is expressed by means of

$$\phi_{xy}(\tau) = \overline{x(t)y(t + \tau)} \qquad (7.1\text{-}3)$$

Thus, Eq. (7.1-2) may be rewritten in terms of autocorrelation and cross-correlation functions as

$$\overline{\epsilon^2} = \phi_{ss}(0) - 2\int_0^\infty \psi(T + \tau)W(\tau)\, d\tau$$
$$+ \int_0^\infty W(\tau_1)\, d\tau_1 \int_0^\infty W(\tau_2)\phi(\tau_2 - \tau_1)\, d\tau_2 \qquad (7.1\text{-}4)$$

where, for convenience, we have introduced the notation

$$\psi(\tau) = \phi_{ss}(\tau) + \phi_{ns}(\tau) \qquad (7.1\text{-}5)$$
$$\phi(\tau) = \phi_{ss}(\tau) + \phi_{ns}(\tau) + \phi_{sn}(\tau) + \phi_{nn}(\tau) \qquad (7.1\text{-}6)$$

Our problem may now be stated as follows: Given the correlation functions appearing in Eqs. (7.1-5) and (7.1-6), we must find a weighting function $W(t)$ which minimizes the mean-squared error $\overline{\epsilon^2}$ defined by Eq. (7.1-4). We note that the condition of physical realizability is automatically satisfied, since we may take $W(t) = 0$ for $t < 0$.

An alternate expression for the mean-squared error may be obtained directly in terms of the spectral densities of the input signals and the transfer function of the predicting-smoothing filter. We assume first that the signal and the noise are completely uncorrelated so that the cross-power spectral densities $G_{sn}(\omega)$ and $G_{ns}(\omega)$ are identically zero. Let $Y(j\omega)$ be the frequency response function of the filter.

We first consider the components of signal and noise at a particular frequency ω. At this frequency the error power density produced by the noise is equal to $|Y(j\omega)|^2 G_{nn}(\omega)$, where $G_{nn}(\omega)$ is the power spectral density of the input noise.

In the absence of noise the frequency-response function of the ideal predictor operating only upon the signal $s(t)$ is $e^{j\omega T}$. Therefore, the error power density caused by the failure of the filter to perform ideal prediction at the frequency ω is equal to $|Y(j\omega) - e^{j\omega T}|^2 G_{ss}(\omega)$, where $G_{ss}(\omega)$ is the power spectral density of input signal.

The total error power spectral density is the sum of these two errors so that

$$G_{\epsilon\epsilon}(\omega) = |Y(j\omega)|^2 G_{nn}(\omega) + |Y(j\omega) - e^{j\omega T}|^2 G_{ss}(\omega) \qquad (7.1\text{-}7)$$

Then the total mean-squared error is obtained from

$$\overline{\epsilon^2} = \int_0^\infty G_{\epsilon\epsilon}(\omega)\, d\omega$$
$$= \int_0^\infty [|Y(j\omega)|^2 G_{nn}(\omega) + |Y(j\omega) - e^{j\omega T}|^2 G_{ss}(\omega)]\, d\omega \qquad (7.1\text{-}8)$$

Thus, an alternate statement of our problem, for the case in which the signal and noise are completely uncorrelated, is as follows: Given the power spectral densities of the signal and the noise, we must find a physically realizable transfer function $Y(p)$ which minimizes the mean-squared error $\overline{\epsilon^2}$ defined by Eq. (7.1-8).

When there exists a nonzero correlation between the signal and the noise, additional terms, arising from this cross correlation, will appear in Eq. (7.1-8). The total mean-squared error is then given by

$$\overline{\epsilon^2} = \int_0^\infty \{|Y(j\omega)|^2 G_{nn}(\omega) + [Y(j\omega) - e^{j\omega T}]Y(-j\omega)G_{ns}(\omega)$$
$$+ [Y(-j\omega) - e^{-j\omega T}]Y(j\omega)G_{sn}(\omega) + |Y(j\omega) - e^{j\omega T}|^2 G_{ss}(\omega)\}\, d\omega \qquad (7.1\text{-}9)$$

following the discussion of Sec. 5.4. However, the physical nature of these added terms is not as evident as that of the uncorrelated terms.

Referring again to the expression for the mean-squared error given by Eq. (7.1-4), the next step in the argument is to find a necessary and sufficient condition that $W(t)$ must satisfy in order that $\overline{\epsilon^2}$ will be a minimum. If $W(t)$ actually minimizes $\overline{\epsilon^2}$ and if we replace $W(t)$ by $W(t) + aK(t)$, where a is a real number and $K(t)$ is an arbitrary function of t, the effect will be to increase $\overline{\epsilon^2}$. Thus, for a fixed $K(t)$, $\overline{\epsilon^2}$ will be a function of a,

$$\overline{\epsilon^2(a)} = \phi_{ss}(0) - 2\int_0^\infty \psi(T + \tau)[W(\tau) + aK(\tau)]\, d\tau$$
$$+ \int_0^\infty d\tau_1 \int_0^\infty d\tau_2 [W(\tau_1)W(\tau_2) + aW(\tau_1)K(\tau_2)$$
$$+ aW(\tau_2)K(\tau_1) + a^2 K(\tau_1)K(\tau_2)]\phi(\tau_2 - \tau_1) \qquad (7.1\text{-}10)$$

which assumes its minimum value when $a = 0$. Therefore, the derivative of $\overline{\epsilon^2(a)}$ with respect to a must vanish for $a = 0$. If we differentiate

Eq. (7.1-10) with respect to a, then set $a = 0$, and use the fact that $\phi(\tau_2 - \tau_1) = \phi(\tau_1 - \tau_2)$, we obtain

$$\int_0^\infty K(\tau_2) \left[\psi(T + \tau_2) - \int_0^\infty W(\tau_1) \phi(\tau_2 - \tau_1) \, d\tau_1 \right] d\tau_2 = 0 \quad (7.1\text{-}11)$$

Since this must hold for all functions $K(t)$, then

$$\psi(t + T) = \int_0^\infty W(\tau) \phi(t - \tau) \, d\tau \qquad \text{for } t \geq 0 \qquad (7.1\text{-}12)$$

is a necessary condition which $W(t)$ must satisfy in order that $\overline{\epsilon^2}$ will be a minimum.

This condition is also sufficient as seen from the following argument. Equation (7.1-10) may be written in the form

$$\overline{\epsilon^2(a)} = \overline{\epsilon^2(0)} + 2a \int_0^\infty K(t) \left[-\psi(T + t) + \int_0^\infty W(\tau) \phi(t - \tau) \, d\tau \right] dt$$
$$+ a^2 \int_0^\infty \int_0^\infty K(\tau_1) K(\tau_2) \phi(\tau_2 - \tau_1) \, d\tau_1 \, d\tau_2 \quad (7.1\text{-}13)$$

The last term in this expression may be written as

$$\overline{\left\{ a \int_0^\infty K(\tau)[s(t - \tau) + n(t - \tau)] \, d\tau \right\}^2}$$

which places in evidence the fact that this term is always positive. Now if we write I_1 for the integral in the second term of Eq. (7.1-13) and I_2 for the integral in the third term, we have

$$\overline{\epsilon^2(a)} = \overline{\epsilon^2(0)} + 2aI_1 + a^2 I_2 \qquad (7.1\text{-}14)$$

where I_2 is positive. Thus, if $I_1 = 0$ we see that

$$\overline{\epsilon^2(a)} \geq \overline{\epsilon^2(0)} \qquad (7.1\text{-}15)$$

The mean-squared error is therefore not decreased by perturbing $W(t)$, if $I_1 = 0$; that is, if Eq. (7.1-12) is satisfied.

We have now succeeded in showing that the problem of finding a function $W(t)$ which minimizes $\overline{\epsilon^2}$, as expressed by Eq. (7.1-4), is entirely equivalent to finding a solution of Eq. (7.1-12) which is a Wiener-Hopf integral equation of the first kind. Two different methods of solving this integral equation are presented in following sections.

When the mean-squared error is expressed by Eq. (7.1-9), the chief difficulty in minimizing $\overline{\epsilon^2}$ lies in choosing an appropriate side condition to ensure that the transfer function $Y(p)$ is physically realizable. This problem is treated in a later section.

7.2 Pure Prediction

The present section will be devoted to the simplest type of prediction problem—that for which the input is a noise-free signal whose value we wish to predict at time $t + T$ from a knowledge of the signal previous to time t. We solve this problem here from purely physical reasoning. The same result may be obtained, of course, as a special case of the more general problem to be solved later. However, the derivation is sufficiently simple and instructive as to warrant a separate discussion.

As discussed in Sec. 5.5, a shaping filter may be constructed such that a white-noise input to the filter will result in a signal having a spectrum which is identical with the spectrum $G_{ss}(\omega)$ of our signal $s(t)$. Let $Y_1(p)$ be the transfer function of this shaping filter and let $W_1(t)$ be the corresponding weighting function. The filter $Y_1^{-1}(p)$ is physically realizable, and we can pass the signal $s(t)$ through $Y_1^{-1}(p)$ to obtain a white noise. Our problem will be solved if we can find the best operation to apply to this white noise in order to approximate $s(t + T)$.

As the first step, we express the desired quantity $s(t + T)$ in terms of the white noise $n(t)$ by the relation

$$s(t + T) = \int_{-\infty}^{t+T} W_1(t + T - \tau)n(\tau)\,d\tau$$

Writing

$$I_p = \int_{-\infty}^{t} W_1(t + T - \tau)n(\tau)\,d\tau$$

$$I_f = \int_{t}^{t+T} W_1(t + T - \tau)n(\tau)\,d\tau$$

we see that

$$s(t + T) = I_p + I_f$$

Now the integrand in the expression for I_p depends upon values of $n(\tau)$ for $\tau < t$, that is, upon past values of n. The expression for I_f, on the other hand, depends solely upon future values of the white noise. Since future values of a white noise are unpredictable from its past behavior, I_p is essentially known to us and I_f is essentially unknown. We are therefore tempted to conclude that I_p represents the best available estimate for the quantity $s(t + T)$. We shall now show this to be true in a precise sense.

Considering the quantities I_p and I_f to be random variables, we may readily show them to be uncorrelated. The quantity $E[I_p I_f]$ is given by the double integral expression

$$E[I_p I_f] = \int_{-\infty}^{t} d\tau_1 \int_{t}^{t+T} d\tau_2\, W_1(t + T - \tau_1) W_1(t + T - \tau_2)\delta(\tau_2 - \tau_1)$$

Since the two ranges of integration in these integrals do not overlap, the argument of the delta function is never zero; hence the expression vanishes, giving

$$E[I_p I_f] = 0$$

In addition, we note by similar reasoning that for any random variable V expressible as a linear operation on past values of $n(t)$, the quantities V and I_f are uncorrelated. In other words, if

$$V = \int_{-\infty}^{t} W(t - \tau)n(\tau)\, d\tau$$

then
$$E[VI_f] = 0$$

whatever the choice of W.

Now let an arbitrary W be chosen, in such fashion that the resulting quantity V is to approximate $s(t + T)$ in some sense. The error in approximation is

$$\epsilon = V - s(t + T) = V - I_p - I_f$$

and for $E[\epsilon^2]$ we have

$$E[\epsilon^2] = E[(V - I_p)^2] - 2E[(V - I_p)I_f] + E[I_f^2]$$

Since $E[VI_f] = E[I_p I_f] = 0$, however, it follows that

$$E[\epsilon^2] = E[(V - I_p)^2] + E[I_f^2]$$

Clearly from this relation the best choice for W is that which makes V and I_p identical, as asserted. Denoting this optimum weighting function by $W_2(t)$, we must have

$$W_2(t) = \begin{cases} W_1(t + T) & \text{for } t \geqq 0 \\ 0 & \text{for } t < 0 \end{cases} \qquad (7.2\text{-}1)$$

Representing the corresponding transfer function by $Y_2(p)$, we note that Y_2 operates on the white noise n which is in turn generated from the original signal s by the operation Y_1^{-1}. Combining these results, we see that the optimum predictor to be applied to $s(t)$ has the transfer function

$$Y(p) = Y_1^{-1}(p)Y_2(p) \qquad (7.2\text{-}2)$$

In case the random process $\{s(t)\}$ is Gaussian, even stronger statements can be made concerning these results. In that instance the corresponding white noise is the limiting case of the shot effect; i.e., an infinitely dense collection of infinitesimal and independent impulses. Past and future values are then not only uncorrelated but statistically independent. In particular

$$E[VI_f] = E[V]E[I_f] = 0$$

for any random variable V whatever that depends only upon past values of $n(t)$, since V and I_f are independent and $E[I_f] = 0$.

We now restate the problem for the Gaussian case as follows. What is the optimum operation of any sort, linear or otherwise, that can be applied to past values of $n(t)$ to give the best estimate for $s(t + T)$ in the mean-squared error sense? Denoting the result of the as yet unspecified operation by V, we again have

$$E[\epsilon^2] = E[(V - I_p)^2] + E[I_f^2]$$

showing that the best operation is that which makes V identically equal to I_p. In other words, when the process $\{s(t)\}$ is Gaussian, the optimum linear predictor as derived above is also the optimum predictor of any sort, linear or otherwise.

A further remark is worthwhile. If all one knows about an arbitrary random process $\{s(t)\}$ is its correlation function, then one cannot expect from this knowledge alone to obtain a predictor for $s(t)$ that is better than the optimum linear predictor. This follows from the above results, since there exists a Gaussian process $\{s_1(t)\}$ possessing the same correlation function as that of $\{s(t)\}$. The two processes are therefore indistinguishable, from the standpoint of the amount of knowledge postulated.

For any prediction operator P, let $e(P,s)$ be the mean-squared error

$$e(P,s) = E[\{P(s) - s(t + T)\}^2]$$

and let L be the optimum linear predictor as defined above. Then if $P \neq L$, since L is known to be optimum for s_1,

$$e(P,s_1) > e(L,s_1) = e(L,s)$$

Hence, even if P is an operator that satisfies

$$e(P,s) < e(L,s)$$

then, still $\quad\quad e(P,s_1) > e(L,s)$

It follows that P is actually a poorer predictor than L for a process $\{s_1\}$ that cannot be distinguished from $\{s\}$. The specification of more data than just the correlation function is therefore required if a better prediction is to be obtained.

Example 7.2-1. We shall now apply this procedure to a case in which the signal $s(t)$ has a spectral density given by

$$G_{ss}(\omega) = \frac{1}{1 + \omega^2}$$

The transfer function of the appropriate shaping filter for this spectrum is given by

$$Y_1(p) = \frac{\sqrt{\pi}}{1 + p}$$

and the corresponding weighting function is

$$W_1(t) = \sqrt{\pi}\, e^{-t}$$

From Eq. (7.2-1) we have

$$W_2(t) = \begin{cases} \sqrt{\pi}\, e^{-(t+T)} & \text{for } t \geq 0 \\ 0 & \text{for } t < 0 \end{cases}$$

and the corresponding transfer function is found from Eq. (5.2-42) to be

$$Y_2(p) = \int_0^\infty \sqrt{\pi} \, e^{-(t+T)} e^{-pt} \, dt = \frac{\sqrt{\pi} \, e^{-T}}{1+p}$$

Hence, the transfer function of the optimal predictor, as obtained from Eq. (7.2-2), is given by

$$Y(p) = \frac{1+p}{\sqrt{\pi}} \frac{\sqrt{\pi} \, e^{-T}}{1+p} = e^{-T}$$

Therefore, the optimal prediction of $s(t + T)$ is obtained by taking the product of $s(t)$ and e^{-T}. At first this result seems surprising for it would seem to imply that always the signal $s(t)$ must tend to zero. Actually, of course, it is only the predictable part of $s(t + T)$ which must approach zero and the unpredictable part is as likely to be positive as negative.

The result expressed by Eq. (7.2-2) and the necessary operations which must be performed to obtain the factors in this expression may be summarized in the following formula

$$Y(j\omega) = \frac{1}{2\pi Y_1(j\omega)} \int_0^\infty e^{-j\omega t} \, dt \int_{-\infty}^\infty Y_1(ju)e^{ju(t+T)} \, du \qquad (7.2\text{-}3)$$

which is just a special case of Eq. (7.4-22).

In performing the first integration indicated in Eq. (7.2-3), the following Fourier transforms frequently will be found to be useful.

1. If the imaginary part of α is positive, then

$$\frac{1}{2\pi} \int_{-\infty}^\infty \frac{e^{j\omega t}}{(\omega - \alpha)^n} \, d\omega = \begin{cases} \dfrac{j^n}{(n-1)!} t^{n-1} e^{j\alpha t} & \text{for } t > 0 \\ 0 & \text{for } t < 0 \end{cases} \qquad (7.2\text{-}4)$$

2. If the imaginary part of α is negative, then

$$\frac{1}{2\pi} \int_{-\infty}^\infty \frac{e^{j\omega t}}{(\omega - \alpha)^n} \, d\omega = \begin{cases} \dfrac{j^n}{(n-1)!} t^{n-1} e^{j\alpha t} & \text{for } t < 0 \\ 0 & \text{for } t > 0 \end{cases} \qquad (7.2\text{-}5)$$

7.3   The Method of Bode and Shannon

In Sec. 7.1 we derived an equation for the mean-squared prediction error expressed in terms of the power spectral densities of the signal and noise. We shall now use techniques similar to those employed in Sec. 7.2 to obtain the optimal predicting-smoothing filter.

First, let us suppose that the frequency-response function of the optimal filter is

$$Y(j\omega) = C(\omega)e^{jB(\omega)} \qquad (7.3\text{-}1)$$

where $C(\omega)$ and $B(\omega)$ are real functions of frequency. Then Eq. (7.1-9) may be expressed as

$$\overline{\epsilon^2} = \int_0^\infty [C^2(G_{ss} + G_{ns} + G_{sn} + G_{nn}) + G_{ss}$$
$$- C(G_{ss} + G_{ns})e^{j(\omega T - B)} - C(G_{ss} + G_{sn})e^{-j(\omega T - B)}] \, d\omega \quad (7.3\text{-}2)$$

We recall that, in general, G_{ns} is a complex quantity and G_{sn} is its complex conjugate. Thus, we may write

$$G_{ss} + G_{ns} = A(\omega)e^{j\alpha(\omega)} \quad (7.3\text{-}3)$$

where $A(\omega)$ and $\alpha(\omega)$ are real functions of frequency. Equation (7.3-2) becomes

$$\overline{\epsilon^2} = \int_0^\infty [C^2(G_{ss} + G_{ns} + G_{sn} + G_{nn}) + G_{ss}$$
$$- 2AC \cos(\omega T - B + \alpha)] \, d\omega \quad (7.3\text{-}4)$$

Clearly, the best choice of $B(\omega)$ is

$$B(\omega) = \alpha(\omega) + \omega T \quad (7.3\text{-}5)$$

for this makes the cosine term as large as possible and, therefore, $\overline{\epsilon^2}$ as small as possible.

Next, we complete the square for the terms involving $C(\omega)$ to obtain

$$\overline{\epsilon^2} = \int_0^\infty \left[\left(C \sqrt{G_{ss} + G_{ns} + G_{sn} + G_{nn}} \right. \right.$$
$$\left. - \frac{A}{\sqrt{G_{ss} + G_{ns} + G_{sn} + G_{nn}}} \right)^2$$
$$\left. + G_{ss} - \frac{A^2}{G_{ss} + G_{ns} + G_{sn} + G_{nn}} \right] d\omega \quad (7.3\text{-}6)$$

We observe that $\overline{\epsilon^2}$ will be a minimum if we choose

$$C(\omega) = \frac{A(\omega)}{G_{ss}(\omega) + G_{ns}(\omega) + G_{sn}(\omega) + G_{nn}(\omega)} \quad (7.3\text{-}7)$$

The main difficulty with this approach is that the resulting transfer function $Y(j\omega)$ obtained in this manner is not, in general, physically realizable. Therefore, the remaining problem is to construct from this solution the best physically realizable filter.

Following the procedure of Sec. 7.2, we design a shaping filter for the signal plus noise $s(t) + n(t)$. Let $Y_1(p)$ be the transfer function of this filter. If we pass $s(t) + n(t)$ through the filter $Y_1^{-1}(p)$, the output will be a white noise. Since a knowledge of the input and output of this filter are equivalent, the best linear operation on the white noise will give the same prediction as the best linear operation on the original signal plus noise.

We have just seen that if

$$Y(j\omega) = \frac{A(\omega)}{G_{ss}(\omega) + G_{ns}(\omega) + G_{sn}(\omega) + G_{nn}(\omega)}\, e^{j[\alpha(\omega)+\omega T]}$$

$$= \frac{G_{ss}(\omega) + G_{ns}(\omega)}{G_{ss}(\omega) + G_{ns}(\omega) + G_{sn}(\omega) + G_{nn}(\omega)}\, e^{j\omega T} \qquad (7.3\text{-}8)$$

were physically realizable as a transfer function, it would be the transfer function of the optimum smoothing predictor to be used to filter $s(t) + n(t)$. The equivalent operation to be performed on the white-noise output of $Y_1^{-1}(p)$ would then be

$$Y_2(p) = Y(p)Y_1(p) \qquad (7.3\text{-}9)$$

The weighting function corresponding to this transfer function is simply

$$K_2(t) = \frac{1}{2\pi}\int_{-\infty}^{\infty} Y_2(j\omega)e^{j\omega t}\, d\omega \qquad (7.3\text{-}10)$$

which will, in general, have nonzero values from $t = -\infty$ to $t = +\infty$. For $K_2(t)$ to be physically realizable as an impulse response function, it must be zero for negative values of t.

Again the only impulses, of which our white noise is composed, that are available to be operated upon by our filter are those which have occurred in the past prior to time t. In performing our prediction, it would seem natural to weight those impulses according to Eq. (7.3-10) and to weight the future impulses zero. This is equivalent to operating on the white-noise output of $Y_1^{-1}(p)$ with a filter whose weighting function is defined by

$$K_3(t) = \begin{cases} K_2(t) & \text{for } t \geqq 0 \\ 0 & \text{for } t < 0 \end{cases} \qquad (7.3\text{-}11)$$

with a corresponding transfer function $Y_3(p)$.

To summarize, the optimal least-squares prediction is obtained by passing our signal plus noise $s(t) + n(t)$ through a filter whose transfer function is given by

$$Y_4(p) = Y_1^{-1}(p)Y_3(p) \qquad (7.3\text{-}12)$$

Example 7.3-1. As an illustration of this optimalization procedure, let us consider a case in which the signal and noise are uncorrelated. Let the spectral densities of the signal and noise be given by

$$G_{ss}(\omega) = \frac{6}{\pi}\frac{1}{\omega^2 + \tfrac{9}{4}} \qquad G_{nn}(\omega) = \frac{2}{\pi}\frac{\omega^2 + 2}{\omega^4 + 4}$$

Then

$$G_{ss}(\omega) + G_{nn}(\omega) = \frac{2}{\pi}\frac{4\omega^4 + \tfrac{17}{4}\,\omega^2 + \tfrac{33}{2}}{(\omega^2 + \tfrac{9}{4})(\omega^4 + 4)}$$

from which we obtain

$$jY_1(j\omega) = \frac{2\sqrt{2}\,(\omega - c)(\omega + c^*)}{(\omega - b)(\omega - a)(\omega + a^*)}$$

where $\qquad a = 1 + j \qquad b = j1.5 \qquad c = 0.8658 + j1.1318$

(Quantities with asterisks indicate complex conjugates.)

From Eq. (7.3-8), we obtain

$$Y(j\omega) = \frac{3(\omega^4 + 4)}{4\omega^4 + 17\frac{1}{4}\omega^2 + 33\frac{1}{2}}\,e^{j\omega T}$$

from which we have

$$
\begin{aligned}
jY_2(j\omega) &= \frac{3(\omega - a)(\omega - a^*)(\omega + a)(\omega + a^*)}{4(\omega - c)(\omega - c^*)(\omega + c)(\omega + c^*)}\,e^{j\omega T}\;\frac{2\sqrt{2}\,(\omega - c)(\omega + c^*)}{(\omega - b)(\omega - a)(\omega + a^*)} \\
&= \frac{3}{\sqrt{2}}\,\frac{(\omega - a^*)(\omega + a)}{(\omega - b)(\omega - c^*)(\omega + c)}\,e^{j\omega T} \\
&= \frac{3}{\sqrt{2}}\left(\frac{A}{\omega - b} + \frac{B}{\omega - c^*} + \frac{C}{\omega + c}\right)e^{j\omega T}
\end{aligned}
$$

where A, B, C are constants to be determined. $K_2(t)$ may be computed from Eq. (7.3-10). However, from Eqs. (7.2-4) and (7.2-5), we see that the only term in the expression for $Y_2(j\omega)$, which is physically realizable as a weighting function, is the first. Since $K_3(t)$ is composed of just the physically realizable part of $K_2(t)$, we may discard the terms with coefficients B and C when computing $K_2(t)$. Therefore, we find

$$
\begin{aligned}
jK_2(t) &= \frac{1}{2\pi}\int_{-\infty}^{\infty}\frac{3}{\sqrt{2}}\,\frac{A e^{j\omega T}}{\omega - b}\,e^{j\omega t}\,d\omega \\
&= \frac{3Aj}{\sqrt{2}}\,e^{-3(T+t)/2} \qquad \text{for } T + t > 0
\end{aligned}
$$

so that $\qquad$
$$
\begin{aligned}
Y_3(j\omega) &= \int_{0}^{\infty} K_2(t)e^{-j\omega t}\,dt \\
&= \frac{1}{j}\,\frac{3}{\sqrt{2}}\,\frac{A}{\omega - b}\,e^{-3T/2}
\end{aligned}
$$

The constant A is easily found to be

$$A = \frac{(b + a)(b - a^*)}{(b + c)(b - c^*)} = 0.9445$$

Hence, finally, we have, from Eq. (7.3-12),

$$
\begin{aligned}
Y_4(j\omega) &= \frac{3}{4}\,A\,\frac{(\omega - a)(\omega + a^*)}{(\omega - c)(\omega + c^*)}\,e^{-3T/2} \\
&= 0.708\,\frac{\omega^2 - 2j\omega - 2}{\omega^2 - 2.2636j\omega - 2.0306}\,e^{-3T/2}
\end{aligned}
$$

so that $\qquad Y_4(p) = 0.708\,\dfrac{p^2 + 2p + 2}{p^2 + 2.2636p + 2.0306}\,e^{-3T/2}$

is obtained as the transfer function of the required smoothing and predicting filter.

All the necessary operations to be performed in computing the optimal transfer function may be summarized in a single formula. This formula is derived in a different manner in Sec. 7.4 and appears as the final result of that section. It is an interesting exercise for the reader to compare the results of this section and the next to verify that the two procedures are actually identical.

7.4 Analytic Solution of the Wiener-Hopf Equation Using Complex Variable Techniques

In Sec. 7.1 it was shown that a necessary and sufficient condition for $W(t)$ to be the weighting function of the optimal linear smoothing-predicting filter for the signal plus noise $s(t) + n(t)$ is that $W(t)$ be a solution of the Wiener-Hopf integral equation (7.1-12). In Sec. 7.5 this equation will be solved for a wide class of problems, using very elementary mathematical techniques. However, in the present section we shall use function-theory methods to derive the general solution of this integral equation.

There are two important facts from function theory which we will need in order to obtain the required solution.

THEOREM 1. Let $f(t)$ be an integrable function which vanishes over the range $(-\infty, 0)$ and possesses a Fourier transform $F(\omega)$. Then

$$F(\omega) = \int_{-\infty}^{\infty} f(t)e^{-i\omega t}\, dt = \int_{0}^{\infty} f(t)e^{-i\omega t}\, dt \tag{7.4-1}$$

is an analytic and bounded function of the complex variable ω in the lower half of the complex plane. Conversely, let $F(\omega)$ be an analytic and bounded function of the complex variable ω in the lower half of the complex plane. Then if $F(\omega)$ is the Fourier transform of a function $f(t)$ so that

$$f(t) = \frac{1}{2\pi} \int_{-\infty}^{\infty} F(\omega)e^{i\omega t}\, d\omega \tag{7.4-2}$$

it is also true that $f(t)$ vanishes over the range $(-\infty, 0)$. A similar theorem is true if we replace $(-\infty, 0)$ by $(0, \infty)$ and "lower" by "upper."

THEOREM 2. If $A(\omega)$ is a positive and real-valued function defined for real values of ω for which

$$\int_{-\infty}^{\infty} \frac{|\log|A(\omega)||}{1 + \omega^2}\, d\omega < \infty \tag{7.4-3}$$

then there exist two functions of a complex variable, $A_1(\omega)$ and $A_2(\omega)$, such that

$$A(\omega) = A_1(\omega)A_2(\omega) \tag{7.4-4}$$

holds for real values of ω. Furthermore, $A_1(\omega)$ is analytic, bounded, and free from zeros and singularities in the upper half plane. Also, $A_2(\omega)$ is analytic, bounded, and free from zeros and singularities in the lower half plane.   Finally,

$$A_1(\omega) = A_2^*(\omega) \tag{7.4-5}$$

for real values of ω.

Returning to the problem at hand, let us define

$$f(t) = -\psi(t + T) + \int_{-\infty}^{\infty} W(\tau)\phi(t - \tau)\, d\tau \tag{7.4-6}$$

From Eq. (7.1-12) we know that

$$f(t) = 0 \qquad \text{for } t \geq 0 \tag{7.4-7}$$

Define

$$F(\omega) = \int_{-\infty}^{\infty} f(t)e^{-j\omega t}\, dt \tag{7.4-8}$$

as the Fourier transform of $f(t)$.   Thus, from Eq. (7.4-6), we have

$$F(\omega) = -\int_{-\infty}^{\infty} \psi(t + T)e^{-j\omega t}\, dt$$
$$+ \int_{-\infty}^{\infty} e^{-j\omega t}\, dt \int_{-\infty}^{\infty} W(\tau)\phi(t - \tau)\, d\tau \tag{7.4-9}$$

The first integral in this expression may be written as

$$\int_{-\infty}^{\infty} \psi(t + T)e^{-j\omega t}\, dt = e^{j\omega T}\int_{-\infty}^{\infty} \psi(u)e^{-j\omega u}\, du$$
$$= \pi G_2(\omega)e^{j\omega T} \tag{7.4-10}$$

where $G_2(\omega)$ is the cross-power spectral density of $s(t)$ and $s(t) + n(t)$. That is,

$$G_2(\omega) = G_{ss}(\omega) + G_{ns}(\omega) \tag{7.4-11}$$

The second integral in Eq. (7.4-9) is treated as follows.

$$\int_{-\infty}^{\infty} e^{-j\omega t}\, dt \int_{-\infty}^{\infty} W(\tau)\phi(t - \tau)\, d\tau$$
$$= \int_{-\infty}^{\infty} W(\tau)\, d\tau \int_{-\infty}^{\infty} \phi(t - \tau)e^{-j\omega t}\, dt$$
$$= \int_{-\infty}^{\infty} \phi(u)e^{-j\omega u}\, du \int_{-\infty}^{\infty} W(\tau)e^{-j\omega\tau}\, d\tau = \pi G_1(\omega)Y(j\omega) \tag{7.4-12}$$

where $G_1(\omega)$ is the power spectral density of $s(t) + n(t)$.   That is

$$G_1(\omega) = G_{ss}(\omega) + G_{ns}(\omega) + G_{sn}(\omega) + G_{nn}(\omega) \tag{7.4-13}$$

Thus, Eq. (7.4-9) becomes

$$\frac{1}{\pi}F(\omega) = Y(j\omega)G_1(\omega) - e^{j\omega T}G_2(\omega) \tag{7.4-14}$$

For convenience, let us define

$$\tilde{Y}(\omega) = Y(j\omega) \tag{7.4-15}$$

Then the poles and zeros of $\tilde{Y}(\omega)$ are rotated $90°$ clockwise from those of the transfer function $Y(p)$. Since $Y(p)$ is a physically realizable transfer function, its poles and zeros are symmetrically placed about the real axis with no poles in the right half plane. Therefore, the poles and zeros of $\tilde{Y}(\omega)$ are symmetric about the imaginary axis with no poles in the lower half plane.

If $G_1(\omega)$ satisfies the requirements of Theorem 2 above, we may write

$$G_1(\omega) = H_1(\omega)H_2(\omega) \tag{7.4-16}$$

where $H_1(\omega)$ is analytic, bounded, and free from zeros and poles in the lower half plane. Let us define

$$H_3(\omega) = \frac{\pi G_2(\omega)}{H_2(\omega)} \tag{7.4-17}$$

so that Eq. (7.4-14) may be written as

$$\frac{1}{\pi}\frac{F(\omega)}{H_2(\omega)} = \tilde{Y}(\omega)H_1(\omega) - e^{j\omega T}H_3(\omega) \tag{7.4-18}$$

From Theorem 1, $F(\omega)$ is a function which is analytic and bounded in the upper half plane. Furthermore, from Theorem 2, $H_2(\omega)$ is analytic, bounded, and free from zeros and poles in the upper half plane. Therefore, $F(\omega)/H_2(\omega)$ is an analytic function of ω in the upper half plane. Furthermore, in all cases of practical interest, $F(\omega)/H_2(\omega)$ is bounded in the upper half plane. Hence, its inverse Fourier transform is zero for t in the range $(0, \infty)$. That is, for $t > 0$ we have

$$\int_{-\infty}^{\infty} \tilde{Y}(\omega)H_1(\omega)e^{j\omega t}\, d\omega = \int_{-\infty}^{\infty} H_3(\omega)e^{j\omega(t+T)}\, d\omega \tag{7.4-19}$$

Now $\tilde{Y}(\omega)$ and $H_1(\omega)$ are both analytic and bounded in the lower half plane, so that the Fourier transform $g(t)$ defined by

$$g(t) = \int_{-\infty}^{\infty} \tilde{Y}(\omega)H_1(\omega)e^{j\omega t}\, d\omega \tag{7.4-20}$$

vanishes for $t < 0$. Taking the inverse Fourier transform, we therefore find

$$\begin{aligned}
2\pi\tilde{Y}(\omega)H_1(\omega) &= \int_{-\infty}^{\infty} g(t)e^{-j\omega t}\, dt \\
&= \int_{0}^{\infty} g(t)e^{-j\omega t}\, dt \\
&= \int_{0}^{\infty} e^{-j\omega t}\, dt \int_{-\infty}^{\infty} \tilde{Y}(u)H_1(u)e^{jut}\, du
\end{aligned} \tag{7.4-21}$$

Over the range $t > 0$, however, Eq. (7.4-19) is valid, and we may thus perform a substitution to obtain

$$2\pi\tilde{Y}(\omega)H_1(\omega) = \int_{0}^{\infty} e^{-j\omega t}\, dt \int_{-\infty}^{\infty} H_3(u)e^{ju(t+T)}\, du$$

or, alternatively,

$$\tilde{Y}(\omega) = Y(j\omega) = \frac{1}{2\pi H_1(\omega)} \int_0^\infty e^{-j\omega t}\, dt \int_{-\infty}^\infty H_3(u)e^{ju(t+T)}\, du \quad (7.4\text{-}22)$$

as a closed expression for the optimum transfer function $Y(j\omega)$.

The real mathematical difficulties of this theory lie in the proof of the factorization of the spectral densities, which we have passed over. However, if the spectral densities (continued analytically into the complex plane) are rational functions, then the steps taken are obviously valid. Furthermore, if $G_1(\omega)$ is rational, $H_1(\omega)$ and hence $H_2(\omega)$ and $H_3(\omega)$ may be found simply from an inspection of the poles and zeros of $G_1(\omega)$. When $H_3(\omega)$ is a rational function of ω, it may be expanded in partial fractions. Then Eqs. (7.2-4) and (7.2-5) may be used to aid in carrying out the operations indicated in Eq. (7.4-22).

The formula for $H_1(\omega)$ in the more general case is

$$H_1(\omega) = e^{\lambda(\omega)} \quad (7.4\text{-}23)$$

where

$$\lambda(\omega) = \frac{j}{\pi} \int_0^\infty \frac{\omega \log G_1(u)}{\omega^2 - u^2}\, du \quad (7.4\text{-}24)$$

7.5 Direct Solution of the Wiener-Hopf Equation for Rational Spectra

In any practical filtering or prediction problem it is usually necessary to make simplifying approximations to the spectral densities before the integrals of Eq. (7.4-22) can be evaluated successfully. The usual procedure is to approximate these quantities by rational functions in order to obtain a transfer function in a useful form. The power spectral density of a function whose correlation function is an exponential or an exponentially damped cosine is rational. Therefore, in many problems arising in practice, it is convenient to approximate empirically obtained correlation functions in this way. In Appendix D it is shown that any correlation function may be approximated to any desired degree of accuracy by a series of exponentials. At times it is also convenient to use exponentially damped cosines in the approximation. In the present section we shall obtain a direct solution of the Wiener-Hopf equation (7.1-12), using correlation functions composed of terms of these types.

Let us suppose that each of the correlation functions has been so approximated. Therefore,

$$\phi_{ss}(\tau) = \Sigma S_i e^{-\alpha_i|\tau|} \quad (7.5\text{-}1)$$
$$\phi_{nn}(\tau) = \Sigma N_i e^{-\beta_i|\tau|} \quad (7.5\text{-}2)$$

where the absolute value of τ is used, since the autocorrelation functions are even in τ. Here α_i and β_i may be complex, to take into account exponentially damped cosine terms. The corresponding expressions for the cross-correlation functions are

$$\phi_{ns}(\tau) = \begin{cases} \Sigma G_i e^{-\gamma_i \tau} & \tau > 0 \\ \Sigma H_i e^{\delta_i \tau} & \tau < 0 \end{cases} \qquad (7.5\text{-}3)$$

$$\phi_{sn}(\tau) = \begin{cases} \Sigma H_i e^{-\delta_i \tau} & \tau > 0 \\ \Sigma G_i e^{\gamma_i \tau} & \tau < 0 \end{cases} \qquad (7.5\text{-}4)$$

for, although the cross-correlation functions are not even in τ, they do satisfy Eq. (3.5-14). Therefore, from Eqs. (7.1-5) and (7.1-6), we have

$$\psi(\tau) = \Sigma S_i e^{-\alpha_i \tau} + \Sigma G_i e^{-\gamma_i \tau} \qquad \tau > 0$$
$$\phi(\tau) = \Sigma S_i e^{-\alpha_i |\tau|} + \Sigma G_i e^{-\gamma_i |\tau|} + \Sigma H_i e^{-\delta_i |\tau|} + \Sigma N_i e^{-\beta_i |\tau|} \qquad (7.5\text{-}5)$$

These relations may be formally simplified by combining terms and writing

$$\psi(\tau) = \sum_{k=1}^{p} C_k e^{-c_k \tau} \qquad \text{for } \tau > 0 \qquad (7.5\text{-}6)$$

$$\phi(\tau) = \sum_{j=1}^{m} B_j e^{-b_j |\tau|} + \sum_{k=1}^{p} C_k e^{-c_k |\tau|} \qquad (7.5\text{-}7)$$

It should be noted that Eq. (7.5-6) holds only when the argument is positive, while Eq. (7.5-7) is valid for all τ. It is not necessary to consider $\psi(\tau)$ for negative τ since the Wiener-Hopf equation, Eq. (7.1-12), must be satisfied only for positive values of the argument.

The method of solution of Eq. (7.1-12) that we shall employ is based on a method of undetermined coefficients. Since the filter to be designed is composed of linear time-invariant components, it seems reasonable to suppose, from the physical standpoint, that its response to a unit-impulse input includes stable exponential and exponential sine and cosine terms, as well as perhaps a direct amplification of the input. Therefore, we might assume the weighting function $W(\tau)$ to be of the form

$$W(\tau) = \sum_{s=1}^{N} A_s e^{-a_s \tau} + A \delta(\tau) \qquad (7.5\text{-}8)$$

where $\delta(\tau)$ is the unit-impulse function. Here, the number of exponential terms N is unknown at present; but, as we shall see, it is determined by the number of terms used in the approximation of the correlation functions. In order to determine N, as well as the A's and a's appearing in Eq. (7.5-8), we substitute Eqs. (7.5-6), (7.5-7), and (7.5-8) directly into Eq. (7.1-12), and require that this relation hold identically for all positive values of t. The result of this substitution, after the indicated integration has been performed, yields

$$\sum_{k=1}^{p} C_k e^{-c_k(t+T)} = \sum_{s=1}^{N} A_s \left[\sum_{j=1}^{m} \left(\frac{B_j}{a_s - b_j} e^{-b_j t} - \frac{2 b_j B_j}{a_s^2 - b_j^2} e^{-a_s t} \right) \right.$$
$$\left. + \sum_{k=1}^{p} \left(\frac{C_k}{a_s - c_k} e^{-c_k t} - \frac{2 c_k C_k}{a_s^2 - c_k^2} e^{-a_s t} \right) \right]$$
$$+ A \left(\sum_{j=1}^{m} B_j e^{-b_j t} + \sum_{k=1}^{p} C_k e^{-c_k t} \right) \quad (7.5\text{-}9)$$

Several conditions must be satisfied if Eq. (7.5-9) is to hold identically for all positive t. First, the coefficients of $e^{-a_s t}$ on the right-hand side must vanish. This leads to the following N equations:

$$\sum_{j=1}^{m} \frac{b_j B_j}{a_s^2 - b_j^2} + \sum_{k=1}^{p} \frac{c_k C_k}{a_s^2 - c_k^2} = 0 \qquad s = 1, \ldots, N \quad (7.5\text{-}10)$$

for determining $a_1, a_2, \ldots, a_N$. Thus, the exponential parts of which the weighting function is composed in Eq. (7.5-8) may be obtained as the roots with positive real parts of the function

$$P(x) = \sum_{j=1}^{m} \frac{b_j B_j}{x^2 - b_j^2} + \sum_{k=1}^{p} \frac{c_k C_k}{x^2 - c_k^2} \quad (7.5\text{-}11)$$

There will be in general $m + p - 1$ such roots so that N should be taken as $m + p - 1$.† [Appendix H describes certain techniques which may be used to aid in obtaining the roots of $P(x)$.]

After these exponents are determined, the coefficients $A, A_1, A_2, \ldots, A_{m+p-1}$ are computed as the solution of the following $m + p$ linear algebraic equations:

$$\sum_{s=1}^{N} \frac{A_s}{a_s - b_j} + A = 0 \qquad j = 1, \ldots, m$$
$$\qquad\qquad\qquad\qquad\qquad\qquad\qquad (7.5\text{-}12)$$
$$\sum_{s=1}^{N} \frac{A_s}{a_s - c_k} + A = e^{-c_k T} \qquad k = 1, \ldots, p$$

† It might happen that the coefficients in Eq. (7.5-11) are so related that fewer than $m + p - 1$ values of a_s can be determined. In this case, it can be shown that the optimum filter will, of necessity, involve differentiators. However, since these coefficients are determined as approximations to the various correlation functions, they could be altered slightly without affecting the accuracy desired in the curve fitting. With this slight degree of flexibility, one can always guarantee that Eq. (7.5-11) will yield the maximum number of roots possible. Furthermore, since differentiators are usually undesirable components in any filter, it would seem advisable to take steps to avoid their use. Hence, we shall restrict our attention here to the case in which Eq. (7.5-11) yields exactly $m + p - 1$ roots.

These equations are the result of equating the coefficients of $e^{-b_j t}$ and $e^{-c_k t}$ in Eq. (7.5-9).

An explicit expression for the mean-squared error may be obtained from Eq. (7.1-4). Substituting from Eqs. (7.5-6) to (7.5-8) and performing the indicated integration, we find that

$$\overline{\epsilon^2} = \phi_{ss}(0) - \sum_{s=1}^{N} A_s \sum_{k=1}^{p} \frac{C_k e^{-c_k T}}{a_s + c_k} - A \sum_{k=1}^{p} C_k e^{-c_k T} \qquad (7.5\text{-}13)$$

The above discussion is valid only when Eq. (7.5-10) does not possess multiple roots. When roots of higher multiplicity than one occur, it is necessary to modify the form of $W(t)$ assumed in Eq. (7.5-8). Otherwise the set of algebraic equations in (7.5-12) will be overdetermined and self-contradictory. We may be guided in our choice for $W(t)$ by considering the analogous procedure for differential equations when the characteristic equation possesses multiple roots. We shall illustrate this by an example.

Suppose $a_1 = a_2$ is a double root of $P(x)$. We replace the first two terms in $W(t)$, corresponding to these exponents, by

$$(A_1 \tau + A_2) e^{-a_1 \tau}$$

The first of Eqs. (7.5-12) is replaced by

$$\sum_{j=1}^{m} \frac{b_j B_j}{(a_1^2 - b_j^2)^2} + \sum_{k=1}^{p} \frac{c_k C_k}{(a_1^2 - c_k^2)^2} = 0$$

and the others are unchanged. This equation states precisely the condition that must be satisfied in order that a_1 be a double root of $P(x)$. Therefore, this relation will be automatically satisfied. The algebraic equations in (7.5-12) become

$$\frac{A_1}{(a_1 - b_j)^2} + \sum_{s=2}^{N} \frac{A_s}{a_s - b_j} + A = 0 \qquad j = 1, \ldots, m$$

$$\frac{A_1}{(a_1 - c_k)^2} + \sum_{s=2}^{N} \frac{A_s}{a_s - c_k} + A = e^{-c_k T} \qquad k = 1, \ldots, p$$

$$(7.5\text{-}14)$$

Real roots of higher multiplicity and multiple complex roots are handled in the obvious way. However, the occurrence of such roots is probably rare, since the coefficients in $P(x)$ are taken from approximations to empirical data. Furthermore, multiple roots can always be removed by slight readjustments in the coefficients of $P(x)$.

Because of the special form of the set of linear algebraic equations in (7.5-12), it is possible to solve these equations explicitly. The matrix of the coefficients of this system has the form

$$M = \begin{Vmatrix} 1 & \dfrac{1}{a_1 - f_0} & \dfrac{1}{a_2 - f_0} & \cdots & \dfrac{1}{a_N - f_0} \\[2ex] 1 & \dfrac{1}{a_1 - f_1} & \dfrac{1}{a_2 - f_1} & \cdots & \dfrac{1}{a_N - f_1} \\[1ex] \cdot & \cdot & \cdot & \cdots & \cdot \\[1ex] 1 & \dfrac{1}{a_1 - f_N} & \dfrac{1}{a_2 - f_N} & \cdots & \dfrac{1}{a_N - f_N} \end{Vmatrix} \qquad (7.5\text{-}15)$$

For convenience we have written

$$\begin{aligned} f_0 &= b_1 & f_1 &= b_2 & \cdots & & f_{m-1} &= b_m \\ f_m &= c_1 & f_{m+1} &= c_2 & \cdots & & f_N &= c_p \end{aligned}$$

so that $N = m + p - 1$. After a rather involved computation it can be shown that the determinant of this matrix can be expressed as

$$|M| = \prod_{j=1}^{N} \frac{f_j - f_0}{(a_j - f_0)(a_j - f_j)} \prod_{k=1}^{N-1} \prod_{i=k+1}^{N} \frac{(f_k - f_i)(a_i - a_k)}{(a_k - f_i)(a_i - f_k)} \qquad (7.5\text{-}16)$$

The cofactors of this determinant may also be expressed in a similar way as a product and, as a result, the elements of the inverse matrix M^{-1} are obtained as a product of factors of the same type as those appearing in Eq. (7.5-16). The calculations are rather tedious, and thus have been omitted from the discussion. The final result may be summarized as follows.

Let us denote by M_{rk}^{-1} the element in the rth row and kth column of the inverse matrix M^{-1}. Then the first row of M^{-1} is

$$M_{1k}^{-1} = \frac{\displaystyle\prod_{i=1}^{N} (a_i - f_{k-1})}{\displaystyle\prod_{j=0}^{N}{}' (f_j - f_{k-1})} \qquad k = 1, \ldots, N+1 \qquad (7.5\text{-}17)$$

The prime on the product symbol in the denominator indicates that j should be extended over all integers from 0 to N, omitting the factor for which $j = k - 1$. The other elements in the matrix may then be written as

$$M_{rk}^{-1} = \frac{\displaystyle\prod_{j=0}^{N}{}' (f_j - a_{r-1})}{\displaystyle\prod_{i=1}^{N}{}' (a_i - a_{r-1})} M_{1k}^{-1} \qquad \begin{aligned} r &= 2, \ldots, N+1 \\ k &= 1, \ldots, N+1 \end{aligned} \qquad (7.5\text{-}18)$$

Again the prime on the product symbol in the numerator indicates the omission of the factor for which $j = k - 1$. Similarly, the prime on the product symbol in the denominator indicates the omission of the factor for which $i = r - 1$.

Using these results and the rule for matrix multiplication, the solution of the equations in (7.5-12) may be written as

$$
A = \sum_{i=1}^{p} M_{1,m+i}^{-1} e^{-c_i T}
$$

$$
A_s = \sum_{i=1}^{p} M_{s+1,m+i}^{-1} e^{-c_i T} \qquad s = 1, \ldots, m + p - 1
$$

(7.5-19)

If multiple roots are present, then the equations in (7.5-14) are the relevant equations and the equations in (7.5-19) do not hold. However, by transferring the first terms in (7.5-14) to the right-hand sides of the equations, the matrix methods as given above may be used to solve the first N equations for each of the A's in terms of A_1. Then the last equation serves to determine A_1.

In general, the process of solving a large number of linear algebraic equations, apart from being rather tedious, can lead to the propagation of errors which can be eliminated by carrying a large number of significant figures in the computation. The advantage of the method presented here is that all operations except the last consist of multiplications and divisions which result in no loss of significant figures.

Before illustrating this technique, a few additional remarks seem appropriate at this time. First, it is possible that $P(x)$ may possess complex roots with positive real parts. Since the coefficients in $P(x)$ are always real, these can only occur in conjugate pairs. We shall now investigate what effect this has on our solution. Suppose

$$
a_1 = \alpha + j\beta
$$
$$
a_2 = \alpha - j\beta
$$

are two such roots. Then if we assume that

$$
A_1 = X + jY
$$
$$
A_2 = X - jY
$$

where X and Y are real numbers, the corresponding terms appearing in Eqs. (7.5-12) may be put in the form

$$
\frac{A_1}{a_1 - b} + \frac{A_2}{a_2 - b} = \frac{2}{(\alpha - b)^2 + \beta^2} [(\alpha - b)X - \beta Y]
$$

Since X and Y are real, this expression is real. Furthermore, since the other coefficients appearing in Eqs. (7.5-12) are real, the solutions themselves will be real.   Hence, the assumption that A_1 and A_2 are complex conjugates is valid.

The corresponding terms in the weighting function, Eq. (7.5-8), become

$$A_1 e^{-a_1 \tau} + A_2 e^{-a_2 \tau} = 2e^{-\alpha \tau}(X \cos \beta \tau + Y \sin \beta \tau)$$

Thus, if two roots of Eq. (7.5-11) are complex conjugates, the corresponding coefficients appearing in the weighting function, obtained as solutions of Eqs. (7.5-12), will also be complex conjugates and the weighting function remains a real quantity.

The second remark concerns the technique to be used when the approximation to the various correlation functions includes exponentially damped cosines.   This may be treated in our computational procedure by writing

$$Be^{-\alpha \tau} \cos \beta \tau = \frac{B}{2} \left[e^{-(\alpha + j\beta)\tau} + e^{-(\alpha - j\beta)\tau} \right]$$

$P(x)$ will still have real coefficients because for every term which is complex in Eq. (7.5-11) there also appears the complex conjugate.   Thus all the comments made above remain valid in this case.   It also follows that the solution of the equations in (7.5-12) will give rise to real or conjugate complex A's.

The computational technique developed in this section may be summarized in the following steps:

1. The approximations to the correlation functions are obtained in the form given by Eqs. (7.5-6) and (7.5-7).

2. The function $P(x)$ defined by Eq. (7.5-11) is then computed and the roots $a_1, a_2, \ldots, a_{m+p-1}$ with positive real parts obtained.

3. When these roots are known, the equations in (7.5-12) for the coefficients $A, A_1, A_2, \ldots, A_{m+p-1}$ may be found.   The solution of these equations is obtained immediately from the equations in (7.5-19).

4. Using the results of steps 2 and 3, we can form the weighting function for the optimum filter immediately from Eq. (7.5-8).

Example 7.5-1.   To illustrate this procedure, let us solve again the problem discussed in Example 7.3-1.   The correlation functions corresponding to the spectral densities used in that example are easily found to be

$$\psi(\tau) = 2e^{-3\tau/2}$$
$$\phi(\tau) = 2e^{-3\tau/2} + e^{-\tau} \cos \tau$$

so that $p = 1$ and $m = 2$.   Comparing these with Eqs. (7.5-6) and (7.5-7), we see that

$$C_1 = 2 \qquad B_1 = \tfrac{1}{2} \qquad B_2 = \tfrac{1}{2}$$
$$c_1 = \tfrac{3}{2} \qquad b_1 = 1 + j \qquad b_2 = 1 - j$$

Using these values, we obtain for $P(x)$

$$P(x) = \frac{4x^4 - 17\tfrac{1}{4}x^2 + 33\tfrac{3}{4}}{(x^4 + 4)(x^2 - \tfrac{9}{4})}$$

which yields two roots with positive real parts

$$a_1 = 1.1318 + j0.8658$$
$$a_2 = 1.1318 - j0.8658$$

The coefficients in the weighting function are found immediately from

$$A = M_{13}^{-1} = \frac{(a_1 - f_2)(a_2 - f_2)}{(f_0 - f_2)(f_1 - f_2)} e^{-c_1 T}$$

$$= \frac{(a_1 - c_1)(a_2 - c_1)}{(b_1 - c_1)(b_2 - c_1)} e^{-c_1 T}$$

$$= 0.7082 e^{-3T/2}$$

$$A_1 = M_{23}^{-1} = \frac{(f_0 - a_1)(f_1 - a_1)}{a_2 - a_1} M_{13}^{-1} e^{-c_1 T}$$

$$= \frac{(b_1 - a_1)(b_2 - a_1)}{a_2 - a_1} M_{13}^{-1} e^{-c_1 T}$$

$$= (-0.0933 + j0.1095) e^{-3T/2}$$

$$A_2 = M_{33}^{-1} = (-0.0933 - j0.1095) e^{-3T/2}$$

Therefore, the weighting function is simply

$$W(t) = [0.708\delta(t) + (-0.093 + j0.110)e^{-(1.132+j0.866)t}$$
$$+ (-0.093 - j0.110)e^{-(1.132-j0.866)t}]e^{-3T/2}$$
$$= \{0.708\delta(t) - e^{-1.132t}[0.186 \cos (0.866t) - 0.220 \sin (0.866t)]\}e^{-3T/2}$$

In order to compare this with the result obtained in the example of Sec. 7.3, we note that the transfer function obtained there may be put in the form

$$Y_4(p) = 0.708 \left[1 - \frac{0.2636p + 0.0306}{(p + 1.132)^2 + (0.866)^2} \right] e^{-3T/2}$$

Taking the inverse Laplace transform of $Y_4(p)$ gives us the weighting function obtained above.

PROBLEMS

7-1. Determine the mean-squared error for the optimum predictor designed in Examples 7.3-1 and 7.5-1.

7-2. Design an optimum predictor for a noise-free signal whose spectral density is given by

$$G_{ss}(\omega) = \frac{1}{(1 + \omega^2)^2}$$

7-3. Design an optimum differentiating filter for an input consisting of a signal and noise with spectral densities given by

$$G_{ss}(\omega) = \frac{1}{1 + \omega^2} \qquad G_{nn}(\omega) = 1$$

7-4. Design an optimum linear filter for the signal and noise whose spectra are given in Prob. 5-11. Compare the resulting mean-squared error with the minimum obtainable error for Prob. 5-11.

7-5. Design an optimum linear filter to separate a noise $n(t)$ from a signal $s(t)$ when the spectral densities for the signal and noise are given by

$$G_{ss}(\omega) = \frac{1}{\omega^2 + 1} \qquad G_{nn}(\omega) = \frac{2\omega^2}{\omega^4 + 1}$$

CHAPTER 8

OPTIMUM OPERATIONS WITH FINITE DATA

8.1 Introductory Remarks

In the first section of Chap. 7 it was stated that the Wiener prediction theory was based on the assumptions that

1. the device to be used must be physically realizable
2. the device is to perform a linear operation
3. the criterion used in selecting the best device is rms error
4. the signal and noise are each members of stationary random processes

One further implied assumption is that

5. the device is permitted to operate on the entire past history of the signal and noise data

The first of these requirements is necessary in any practical theory. However, there are excellent reasons for wishing to remove or weaken any or all of the remaining four. In the present chapter some consideration will be given to the effects of eliminating each of these four assumptions.

By and large we are primarily concerned here with problems in which a filter or predictor is allowed to operate only on the portion of its input data defined over some time interval of finite length. We may ask, for example, that a system which is inactive prior to time $t = 0$ should produce the best possible filtering of a signal from a noise at an arbitrary later time $t = T$. Even though the signal and noise may belong to stationary random processes, the characteristics of the desired filter may be quite different from those obtained in Chap. 7 unless T is large. In case either the signal or noise is nonstationary, the procedures of Chap. 7 are not applicable at all. Alternately, we may require that the predictor output at time t be substantially independent of events occurring prior to time $t - T$. In this case we may say that the system operates only on the data between $t - T$ and t.

The filters or predictors studied here are required to be "physically realizable" in the precise mathematical sense that they are allowed to utilize only past data for their inputs.[1]   At the same time, by virtue of their complexity, they are seldom "practically mechanizable" in the sense of lending themselves to a simple and direct instrumentation in terms of conventional lumped-parameter systems.   We do not start with the premise that the "systems" under study satisfy any particular class of differential equations, or in fact any differential equations whatever, but rather seek directly for optimum weighting functions.   In view of these facts, the reader may well question the relevance of this material in a work devoted to automatic control.

The reasons for its inclusion are twofold.   To begin with, in the practical analysis or synthesis of a system to perform a given task, it is often of considerable value to have a standard of reference representing the maximum attainable performance that could be expected from an optimum system.   If, for example, one is attempting to design a system with a prescribed solution time to predict a signal in the presence of noise, it is important to know that there are intrinsic limits on the quality of prediction attainable which are imposed by the nature of the data and the solution time.   In particular it is of the utmost importance to know that the quality of prediction generally deteriorates completely as the solution time approaches zero.   A systems analyst unaware of this fact could readily make the serious mistake of attempting an unworkable system possessing the deceptive advantage of a very short solution time, or at the very least could fall into the erroneous assumption that the poor performance of his system was due to its specific properties rather than to an intrinsic property of the data itself.   By considering the theoretical performance capabilities of optimum systems, one can avoid these pitfalls and can often show that a simple practical system under study may differ so little from optimum as to make further refinements unnecessary.

A second reason for studying optimum filters of the class considered here lies in the fact that, even though they may not of themselves be easily mechanized, they can often be approximated by practical devices. No very general and well-organized body of technique for carrying out such approximations is known to the authors, and we therefore do not consider this point at length.   It is nevertheless true that a substantial amount of early work in the fire-control field was based upon exactly such an approach.

In seeking to relax the assumptions imposed by the Wiener prediction theory, we might pose the following general problem.   Consider a random process $\{x(t)\}$ consisting of the sum of a signal $\{s(t)\}$ and a noise $\{n(t)\}$. Let Z be a random variable determined by the signal; e.g., let

---

[1] However, our techniques are equally applicable to the problem of interpolation; i.e., to the problem of obtaining the best estimate of a signal s at time t in the presence of noise, from observation over an interval which contains t in its interior.

$$Z = s(T + \alpha)$$

or
$$Z = \int_{-\infty}^{t} K(t - \tau)s(\tau) \, d\tau$$

for some value of t. Then we wish to "predict" Z by a physically realizable operation $P[x(t)]$ which is permitted to operate on the observed values of $x(t)$ only in the interval $0 \leq t \leq T$. The basis for selecting the optimum operator P is that the expectation of $\phi(\epsilon)$ be a minimum, where ϕ is some specified function of the error $\epsilon = P[x] - Z$.

The advantage for certain problems of choosing

$$\phi(\epsilon) = \begin{cases} 0 & \text{if } |\epsilon| < a \\ 1 & \text{if } |\epsilon| > a \end{cases}$$

was mentioned in Sec. 5.1. Certainly, we can, in general, hope for a better prediction if we do not require $P[x]$ to be a linear operation on $x(t)$. The Wiener theory allows P to operate on the semi-infinite interval $-\infty < t < T$, but a finite known past more nearly approximates the physical situation usually encountered.

Unfortunately, very little has been accomplished with the general problem as formulated above. The importance of the Wiener theory lies partly in the fact that it gives an explicit and practical solution to an important but restricted class of problems. The work that has been done in extending the Wiener theory has been a step-by-step process of replacing one or another of the requirements (2) to (5) by other assumptions. Care must be exercised, however, in selecting alternate hypotheses, if the results are to have practical significance. For example, if, in the general problem, we only add the specification that $\phi(\epsilon) = \epsilon^2$, then the optimal operation can be shown to be

$$P[x] = E[z \mid x(t); 0 \leq t \leq T]$$

That is, the optimal operator is the conditional expectation of z, given $x(t)$ in the interval $0 \leq t \leq T$. This solution as such has little practical value since the calculation of conditional expectation usually involves a more detailed knowledge of the random process (in particular, the joint distribution functions) than is usually available.

Most of the work that has been done assumes $\phi(\epsilon) = \epsilon^2$ (that is, the rms criterion) and a linear prediction device. However, in Sec. 8.6 an approach is considered in which both of these assumptions have been eliminated. In general, most authors will introduce additional assumptions which are needed to render their results significant and these will vary from one author to the next. Usually some restriction on the signal and noise processes will be involved.

In the next two sections we shall consider two related general classes of prediction problems. The solution of each of these problems will be shown to depend upon the solution of a certain integral equation.   Then in later sections general solutions of this integral equation will be obtained.   Before proceeding to formulate these problems, however, we consider three examples to motivate the discussion.

Example 8.1-1.   We consider the problem of predicting a future position of a moving target by a system which receives target data, in the presence of noise, starting at time $t = 0$.   For simplicity, we assume that at time t we desire a prediction of future target position at time $t + \alpha$, where α is a fixed constant.   We further assume that the target is moving at a constant vector velocity, so that its position with respect to each of a set of rectangular coordinate axes is an arbitrary and unknown linear function of time.   As a result we may consider the prediction of a single coordinate by itself to simplify calculations.

Letting $s_1(t)$ be the target position, we have

$$s_1(t) = C_1 + C_2 t$$

where C_1 and C_2 are unknown coefficients.   The observed data $x(t)$ is assumed to consist of the sum of $s_1(t)$ and a stationary random noise $n(t)$.

$$x(t) = n(t) + C_1 + C_2 t$$

Now let $W(t,\tau)$ be the weighting function for a filter or general prediction operator that receives $x(t)$ as input over the interval from 0 to t.   The output $y(t)$ is then

$$y(t) = \int_0^t W(t,\tau)[n(\tau) + C_1 + C_2\tau]\, d\tau \tag{8.1-1}$$

and we wish to pick W so that the mean-squared value of the error ϵ is minimized, where

$$\epsilon = y(t) - s_1(t + \alpha)$$

Example 8.1-2.   We now reconsider roughly the same problem from a slightly different point of view.   Suppose that the target is capable of large random discontinuous changes in both its position and velocity occurring at random time instants (or the equivalent proposition that the predictor is switched from one target to another). At the time such a jump occurs, all past data becomes invalid for any subsequent prediction.   In consequence, it is desirable to construct a predictor with a "memory" that is relatively short in comparison with the average time interval between jumps in order that its prediction should not be influenced unduly by previous invalid information.

As an idealization, we assume that the weighting function $W(t,\tau)$ is zero for $\tau < t - T$; that is, we assume that all data more than T units in the past is discarded.   Considering only the prediction T or more time units after a jump, the output $y(t)$ is given by

$$y(t) = \int_{t-T}^t W(t,\tau)[n(\tau) + C_1 + C_2\tau]\, d\tau \tag{8.1-2}$$

and the prediction error, when $t + \alpha$ is in the same interval, is given by the same formula as in Example 8.1-1.

Although these two examples differ somewhat in their formal statement and notation, from the mathematical standpoint they are essentially identical.   In each instance we are given a finite interval of data consisting of the sum of an unknown linear function of time with a superimposed stationary noise $n(t)$. From this data we wish to extract a predicted value for the linear function, by a process which amounts mathematically to multiplying the observed data x by a suitable function W and integrating the product over the observed interval.

In many ways, the nature of the problem and the solution thereto is more readily grasped if one forgets for the time being any questions of possible instrumentation. We are searching here for optimum operations to be applied to a set of data, and have already pointed out that the operations derived are seldom capable of practical and direct mechanization. In bridging the gap to reality, one may imagine that we are presented with an infinitely accurate recording of the data (with the noise included) as it was perceived by an actual instrument. We are then executing a post-mortem analysis of the data, by numerical techniques, under rules which permit us to use at any point of the record only a prescribed interval of the preceding data and none of the later data whatever. Clearly, by such devices as the point-by-point numerical solution to differential equations, we can reproduce the idealized action of any linear network or system. In consequence, the optimum linear operators studied in this chapter are drawn from a class of operators that includes the lumped-parameter systems as special cases. We should therefore generally expect to attain smaller rms errors by these techniques than can be realized by workable devices. We are here studying the intrinsic properties of the data itself, and can thereby study the inherent limitations of the problem which no linear instrument can circumvent.

With the foregoing discussion as background, we reconsider Examples 8.1-1 and 8.1-2. From Eq. (8.1-2), by a change of variable, we have

$$y(t) = \int_0^T W(t, t - T + \tau)[n(t - T + \tau)$$
$$+ (C_1 + C_2 t - C_2 T) + C_2 \tau] \, d\tau \quad (8.1\text{-}3)$$

Now the random process $\{n\}$ is assumed to be stationary; if we write

$$n_1(\tau) = n(t - T + \tau)$$

then the process $\{n_1\}$ has statistical properties that are identical with those of the process $\{n\}$. In addition, if the constants C_1 and C_2 are arbitrary, then so also are the constants

$$C_1' = C_1 + C_2 t - C_2 T$$
$$C_2' = C_2$$

Finally, by the preceding arguments, the values of t and $t - T$ appear in the problem as rather incidental parameters and can be suppressed; the only significant parameter is the interval length T. Consequently, we may write $W_1(\tau) = W(t, t - T + \tau)$ to obtain

$$y = \int_0^T W_1(\tau)[n_1(\tau) + C_1' + C_2'\tau] \, d\tau \tag{8.1-4}$$

and the prediction error ϵ is

$$\epsilon = y - C_1' - C_2'(T + \alpha) \tag{8.1-5}$$

The integral introduced in Example 8.1-1 may be cast into an identical form quite simply. In Eq. (8.1-1) let us concentrate our attention initially on a certain fixed time instant t and identify t with T. Again suppressing the t appearing in the weighting function, by writing $W_1(\tau) = W(t,\tau)$, we have

$$y = \int_0^T W_1(\tau)[n(\tau) + C_1 + C_2\tau] \, d\tau \tag{8.1-6}$$

and ϵ is given by (8.1-5). Since n and n_1 are identical statistically, and since all that is known of the coefficients is that they are arbitrary constants, Eqs. (8.1-4) and (8.1-6) are essentially equivalent.

In effect, we have achieved this equivalence by the device of considering each time instant t to present a new and distinct problem whose solution need bear no resemblance or dynamic relation to any solution obtained for previous values of t. This must be clearly kept in mind in any attempt to mechanize such results by continuous devices.

In the problem posed by Example 8.1-2, we can in fact obtain from the function $W_1(t)$ the unit-impulse response of a suitable time-invariant linear device (albeit not a lumped-parameter network). To see this, let us write

$$W_2(\tau) = \begin{cases} W_1(T - \tau) & 0 \leqq \tau \leqq T \\ 0 & \text{otherwise} \end{cases}$$

Then (8.1-3) gives by transformation of the variable of integration

$$\begin{aligned} y(t) &= \int_0^T W_2(T - \tau)[n(t - T + \tau) + C_1 + C_2(t - T + \tau)] \, d\tau \\ &= \int_0^\infty W_2(\tau)[n(t - \tau) + C_1 + C_2(t - \tau)] \, d\tau \end{aligned}$$

The last integral, however, identifies y at any time t as the response to $n(t) + C_1 + C_2 t$ of a device whose unit-impulse response is W_2. We can thus define a corresponding transfer function in terms of the Laplace transform of $W_2(t)$. Finally, we may approximate this transfer function by a suitable rational function to obtain a legitimate lumped-parameter prediction filter that approximates the optimum and whose unit-impulse response is approximately zero for impulses more than T time units in the past.

The same techniques applied blindly to Example 8.1-1, however, can lead to serious errors of interpretation. In that example, the interval length is variable. Only by fixing on a particular value of t and identifying it with T are we able to write Eq. (8.1-6). To solve the general problem (that is, with t variable), we require a different solution W_1 for each t considered. The problem is thus truly nonstationary in character; the weighting function depends intrinsically upon both t and τ and not merely upon their difference. As a result, transform methods cannot be used in general to lead to any simple lumped-parameter system, even as an approximation.

A final remark is appropriate before considering the next example. The error ϵ can be written in the form

$$\epsilon = \int_0^T W_1(\tau)n(\tau)\, d\tau + C_1' \left[\int_0^T W_1(\tau)\, d\tau - 1 \right]$$
$$+ C_2' \left[\int_0^T \tau W_1(\tau)\, d\tau - (T + \alpha) \right] \quad (8.1\text{-}7)$$

by means of (8.1-4) and (8.1-5). If the coefficients C_1' and C_2' can be arbitrarily large, then so also can the error unless the bracketed quantities in (8.1-7) both vanish. If this is the case, however, then the predictor is free from error whenever noise is absent.

We are thus led to consider the class of predictors which are *exact* for certain standard forms of signal, e.g., for all linear functions of time. This class of predictors is generally useful under circumstances in which the signal is large in comparison with the noise. When this is the case, the predictor cannot afford to improve its filtering of the noise at the expense of a poorer prediction of the signal, since even slight relative errors in the signal prediction may completely dominate the uncertainties due to noise. This situation presents a marked contrast to that of Example 8.1-3 in which noise and signal are comparable in magnitude. Under the latter circumstances, the requirement of exactness for the signal unduly penalizes the filtering of noise. Instead, by assuming the coefficients C_i to be random variables with a known set of variances and covariances, we are led to minimize the total mean-squared error due both to noise and to imperfect predicting of the signal. The mathematics in the two cases turns out to be roughly the same. The quality of prediction, however, is shown in subsequent examples to be quite different for moderate values of signal-to-noise ratio.

Example 8.1-3. In the testing of high-precision gyroscopic instruments, one possibility consists in allowing a gyro to stabilize a test table whose axis of rotation is parallel to that of the earth. Under these conditions, the table ideally remains nonrotating with respect to inertial space. Relative to an observer on the earth, the table rotates at a rate equal and opposite to earth's rate.

If the mass of the gyro is not ideally centered, a torque on the gyro will be exerted by gravity which is proportional to a component of gravity along a direction moving with the table. Since the table rotates with respect to the earth, the end result will be a drift of the gyro that is a sinusoidally varying function of time. Including possible constant torques, we are led to the problem of detecting signals of the form

$$C_1 + C_2 \cos \omega t + C_3 \sin \omega t$$

in the presence of noise. We further may presume the signal and noise to be comparable in magnitude, since the gyro is presumably balanced as well as possible before the test. As in the preceding examples, the time interval over which the data is defined is finite; in fact, in view of the time required for a full rotation of the table, a significant question is how short a time interval we can choose and still obtain valid results.

To give a formal statement of the two general classes of problems to be solved in Secs. 8.2 to 8.5, let $\{x(t)\}$ be a random process composed of a random signal $\{s(t)\}$, a random noise $\{n(t)\}$, and a series of known functions of time $f_1(t)$, . . . , $f_n(t)$ with unknown but fixed coefficients C_1, . . . , C_n. Thus

$$x(t) = n(t) + s(t) + \sum_{k=1}^{n} C_k f_k(t) \tag{8.1-8}$$

The total signal $s_1(t)$ is given by

$$s_1(t) = s(t) + \sum_{k=1}^{n} C_k f_k(t) \tag{8.1-9}$$

Consider a linear device whose weighting function is given by $W(t,\tau)$, and let $y(t)$ be the response of the system when $x(t)$ is the input. Then we may write

$$y(t) = \int_0^T W(t,\tau)x(\tau) \, d\tau \tag{8.1-10}$$

where we shall require $W(t,\tau)$ to vanish for τ outside the interval $(0,T)$.

Finally, let us define $z(t)$, the quantity to be approximated by $y(t)$, as a random process which is functionally related to the signal $s_1(t)$ as indicated by

$$z(t) = \int_{-\infty}^{\infty} K(t,\tau)s_1(\tau) \, d\tau \tag{8.1-11}$$

Here, $K(t,\tau)$ may be thought of as an ideal weighting function having properties analogous to those discussed in Sec. 5.4. Thus, the doubly infinite limits of integration used in Eq. (8.1-11) are necessary since no assumptions are made about the physical realizability and, hence, the vanishing of $K(t,\tau)$ for any value of τ.

The problem to be solved is that of choosing $W(t,\tau)$ so as to minimize the mean-squared difference between the actual and the desired output, i.e.,

$$\overline{\epsilon(t)^2} = E[\{y(t) - z(t)\}^2] \tag{8.1-12}$$

The distinction between the two classes of problems to be solved lies solely in the assumptions made about the coefficients $C_1, \ldots, C_n$. In Sec. 8.2 we assume that these quantities are unknown and may be arbitrarily large. We then must require the operator W to be exact for each of the functions $f_k(t)$. From Eqs. (8.1-8) to (8.1-11), we have

$$\epsilon(t) = \int_0^T W(t,\tau)[s(\tau) + n(\tau)] \, d\tau - \int_{-\infty}^{\infty} K(t,\tau)s(\tau) \, d\tau$$

$$+ \sum_{k=1}^{n} C_k \left[\int_0^T W(t,\tau)f_k(\tau) \, d\tau - \int_{-\infty}^{\infty} K(t,\tau)f_k(\tau) \, d\tau \right] \tag{8.1-13}$$

The requirement that ϵ shall be independent of the coefficients C_k then leads to the set of equations

$$\int_{-\infty}^{\infty} K(t,\tau)f_k(\tau) \, d\tau = \int_0^T W(t,\tau)f_k(\tau) \, d\tau \qquad k = 1, 2, \ldots, n \tag{8.1-14}$$

The weighting function $W(t,\tau)$ must then be so chosen as to minimize the mean-squared value of $\epsilon(t)$, subject to the equations of constraint (8.1-14). For convenience, we assume throughout that

$$E[s(t)] = E[n(t)] = 0 \tag{8.1-15}$$

although this is not really essential to our development.

In Sec. 8.3 we consider the second class of problems wherein the quantities C_i are postulated to be random variables with $E[C_iC_j]$ known. In this instance, $W(t,\tau)$ must minimize the mean-squared error with no constraining relations.

In each of these two sections we show that the problem leads to the solution of a certain integral equation which is the same in form for both cases. In Secs. 8.4 and 8.5, fairly general solutions to this integral equation are developed, under the respective assumptions that $s(t)$ and $n(t)$ are stationary (Sec. 8.4) or nonstationary (Sec. 8.5).

The material of Sec. 8.6 differs somewhat in nature from that of the rest of the chapter. There we make the restrictive assumptions that (1) the noise $n(t)$ is Gaussian, and (2) the signal consists solely of a linear combination of known functions with coefficients that are random variables whose joint probability density function is known.

As a result of these restrictions, we are able to indicate a technique for solution to the problem of minimizing $E[\phi(\epsilon)]$, where $\phi(\epsilon)$ is a general nonnegative function of the error ϵ. The resulting solution is nonlinear and represents the absolute optimum filtering or prediction attainable for the problem posed.

8.2 Prediction Involving Unknown Linear Combinations of Known Functions in the Presence of Noise

In this section we attack the first of the two general classes of problems posed in Sec. 8.1, namely, that in which the coefficients C_k are completely unknown. The mean-squared value of the error, as given by Eq. (8.1-13), may be expressed in terms of the correlation functions of $x(t)$ and $z(t)$ in the usual way. The resulting expression to be minimized is given by

$$\overline{\epsilon(t)^2} = \phi_{zz}(t,t) - 2 \int_0^T W(t,\tau)\phi_{zx}(t,\tau) \, d\tau$$
$$+ \int_0^T \int_0^T W(t,\tau_1)W(t,\tau_2)\phi_{xx}(\tau_1,\tau_2) \, d\tau_1 \, d\tau_2 \quad (8.2\text{-}1)$$

Then the problem of minimizing Eq. (8.2-1) subject to the equations of constraint (8.1-14) is equivalent to the free problem of minimizing the expression

$$J(W) = \overline{\epsilon(t)^2} - 2 \sum_{k=1}^n \lambda_k(t) \left[\int_0^T W(t,\tau)f_k(\tau) \, d\tau \right.$$
$$\left. - \int_{-\infty}^\infty K(t,\tau)f_k(\tau) \, d\tau \right] \quad (8.2\text{-}2)$$

where $\lambda_k(t)$ are the well-known Lagrangian multipliers.

In order to obtain a necessary and sufficient condition for J to have a minimum, we apply the usual techniques of the calculus of variations. Thus, if we let W take on a variation δW, we obtain

$$\delta J = -2 \int_0^T \delta W(t,\tau)\phi_{zx}(t,\tau) \, d\tau$$
$$+ 2 \int_0^T \delta W(t,\tau) \, d\tau \int_0^T W(t,\rho)\phi_{xx}(\tau,\rho) \, d\rho$$
$$- 2 \sum_{k=1}^n \lambda_k(t) \int_0^T \delta W(t,\tau)f_k(\tau) \, d\tau \quad (8.2\text{-}3)$$

Therefore, if δJ is to vanish for all variations δW, we must have

$$\sum_{k=1}^n \lambda_k(t)f_k(\tau) + \phi_{zz}(t,\tau) = \int_0^T W(t,\rho)\phi_{xx}(\tau,\rho) \, d\rho \qquad 0 \leqq \tau \leqq T \quad (8.2\text{-}4)$$

as a necessary condition to be satisfied by the optimal weighting function $W(t,\tau)$.

To show that this condition is also sufficient we replace the optimal $W(t,\tau)$ by another weighting function of the form $W(t,\tau) - Y(t,\tau)$. Then

Eq. (8.2-2) may be written as

$$J(W - Y) = J(W) + 2 \int_0^T Y(t,\tau) \left[\phi_{zx}(t,\tau) + \sum_{k=1}^n \lambda_k(t) f_k(\tau) \right.$$
$$\left. - \int_0^T W(t,\rho) \phi_{xx}(\rho,\tau) \, d\rho \right] d\tau + E \left[\left\{ \int_0^T Y(t,\tau) x(\tau) \, d\tau \right\}^2 \right]$$

Thus, if Eq. (8.2-4) is satisfied, we have

$$J(W - Y) = J(W) + E \left[\left\{ \int_0^T Y(t,\tau) x(\tau) \, d\tau \right\}^2 \right]$$

Hence, the value of J is not decreased by perturbing $W(t,\tau)$ if condition (8.2-4) holds.

The correlation functions appearing in Eq. (8.2-4) may be calculated using Eqs. (8.1-8) and (8.1-11) with the result that

$$\phi_{xx}(\tau,\rho) = \phi(\tau,\rho) + \sum_{i=1}^n \sum_{j=1}^n C_i C_j f_i(\tau) f_j(\rho) \qquad (8.2\text{-}5)$$

and $\quad \phi_{zx}(t,\tau) = \int_{-\infty}^\infty K(t,\rho) \psi(\rho,\tau) \, d\rho$

$$+ \sum_{i=1}^n \sum_{j=1}^n C_i C_j f_i(\tau) \int_{-\infty}^\infty K(t,\rho) f_j(\rho) \, d\rho \quad (8.2\text{-}6)$$

where
$$\phi(t,\tau) = \phi_{ss}(t,\tau) + \phi_{sn}(t,\tau) + \phi_{ns}(t,\tau) + \phi_{nn}(t,\tau) \qquad (8.2\text{-}7)$$
$$\psi(t,\tau) = \phi_{ss}(t,\tau) + \phi_{sn}(t,\tau) \qquad (8.2\text{-}8)$$

Substituting Eqs. (8.2-5) and (8.2-6) into Eq. (8.2-4) and using Eq. (8.1-14) yields

$$\sum_{k=1}^n \lambda_k(t) f_k(\tau) + \int_{-\infty}^\infty K(t,\rho) \psi(\rho,\tau) \, d\rho = \int_0^T W(t,\rho) \phi(\tau,\rho) \, d\rho$$

$$0 \leqq \tau \leqq T \quad (8.2\text{-}9)$$

In obtaining the solution of the optimalization problem, it is convenient to define functions $u_k(\tau)$ and $v(t,\tau)$ as solutions of the integral equations

$$f_k(\tau) = \int_0^T \phi(\tau,\rho) u_k(\rho) \, d\rho \qquad 0 \leqq \tau \leqq T \qquad (8.2\text{-}10)$$

$$\int_{-\infty}^\infty K(t,\rho) \psi(\rho,\tau) \, d\rho = \int_0^T \phi(\tau,\rho) v(t,\rho) \, d\rho \qquad 0 \leqq \tau \leqq T \quad (8.2\text{-}11)$$

so that Eq. (8.2-9) may be written as

$$\int_0^T \phi(\tau,\rho) \left[W(t,\rho) - v(t,\rho) - \sum_{k=1}^n \lambda_k(t) u_k(\rho) \right] d\rho = 0 \quad (8.2\text{-}12)$$

[The functions $u_k(\tau)$ and $v(t,\tau)$ are required to vanish for the same values of τ as $W(t,\tau)$.] The function

$$W(t,\tau) = v(t,\tau) + \sum_{k=1}^{n} \lambda_k(t)u_k(\tau) \qquad (8.2\text{-}13)$$

is then clearly the desired solution to (8.2-9).

To obtain the λ_k's, we substitute this expression for $W(t,\tau)$ into Eq. (8.1-14). There results the following nth-order system of linear algebraic equations

$$\sum_{j=1}^{n} \beta_{ij}\lambda_j(t) = \mu_i(t) \qquad (8.2\text{-}14)$$

where we have defined

$$\beta_{ij} = \int_0^T f_i(\rho)u_j(\rho)\,d\rho \qquad (8.2\text{-}15)$$

$$\mu_i(t) = \int_{-\infty}^{\infty} K(t,\rho)f_i(\rho)\,d\rho - \int_0^T v(t,\rho)f_i(\rho)\,d\rho \qquad (8.2\text{-}16)$$

At this point it is convenient to introduce matrix notation. Let us define

$$\begin{aligned} B &= \|\beta_{ij}\| & \mathbf{\mu}(t) &= \{\mu_i(t)\} \\ \mathbf{\lambda} &= \{\lambda_i\} & \mathbf{u}(t) &= \{u_i(t)\} \\ & & \mathbf{f}(t) &= \{f_i(t)\} \end{aligned} \qquad (8.2\text{-}17)$$

so that Eq. (8.2-14) becomes

$$B\mathbf{\lambda}(t) = \mathbf{\mu}(t) \qquad (8.2\text{-}18)$$

which has for a solution

$$\mathbf{\lambda}(t) = B^{-1}\mathbf{\mu}(t) \qquad (8.2\text{-}19)$$

Hence, from Eq. (8.2-13), our optimal weighting function is given by

$$W(t,\tau) = v(t,\tau) + [B^{-1}\mathbf{\mu}(t)] \cdot \mathbf{u}(t) \qquad (8.2\text{-}20)$$

One observes that in the solution of these equations the variable t merely plays the role of a parameter which may be kept constant as far as the intermediate computations are concerned. Furthermore, we note that the relevant integral equations to be solved are of the form discussed in Secs. 8.4 and 8.5.

The expression for the mean-squared error, as given by Eq. (8.2-1), will now be put in a more convenient form. The autocorrelation function of $z(t)$ is obtained, using Eqs. (8.1-9) and (8.1-11) in the form

$$\overline{\phi_{zz}(t,\tau)} = \int_{-\infty}^{\infty} \int_{-\infty}^{\infty} K(t,\tau_1)K(t,\tau_2)\left[\phi_{ss}(\tau_1,\tau_2) \right.$$
$$\left. + \sum_{i=1}^{n}\sum_{j=1}^{n} C_iC_jf_i(\tau_1)f_j(\tau_2) \right] d\tau_1\,d\tau_2 \qquad (8.2\text{-}21)$$

Substituting this, together with Eqs. (8.2-5) and (8.2-6), into Eq. (8.2-1) and using Eq. (8.1-14) we have

$$\overline{\epsilon(t)^2} = \int_{-\infty}^{\infty} \int_{-\infty}^{\infty} K(t,\tau_1)K(t,\tau_2)\phi_{ss}(\tau_1,\tau_2) \, d\tau_1 \, d\tau_2$$
$$- 2 \int_{-\infty}^{\infty} \int_0^T W(t,\tau_1)K(t,\tau_2)\psi(\tau_2,\tau_1) \, d\tau_1 \, d\tau_2$$
$$+ \int_0^T \int_0^T W(t,\tau_1)W(t,\tau_2)\phi(\tau_1,\tau_2) \, d\tau_1 \, d\tau_2 \quad (8.2\text{-}22)$$

or, alternately, using Eqs. (8.2-9) and (8.1-14),

$$\overline{\epsilon(t)^2} = \int_{-\infty}^{\infty} \int_{-\infty}^{\infty} K(t,\tau_1)K(t,\tau_2)\phi_{ss}(\tau_1,\tau_2) \, d\tau_1 \, d\tau_2$$
$$- \int_{-\infty}^{\infty} \int_0^T W(t,\tau_1)K(t,\tau_2)\psi(\tau_2,\tau_1) \, d\tau_1 \, d\tau_2$$
$$+ \int_{-\infty}^{\infty} K(t,\tau)\boldsymbol{\lambda}(t) \cdot \mathbf{f}(\tau) \, d\tau \quad (8.2\text{-}23)$$

Example 8.2-1. We solve here a specific case of the problem posed by Examples 8.1-1 and 8.1-2. The input function $x(t)$ is composed of a stationary random noise with correlation function

$$\phi_{nn}(t) = A e^{-b|t|}$$

together with a linear function of t. Thus

$$x(t) = n(t) + C_1 + C_2 t$$

In the notation of this section we have

$$\phi(t) = A e^{-b|t|} \qquad \psi(t) = 0$$
$$f_1(t) = 1 \qquad f_2(t) = t$$

Also, for the case of prediction at time $T + \alpha$, we have

$$K(\tau) = \delta(\tau - T - \alpha)$$

Hence, the appropriate integral equations to be solved are

$$1 = A \int_0^T e^{-b|t-\tau|} u_1(\tau) \, d\tau \qquad 0 \leq t \leq T$$
$$t = A \int_0^T e^{-b|t-\tau|} u_2(\tau) \, d\tau \qquad 0 \leq t \leq T$$

The solutions are obtained using the methods discussed in Sec. 8.4 with the result that

$$u_1(t) = \frac{1}{2A} [b + \delta(t) + \delta(T - t)]$$
$$u_2(t) = \frac{1}{2Ab} [b^2 t - \delta(t) + (1 + bT)\delta(T - t)]$$

The constants β_{ij} are computed from Eq. (8.2-15), giving

$$\beta_{11} = \int_0^T u_1(t)\, dt = \frac{1}{2A}\,(2 + bT)$$

$$\beta_{12} = \beta_{21} = \int_0^T t u_1(t)\, dt = \frac{T}{4A}\,(2 + bT)\dagger$$

$$\beta_{22} = \int_0^T t u_2(t)\, dt = \frac{1}{6Ab^2}\,(3bT + 3b^2T^2 + b^3T^3)$$

Using Eqs. (8.2-16), we compute μ_j to obtain

$$\mu_1 = \int_{-\infty}^{\infty} \delta(\tau - T - \alpha)\, d\tau = 1$$

$$\mu_2 = \int_{-\infty}^{\infty} \tau \delta(\tau - T - \alpha)\, d\tau = T + \alpha$$

The inverse of the matrix

$$B = \begin{pmatrix} \beta_{11} & \beta_{12} \\ \beta_{21} & \beta_{22} \end{pmatrix}$$

is readily found to be

$$B^{-1} = \frac{1}{|B|} \begin{pmatrix} \dfrac{1}{6Ab^2}\,(3\tau + 3\tau^2 + \tau^3) & -\dfrac{T}{4A}\,(2 + \tau) \\[2ex] -\dfrac{T}{4A}\,(2 + \tau) & \dfrac{1}{2A}\,(2 + \tau) \end{pmatrix}$$

where we have written

$$\tau = bT$$

and where

$$|B| = \frac{1}{48A^2b^2}\,(24\tau + 24\tau^2 + 8\tau^3 + \tau^4)$$

Writing $a = b\alpha$, we have

$$\lambda = B^{-1}\mu = \begin{pmatrix} \lambda_1 \\ \lambda_2 \end{pmatrix}$$

where

$$\lambda_1 = \frac{1}{12Ab^2|B|}\,[6\tau(1 - a) - 3a\tau^2 - \tau^3]$$

$$\lambda_2 = \frac{1}{4Ab|B|}\,[4a + 2\tau(1 + a) + \tau^2]$$

which gives

$$W(t) = \lambda_1 u_1(t) + \lambda_2 u_2(t)$$

The mean-squared error may be computed using Eq. (8.2-23). We have

$$\begin{aligned}
\overline{\epsilon^2} &= \int_{-\infty}^{\infty} \delta(t - T - \alpha)\lambda \cdot \mathbf{f}(t)\, dt \\
&= \lambda_1 + \lambda_2(T + \alpha) \\
&= \frac{1}{6Ab^2|B|}\,[6a^2 + 3\tau(1 + a)^2 + 3\tau^2(1 + a) + \tau^3] \\
&= \frac{8A[6a^2 + 3\tau(1 + a)^2 + 3\tau^2(1 + a) + \tau^3]}{24\tau + 24\tau^2 + 8\tau^3 + \tau^4}
\end{aligned}$$

† We note that in general

$$\beta_{ij} = \int_0^T f_i(\tau)u_j(\tau)\, d\tau = \int_0^T d\tau \int_0^T dt\; \phi(t,\tau)u_i(t)u_j(\tau) = \beta_{ji}$$

We observe that as the interval T of observation of the data tends toward zero, with the time α of prediction held fixed, the mean-squared error approaches the expression $2Ab\alpha^2/T$ and thus becomes infinite in the limit. On the other hand, for very large intervals of observation the mean-squared error approaches $8A/bT$ and thus tends to zero. If we take the special case in which $\alpha = 0$ (that is, require no prediction but consider only filtering), then the mean-squared error is uniformly less than the mean-squared value A of the noise for all values of T, as is evident from the expression

$$(\overline{\epsilon^2})_{\alpha=0} = \frac{24 + 24\tau + 8\tau^2}{24 + 24\tau + 8\tau^2 + \tau^3} A$$

8.3 Prediction Involving Statistically Known Linear Combinations of Known Functions in the Presence of Noise

We shall now consider a modified version of the problem discussed in Sec. 8.2. The input function $x(t)$ has the same form as given in Eq. (8.1-8) except that the coefficients $C_1, \ldots, C_n$ are random variables with a prescribed joint correlation given by

$$E[C_iC_j] = \gamma_{ij} \qquad i, j = 1, \ldots, n \qquad (8.3\text{-}1)$$

Thus the present problem differs from the one considered previously in that, by knowing the statistical behavior of the coefficients, we can no longer impose the condition of unbias (8.1-14).

The mean-squared error is obtained as before and is given by Eq. (8.2-1). However, the correlation functions of $z(t)$ and $x(t)$ have the C_iC_j product replaced by the correlation matrix γ_{ij}. Thus, if we assume that

$$E[C_k s(t)] = E[C_k n(t)] = 0 \qquad (8.3\text{-}2)$$

we have

$$\phi_{zz}(t,t) = \int_{-\infty}^{\infty} \int_{-\infty}^{\infty} K(t,\tau_1)K(t,\tau_2)\left[\phi_{ss}(\tau_1,\tau_2) \right.$$
$$\left. + \sum_{i=1}^{n}\sum_{j=1}^{n} \gamma_{ij}f_i(\tau_1)f_j(\tau_2) \right] d\tau_1\,d\tau_2 \qquad (8.3\text{-}3)$$

$$\phi_{xx}(\tau,\rho) = \phi(\tau,\rho) + \sum_{i=1}^{n}\sum_{j=1}^{n} \gamma_{ij}f_i(\tau)f_j(\rho) \qquad (8.3\text{-}4)$$

$$\phi_{zx}(t,\tau) = \int_{-\infty}^{\infty} K(t,\rho)\psi(\rho,\tau)\,d\rho$$
$$+ \sum_{i=1}^{n}\sum_{j=1}^{n} \gamma_{ij}f_i(\tau)\int_{-\infty}^{\infty} K(t,\rho)f_j(\rho)\,d\rho \qquad (8.3\text{-}5)$$

where $\phi(t,\tau)$ and $\psi(t,\tau)$ are given by Eqs. (8.2-7) and (8.2-8).

Following the arguments of Sec. 8.2 for the problem at hand, we find that a necessary and sufficient condition for $W(t,\tau)$ to provide the optimum solution to the problem of minimizing $\overline{\epsilon(t)^2}$ is that $W(t,\tau)$ satisfy the integral equation

$$\phi_{zz}(t,\tau) = \int_0^T W(t,\rho)\phi_{zz}(\tau,\rho) \, d\rho = \int_0^T W(t,\rho)\phi(\tau,\rho) \, d\rho$$

$$+ \sum_{i=1}^n \sum_{j=1}^n \gamma_{ij} f_i(\tau) \int_0^T W(t,\rho)f_j(\rho) \, d\rho \qquad 0 \leq \tau \leq T \quad (8.3\text{-}6)$$

For convenience of notation let us define

$$\alpha_i(t) = \sum_{j=1}^n \gamma_{ij} \left[\int_{-\infty}^\infty K(t,\rho)f_j(\rho) \, d\rho - \int_0^T W(t,\rho)f_j(\rho) \, d\rho \right] \quad (8.3\text{-}7)$$

so that Eq. (8.3-6) becomes

$$\sum_{k=1}^n \alpha_k(t)f_k(\tau) + \int_{-\infty}^\infty K(t,\rho)\psi(\rho,\tau) \, d\rho = \int_0^T W(t,\rho)\phi(\tau,\rho) \, d\rho$$

$$0 \leq \tau \leq T \quad (8.3\text{-}8)$$

This equation has exactly the same form as Eq. (8.2-9) except that it cannot be solved directly for $W(t,\tau)$, using the methods described above, because the quantities $\alpha_k(t)$ themselves depend upon $W(t,\tau)$. However, to circumvent this difficulty, we may proceed as follows.

As before, we define functions $u_k(\tau)$ and $v(t,\tau)$ as solutions of the integral equations (8.2-10) and (8.2-11) and find that the optimal weighting function is expressible as

$$W(t,\tau) = v(t,\tau) + \sum_{k=1}^n \alpha_k(t)u_k(\tau) \qquad (8.3\text{-}9)$$

To find $\alpha_k(t)$, we substitute Eq. (8.3-9) into Eq. (8.3-7) to obtain

$$\alpha_i(t) = \sum_{j=1}^n \gamma_{ij} \left[\mu_j(t) - \sum_{k=1}^n \beta_{jk}\alpha_k(t) \right] \qquad i = 1, 2, \ldots, n \quad (8.3\text{-}10)$$

where β_{ij} and $\mu_j(t)$ are given by Eqs. (8.2-15) and (8.2-16). Using matrix notation we may rewrite Eq. (8.3-10) as

$$\boldsymbol{\alpha}(t) = \Gamma \boldsymbol{\mu}(t) - \Gamma B \boldsymbol{\alpha}(t) \qquad (8.3\text{-}11)$$

where we have defined

$$\Gamma = \|\gamma_{ij}\| \qquad \boldsymbol{\alpha}(t) = \{\alpha_i(t)\} \qquad (8.3\text{-}12)$$

in addition to the vectors and matrices defined previously by Eq. (8.2-17). Solving Eq. (8.3-11) for $\boldsymbol{\alpha}(t)$, we obtain

$$\boldsymbol{\alpha}(t) = P\Gamma\boldsymbol{\mu}(t) \qquad (8.3\text{-}13)$$

where

$$P = (I + \Gamma B)^{-1} \qquad (8.3\text{-}14)$$

and I is the $n \times n$ identity matrix. Hence, from Eq. (8.3-9), the optimal weighting function is found to be

$$W(t,\tau) = v(t,\tau) + [P\Gamma\mathbf{y}(t)] \cdot \mathbf{u}(\tau) \qquad (8.3\text{-}15)$$

In order to obtain a convenient expression for the mean-squared error we first make the following observation. Equation (8.3-7) may be written in matrix form as

$$\boldsymbol{\alpha}(t) = \int_{-\infty}^{\infty} [K(t,\rho) - W(t,\rho)]\Gamma\mathbf{f}(\rho) \, d\rho \qquad (8.3\text{-}16)$$

from which it follows that

$$\int_{-\infty}^{\infty} K(t,\rho)\mathbf{f}(\rho) \, d\rho - \int_{0}^{T} W(t,\rho)\mathbf{f}(\rho) \, d\rho = \Gamma^{-1}\boldsymbol{\alpha}(t) \qquad (8.3\text{-}17)$$

Then by substituting Eqs. (8.3-3) to (8.3-5) into Eq. (8.2-1) and using Eqs. (8.3-8) and (8.3-17) there results the following expression for the mean-squared error.

$$\overline{\epsilon(t)^2} = \boldsymbol{\alpha}(t)*\Gamma^{-1}\boldsymbol{\alpha}(t) + \int_{-\infty}^{\infty}\int_{-\infty}^{\infty} K(t,\tau_1)K(t,\tau_2)\phi_{ss}(\tau_1,\tau_2) \, d\tau_1 \, d\tau_2$$
$$- \int_{-\infty}^{\infty}\int_{0}^{T} W(t,\tau_1)K(t,\tau_2)\psi(\tau_2,\tau_1) \, d\tau_1 \, d\tau_2$$
$$+ \int_{0}^{T} W(t,\tau)\boldsymbol{\alpha}(t) \cdot \mathbf{f}(\tau) \, d\tau \qquad (8.3\text{-}18)$$

where the asterisk denotes the transpose of the indicated vector.

It is interesting to compare Eqs. (8.3-18) and (8.2-23). The quantities $\alpha_k(t)$ play a role analogous to the Lagrangian multipliers $\lambda_k(t)$. The terms of which the mean-squared error is composed are identical for the two cases except for the additional term in Eq. (8.3-18) which is attributed to the systematic error resulting from the distortion of the functions $f_k(t)$ due to the fact that the optimal prediction does not behave in an ideal manner. In the case considered in Sec. 8.2 we did not encounter such a term because the requirement imposed by the condition of unbias eliminated this systematic error.

Example 8.3-1. To illustrate the techniques developed above, we reconsider the problem discussed in Example 8.2-1, where we now assume the coefficients C_1 and C_2 to be random variables. For simplicity, we use numerical values here since the algebra is generally more complicated than in Example 8.2-1. We choose here for the desired operation a filtering in which

$$K(\tau) = \delta(\tau)$$

so that we are seeking a value for the signal at $t = 0$ (that is, the quantity C_1). From our previous results this is equivalent to choosing $\alpha = -T$, giving as a mean-squared error from Example 8.2-1,

$$\overline{\epsilon^2} = \frac{24 + 24\tau + 8\tau^2}{24 + 24\tau + 8\tau^2 + \tau^3} A$$

It will be noted that this is the same result obtained for $\alpha = 0$.

We now choose $b = 1$, $A = 1$, $T = 1$ so that

$$\overline{\epsilon^2} = {}^{56}\!\%_7 = 0.98246$$

To apply the techniques of the present section, we let the coefficients C_1, C_2 have a correlation matrix given by

$$\Gamma = \begin{pmatrix} \gamma_{11} & \gamma_{12} \\ \gamma_{21} & \gamma_{22} \end{pmatrix} = \begin{pmatrix} 1 & 1 \\ 1 & 2 \end{pmatrix}$$

The signal-to-noise ratio is thus of the order of magnitude of unity, with $A = 1$, and we should expect the techniques of this section to show up to good advantage.

Substituting numerical values, we obtain

$$B = \begin{pmatrix} \tfrac{3}{2} & \tfrac{3}{4} \\ \tfrac{3}{4} & \tfrac{7}{6} \end{pmatrix}$$

and hence

$$I + \Gamma B = \begin{pmatrix} 1\tfrac{3}{4} & 2\tfrac{3}{12} \\ 3 & 4\tfrac{9}{12} \end{pmatrix}$$

From this

$$P = (I + \Gamma B)^{-1} = \tfrac{4}{361} \begin{pmatrix} 49 & -36 \\ -23 & 39 \end{pmatrix}$$

and

$$\alpha = P\Gamma\mu = \tfrac{4}{361} \begin{pmatrix} 13 \\ 16 \end{pmatrix}$$

For this example we have

$$\mu(t) = \tfrac{1}{2} \begin{pmatrix} 1 + \delta(t) + \delta(1 - t) \\ t - \delta(t) + 2\delta(1 - t) \end{pmatrix}$$

so that the optimal weighting function, as obtained from Eq. (8.3-15), is

$$W(t) = \tfrac{2}{361}[13 + 16t - 3\delta(t) + 45\delta(1 - t)]$$

The value of the mean-squared error is obtained from Eq. (8.3-18) in the form

$$\overline{\epsilon^2} = \alpha^* \Gamma^{-1} \alpha + \int_0^1 W(t)\alpha \cdot f(t)\, d\tau$$

Now

$$\Gamma^{-1} = \begin{pmatrix} 2 & -1 \\ -1 & 1 \end{pmatrix}$$

and thus

$$\alpha^* \Gamma^{-1} \alpha = \frac{2016}{130{,}321}$$

Furthermore,

$$\alpha \cdot f(t) = \tfrac{4}{361}(13 + 16t)$$

so that

$$\int_0^1 W(t)\alpha \cdot f(t)\, dt = \frac{41{,}480}{390{,}363}$$

Thus

$$\overline{\epsilon^2} = \frac{47{,}528}{390{,}363} = 0.12175$$

in comparison with the mean-squared error of 0.98246 obtained in Example 8.2-1. Since the mean-squared value of the noise for both cases is unity, we see that knowing the distribution matrix for the coefficients permits one to do a much better job of filtering than would be possible if these coefficients were completely arbitrary.

As we have seen from the example problems discussed in this section and in Sec. 8.2, the important distinction between the two treatments lies in the fact that in one case the filter must be exact for all functions $f_k(t)$ considered, while in the other case the coefficients C_k are random variables with known statistical properties. In the latter case the system is allowed to produce an error from the message, and it is the total error from message and noise that is minimized in the root-mean-square sense. For small or moderate values of signal-to-noise ratio this distinction is significant. If the message is dominated by the noise, a much smaller total error can be achieved by knowing the distribution of coefficients. For large values of signal-to-noise ratio, the second case approaches the first case in the limit. This is to be expected, since the relative error in the message that can be tolerated must necessarily approach zero as the level of the message itself becomes infinite.

We shall now show analytically that the results for the two cases actually do approach each other in the limit of increasing signal-to-noise ratio. From Eq. (8.3-11) we have

$$B\boldsymbol{\alpha}(t) + \Gamma^{-1}\boldsymbol{\alpha}(t) = \boldsymbol{\mu}(t) \qquad (8.3\text{-}19)$$

so that as $\Gamma \to \infty$, $\Gamma^{-1} \to 0$ and Eq. (8.3-19) tends to

$$B\boldsymbol{\alpha}(t) = \boldsymbol{\mu}(t) \qquad (8.3\text{-}20)$$

in the limit. Furthermore, from Eq. (8.3-17), we have

$$\int_{-\infty}^{\infty} [K(t,\rho) - W(t,\rho)]\mathbf{f}(\rho)\, d\rho = 0 \qquad (8.3\text{-}21)$$

in the limit. Now Eq. (8.3-21) is simply the condition of unbias stated in Eq. (8.1-14) and Eqs. (8.3-20) and (8.2-18) show that $\boldsymbol{\alpha}(t) \to \boldsymbol{\lambda}(t)$ in the limit. Finally, by comparing Eqs. (8.2-20) and (8.3-15), we have the desired result.

8.4 The Integral Equation for the Stationary Case

In order to solve the optimalization problems posed in the previous two sections, it was seen to be necessary to obtain the solution of a certain integral equation. In this section and in Sec. 8.5 we shall carry out the detailed solution of this integral equation. Specifically, in the present section we shall be concerned with the case in which $\{s(t) + n(t)\}$ is a stationary random process such that its correlation function, as given by the stationary form of Eq. (8.2-7), can be expressed as a sum of negative exponential functions (cf. Sec. 5.5 and Appendix D). The integral equation to be solved for $W(\tau)$ is

$$f(t) = \int_0^T W(\tau)\phi(t - \tau)\, d\tau \qquad 0 \le t \le T \qquad (8.4\text{-}1)$$

where the function $f(t)$ is assumed to be a known differentiable function of t defined over the interval $0 \le t \le T$.

A random process with a rational spectrum has a correlation function which is expressible as a sum of exponentials. If we denote the degree in the variable ω^2 of the denominator of the spectrum by N, the degree of the numerator by m, and let $n = N - m$, we may write

$$\phi(\tau) = \sum_{k=1}^{N} \phi_k e^{-\gamma_k |\tau|}$$

$$= \sum_{r=1}^{n} \phi_r e^{-\gamma_r |\tau|} + \sum_{s=1}^{m} \phi_{n+s} e^{-\rho_s |\tau|} \tag{8.4-2}$$

The decomposition of the correlation function into two sums of n and m terms, respectively, is made for convenience in the sequel. The precise order for grouping these terms is immaterial. Although the correlation function $\phi(\tau)$ is real for real values of τ, the constants ϕ_k and γ_k may be complex. Notice that we have defined

$$\rho_s = \gamma_{n+s} \qquad s = 1, 2, \ldots, m \tag{8.4-3}$$

The corresponding spectral density, computed as the Fourier transform of Eq. (8.4-2), is

$$G(\omega^2) = \frac{1}{\pi} \sum_{k=1}^{N} \frac{2\gamma_k \phi_k}{\omega^2 + \gamma_k^2} \tag{8.4-4}$$

where for convenience we have indicated that the independent variable in G is ω^2 rather than ω. This quantity may alternately be expressed as

$$\pi G(\omega^2) = \frac{\displaystyle\sum_{s=0}^{m} \theta_{2s} \omega^{2(m-s)}}{\omega^{2N} + \displaystyle\sum_{k=1}^{N} \lambda_{2k} \omega^{2(N-k)}}$$

$$= \theta_0 \frac{\displaystyle\prod_{s=1}^{m} (\omega^2 + \alpha_s^2)}{\displaystyle\prod_{k=1}^{N} (\omega^2 + \gamma_k^2)}$$

$$= \theta_0 \frac{\displaystyle\prod_{s=1}^{m} (\omega^2 + \alpha_s^2)}{\displaystyle\prod_{r=1}^{n} (\omega^2 + \gamma_s^2) \prod_{s=1}^{m} (\omega^2 + \rho_s^2)} \tag{8.4-5}$$

Here the constants θ_{2s} and λ_{2k} are the real coefficients of the polynomials of the numerator and denominator of the spectrum. The quantities

$\pm j\alpha_s$ and $\pm j\gamma_k$ are the roots of the numerator and denominator polynomials, respectively. The numbers α_s and γ_k will, in general, be complex and are taken to have positive real parts. The integers m and N are the degrees of the numerator and denominator polynomials, respectively, while the integer n is such that

$$n + m = N \tag{8.4-6}$$

The computational procedure necessary to obtain the solution of the integral equation (8.4-1) is rather lengthy in the general case so that we shall present first a summary of the steps to be carried out, together with a numerical example, before giving the detailed proof. We shall find it convenient to use matrix notation and in order to avoid confusion we adopt the following conventions.

1. A matrix will always be represented by an upper-case letter with two subscripts used to specify the number of rows and columns, respectively. Thus, the matrix A_{mn} has m rows and n columns.

2. The general element of a matrix will usually involve the indices i and j which will always indicate that that element is in the ith row and jth column of the matrix. Thus, the element a_{ij} may be the element of the ith row and jth column of the matrix A_{mn}. Hence, i would take on the values $1, 2, \ldots, m$ and j would take on the values $1, 2, \ldots, n$. We would write

$$A_{mn} = \|a_{ij}\|$$

3. A vector will always be represented by a boldface lower-case letter with a single subscript used to specify the number of elements. Thus, $\mathbf{a}_n$ would be an n-dimensional vector whose general element might be specified by a_i. Hence, we would write

$$\mathbf{a}_n = \{a_i\}$$

and i would take on the values $1, 2, \ldots, n$.

4. In many of the equations that we write involving summation or product symbols certain terms or factors must sometimes be omitted. This will be indicated by a superscript on the operation symbol. For example, the symbols

$$\sum_{r=1}^{N}{}^{k} a_r \qquad \prod_{r=1}^{N}{}^{k} a_r$$

indicate that r takes on all integer values from 1 to N with the exception of the integer k.

Before beginning the computational procedure to be outlined below, it is necessary to obtain the spectral density in the form given in both Eqs. (8.4-4) and (8.4-5). Thus, we need to know numerical values for the quantities $\phi_k, \gamma_k, \theta_{2s}, \lambda_{2k}$, and α_s for all values of the subscripts. Furthermore, it must be emphasized that the exact procedure, as described here, applies only when the zeros and poles of the spectrum are all simple, i.e., all roots α_s and γ_k are distinct. For the case of multiple zeros and poles suitable modifications must be introduced.

The steps to be performed in the computation involve the addition and multiplication of various matrices all but one of which are given in explicit form. This one exception is the inverse of a certain $m \times m$ matrix.

Summary of the Computation

I. Obtain the following matrices whose elements are formed from the roots of the spectrum:

1. $V_{nn}^{(1)-1}$ is the inverse of the Vandermonde matrix

$$V_{nn}^{(1)} = \|\gamma_i{}^{j-1}\| \tag{8.4-7}$$

and is given by

$$V_{nn}^{(1)-1} = \left\| (-1)^{i+1} \frac{\displaystyle\sum_{1 \leq r < s < \cdots < t \leq n}^{(n-i)} \gamma_r \gamma_s \cdots \gamma_t}{\displaystyle\prod_{k=1}^{n}{}^{j} (\gamma_k - \gamma_j)} \right\| \tag{8.4-8}$$

The notation used in the numerator is to denote the sum of products of all possible combinations of the γ's taken $(n - i)$ at a time. As stated above, superscript j on the summation and product symbols indicates that the factors for which $k, r, s, \ldots, t = j$ are omitted. The numerator in the last row of the matrix is $(-1)^{n+1}$. For example, if $n = 4$, the element in the second row and first column ($i = 2, j = 1$) is

$$(-1)^{2+1} \frac{\gamma_2\gamma_3 + \gamma_2\gamma_4 + \gamma_3\gamma_4}{(\gamma_2 - \gamma_1)(\gamma_3 - \gamma_1)(\gamma_4 - \gamma_1)}$$

2. $M_{mm}^{(2)-1}$ is the inverse of the matrix

$$M_{mm}^{(2)} = \left\| \frac{1}{\alpha_j - \rho_i} \right\| \tag{8.4-9}$$

and is given by

$$M_{mm}^{(2)-1} = \left\| \frac{\displaystyle\prod_{r=1}^{m} (\alpha_r - \rho_j)}{\displaystyle\prod_{s=1}^{m}{}^{i} (\alpha_s - \alpha_i)} \prod_{t=1}^{m}{}^{j} \left(\frac{\rho_t - \alpha_i}{\rho_t - \rho_j} \right) \right\| \tag{8.4-10}$$

3. $T_{nn}^{(2)}$ is a triangular matrix with one's on the main diagonal, zero's below the main diagonal, and the other elements given by

$$(-1)^{i+j} \sum_{1 \leq r < s < \cdots < t \leq j-1}^{(j-i)} \gamma_r \gamma_s \cdots \gamma_t$$

4. $R_{mn}^{(1)}$ is a rectangular matrix given by

$$R_{mn}^{(1)} = \left\| \frac{1}{\gamma_j - \rho_i} \right\| \tag{8.4-11}$$

5. $R_{nm}^{(2)}$ is a rectangular matrix with one's in the last row. The other elements are given by

$$\prod_{r=i+1}^{n} (\alpha_j - \gamma_r)$$

6. D_{nn} is a diagonal matrix given by

$$D_{nn} = \left\| \frac{\delta_{ij}}{\displaystyle\prod_{r=1}^{n}{}^{i} (\gamma_i - \gamma_r)} \right\| \tag{8.4-12}$$

The symbol δ_{ij} is the well-known Kronecker delta which is either one or zero according as the subscripts i and j are or are not the same.

7. $D_{mm}^{(1)}$ is a diagonal matrix given by

$$D_{mm}^{(1)} = \left\| \frac{\delta_{ij}}{\displaystyle\prod_{r=1}^{n} (\rho_i - \gamma_r)} \right\| \tag{8.4-13}$$

8. $D_{mm}^{(2)}$ is a diagonal matrix given by

$$D_{mm}^{(2)} = \left\| \delta_{ij} \prod_{r=1}^{n} (\alpha_i - \gamma_r) \right\| \tag{8.4-14}$$

II. Perform the matrix operations indicated in the following equations:

$$B_{nn}^{(1)} = V_{nn}^{(1)-1} - T_{nn}^{\prime(2)} R_{nm}^{(2)} M_{mm}^{(2)-1} R_{mn}^{(1)} D_{nn} \tag{8.4-15}$$

$$B_{nm}^{(2)} = -T_{nn}^{\prime(2)} R_{nm}^{(2)} M_{mm}^{(2)-1} D_{mm}^{(1)} \tag{8.4-16}$$

$$C_{mn}^{(1)} = D_{mm}^{(2)} M_{mm}^{(2)-1} R_{mn}^{(1)} D_{nn} \tag{8.4-17}$$

$$C_{mm}^{(2)} = D_{mm}^{(2)} M_{mm}^{(2)-1} D_{mm}^{(1)} \tag{8.4-18}$$

III. Obtain the following matrices:

$$\Gamma_{N,2m} = \left\| \gamma_i^{j-1} \right\| \qquad \Gamma_{N,2N} = \left\| \gamma_i^{j-1} \right\| \tag{8.4-19}$$

$$\Delta_{NN}^{(1)} = \left\| \frac{\delta_{ij}}{\displaystyle 2\phi_i\gamma_i \prod_{r=1}^{N}{}^{i} (\gamma_i^2 - \gamma_r^2)} \right\| \tag{8.4-20}$$

$$\Delta_{2m,2m}^{(2)} = \left\| (-1)^i \delta_{ij} \right\| \qquad \Delta_{2N,2N}^{(2)} = \left\| (-1)^i \delta_{ij} \right\| \tag{8.4-21}$$

$$\Theta_{2m,2m} = (-1)^n \left\| (-1)^{\frac{i+j+1}{2}} \theta_{2m+1-i-j} \right\| \tag{8.4-22}$$

$$\Lambda_{2N,2N} = \left\| (-1)^{\frac{i+j+1}{2}} \lambda_{2N+1-i-j} \right\| \tag{8.4-23}$$

In the matrices of Eqs. (8.4-22) and (8.4-23) it is understood that θ_k and λ_k are zero whenever k is an odd or negative integer. Furthermore, we have defined $\lambda_0 = 1$.

IV. Form the three matrices B_{nN}, C_{mN}, and Q_{Nm} as follows. The first n columns of B_{nN} are the columns of $B_{nn}^{(1)}$ while the last m columns are the columns of $B_{nm}^{(2)}$. Thus, we may write

$$B_{nN} = \|B_{nn}^{(1)} \quad B_{nm}^{(2)}\| \tag{8.4-24}$$

The matrix C_{mN} is formed in a similar manner so that we have

$$C_{mN} = \|C_{mn}^{(1)} \quad C_{mm}^{(2)}\| \tag{8.4-25}$$

The matrix Q_{Nm} is given by

$$Q_{Nm} = \left\|\frac{e^{-\alpha_i T}}{\alpha_j + \gamma_i}\right\| \tag{8.4-26}$$

V. Obtain the matrix H_{mm} as the inverse of the matrix

$$I_{mm} - (C_{mN}Q_{Nm})^2$$

where I_{mm} is the $m \times m$ identity matrix defined by

$$I_{mm} = \|\delta_{ij}\|$$

VI. Find a particular solution of the differential equation

$$\pi G(-p^2) W_p(t) = f(t) \tag{8.4-27}$$

where $G(-p^2)$ is the operator formed by replacing ω^2 by $-p^2$ in the expression for the spectral density. Here, of course, p is the differential operator d/dt. Then form the following two vectors:

$$\mathbf{w}_{2m}(t) = \{W_p^{(i-1)}(t)\} \qquad \mathbf{f}_{2N}(t) = \{f^{(i-1)}(t)\} \tag{8.4-28}$$

VII. Compute the following two vectors:

$$\mathbf{c}_N = \Delta_{NN}^{(1)}[\Gamma_{N,2m}\Theta_{2m,2m}\Delta_{2m,2m}^{(2)}\mathbf{w}_{2m}(0) - \Gamma_{N,2N}\Lambda_{2N,2N}\Delta_{2N,2N}^{(2)}\mathbf{f}_{2N}(0)] \tag{8.4-29}$$

$$\mathbf{d}_N = \Delta_{NN}^{(1)}[\Gamma_{N,2N}\Lambda_{2N,2N}\mathbf{f}_{2N}(T) - \Gamma_{N,2m}\Theta_{2m,2m}\mathbf{w}_{2m}(T)] \tag{8.4-30}$$

VIII. Obtain the following four vectors:

$$a_m^{(2)} = H_{mm}C_{mN}(\mathbf{c}_N + Q_{Nm}C_{mN}\mathbf{d}_N) \tag{8.4-31}$$
$$b_m^{(2)} = H_{mm}C_{mN}(\mathbf{d}_N + Q_{Nm}C_{mN}\mathbf{c}_N) \tag{8.4-32}$$
$$a_n^{(1)} = B_{nN}Q_{Nm}C_{mN}(Q_{Nm}a_m^{(2)} + \mathbf{d}_N) + B_{nN}\mathbf{c}_N \tag{8.4-33}$$
$$b_n^{(1)} = B_{nN}Q_{Nm}C_{mN}(Q_{Nm}b_m^{(2)} + \mathbf{c}_N) + B_{nN}\mathbf{d}_N \tag{8.4-34}$$

IX. The solution of the integral equation (8.4-1) is then given by

$$W(t) = \sum_{i=1}^{n} (-1)^{i-1} [a_i^{(1)}\delta^{(i-1)}(t) + b_i^{(1)}\delta^{(i-1)}(T - t)]$$

$$+ \sum_{j=1}^{m} [a_j^{(2)}e^{-\alpha_j t} + b_j^{(2)}e^{-\alpha_j(T-t)}] + W_p(t) \qquad 0 \leq t \leq T \tag{8.4-35}$$

where the coefficients are obtained as components of the vectors

$$\mathbf{a}_n^{(1)} = \{a_i^{(1)}\} \qquad \mathbf{b}_n^{(1)} = \{b_i^{(1)}\} \qquad (8.4\text{-}36)$$
$$\mathbf{a}_m^{(2)} = \{a_i^{(2)}\} \qquad \mathbf{b}_m^{(2)} = \{b_i^{(2)}\}$$

Steps I through V in this computation depend only upon the correlation function $\phi(t)$ and are independent of the choice of the function $f(t)$.

Example 8.4-1. We shall now illustrate the above described computational procedure by solving the following integral equation

$$\sin\left(\frac{\pi}{2}t\right) = \int_0^1 W(\tau)\phi(t-\tau)\,d\tau$$

where

$$\phi(\tau) = 2e^{-|\tau|}\cos\tau - e^{-2|\tau|}$$
$$= e^{-(1+j)|\tau|} + e^{-(1-j)|\tau|} - e^{-2|\tau|}$$

The corresponding spectral density is given by

$$G(\omega^2) = \frac{1}{\pi}\frac{24\omega^2 + 16}{\omega^6 + 4\omega^4 + 4\omega^2 + 16}$$

For this example we have

$$\begin{array}{lllll}
\theta_0 = 24 & \lambda_2 = 4 & m = 1 & \gamma_1 = 1 + j \\
\theta_2 = 16 & \lambda_4 = 4 & n = 2 & \gamma_2 = 1 - j \\
& \lambda_6 = 16 & N = 3 & \gamma_3 = \rho_1 = 2 \\
& \phi_1 = 1 & \alpha_1 = \sqrt{2/3} & \\
& \phi_2 = 1 & T = 1 & \\
& \phi_3 = -1 & f(t) = \sin\left(\frac{\pi}{2}t\right) &
\end{array}$$

I. 1.

$$V_{22}^{(1)-1} = \begin{pmatrix} \dfrac{\gamma_2}{\gamma_2 - \gamma_1} & \dfrac{\gamma_1}{\gamma_1 - \gamma_2} \\ \dfrac{-1}{\gamma_2 - \gamma_1} & \dfrac{-1}{\gamma_1 - \gamma_2} \end{pmatrix} = 0.5\begin{pmatrix} 1+j & 1-j \\ -j & j \end{pmatrix}$$

which is the inverse of the matrix

$$V_{22}^{(1)} = \begin{pmatrix} 1 & \gamma_1 \\ 1 & \gamma_2 \end{pmatrix} = \begin{pmatrix} 1 & 1+j \\ 1 & 1-j \end{pmatrix}$$

2.

$$M_{11}^{(2)-1} = \alpha_1 - \rho_1 = -1.1835$$

which is the inverse of

$$M_{11}^{(2)} = \frac{1}{\alpha_1 - \rho_1} = -0.8450$$

3.

$$T_{22}^{(2)} = \begin{pmatrix} 1 & -\gamma_1 \\ 0 & 1 \end{pmatrix} = \begin{pmatrix} 1 & -(1+j) \\ 0 & 1 \end{pmatrix}$$

4.

$$R_{12}^{(1)} = \begin{pmatrix} \dfrac{1}{\gamma_1 - \rho_1} & \dfrac{1}{\gamma_2 - \rho_1} \end{pmatrix} = -0.5(1+j \quad 1-j)$$

5.

$$R_{21}^{(2)} = \begin{pmatrix} \alpha_1 - \gamma_2 \\ 1 \end{pmatrix} = \begin{pmatrix} -0.1835 + j \\ 1 \end{pmatrix}$$

6.

$$D_{22} = \begin{pmatrix} \dfrac{1}{\gamma_1 - \gamma_2} & 0 \\ 0 & \dfrac{1}{\gamma_2 - \gamma_1} \end{pmatrix} = 0.5 \begin{pmatrix} -j & 0 \\ 0 & j \end{pmatrix}$$

7.

$$D_{11}^{(1)} = \frac{1}{(\rho_1 - \gamma_1)(\rho_1 - \gamma_2)} = 0.5$$

8.

$$D_{11}^{(2)} = (\alpha_1 - \gamma_1)(\alpha_1 - \gamma_2) = 1.0337$$

II.

$$B_{22}^{(1)} = V_{22}^{(1)-1} - T_{22}^{(2)} R_{21}^{(2)} M_{11}^{(2)-1} R_{12}^{(1)} D_{22}$$
$$= \begin{pmatrix} 0.8502 + j0.1498 & 0.8502 - j0.1498 \\ -0.2959 - j0.2041 & -0.2959 + j0.2041 \end{pmatrix}$$
$$B_{21}^{(2)} = -T_{22}^{(2)} R_{21}^{(2)} M_{11}^{(2)-1} D_{11}^{(1)}$$
$$= \begin{pmatrix} -0.7004 \\ 0.5918 \end{pmatrix}$$
$$C_{12}^{(1)} = D_{11}^{(2)} M_{11}^{(2)-1} R_{12}^{(1)} D_{22}$$
$$= (0.3059 - j0.3059 \quad 0.3059 + j0.3059)$$
$$C_{11}^{(2)} = D_{11}^{(2)} M_{11}^{(2)-1} D_{11}^{(1)}$$
$$= -0.6117$$

III.

$$\Gamma_{32} = \begin{pmatrix} 1 & \gamma_1 \\ 1 & \gamma_2 \\ 1 & \gamma_3 \end{pmatrix} = \begin{pmatrix} 1 & 1+j \\ 1 & 1-j \\ 1 & 2 \end{pmatrix}$$

$$\Gamma_{36} = \begin{pmatrix} 1 & \gamma_1 & \gamma_1^2 & \gamma_1^3 & \gamma_1^4 & \gamma_1^5 \\ 1 & \gamma_2 & \gamma_2^2 & \gamma_2^3 & \gamma_2^4 & \gamma_2^5 \\ 1 & \gamma_3 & \gamma_3^2 & \gamma_3^3 & \gamma_3^4 & \gamma_3^5 \end{pmatrix}$$
$$= \begin{pmatrix} 1 & 1+j & 2j & -2(1-j) & -4 & -4(1+j) \\ 1 & 1-j & -2j & -2(1+j) & -4 & -4(1-j) \\ 1 & 2 & 4 & 8 & 16 & 32 \end{pmatrix}$$

$$\Delta_{33}^{(1)} = \begin{pmatrix} \dfrac{1}{2\phi_1\gamma_1(\gamma_1^2 - \gamma_2^2)(\gamma_1^2 - \gamma_3^2)} & 0 & 0 \\ 0 & \dfrac{1}{2\phi_2\gamma_2(\gamma_2^2 - \gamma_1^2)(\gamma_2^2 - \gamma_3^2)} & 0 \\ 0 & 0 & \dfrac{1}{2\phi_3\gamma_3(\gamma_3^2 - \gamma_1^2)(\gamma_3^2 - \gamma_2^2)} \end{pmatrix}$$
$$= \frac{1}{160} \begin{pmatrix} 1 + 3j & 0 & 0 \\ 0 & 1 - 3j & 0 \\ 0 & 0 & -2 \end{pmatrix}$$

$$\Delta_{22}^{(2)} = \begin{pmatrix} -1 & 0 \\ 0 & 1 \end{pmatrix}$$

$$\Delta_{66}^{(2)} = \begin{pmatrix} -1 & 0 & 0 & 0 & 0 & 0 \\ 0 & 1 & 0 & 0 & 0 & 0 \\ 0 & 0 & -1 & 0 & 0 & 0 \\ 0 & 0 & 0 & 1 & 0 & 0 \\ 0 & 0 & 0 & 0 & -1 & 0 \\ 0 & 0 & 0 & 0 & 0 & 1 \end{pmatrix}$$

$$\Theta_{22} = (-1)^2 \begin{pmatrix} 0 & \theta_0 \\ \theta_0 & 0 \end{pmatrix} = \begin{pmatrix} 0 & 24 \\ 24 & 0 \end{pmatrix}$$

$$\Lambda_{66} = \begin{pmatrix} 0 & \lambda_4 & 0 & -\lambda_2 & 0 & 1 \\ \lambda_4 & 0 & -\lambda_2 & 0 & 1 & 0 \\ 0 & -\lambda_2 & 0 & 1 & 0 & 0 \\ -\lambda_2 & 0 & 1 & 0 & 0 & 0 \\ 0 & 1 & 0 & 0 & 0 & 0 \\ 1 & 0 & 0 & 0 & 0 & 0 \end{pmatrix}$$

$$= \begin{pmatrix} 0 & 4 & 0 & -4 & 0 & 1 \\ 4 & 0 & -4 & 0 & 1 & 0 \\ 0 & -4 & 0 & 1 & 0 & 0 \\ -4 & 0 & 1 & 0 & 0 & 0 \\ 0 & 1 & 0 & 0 & 0 & 0 \\ 1 & 0 & 0 & 0 & 0 & 0 \end{pmatrix}$$

IV.

$$\begin{aligned} B_{23} &= \begin{pmatrix} 0.8502 + j0.1498 & 0.8502 - j0.1498 & -0.7004 \\ -0.2959 - j0.2041 & -0.2959 + j0.2041 & 0.5918 \end{pmatrix} \\ C_{13} &= \begin{pmatrix} (0.3059 - j0.3059 & 0.3059 + j0.3059 & -0.6117) \end{pmatrix} \end{aligned}$$

$$Q_{31} = \begin{pmatrix} \dfrac{e^{-\alpha_1 T}}{\alpha_1 + \gamma_1} \\ \dfrac{e^{-\alpha_1 T}}{\alpha_1 + \gamma_2} \\ \dfrac{e^{-\alpha_1 T}}{\alpha_1 + \gamma_3} \end{pmatrix} = \begin{pmatrix} 0.1867 - j0.1028 \\ 0.1867 + j0.1028 \\ 0.1569 \end{pmatrix}$$

As a check the matrix $\left\| \begin{matrix} B_{23} \\ C_{13} \end{matrix} \right\|$ is the inverse of the matrix

$$A_{33} = \begin{pmatrix} 1 & \gamma_1 & \dfrac{1}{\alpha_1 - \gamma_1} \\ 1 & \gamma_2 & \dfrac{1}{\alpha_1 - \gamma_2} \\ 1 & \rho_1 & \dfrac{1}{\alpha_1 - \rho_1} \end{pmatrix}$$

$$= \begin{pmatrix} 1 & 1+j & -0.1775 + j0.9674 \\ 1 & 1-j & -0.1775 - j0.9674 \\ 1 & 2 & -0.8450 \end{pmatrix}$$

V.

$$H_{11}^{-1} = I_{11} - (C_{13}Q_{31})^2 = 0.9980$$

Therefore

$$H_{11} = 1.0020$$

VI. The function $W_p(t)$ is obtained as a particular solution of the following differential equation

$$(p^6 - 4p^4 + 4p^2 - 16) \sin\left(\frac{\pi}{2} t\right) = (24p^2 - 16) W_p(t)$$

Thus

$$W_p(t) = 0.8674 \sin\left(\frac{\pi}{2} t\right)$$

$$\mathbf{w}_2(t) = \begin{pmatrix} W_p(t) \\ \dfrac{dW_p(t)}{dt} \end{pmatrix} = \begin{pmatrix} 0.8674 \sin\left(\dfrac{\pi}{2}t\right) \\ 1.3625 \cos\left(\dfrac{\pi}{2}t\right) \end{pmatrix}$$

$$\mathbf{f}_6(t) = \begin{Bmatrix} f(t) \\ \dfrac{df(t)}{dt} \\ \dfrac{d^2f(t)}{dt^2} \\ \dfrac{d^3f(t)}{dt^3} \\ \dfrac{d^4f(t)}{dt^4} \\ \dfrac{d^5f(t)}{dt^5} \end{Bmatrix} = \begin{Bmatrix} \sin\left(\dfrac{\pi}{2}t\right) \\ 1.5708 \cos\left(\dfrac{\pi}{2}t\right) \\ -2.4674 \sin\left(\dfrac{\pi}{2}t\right) \\ -3.8758 \cos\left(\dfrac{\pi}{2}t\right) \\ 6.0880 \sin\left(\dfrac{\pi}{2}t\right) \\ 9.5630 \cos\left(\dfrac{\pi}{2}t\right) \end{Bmatrix}$$

VII.

$$\mathbf{c}_3 = \Delta_{33}^{(1)}[\Gamma_{32}\Theta_{22}\Delta_{22}^{(2)}\mathbf{w}_2(0) - \Gamma_{36}\Lambda_{66}\Delta_{66}^{(2)}\mathbf{f}_6(0)]$$
$$= \begin{pmatrix} -0.3333 + j0.2701 \\ -0.3333 - j0.2701 \\ -0.2107 \end{pmatrix}$$

$$\mathbf{d}_3 = \Delta_{33}^{(1)}[\Gamma_{36}\Lambda_{66}\mathbf{f}_6(1) - \Gamma_{32}\Theta_{22}\mathbf{w}_2(1)]$$
$$= \begin{pmatrix} 0.3841 + j0.0402 \\ 0.3841 - j0.0402 \\ 0.2682 \end{pmatrix}$$

VIII.

$$\mathbf{a}_1^{(2)} = H_{11}C_{13}(\mathbf{c}_3 + Q_{31}C_{13}\mathbf{d}_3)$$
$$= 0.0861$$
$$\mathbf{b}_1^{(2)} = H_{11}C_{13}(\mathbf{d}_3 + Q_{31}C_{13}\mathbf{c}_3)$$
$$= 0.0917$$
$$\mathbf{a}_2^{(1)} = B_{23}Q_{31}C_{13}(Q_{31}\mathbf{a}_1^{(2)} + \mathbf{d}_3) + B_{23}\mathbf{c}_3$$
$$= \begin{pmatrix} -0.4782 \\ 0.1773 \end{pmatrix}$$
$$\mathbf{b}_{21}^{(1)} = B_{23}Q_{31}C_{13}(Q_{31}\mathbf{b}_1^{(2)} + \mathbf{c}_3) + B_{23}\mathbf{d}_3$$
$$= \begin{pmatrix} 0.4737 \\ -0.0573 \end{pmatrix}$$

IX.

$$W(t) = a_1^{(1)}\delta(t) - a_2^{(1)}\delta'(t) + b_1^{(1)}\delta(1 - t)$$
$$- b_2^{(1)}\delta'(1 - t) + a_1^{(2)}e^{-\alpha_1 t} + b_1^{(2)}e^{-\alpha_1(1-t)} + W_p(t)$$
$$= -0.4782\delta(t) - 0.1773\delta'(t) + 0.4737\delta(1 - t)$$
$$+ 0.0573\delta'(1 - t) + 0.0861e^{-0.8165t} + 0.0917e^{-0.8165(1-t)} + 0.8674 \sin\left(\frac{\pi}{2}t\right)$$

Most of the remainder of this section will be devoted to showing that the above-described computational procedure actually does yield the solution of the integral equation.

As a preliminary we observe that Green's function for the self-adjoint singular boundary-value problem

$$L_{(\gamma)}y = \frac{d^2y}{dt^2} - \gamma^2 y$$

$$y \to 0 \text{ as } t \to \pm \infty \tag{8.4-37}$$

is given by

$$K(t,\tau) = -\frac{1}{2\gamma} e^{-\gamma|t-\tau|} \tag{8.4-38}$$

It is readily verified that this function $K(t,\tau)$ satisfies the relationship

$$L_{(\gamma)}K(t,\tau) = \delta(t - \tau)$$

as is required by a Green's function. Hence, from Eq. (8.4-37) and (8.4-38), we have

$$L_{(\gamma)}e^{-\gamma|t-\tau|} = -2\gamma\delta(t - \tau) \tag{8.4-39}$$

By combining Eqs. (8.4-1) and (8.4-2), our integral equation may be written in the form

$$f(t) = \sum_{k=1}^{N} \phi_k \int_0^T W(\tau)e^{-\gamma_k|t-\tau|} \, d\tau \qquad 0 \leq t \leq T \tag{8.4-40}$$

We now apply the operation

$$L_t = \prod_{k=1}^{N} L_{(\gamma_k)} = \prod_{k=1}^{N} (p^2 - \gamma_k^2) \tag{8.4-41}$$

to both sides of Eq. (8.4-40) in the open interval $0 < t < T$ to obtain

$$\prod_{k=1}^{N} (p^2 - \gamma_k^2)f(t) = -2 \sum_{k=1}^{N} \gamma_k \phi_k \prod_{r=1}^{k} (p^2 - \gamma_r^2)W(t)$$

$$0 < t < T \tag{8.4-42}$$

By comparing Eqs. (8.4-42) and (8.4-4) we see that $f(t)$ and $W(t)$ are related by

$$\pi G(-p^2)W(t) = f(t) \qquad 0 < t < T \tag{8.4-43}$$

Equation (8.4-43) provides us with a linear constant-coefficient differential equation to be solved for $W(t)$. Thus, the general solution of Eq. (8.4-43) consists of the complete solution of the homogeneous equation

$$\pi G(-p^2)W_h(t) = 0 \qquad 0 < t < T \tag{8.4-44}$$

together with a particular solution $W_p(t)$ of Eq. (8.4-43). Hence, we have

$$W(t) = \sum_{j=1}^{m} (a_j^{(2)}e^{-\alpha_j t} + b_j^{(2)}e^{-\alpha_j(T-t)}) + W_p(t) \qquad 0 < t < T \tag{8.4-45}$$

where $\alpha_1, \alpha_2, \ldots, \alpha_m$ are the roots with positive real part of

$$G(-\alpha^2) = 0 \tag{8.4-46}$$

According to the discussion given in Appendix I, the solution of the original integral equation must contain n δ-function terms at each of the end points of the interval $t = 0$ and $t = T$ where n, m, and N are related by Eq. (8.4-6). Therefore, the solution of the integral equation may be sought in the form specified by Eq. (8.4-35) where the constant coefficients $a_i^{(1)}$, $b_i^{(1)}$, $a_j^{(2)}$, $b_j^{(2)}$ are to be determined.

To obtain these constants, we substitute this expression for $W(t)$ into Eq. (8.4-40) and require that the resulting equation be identically satisfied for all t in the interval $(0,T)$. We have

$$
\begin{aligned}
f(t) - \int_0^T W_p(\tau)\phi(t-\tau)\,d\tau = \sum_{k=1}^N \phi_k \Bigg(& \sum_{i=1}^n a_i^{(1)}\gamma_k^{i-1}e^{-\gamma_k t} \\
& + \sum_{i=1}^n b_i^{(1)}\gamma_k^{i-1}e^{-\gamma_k(T-t)} + \sum_{j=1}^m \frac{a_j^{(2)}}{\alpha_j - \gamma_k}e^{-\gamma_k t} \\
& - \sum_{j=1}^m \frac{2\gamma_k a_j^{(2)}}{\alpha_j^2 - \gamma_k^2}e^{-\alpha_j t} - \sum_{j=1}^m \frac{a_j^{(2)}e^{-\alpha_j T}}{\alpha_j + \gamma_k}e^{-\gamma_k(T-t)} \\
& - \sum_{j=1}^m \frac{b_j^{(2)}e^{-\alpha_j T}}{\alpha_j + \gamma_k}e^{-\gamma_k t} - \sum_{j=1}^m \frac{2\gamma_k b_j^{(2)}e^{-\alpha_j T}}{\alpha_j^2 - \gamma_k^2}e^{\alpha_j t} \\
& + \sum_{j=1}^m \frac{b_j^{(2)}}{\alpha_j - \gamma_k}e^{-\gamma_k(T-t)} \Bigg)
\end{aligned} \tag{8.4-47}
$$

The coefficients of $e^{-\alpha_j t}$ and $e^{\alpha_j t}$ vanish because α_j is a root of Eq. (8.4-46). Furthermore, if Eq. (8.4-47) is to be an identity in t, we must have the left-hand side of Eq. (8.4-47) expressible by the same functional form in t as the right-hand side. Thus, we must have

$$f(t) - \int_0^T W_p(t)\phi(t-\tau)\,d\tau = \sum_{k=1}^N \phi_k(c_k e^{-\gamma_k t} + d_k e^{-\gamma_k(T-t)}) \tag{8.4-48}$$

where the constants c_k and d_k depend upon the particular functions $f(t)$ and $\phi(t)$.

Substituting Eq. (8.4-48) into Eq. (8.4-47) and equating the coefficients of $e^{-\gamma_k t}$ and $e^{-\gamma_k(T-t)}$, we obtain

$$
\sum_{i=1}^n a_i^{(1)}\gamma_k^{i-1} + \sum_{j=1}^m \left(\frac{a_j^{(2)}}{\alpha_j - \gamma_k} - \frac{b_j^{(2)}e^{-\alpha_j T}}{\alpha_j + \gamma_k} \right) = c_k
$$

$$
\sum_{i=1}^n b_i^{(1)}\gamma_k^{i-1} + \sum_{j=1}^m \left(\frac{b_j^{(2)}}{\alpha_j - \gamma_k} - \frac{a_j^{(2)}e^{-\alpha_j T}}{\alpha_j + \gamma_k} \right) = d_k
$$

$$\tag{8.4-49}$$

$$k = 1, 2, \ldots, N$$

which is a set of $2N$ linear algebraic equations to be solved for the a's and b's. These equations may be written more conveniently in matrix form as follows:

$$A_{NN}\mathbf{a}_N - S_{NN}\mathbf{b}_N = \mathbf{c}_N$$
$$-S_{NN}\mathbf{a}_N + A_{NN}\mathbf{b}_N = \mathbf{d}_N \tag{8.4-50}$$

where

$$A_{NN} \equiv \left\| \begin{array}{cc} V_{nn}^{(1)} & M_{nm}^{(1)} \\ V_{mn}^{(2)} & M_{mm}^{(2)} \end{array} \right\| \tag{8.4-51}$$

and

$$S_{NN} = \left\| \begin{array}{cc} O_{nn}^{(1)} & Q_{nm}^{(1)} \\ O_{mn}^{(2)} & Q_{mm}^{(2)} \end{array} \right\| = \left\| O_{Nn} \quad Q_{Nm} \right\| \tag{8.4-52}$$

are two $N \times N$ matrices which have been partitioned into submatrices as indicated. These submatrices are defined by

$$V_{nn}^{(1)} \equiv \|\gamma_i^{j-1}\| \qquad M_{nm}^{(1)} \equiv \left\| \frac{1}{\alpha_j - \gamma_i} \right\|$$
$$V_{mn}^{(2)} \equiv \|\rho_i^{j\ 1}\| \qquad M_{mm}^{(2)} \equiv \left\| \frac{1}{\alpha_j - \rho_i} \right\| \tag{8.4-53}$$

and

$$O_{nn}^{(1)} \equiv \|0\| \qquad Q_{nm}^{(1)} \equiv \left\| \frac{e^{-\alpha_i T}}{\alpha_j + \gamma_i} \right\|$$
$$O_{mn}^{(2)} \equiv \|0\| \qquad Q_{mm}^{(2)} \equiv \left\| \frac{e^{-\alpha_i T}}{\alpha_j + \rho_i} \right\| \tag{8.4-54}$$

The column vectors $\mathbf{a}_N$ and $\mathbf{b}_N$ are partitioned as follows:

$$\mathbf{a}_N \equiv \left\| \begin{array}{c} \mathbf{a}_n^{(1)} \\ \mathbf{a}_m^{(2)} \end{array} \right\| \qquad \mathbf{b}_N \equiv \left\| \begin{array}{c} \mathbf{b}_n^{(1)} \\ \mathbf{b}_m^{(2)} \end{array} \right\| \tag{8.4-55}$$

where the subvectors are defined by Eq. (8.4-36).

The vectors $\mathbf{c}_N$ and $\mathbf{d}_N$ are given by

$$\mathbf{c}_N = \{c_i\} \qquad \mathbf{d}_N = \{d_i\} \tag{8.4-56}$$

The inverse of the nonsingular square matrix A_{NN} may be obtained explicitly, as shown in Appendix J. We denote this inverse by the following partitioned matrix:

$$A_{NN}^{-1} = \left\| \begin{array}{cc} B_{nn}^{(1)} & B_{nm}^{(2)} \\ C_{mn}^{(1)} & C_{mm}^{(2)} \end{array} \right\| = \left\| \begin{array}{c} B_{nN} \\ C_{mN} \end{array} \right\| \tag{8.4-57}$$

By premultiplying each of Eqs. (8.4-50) by A_{NN}^{-1} we may reduce these equations to two separate sets of N linear algebraic equations to be solved for $\mathbf{a}_N$ and $\mathbf{b}_N$. We obtain

$$[I_{NN} - (A_{NN}^{-1}S_{NN})^2]\mathbf{a}_N = (A_{NN}^{-1}\mathbf{c}_N + S_{NN}A_{NN}^{-1}\mathbf{d}_N)$$
$$[I_{NN} - (A_{NN}^{-1}S_{NN})^2]\mathbf{b}_N = (A_{NN}^{-1}\mathbf{d}_N + S_{NN}A_{NN}^{-1}\mathbf{c}_N) \tag{8.4-58}$$

where I_{NN} is the $N \times N$ identity matrix. Thus, by knowing A_{NN}^{-1} we may replace the system of algebraic equations of order $2N$ by two uncoupled sets of algebraic equations each of order N and each having identical coefficient matrices.

From Eqs. (8.4-52) and (8.4-57) we have

$$(A_{NN}^{-1}S_{NN}) = \left\| \begin{matrix} O_{nn} & B_{nN}Q_{Nm} \\ O_{mn} & C_{mN}Q_{Nm} \end{matrix} \right\| \tag{8.4-59}$$

and

$$(A_{NN}^{-1}S_{NN})^2 = \left\| \begin{matrix} O_{nn} & B_{nN}Q_{Nm}C_{mN}Q_{Nm} \\ O_{mn} & (C_{mN}Q_{Nm})^2 \end{matrix} \right\| \tag{8.4-60}$$

Thus

$$I_{NN} - (A_{NN}^{-1}S_{NN})^2 = \left\| \begin{matrix} I_{nn} & B_{nN}Q_{Nm}C_{mN}Q_{Nm} \\ O_{mn} & I_{mm} - (C_{mN}Q_{Nm})^2 \end{matrix} \right\| \tag{8.4-61}$$

Hence, from Eqs. (8.4-57), (8.4-61), and

$$A_{NN}^{-1}S_{NN}A_{NN}^{-1} = \left\| \begin{matrix} B_{nN}Q_{Nm}C_{mN} \\ C_{mN}Q_{Nm}C_{mN} \end{matrix} \right\| \tag{8.4-62}$$

the pair of Nth-order equations (8.4-58) may be written in the form given by Eqs. (8.4-31) to (8.4-34). Therefore, to obtain the quantities $\mathbf{a}_N$ and $\mathbf{b}_N$, we need only invert a single $m \times m$ matrix

$$H_{mm} = \left\| I_{mm} - (C_{mN}Q_{Nm})^2 \right\|^{-1} \tag{8.4-63}$$

The vectors $\mathbf{a}_N$ and $\mathbf{b}_N$ are then determined immediately by matrix addition and multiplication.

In order to complete the proof, it is necessary to show that the vectors $\mathbf{c}_N$ and $\mathbf{d}_N$ may be obtained from Eqs. (8.4-29) and (8.4-30). From Eqs. (8.4-2), (8.4-39), and (8.4-41) we observe that

$$L_t \phi(t - \tau) = M_t \delta(t - \tau) \tag{8.4-64}$$

where the operators L_t and M_t are defined by Eqs. (8.4-41) and

$$M_t = -2 \sum_{k=1}^{N} \gamma_k \phi_k \prod_{r=1}^{k} (p^2 - \gamma_r^2) \tag{8.4-65}$$

respectively.

In the following argument we shall have occasion to apply Green's formula for a self-adjoint constant-coefficient linear differential operator. Green's formula states that for such an operator L and any two functions $u(t)$ and $v(t)$ we have

$$\int_0^T [vL(u) - uL(v)] \, dt = [P(u,v)]_0^T \tag{8.4-66}$$

where $P(u,v)$, called the bilinear concomitant,[1] is a given function which

[1] E. L. Ince, "Ordinary Differential Equations," Dover Publications, New York.

is bilinear in u, v and their derivatives. For example, the bilinear concomitant for the self-adjoint constant-coefficient linear differential operator

$$L = p_{2n} + p_{2n-2}\frac{d^2}{dt^2} + \cdots + p_2\frac{d^{2n-2}}{dt^{2n-2}} + p_0\frac{d^{2n}}{dt^{2n}} \qquad (8.4\text{-}67)$$

is

$$
\begin{aligned}
P(u,v) = & -u\left(p_{2n-2}\frac{dv}{dt} + p_{2n-4}\frac{d^3v}{dt^3} + \cdots + p_0\frac{d^{2n-1}v}{dt^{2n-1}}\right) \\
& + \frac{du}{dt}\left(p_{2n-2}v + p_{2n-4}\frac{d^2v}{dt^2} + \cdots + p_0\frac{d^{2n-2}v}{dt^{2n-2}}\right) \\
& - \frac{d^2u}{dt^2}\left(p_{2n-4}\frac{dv}{dt} + p_{2n-6}\frac{d^3v}{dt^3} + \cdots + p_0\frac{d^{2n-3}v}{dt^{2n-3}}\right) \\
& + \frac{d^3u}{dt^3}\left(p_{2n-4}v + p_{2n-6}\frac{d^2v}{dt^2} + \cdots + p_0\frac{d^{2n-4}v}{dt^{2n-4}}\right) \\
& - \cdots \cdots \cdots \\
& - \frac{d^{2n-2}u}{dt^{2n-2}}\left(p_0\frac{dv}{dt}\right) + \frac{d^{2n-1}u}{dt^{2n-1}}(p_0v) \qquad (8.4\text{-}68)
\end{aligned}
$$

Using matrix notation, Eq. (8.4-68) may be written as

$$P(u,v) = \mathbf{u}_{2n}(t)P_{2n,2n}\mathbf{v}_{2n}(t) = \mathbf{v}_{2n}(t)P_{2n,2n}\mathbf{u}_{2n}(t) \qquad (8.4\text{-}69)$$

where

$$\mathbf{u}_{2n}(t) = \left\{(-1)^i\frac{d^{i-1}u}{dt^{i-1}}\right\} \qquad \mathbf{v}_{2n}(t) = \left\{\frac{d^{i-1}v}{dt^{i-1}}\right\} \qquad (8.4\text{-}70)$$

and $P_{2n,2n}$ is a symmetrical triangular matrix of the form

$$
P_{2n,2n} = \left\|
\begin{array}{ccccccccc}
0 & p_{2n-2} & 0 & p_{2n-4} & \cdots & 0 & p_2 & 0 & p_0 \\
p_{2n-2} & 0 & p_{2n-4} & 0 & \cdots & p_2 & 0 & p_0 & 0 \\
0 & p_{2n-4} & 0 & p_{2n-6} & \cdots & 0 & p_0 & 0 & 0 \\
p_{2n-4} & 0 & p_{2n-6} & 0 & \cdots & p_0 & 0 & 0 & 0 \\
\cdots & \cdots & \cdots & & & & & & \\
0 & p_0 & 0 & 0 & \cdots & 0 & 0 & 0 & 0 \\
p_0 & 0 & 0 & 0 & \cdots & 0 & 0 & 0 & 0
\end{array}
\right\|
$$

$$(8.4\text{-}71)$$

We will now show that

$$
\begin{aligned}
f(t) - \int_0^T W_p(\tau)\phi(t-\tau)\,d\tau \\
= \sum_{k=1}^{N}\left[\frac{P_L[f(\tau),\ \phi_k e^{-\gamma_k|t-\tau|}] - P_M[W_p(\tau),\ \phi_k e^{-\gamma_k|t-\tau|}]}{2\gamma_k\phi_k\displaystyle\prod_{r=1}^{k}(\gamma_k^2 - \gamma_r^2)}\right]_0^T \qquad (8.4\text{-}72)
\end{aligned}
$$

where P_L and P_M are the bilinear concomitants for the operators L_t and

M_t. For this purpose, we first observe that Eq. (8.4-43) may be written as

$$L_t f(t) = M_t W_p(t) \qquad 0 < t < T \tag{8.4-73}$$

so that

$$\int_0^T \phi_k e^{-\gamma_k |t-\tau|} L_\tau f(\tau) \, d\tau = \int_0^T \phi_k e^{-\gamma_k |t-\tau|} M_\tau W_p(\tau) \, d\tau \tag{8.4-74}$$

Using Green's formula (8.4-66), Eq. (8.4-74) becomes

$$\int_0^T \phi_k e^{-\gamma_k |t-\tau|} L_\tau f(\tau) \, d\tau = P_M[W_p(\tau), \phi_k e^{-\gamma_k |t-\tau|}]_0^T$$
$$+ \int_0^T W_p(\tau) M_\tau \phi_k e^{-\gamma_k |t-\tau|} \, d\tau \tag{8.4-75}$$

Alternatively, we may write

$$\int_0^T \phi_k e^{-\gamma_k |t-\tau|} L_\tau f(\tau) \, d\tau = P_L[f(\tau), \phi_k e^{-\gamma_k |t-\tau|}]_0^T$$
$$+ \int_0^T f(\tau) L_\tau \phi_k e^{-\gamma_k |t-\tau|} \, d\tau \tag{8.4-76}$$

From Eqs. (8.4-39) and (8.4-41) the second term on the right-hand side of Eq. (8.4-76) becomes

$$\int_0^T f(\tau) L_\tau \phi_k e^{-\gamma_k |t-\tau|} \, d\tau = \int_0^T f(\tau) \left[-2\gamma_k \phi_k \prod_{r=1}^{N}{}^{k} (p^2 - \gamma_r^2) \delta(t - \tau) \right] d\tau$$
$$= -2\gamma_k \phi_k \prod_{r=1}^{N}{}^{k} (p^2 - \gamma_r^2) f(t) \tag{8.4-77}$$

By combining Eqs. (8.4-75) to (8.4-77) we find that

$$\int_0^T W_p(\tau) M_\tau \phi_k e^{-\gamma_k |t-\tau|} \, d\tau = -P_M[W_p(\tau), \phi_k e^{-\gamma_k |t-\tau|}]_0^T$$
$$+ P_L[f(\tau), \phi_k e^{-\gamma_k |t-\tau|}]_0^T - 2\gamma_k \phi_k \prod_{r=1}^{N}{}^{k} (p^2 - \gamma_r^2) f(t) \tag{8.4-78}$$

To obtain the result expressed by Eq. (8.4-72), we divide Eq. (8.4-78) by $2\gamma_k \phi_k \prod_{r=1}^{N}{}^{k} (\gamma_k^2 - \gamma_r^2)$ and sum on k from 1 to N. It now remains to show that

$$\sum_{k=1}^{N} \prod_{r=1}^{N}{}^{k} \frac{p^2 - \gamma_r^2}{\gamma_k^2 - \gamma_r^2} = 1 \tag{8.4-79}$$

and

$$\sum_{k=1}^{N} \frac{M_\tau \phi_k e^{-\gamma_k |t-\tau|}}{2\gamma_k \phi_k \prod_{r=1}^{N}{}^{k} (\gamma_k^2 - \gamma_r^2)} = -\phi(t - \tau) \tag{8.4-80}$$

To prove Eq. (8.4-79), we define the following analytic function of the complex variable z.

$$F(z) = \prod_{r=1}^{N} \frac{p^2 - \gamma_r^2}{(p^2 - z)(z - \gamma_r^2)} \qquad (8.4\text{-}81)$$

which has simple poles at $z = p^2, \gamma_1^2, \gamma_2^2, \ldots, \gamma_N^2$ and is analytic at infinity. The residues at each of these poles are easily found to be

$$R(p^2) = -1 \qquad R(\gamma_k^2) = \prod_{r=1}^{N}{}^{k} \frac{p^2 - \gamma_r^2}{\gamma_k^2 - \gamma_r^2} \qquad (8.4\text{-}82)$$

If we now integrate $F(z)$ around a closed contour in the z plane which encloses all the poles of $F(z)$, the result is

$$\oint_C F(z)\, dz = 2\pi j \left[R(p^2) + \sum_{k=1}^{N} R(\gamma_k^2) \right] \qquad (8.4\text{-}83)$$

However, since $F(z)$ is analytic at infinity, this integral is zero, and Eq. (8.4-79) is established.

To prove Eq. (8.4-80), we use Eq. (8.4-65) to write the left-hand side of (8.4-80) as

$$\sum_{k=1}^{N} \frac{-2 \displaystyle\sum_{s=1}^{N} \gamma_s \phi_s \prod_{r=1}^{N}{}^{s} (p^2 - \gamma_r^2)}{2\gamma_k \phi_k \displaystyle\prod_{r=1}^{N}{}^{k} (\gamma_k^2 - \gamma_r^2)} \phi_k e^{-\gamma_k |t - \tau|}$$

$$= -\sum_{s=1}^{N} \frac{\gamma_s \phi_s}{(p^2 - \gamma_s^2)} \sum_{k=1}^{N} \frac{\displaystyle\prod_{r=1}^{N} (p^2 - \gamma_r^2)}{\gamma_k \displaystyle\prod_{r=1}^{N}{}^{k} (\gamma_k^2 - \gamma_r^2)} e^{-\gamma_k |t - \tau|} \qquad (8.4\text{-}84)$$

Since $\displaystyle\prod_{r=1}^{N} (p^2 - \gamma_r^2) e^{-\gamma_k |t-\tau|} = -2\gamma_k \prod_{r=1}^{N}{}^{k} (p^2 - \gamma_r^2) \delta(t - \tau)$

and $\dfrac{-2\gamma_s \delta(t - \tau)}{p^2 - \gamma_s^2} = e^{-\gamma_s |t - \tau|}$

the right-hand side of Eq. (8.4-84) may be written as

$$-\sum_{s=1}^{N} \phi_s \sum_{k=1}^{N} \prod_{r=1}^{N}{}^{k} \frac{p^2 - \gamma_r^2}{\gamma_k^2 - \gamma_r^2} e^{-\gamma_s |t - \tau|}$$

which, from Eq. (8.4-79), becomes

$$-\sum_{s=1}^{N} \phi_s e^{-\gamma_s|t-\tau|} = -\phi(t-\tau)$$

This establishes Eq. (8.4-80) and, finally, the result stated in Eq. (8.4-72). By comparing Eqs. (8.4-72) and (8.4-48) we see that

$$c_k = \left. \frac{P_M[W_p(\tau), e^{\gamma_k \tau}] - P_L[f(\tau), e^{\gamma_k \tau}]}{2\gamma_k \phi_k \displaystyle\prod_{r=1}^{k} (\gamma_k^2 - \gamma_r^2)} \right|_{\tau=0} \tag{8.4-85}$$

$$d_k = \left. \frac{P_L[f(\tau), e^{-\gamma_k(\tau-T)}] - P_M[W_p(\tau), e^{-\gamma_k(\tau-T)}]}{2\gamma_k \phi_k \displaystyle\prod_{r=1}^{k} (\gamma_k^2 - \gamma_r^2)} \right|_{\tau=T} \tag{8.4-86}$$

In terms of the coefficients of the spectral density function the operators L_t and M_t may be written as

$$L_t = \frac{d^{2N}}{dt^{2N}} - \lambda_2 \frac{d^{2N-1}}{dt^{2N-1}} + \cdots + (-1)^N \lambda_{2N} \tag{8.4-87}$$

$$M_t = (-1)^n \left[\theta_0 \frac{d^{2m}}{dt^{2m}} - \theta_2 \frac{d^{2m-1}}{dt^{2m-1}} + \cdots + (-1)^m \theta_{2m} \right] \tag{8.4-88}$$

Thus, by using Eqs. (8.4-69) to (8.4-71), we find

$$P_M[W_p(\tau), e^{\gamma_k \tau}]\Big|_{\tau=0} = \boldsymbol{\gamma}_{2m}(k) \Theta_{2m,2m} \Delta_{2m,2m}^{(2)} \mathbf{w}_{2m}(0) \tag{8.4-89}$$

$$P_L[f(\tau), e^{\gamma_k \tau}]\Big|_{\tau=0} = \boldsymbol{\gamma}_{2N}(k) \Lambda_{2N,2N} \Delta_{2N,2N}^{(2)} \mathbf{f}_{2N}(0) \tag{8.4-90}$$

$$P_L[f(\tau), e^{-\gamma_k(\tau-T)}]\Big|_{\tau=T} = \boldsymbol{\gamma}_{2N}(k) \Lambda_{2N,2N} \mathbf{f}_{2N}(T) \tag{8.4-91}$$

$$P_M[W_p(\tau), e^{-\gamma_k(\tau-T)}]\Big|_{\tau=T} = \boldsymbol{\gamma}_{2m}(k) \Theta_{2m,2m} \mathbf{w}_{2m}(T) \tag{8.4-92}$$

where $\qquad \boldsymbol{\gamma}_{2m}(k) = \{\gamma_k^{i-1}\} \qquad \boldsymbol{\gamma}_{2N}(k) = \{\gamma_k^{i-1}\} \tag{8.4-93}$

The other vectors and matrices appearing in Eqs. (8.4-89) to (8.4-92) are defined by Eqs. (8.4-19) to (8.4-23) and (8.4-28). The expressions for the vectors $\mathbf{c}_k$ and $\mathbf{d}_k$, as given in Eqs. (8.4-29) and (8.4-30), follow immediately from the above calculations together with Eqs. (8.4-85) and (8.4-86).

Before closing this section it is worthwhile to point out several important limiting cases of our solution.

Case I. $\qquad m = 0 \qquad n = N$

Equations (8.4-50) reduce to

$$V_{nn}^{(1)}\mathbf{a}_n = \mathbf{c}_n \qquad V_{nn}^{(1)}\mathbf{b}_n = \mathbf{d}_n \qquad (8.4\text{-}94)$$

$V_{nn}^{(1)}$ is the Vandermonde matrix whose inverse is given by Eq. (8.4-8). The solution of the integral equation consists entirely of δ-function terms and their derivatives plus the particular integral $W_p(t)$.

The formulas used to obtain the vectors $\mathbf{c}_n$ and $\mathbf{d}_n$ are altered slightly. For this case we have

$$M_t = (-1)^n\theta_0 \qquad (8.4\text{-}95)$$

Therefore $\qquad\qquad L_t\phi(t - \tau) = (-1)^n\theta_0\delta(t - \tau) \qquad (8.4\text{-}96)$

and $\qquad\qquad\qquad L_tf(t) = (-1)^n\theta_0W_p(t) \qquad (8.4\text{-}97)$

Now

$$\int_0^T \phi(t - \tau)L_\tau f(\tau)\, d\tau = (-1)^n\theta_0 \int_0^T \phi(t - \tau)W_p(\tau)\, d\tau$$
$$= P_L[f(\tau),\phi(t - \tau)]_0^T + (-1)^n\theta_0 f(t) \qquad (8.4\text{-}98)$$

Hence

$$f(t) - \int_0^T W_p(\tau)\phi(t - \tau)\, d\tau = \frac{(-1)^n}{\theta_0} P_L[f(\tau),\phi(t - \tau)]_T^0 \qquad (8.4\text{-}99)$$

and, thus,

$$c_k = \frac{(-1)^n}{\theta_0} P_L[f(\tau),e^{\gamma_k\tau}]\Big|_{\tau=0} \qquad (8.4\text{-}100)$$

$$d_k = \frac{(-1)^n}{\theta_0} P_L[f(\tau),e^{-\gamma_k(\tau-T)}]\Big|_{\tau=T} \qquad (8.4\text{-}101)$$

Using Eqs. (8.4-90) and (8.4-91), we have

$$\mathbf{c}_n = \frac{(-1)^n}{\theta_0} \Gamma_{n,2n}\Lambda_{2n,2n} \Delta_{2n,2n}^{(2)}\mathbf{f}_{2n}(0) \qquad (8.4\text{-}102)$$

$$\mathbf{d}_n = \frac{-(-1)^n}{\theta_0} \Gamma_{n,2n}\Lambda_{2n,2n}\mathbf{f}_{2n}(T) \qquad (8.4\text{-}103)$$

Case II. $\qquad m = N \qquad n = 0$

Equations (8.4-50) reduce to

$$M_{mm}^{(2)}\mathbf{a}_m = \mathbf{c}_m \qquad M_{mm}^{(2)}\mathbf{b}_m = \mathbf{d}_m \qquad (8.4\text{-}104)$$

The inverse of the matrix $M_{mm}^{(2)}$ is given by Eq. (8.4-10).

Case III. $\qquad m = N - 1 \qquad n = 1$

This is the case which is most likely to arise if the correlation function is obtained empirically and approximated by a series of exponentials in the manner discussed in Sec. 7.5. The matrix A_{NN} then has the same form as the matrix M defined by Eq. (7.5-15). The inverse of A_{NN} is obtained from Eqs. (7.5-17) and (7.5-18). In terms of the present notation we have

$$B_{1N} = \left\| \frac{\displaystyle\prod_{r=1}^{m} (\alpha_r - \gamma_j)}{\displaystyle\prod_{s=1}^{N}{}^{j} (\gamma_s - \gamma_j)} \right\| \tag{8.4-105}$$

$$C_{mN} = \left\| \prod_{r=1}^{N}{}^{j} \left(\frac{\gamma_r - \alpha_i}{\gamma_r - \gamma_j} \right) \frac{\displaystyle\prod_{s=1}^{m} (\alpha_s - \gamma_j)}{\displaystyle\prod_{s=1}^{m}{}^{i} (\alpha_s - \alpha_i)} \right\| \tag{8.4-106}$$

These matrices are, of course, identical with the ones computed from Eqs. (8.4-15) to (8.4-18) for the special case considered. However, the computations indicated by Eqs. (8.4-105) and (8.4-106) are much more readily performed.

Case IV. $\qquad\qquad\qquad T \to \infty$

As discussed in the earlier sections of this chapter, T is the time interval during which our predictor is permitted to make observations. In the limiting case, $T \to \infty$, the entire past history of the signal and noise data are available to the predictor. Furthermore, as might be expected, the computations to be performed in computing the optimal weighting function are considerably reduced.

From Eqs. (8.4-52) and (8.4-54) we see that in the limit of increasing T we have $S_{NN} = 0$. Similarly, from Eq. (8.4-86) and the fact that $f(t)$ and $W_p(t)$, together with their derivatives, must tend to zero as t increases, we have $\mathbf{d}_N = 0$. Therefore, Eqs. (8.4-50) reduce to

$$A_{NN}\mathbf{a}_N = \mathbf{c}_N \qquad \mathbf{b}_N = \{0\} \tag{8.4-107}$$

The solution of the integral equation is then

$$W(t) = \sum_{i=1}^{n} a_i^{(1)} \delta^{(i-1)}(t) + \sum_{j=1}^{m} a_j^{(2)} e^{-\alpha_j t} + W_p(t) \tag{8.4-108}$$

where
$$\mathbf{a}_n^{(1)} = B_{nN}\mathbf{c}_N \qquad \mathbf{a}_m^{(2)} = C_{mN}\mathbf{c}_N \tag{8.4-109}$$

Case V. *Pure Prediction.* For the special problem in which the predictor is required to predict a random signal in the presence of a random noise, the integral equation to be solved is

$$\psi(t + t_p) = \int_0^T W(\tau)\phi(t - \tau)\,d\tau \qquad 0 \leqq t \leqq T \tag{8.4-110}$$

where $\phi(\tau)$ and $\psi(\tau)$ are defined by Eqs. (8.2-17) and (8.2-18) and t_p is the prediction time.   In terms of the notation of this section we may write

$$\phi(\tau) = \sum_{k=1}^{N} \phi_k e^{-\gamma_k|\tau|}$$

$$\psi(\tau) = \sum_{u=1}^{q} \phi_u e^{-\gamma_u|\tau|}$$

(8.4-111)

where $q \leqq N$.

From Eq. (8.4-42) we see that $W_p(t) = 0$ and, therefore,

$$\mathbf{c}_N = \left\| \begin{matrix} \mathbf{c}_q \\ \mathbf{c}_{N-q} \end{matrix} \right\| \qquad \mathbf{d}_N = \{0\} \qquad (8.4\text{-}112)$$

where $\qquad \mathbf{c}_q = \{e^{-\gamma_i t_p}\} \qquad \mathbf{c}_{N-q} = \{0\} \qquad (8.4\text{-}113)$

The Wiener theory, discussed in Chap. 7, is a combination of the two special cases IV and V.

8.5   The Integral Equation for the Nonstationary Case

In Sec. 8.4 we described a computational procedure for solving the integral equation (8.4-1).   When the associated random process has non-stationary statistical characteristics, the solution is considerably more complex.   Here we shall discuss the solution of

$$f(t) = \int_0^T W(\tau)\phi(t,\tau) \, d\tau \qquad 0 \leqq t \leqq T \qquad (8.5\text{-}1)$$

where $\phi(t,\tau)$ is the correlation function of a nonstationary random process $\{y(t)\}$.   We shall assume that the process $\{y(t)\}$ is obtained from a white noise $\{x(t)\}$ by use of a linear time-varying filter described by

$$L_t y(t) = M_t x(t) \qquad (8.5\text{-}2)$$

where $\qquad L_t y(t) = \sum_{k=0}^{N} \beta_k(t) \frac{d^{N-k} y}{dt^{N-k}} \qquad (8.5\text{-}3)$

$$M_t x(t) = \sum_{s=0}^{m} \mu_s(t) \frac{d^{m-s} x}{dt^{m-s}} \qquad (8.5\text{-}4)$$

We shall further assume that $N > m$ and the coefficients $\beta_k(t)$ and $\mu_s(t)$ have as many continuous derivatives as we require.

It is to be noted that in one sense the assumptions made concerning $\phi(t,\tau)$ are somewhat more restrictive than the corresponding ones made in Sec. 8.4.   If we are given an arbitrary correlation function for a stationary process (e.g., one obtained from empirical data), it has been shown previously how this correlation function can be approximated by a sum

of negative exponential functions.   Thus the considerations of Sec. 8.4
are applicable to a very broad class of stationary problems.   No corresponding technique appears to have been developed for an arbitrary
nonstationary correlation function, so that it is not apparent in general
how one can determine a white noise $x(t)$ and differential operators
L_t and M_t such that (8.5-2) to (8.5-5) are valid.

A commonly occurring situation is one in which $y(t) = s(t) + n(t)$,
where $s(t)$ and $n(t)$ can each be regarded as arising from the passage of
separate white-noise signals through suitable variable-parameter filters.
Thus ϕ_{ss} and ϕ_{nn} may themselves satisfy the required conditions.   Even
here, however, it is far from clear how a single filter and a single white
noise can be constructed so that $\phi(t,\tau)$, as expressed by the sum (8.2-7)
of autocorrelation and cross-correlation functions, meets our requirements.   Analytically, it is required that

$$\phi(t,\tau) = \int_{-\infty}^{\infty} W(t,\tau_1) W(\tau,\tau_1) \, d\tau_1$$

where $W(t,\tau)$ is the weighting function for some lumped-parameter system
of the form (8.5-2) to (8.5-4).   However, it has not yet been found possible to apply this relation in any useful way to determine $W(t,\tau)$ or the
desired differential operators.

The solution to (8.5-1) may be obtained most conveniently using the
notion of integral operators.   Therefore, before proceeding with the
problem at hand we shall first introduce as much of the concept of integral operators as will be needed.

Given a function of two variables $K(t,\tau)$ and any function $g(t)$, we define
the operation $K(g)$ by

$$K(g)(t) = \int_{-\infty}^{\infty} K(t,\tau)g(\tau) \, d\tau \qquad (8.5\text{-}5)$$

K is called the *integral operator* and $K(t,\tau)$ is referred to as the *kernel*.
The expression $K(g)(t)$ is the function of t resulting from the application
of the operator K to the function g, in the manner indicated.   We define
the adjoint operator K^* as having a kernel $K^*(t,\tau)$ given by

$$K^*(t,\tau) = K(\tau,t) \qquad (8.5\text{-}6)$$

We indicate the result of applying successively two integral operations
K_1 and K_2 to $g(t)$ by

$$(K_2 \circ K_1)(g)(t) = \int_{-\infty}^{\infty} \int_{-\infty}^{\infty} K_2(t,\rho)K_1(\rho,\tau)g(\tau) \, d\rho \, d\tau \qquad (8.5\text{-}7)$$

Comparing this with Eq. (8.5-5), we see that the kernel $(K_2 \circ K_1)(t,\tau)$
for the operator $(K_2 \circ K_1)$ is expressible in terms of the kernels $K_1(t,\tau)$

and $K_2(t,\tau)$ as follows:

$$(K_2 \circ K_1)(t,\tau) = \int_{-\infty}^{\infty} K_2(t,\rho)K_1(\rho,\tau) \, d\rho \qquad (8.5\text{-}8)$$

Obviously, this can be extended to include the composition of any number of integral operators. It is easy to show that integral operators are associative but, in general, do not commute. That is

$$(K_1 \circ K_2) \circ K_3 = K_1 \circ (K_2 \circ K_3) \qquad (8.5\text{-}9)$$
$$K_1 \circ K_2 \neq K_2 \circ K_1 \qquad (8.5\text{-}10)$$

The identity operator δ has the unit-impulse function $\delta(t - \tau)$ for its kernel because

$$\delta(g)(t) = \int_{-\infty}^{\infty} \delta(t - \tau)g(\tau) \, d\tau = g(t) \qquad (8.5\text{-}11)$$

We define the inverse operator K^{-1} by

$$K \circ K^{-1} = K^{-1} \circ K = \delta \qquad (8.5\text{-}12)$$

The adjoint of the composition of two integral operators is expressible in terms of the adjoint of the individual operators as

$$(K_2 \circ K_1)^* = K_1^* \circ K_2^* \qquad (8.5\text{-}13)$$

This follows from the fact that

$$(K_2 \circ K_1)^*(t,\tau) = (K_2 \circ K_1)(\tau,t) = \int_{-\infty}^{\infty} K_2(\tau,\rho)K_1(\rho,t) \, d\rho$$
$$= \int_{-\infty}^{\infty} K_1^*(t,\rho)K_2^*(\rho,\tau) \, d\rho = (K_1^* \circ K_2^*)(t,\tau) \qquad (8.5\text{-}14)$$

Furthermore,

$$(K_1 \circ K_2)^{-1} = K_2^{-1} \circ K_1^{-1} \qquad (8.5\text{-}15)$$

because

$$(K_1 \circ K_2) \circ (K_2^{-1} \circ K_1^{-1}) = K_1 \circ (K_2 \circ K_2^{-1}) \circ K_1^{-1}$$
$$= K_1 \circ K_1^{-1} = \delta \qquad (8.5\text{-}16)$$

It is also easy to show that the adjoint of the inverse operator is identical with the inverse of the adjoint operator. That is,

$$(K^{-1})^* = (K^*)^{-1} \qquad (8.5\text{-}17)$$

which follows from a comparison of

$$(K \circ K^{-1})^* = (K^{-1})^* \circ K^* = \delta^* = \delta$$

and

$$(K^*)^{-1} \circ K^* = \delta$$

We require a few additional facts before proceeding with the solution of the integral equation.

1. The adjoints of the differential expressions (8.5-3) and (8.5-4) are defined by

$$L_t^* y(t) = \sum_{k=0}^{N} (-1)^{N-k} \frac{d^{N-k}}{dt^{N-k}} [\beta_k(t) y(t)]$$

$$M_t^* x(t) = \sum_{s=0}^{m} (-1)^{m-s} \frac{d^{m-s}}{dt^{m-s}} [\mu_s(t) x(t)]$$

(8.5-18)

2. Green's formula states that for any two functions $u(t)$ and $v(t)$ and any linear differential operation L_t, we have

$$\int_a^b [v(t) L_t u(t) - u(t) L_t^* v(t)] \, dt = P_L[u(t), v(t)]_a^b$$

(8.5-19)

where $P_L(u,v)$, called the bilinear concomitant, is the following bilinear form in u, v and their derivatives:

$$
P_L(u,v) = u \left[\beta_{N-1} v - \frac{d}{dt} (\beta_{N-2} v) + \cdots + (-1)^{N-1} \frac{d^{N-1}(\beta_0 v)}{dt^{N-1}} \right]
$$
$$
+ \frac{du}{dt} \left[\beta_{N-2} v - \frac{d}{dt} (\beta_{N-3} v) + \cdots + (-1)^{N-2} \frac{d^{N-2}(\beta_0 v)}{dt^{N-2}} \right]
$$
$$
+ \cdots \cdots \cdots \cdots \cdots \cdots \cdots \cdots \cdots \cdots \cdots
$$
$$
+ \frac{d^{N-1} u}{dt^{N-1}} \beta_0 v
$$

(8.5-20)

3. For any linear differential operator L_t, we have

$$L_t \delta(t - \tau) = L_t \delta(\tau - t)$$

(8.5-21)

since the delta function is an even function of its argument, and,

$$L_t \delta(t - \tau) = L_\tau^* \delta(\tau - t)$$

(8.5-22)

To prove the second relationship, let us consider the following two integrals

$$I_1 = \int_{-\infty}^{\infty} \int_{-\infty}^{\infty} [L_t \delta(t - \tau)] u(t) v(\tau) \, dt \, d\tau$$

$$I_2 = \int_{-\infty}^{\infty} \int_{-\infty}^{\infty} [L_\tau^* \delta(\tau - t)] u(t) v(\tau) \, dt \, d\tau$$

where $u(t)$, $v(\tau)$ are arbitrary functions which vanish, together with their various derivatives, at $t = \pm \infty$. Applying Green's formula we have[1]

$$I_1 = \int_{-\infty}^{\infty} v(\tau) \, d\tau \int_{-\infty}^{\infty} \delta(t - \tau) L_t^* u(t) \, dt = \int_{-\infty}^{\infty} v(\tau) L_\tau^* u(\tau) \, d\tau$$

and $$I_2 = \int_{-\infty}^{\infty} u(t) \, dt \int_{-\infty}^{\infty} \delta(\tau - t) L_\tau v(\tau) \, d\tau = \int_{-\infty}^{\infty} u(t) L_t v(t) \, dt$$

Hence, according to Green's formula $I_1 = I_2$. Since this is true identically for all functions $u(t)$, $v(\tau)$, it follows that Eq. (8.5-22) must hold.

[1] Note that the bilinear concomitant is zero here.

Returning to our original problem, let us associate with the differential operators L_t and M_t the integral operators L and M whose kernels are defined by

$$L(t,\tau) = L_t \delta(t - \tau) = L_\tau^* \delta(\tau - t) \tag{8.5-23}$$
$$M(t,\tau) = M_t \delta(t - \tau) = M_\tau^* \delta(\tau - t) \tag{8.5-24}$$

Then

$$L(g)(t) = \int_{-\infty}^{\infty} L(t,\tau)g(\tau)\, d\tau = \int_{-\infty}^{\infty} [L_\tau^* \delta(\tau - t)]g(\tau)\, d\tau$$
$$= \int_{-\infty}^{\infty} \delta(\tau - t)L_\tau g(\tau)\, d\tau = L_t g(t) \tag{8.5-25}$$

and

$$L^*(g)(t) = \int_{-\infty}^{\infty} L^*(t,\tau)g(\tau)\, d\tau = \int_{-\infty}^{\infty} L(\tau,t)g(\tau)\, d\tau$$
$$= \int_{-\infty}^{\infty} [L_\tau \delta(\tau - t)]g(\tau)\, d\tau = \int_{-\infty}^{\infty} \delta(\tau - t)L_\tau^* g(\tau)\, d\tau = L_t^* g(t) \tag{8.5-26}$$

with similar relations for $M(g)(t)$ and $M^*(g)(t)$.

Let us define $W_1(t,\tau)$ to be the weighting function associated with the differential operator L_t so that

$$L_t W_1(t,\tau) = \delta(t - \tau) \tag{8.5-27}$$

Let W_1 be the integral operator whose kernel is $W_1(t,\tau)$. Then, since

$$(L \circ W_1)(t,\tau) = \int_{-\infty}^{\infty} L(t,\rho)W_1(\rho,\tau)\, d\rho = \int_{-\infty}^{\infty} [L_\rho^* \delta(\rho - t)]W_1(\rho,\tau)\, d\rho$$
$$= \int_{-\infty}^{\infty} \delta(\rho - t)L_\rho W_1(\rho,\tau)\, d\rho$$
$$= \int_{-\infty}^{\infty} \delta(\rho - t)\delta(\rho - \tau)\, d\rho = \delta(t - \tau) \tag{8.5-28}$$

it follows that

$$W_1 = L^{-1} \tag{8.5-29}$$

The differential equation (8.5-2) may be written in terms of integral operators as

$$L(y)(t) = M(x)(t) \tag{8.5-30}$$

Since

$$(L^{-1} \circ L)(y)(t) = \delta(y)(t) = y(t) \tag{8.5-31}$$

we have

$$y(t) = (L^{-1} \circ M)(x)(t) \tag{8.5-32}$$

Equation (8.5-32) may be written using more conventional notation as follows.

$$y(t) = \int_{-\infty}^{\infty} (L^{-1} \circ M)(t,\tau)x(\tau)\, d\tau$$
$$= \int_{-\infty}^{\infty} \int_{-\infty}^{\infty} W_1(t,\rho)[M_\tau^* \delta(\tau - \rho)]x(\tau)\, d\tau\, d\rho$$
$$= \int_{-\infty}^{\infty} \int_{-\infty}^{\infty} W_1(t,\rho)\delta(\tau - \rho)M_\tau x(\tau)\, d\tau\, d\rho$$
$$= \int_{-\infty}^{\infty} W_1(t,\tau)M_\tau x(\tau)\, d\tau \tag{8.5-33}$$

which should be compared with Eq. (5.2-28).

Using Eq. (8.5-32), we have

$$
\begin{aligned}
\phi(t,\tau) &= \overline{y(t)y(\tau)} = \overline{(L^{-1} \circ M)(x)(t)(L^{-1} \circ M)(x)(\tau)} \\
&= \int_{-\infty}^{\infty}\int_{-\infty}^{\infty} (L^{-1} \circ M)(t,\rho)(L^{-1} \circ M)(\tau,s)\overline{x(\rho)x(s)}\ d\rho\ ds \\
&= \int_{-\infty}^{\infty}\int_{-\infty}^{\infty} (L^{-1} \circ M)(t,\rho)(L^{-1} \circ M)(\tau,s)\delta(\rho - s)\ d\rho\ ds \\
&= \int_{-\infty}^{\infty} (L^{-1} \circ M)(t,\rho)(L^{-1} \circ M)(\tau,\rho)\ d\rho \\
&= \int_{-\infty}^{\infty} (L^{-1} \circ M)(t,\rho)(L^{-1} \circ M)^*(\rho,\tau)\ d\rho \\
&= (L^{-1} \circ M) \circ (L^{-1} \circ M)^*(t,\tau) \\
&= (L^{-1} \circ M \circ M^* \circ L^{*-1})(t,\tau) \tag{8.5-34}
\end{aligned}
$$

so that the correlation function $\phi(t,\tau)$ is actually the kernel of the integral operator

$$
\phi = L^{-1} \circ M \circ M^* \circ L^{*-1} \tag{8.5-35}
$$

Since

$$
\begin{aligned}
(L^{-1} \circ M)(t,\tau) &= \int_{-\infty}^{\infty} W_1(t,\rho)M_\rho\delta(\rho - \tau)\ d\rho = \int_{-\infty}^{\infty} \delta(\rho - \tau)M_\rho^* W_1(t,\rho)\ d\rho \\
&= M_\tau^* W_1(t,\tau) \tag{8.5-36}
\end{aligned}
$$

the correlation function may be written more conventionally as

$$
\phi(t,\tau) = \int_{-\infty}^{\infty} [M_\rho^* W_1(t,\rho)][M_\rho^* W_1(\tau,\rho)]\ d\rho \tag{8.5-37}
$$

which may easily be established directly from Eq. (8.5-33) without the use of integral operators.

The inverse of the operator ϕ is

$$
\phi^{-1} = L^* \circ M^{*-1} \circ M^{-1} \circ L \tag{8.5-38}
$$

In an analogous manner to that used in establishing Eq. (8.5-29) we see that

$$
W_2 = M^{-1} \tag{8.5-39}
$$

where W_2 is an integral operator whose kernel $W_2(t,\tau)$ is given by

$$
M_t W_2(t,\tau) = \delta(t - \tau) \tag{8.5-40}
$$

Now $\quad (M^{-1} \circ L)(t,\tau) = \int_{-\infty}^{\infty} W_2(t,\rho)L_\rho\delta(\rho - \tau)\ d\rho = L_\tau^* W_2(t,\tau) \quad (8.5\text{-}41)$

and, similarly,

$$
\begin{aligned}
(L^* \circ M^{*-1})(t,\tau) &= \int_{-\infty}^{\infty} L^*(t,\rho)M^{*-1}(\rho,\tau)\ d\rho = \int_{-\infty}^{\infty} L(\rho,t)M^{-1}(\tau,\rho)\ d\rho \\
&= \int_{-\infty}^{\infty} W_2(\tau,\rho)L_\rho\delta(\rho - t)\ d\rho = \overline{L_t^* W_2(\tau,t)} \tag{8.5-42}
\end{aligned}
$$

Hence, the kernel of the inverse operator ϕ^{-1} may be written as

$$
\phi^{-1}(t,\tau) = \int_{-\infty}^{\infty} L_t^* W_2(\rho,t)L_\tau^* W_2(\rho,\tau)\ d\rho \tag{8.5-43}
$$

The weighting function $W_2(t,\tau)$ has a jump in its $(m - 1)$st derivative and since L_t is a differential operator of order $N > m$ the kernel $\phi^{-1}(t,\tau)$ will contain δ functions and their derivatives.

The advantage of the integral operator concept is evident immediately if we observe that the solution of the integral equation

$$f(t) = \int_{-\infty}^{\infty} \phi(t,\tau) W(\tau) \, d\tau = \phi(W)(t) \qquad -\infty < t < \infty \qquad (8.5\text{-}44)$$

is simply

$$W(t) = \phi^{-1}(f)(t) = \int_{-\infty}^{\infty} \phi^{-1}(t,\tau) f(\tau) \, d\tau \qquad (8.5\text{-}45)$$

where the kernel $\phi^{-1}(t,\tau)$ is obtained from Eq. (8.5-43).

Unfortunately, the problem at hand is not quite so simple because the integral equation (8.5-1) has finite limits. Since the integral expression in (8.5-1) is required to equal $f(t)$ only over the finite interval $0 \leqq t \leqq T$, in seeking to apply Eq. (8.5-45) values of $f(t)$ outside of this interval may be arbitrarily chosen. In particular, we show that by proper selection of $f(t)$ for $t < 0$ and $t > T$ the function $W(t)$ defined by (8.5-45) can be made to vanish for $-\infty < t < 0$ and $T < t < \infty$. A comparison of Eqs. (8.5-44) and (8.5-45) shows that the resulting function $W(t)$ will then in fact satisfy the desired integral equation with finite limits of integration, since

$$f(t) = \int_{-\infty}^{\infty} \phi(t,\tau) W(\tau) \, d\tau = \int_{0}^{T} \phi(t,\tau) W(\tau) \, d\tau \qquad (8.5\text{-}46)$$

The final solution obtained for $W(t)$ may be expressed in the form

$$W(t) = L_t^* u(t) \qquad -\infty < t < \infty \qquad (8.5\text{-}47)$$

in terms of an auxiliary function $u(t)$ satisfying, together with a second such function $z(t)$, the relations

$$\begin{align}
L_t z(t) &= M_t M_t^* u(t) & -\infty < t < \infty & \qquad (8.5\text{-}48) \\
z(t) &= f(t) & 0 \leqq t \leqq T & \qquad (8.5\text{-}49) \\
L_t^* u(t) &= 0 & -\infty < t < 0 & \qquad (8.5\text{-}50) \\
u(t) &= 0 & T < t < \infty & \qquad (8.5\text{-}51)
\end{align}$$

Equations (8.5-47) and (8.5-48) are shown to be sufficient conditions for the relation $z(t) = \phi(W)(t)$ to hold for all values of t. Equations (8.5-50) and (8.5-51) guarantee that the function $W(t)$ thus defined vanishes outside of the interval $0 \leqq t \leqq T$. Finally Eq. (8.5-49) identifies $z(t)$ and hence $\phi(W)(t)$ with the desired function $f(t)$ within this interval. The requirement that $W(t)$ shall possess derivatives of delta functions of order no higher than $N - m - 1$ at $t = 0$ and $t = T$ (cf. Appendix I) is shown to be precisely the condition needed to determine all constants of integration in the differential equations resulting from Eqs. (8.5-48) to (8.5-51). As the first step we establish the relationship $W(t) = \phi^{-1}(z)(t)$ from Eqs. (8.5-47) and (8.5-48). We then proceed to a direct step-by-step synthesis of the desired solution, in a form suited to computation.

From Eqs. (8.5-43) and (8.5-48) we have

$$
\begin{aligned}
\phi^{-1}(z)(t) &= \int_{-\infty}^{\infty} d\rho \int_{-\infty}^{\infty} L_t^* W_2(\rho,t)[L_\tau^* W_2(\rho,\tau)]z(\tau)\, d\tau \\
&= \int_{-\infty}^{\infty} d\rho \int_{-\infty}^{\infty} L_t^* W_2(\rho,t) W_2(\rho,\tau) M_\tau M_\tau^* u(\tau)\, d\tau \\
&= \int_{-\infty}^{\infty} d\rho \int_{-\infty}^{\infty} L_t^* W_2(\rho,t)[M_\tau^* W_2(\rho,\tau)]M_\tau^* u(\tau)\, d\tau \\
&= \int_{-\infty}^{\infty} d\rho \int_{-\infty}^{\infty} L_t^* W_2(\rho,t)\delta(\rho - \tau)M_\tau^* u(\tau)\, d\tau \\
&= \int_{-\infty}^{\infty} L_t^* W_2(\rho,t) M_\rho^* u(\rho)\, d\rho \\
&= L_t^* \int_{-\infty}^{\infty} [M_\rho W_2(\rho,t)]u(\rho)\, d\rho \\
&= L_t^* \int_{-\infty}^{\infty} \delta(\rho - t)u(\rho)\, d\rho \\
&= L_t^* u(t) \quad\quad\quad\quad\quad\quad\quad\quad\quad\quad\quad (8.5\text{-}52)
\end{aligned}
$$

By Eq. (8.5-47) we thus find

$$ \phi^{-1}(z)(t) = W(t) \quad\quad\quad (8.5\text{-}53) $$

as asserted.

Let $\bar{v}_i(t)$ for $i = 0, 1, \ldots, m - 1$ be the m linearly independent solutions to the differential equations

$$ M_t \bar{v}_i(t) = 0 \quad\quad 0 \le t \le T \quad\quad\quad (8.5\text{-}54) $$

under the initial conditions

$$ \bar{v}_i^{(k)}(0) = \delta_{ik} \quad\quad i, k = 0, 1, \ldots, m - 1 \quad\quad\quad (8.5\text{-}55) $$

where δ_{ik} is unity if $i = k$, and zero otherwise. Also let $\bar{v}_p(t)$ satisfy

$$ M_t \bar{v}_p(t) = L_t f(t) \quad\quad 0 \le t \le T \quad\quad\quad (8.5\text{-}56) $$

with

$$ \bar{v}_p^{(k)}(0) = 0 \quad\quad k = 0, 1, \ldots, m - 1 \quad\quad\quad (8.5\text{-}57) $$

Then the function

$$ \bar{v}(t) = \bar{v}_p(t) + \sum_{i=0}^{m-1} c_i \bar{v}_i(t) \quad\quad\quad (8.5\text{-}58) $$

where the constants c_i are arbitrary, satisfies

$$ M_t \bar{v}(t) = L_t f(t) \quad\quad 0 \le t \le T \quad\quad\quad (8.5\text{-}59) $$

Now let $\bar{u}_i(t)$ for $i = 0, 1, \ldots, m - 1$, and $\bar{u}_p(t)$ satisfy

$$M_t^* \bar{u}_i(t) = \bar{v}_i(t) \qquad 0 \leq t \leq T \qquad (8.5\text{-}60)$$
$$M_t^* \bar{u}_p(t) = \bar{v}_p(t) \qquad 0 \leq t \leq T \qquad (8.5\text{-}61)$$

with the boundary conditions

$$\bar{u}_i^{(k)}(T) = \bar{u}_p^{(k)}(T) = 0 \qquad i,k = 0, 1, \ldots, m - 1 \qquad (8.5\text{-}62)$$

Then the function

$$\bar{u}(t) = \bar{u}_p(t) + \sum_{i=0}^{m-1} c_i \bar{u}_i(t) \qquad (8.5\text{-}63)$$

satisfies

$$M_t M_t^* \bar{u}(t) = L_t f(t) \qquad 0 \leq t \leq T \qquad (8.5\text{-}64)$$

and vanishes, together with its first $m - 1$ derivatives, at $t = T$. The differential equations (8.5-60) and (8.5-61) may conveniently be integrated backward from $t = T$ toward $t = 0$, using Eqs. (8.5-62) as initial conditions.

We now identify $u(t)$ with $\bar{u}(t)$ over the interval $0 \leq t \leq T$. By (8.5-51) $u(t)$ vanishes identically for $t > T$; therefore, from (8.5-62) the function $u(t)$ and its first $m - 1$ derivatives are continuous at $t = T$. Since according to (8.5-47) $u(t)$ is differentiated N times in obtaining $W(t)$, this degree of continuity is precisely that required to ensure that $W(t)$ contains no derivatives of $\delta(t - T)$ of order higher than $N - m - 1$.

Considering now the interval $-\infty < t < 0$, let $\tilde{u}_i(t)$ for $i = 0, 1, \ldots,$ $N - 1$ satisfy

$$L_t^* \tilde{u}_i(t) = 0 \qquad -\infty < t < 0 \qquad (8.5\text{-}65)$$

and

$$\tilde{u}_i^{(k)}(0) = \delta_{ik} \qquad i,k = 0, 1, \ldots, N - 1 \qquad (8.5\text{-}66)$$

Then the function

$$\tilde{u}(t) = \sum_{i=0}^{N-1} a_i \tilde{u}_i(t) \qquad (8.5\text{-}67)$$

satisfies, for arbitrary values a_i,

$$L_t^* \tilde{u}(t) = 0 \qquad -\infty < t < 0 \qquad (8.5\text{-}68)$$

In solving Eqs. (8.5-65) and (8.5-66) the methods of Sec. 6.4 are useful, since the integration may be carried out with t running backward, starting from the values (8.5-66) as initial conditions.

Identifying $u(t)$ with $\tilde{u}(t)$ over $-\infty < t < 0$, it is seen at once that Eq. (8.5-50) is valid. The requirement that $u(t)$ and its first $m - 1$ derivatives be continuous at $t = 0$ leads at once to m equations between the constants a_i and c_i. From the relations

$$\tilde{u}^{(k)}(0) = \bar{u}^{(k)}(0) \qquad k = 0, 1, \ldots, m - 1 \qquad (8.5\text{-}69)$$

it follows by Eqs. (8.5-63), (8.5-66), and (8.5-67) that

$$a_k = \bar{u}_p^{(k)}(0) + \sum_{i=0}^{m-1} c_i \bar{u}_i^{(k)}(0) \qquad k = 0, 1, \ldots, m-1 \qquad (8.5\text{-}70)$$

There are thus a total of N arbitrary constants, which may be regarded as the set $c_0, c_1, \ldots, c_{m-1}, a_m, \ldots, a_{N-1}$.

We now consider Eq. (8.5-48) as a differential equation to be solved for $z(t)$. For the moment we gloss over details in order to present a general picture of what is involved. A more concrete discussion of the steps which follow is given at a later point in this section. Since $u(t)$ is known for all values of t (to within N arbitrary constants) then so also is $M_t M_t^* u(t)$, in principle. The operator L_t^{-1} may be postulated to be stable over the interval $-\infty < t < 0$; that is, solutions to $L_t y = \delta(t - \tau)$ are bounded for every t and τ in this interval.[1] Thus $z(t)$ may be regarded as the forced response associated with Eq. (8.5-48), without the introduction of additional arbitrary transient terms.

The function $z(t)$ that results from this operation involves N arbitrary constants, and is otherwise completely determined by the preceding calculations. The condition that it be identically equal to $f(t)$ over the interval $0 \le t \le T$ is not automatically satisfied. Equations (8.5-48) and (8.5-64) show, however, that

$$L_t z(t) = L_t f(t) \qquad 0 \le t \le T \qquad (8.5\text{-}71)$$

If, now, the additional conditions

$$z^{(k)}(0+) = f^{(k)}(0+) \qquad k = 0, 1, \ldots, N-1 \qquad (8.5\text{-}72)$$

are imposed, then z and f will themselves be equal for $0 \le t \le T$. The relations (8.5-72) provide a set of N simultaneous linear algebraic equations for determining the constants $c_0, c_1, \ldots, c_{m-1}, a_m, \ldots, a_{N-1}$. The function $u(t)$ may thus be determined and $W(t)$ can then be computed from Eq. (8.5-47).

There are several steps in the preceding derivation that require elaboration in order to be suited to practical computation. Considering first the solution to the differential equations (8.5-54), (8.5-56), (8.5-60), and (8.5-61) over the interval $0 \le t \le T$, it should be noted that in the final substitution of $u(t)$ into Eq. (8.5-47) the first N derivatives of $u(t)$ are required, as well as $u(t)$ itself. Normal procedures for digital or analogue solution to these differential equations would generally result in the computation of the first m derivatives of the functions $\bar{v}_i(t)$, $\bar{v}_p(t)$, $\bar{u}_i(t)$,

---

[1] If this were not the case, the random process $\{y(t)\}$ resulting from solution of (8.5-2) would possess an infinite correlation function.

and $\bar{u}_p(t)$. The values for these derivatives should therefore be preserved for subsequent use.

Since $N > m$, however, further differentiations must be performed on the function $u(t)$. To accomplish this, the differential equation

$$M_t^* \bar{u}(t) = \bar{v}(t) \tag{8.5-73}$$

may itself be successively differentiated with respect to t by analytic means, leading to recursion formulas for the higher derivatives. Thus, for example, if $m = 1$, we have

$$M_t^* \bar{u} = -\mu_0 \frac{d\bar{u}}{dt} + \left(\mu_1 - \frac{d\mu_0}{dt} \right) \bar{u} = \bar{v}$$

and upon differentiation,

$$-\mu_0 \frac{d^2\bar{u}}{dt^2} + \left(\mu_1 - 2\frac{d\mu_0}{dt} \right) \frac{d\bar{u}}{dt} + \left(\frac{d\mu_1}{dt} - \frac{d^2\mu_0}{dt^2} \right) \bar{u} = \frac{d\bar{v}}{dt}$$

This relation may then be solved to give the second derivative of $\bar{u}$ in terms of $\bar{u}$ itself and the first derivatives of $\bar{u}$ and $\bar{v}$. If higher derivatives are required, the process may be repeated; however, if $N > 2m$, it must then also be applied to the relation (8.5-56) to generate derivatives of $\bar{v}$ of higher order than m. In the interests of computational efficiency it is suggested that this procedure be applied to the final functions $\bar{u}$ and $\bar{v}$ after solution of the necessary simultaneous linear equations rather than to the intermediate functions $\bar{v}_i$, $\bar{v}_p$, etc.

For negative values of t we also require derivatives of the functions $\tilde{u}_i(t)$ defined by Eqs. (8.5-65) and (8.5-66) for later use in (8.5-48). By a device to be considered below, however, only the first m derivatives of these functions are required, so that recursive methods are unnecessary here.

We now consider in greater detail the techniques that may be used in solving Eq. (8.5-48), and give a more concrete formulation to the simultaneous equations that must be solved for the N unknown constants. From the evaluation of the functions $\tilde{u}_i(t)$, sufficient derivatives are available to permit calculation of the N functions $\tilde{v}_i(t)$ defined by

$$\tilde{v}_i(t) = M_t^* \tilde{u}_i(t) \qquad i = 0, 1, \ldots, N - 1 \tag{8.5-74}$$

Writing

$$\tilde{v}(t) = \sum_{i=0}^{N-1} a_i \tilde{v}_i(t) \qquad -\infty < t < 0 \tag{8.5-75}$$

Eq. (8.5-48) becomes, over the interval $-\infty < t < 0$,

$$L_t z(t) = M_t \tilde{v}(t) \qquad -\infty < t < 0 \tag{8.5-76}$$

Now the function $u(t)$ is given by two different expressions for $t < 0$ and for $0 \le t \le T$, and generally possesses no more than $m - 1$ continuous derivatives at $t = 0$. The expression $M_t^* u(t)$ therefore possesses a simple discontinuity at $t = 0$, and the quantity $M_t M_t^* u(t)$ contains derivatives of $\delta(t)$ through order $m - 1$. The direct calculation of $M_t M_t^* u(t)$ as a forcing function to be applied to (8.5-48), as well as the integration of (8.5-48) past $t = 0$, thus offers certain complications which we should prefer to avoid.

If, however, we define a function $v(t)$ by

$$v(t) = M_t^* u(t) = \begin{cases} \tilde{v}(t) & -\infty < t < 0 \\ \bar{v}(t) & 0 < t < T \end{cases} \qquad (8.5\text{-}77)$$

then the function $v(t)$ possesses at most a simple discontinuity at $t = 0$. The methods of Sec. 5.2 may now be employed to express the differential equation $L_t z(t) = M_t v(t)$ as a set of N first-order equations, according to Eqs. (5.2-30), (5.2-31), and (5.2-37). In so doing, the function $v(t)$ itself appears as a forcing function, without further differentiation, and the resulting solutions are therefore continuous at $t = 0$. In effect, the essential difficulties associated with the point $t = 0$ are absorbed in the calculations needed to reduce the Nth-order equation to N first-order equations.

To formulate this procedure explicitly, for each value of $i = 0, 1, \ldots, N - 1$, let $z_{ij}(t)$ satisfy the set of equations [cf. Eqs. (5.2-31)].

$$\frac{dz_{i0}}{dt} = z_{i1} + F_1(t)\tilde{v}_i(t)$$

$$\frac{dz_{i1}}{dt} = z_{i2} + F_2(t)\tilde{v}_i(t) \qquad -\infty < t < 0$$

$$\cdots \cdots \cdots \cdots \cdots \cdots \cdots \cdots \cdots \cdots \cdots \cdots \qquad (8.5\text{-}78)$$

$$\frac{dz_{i,N-1}}{dt} = -\beta_1(t)z_{i,N-1} - \cdots - \beta_N(t)z_{i0} + F_N(t)\tilde{v}_i(t) \;.$$

The functions $\tilde{v}_i(t)$ are defined by (8.5-74), and

$$F_j(t) = 0 \qquad j \leq N - m - 1$$
$$F_{N-m}(t) = \mu_0(t)$$

$$F_j(t) = \mu_{j-N+m}(t) - \sum_{k=N-m}^{j-1} \sum_{s=0}^{j-k} \binom{N+s-j}{N-j} \beta_{j-k-s}(t) \frac{d^s F_k}{dt^s} \qquad (8.5\text{-}79)$$
$$j = N - m + 1, \ldots, N$$

by a modification of notation in Eq. (5.2-37).

The function $z(t)$ is itself defined over this interval by

$$z(t) = \sum_{i=0}^{N-1} a_i z_{i0}(t) \qquad -\infty < t < 0 \qquad (8.5\text{-}80)$$

To match the function $z(t)$ thus obtained and its first $N - 1$ derivatives at $t = 0$ to corresponding values for the function $f(t)$, it would appear necessary to differentiate the functions $z_{i0}(t)$ a total of $N - 1$ times. This procedure, however, again leads to difficulties at $t = 0$ since in the differentiation it is necessary to perform an elimination process in Eqs. (8.5-78) leading to differentiation of the discontinuous functions $v_i(t)$ at $t = 0$.

An equivalent and simpler procedure is the following. For $t \geqq 0$, Eq. (8.5-59) may be treated as though it were an Nth-order differential equation for determining the known function $f(t)$, and similarly reduced to a set of N first-order equations. Writing

$$f_0(t) = f(t) \tag{8.5-81}$$

there results the set of equations

$$\frac{df_0}{dt} = f_1 + F_1(t)\bar{v}(t)$$

$$\frac{df_1}{dt} = f_2 + F_2(t)\bar{v}(t) \tag{8.5-82}$$

$$\cdots \cdots \cdots \cdots \cdots \cdots \cdots$$

$$\frac{df_{N-1}}{di} = -\beta_1(t)f_{N-1} - \cdots - \beta_N(t)f_0 + F_N(t)\bar{v}(t)$$

where $F_j(t)$ is again given by (8.5-79). By a successive elimination process the functions $f_j(t)$ thus defined may be expressed in terms of $f(t)$ and $\bar{v}(t)$, giving for $j = 1, 2, \ldots, N - 1$

$$f_j(t) = f^{(j)}(t) - \sum_{k=0}^{j-1} \sum_{r=0}^{k} \binom{k}{r} \frac{d^{k-r}F_{j-k}}{dt^{k-r}} \frac{d^r\bar{v}}{dt^r} \tag{8.5-83}$$

To provide the required identification of $z(t)$ with $f(t)$ over the interval $0 \leq t \leq T$, we now equate the values $f_j(0)$ for $j = 0, 1, \ldots, N - 1$ to the corresponding values of the N quantities:

$$z_j(0) = \sum_{i=0}^{N-1} a_i z_{ij}(0) \qquad j = 0, 1, \ldots, N - 1 \tag{8.5-84}$$

Representing $\bar{v}(t)$ in terms of the functions $\bar{v}_p(t)$ and $\bar{v}_i(t)$ by Eq. (8.5-58), there results the following N simultaneous equations relating the coefficients a_i and c_i.

$$\sum_{i=0}^{N-1} a_i z_{ij}(0) = f^{(j)}(0) - \sum_{k=0}^{m-N+j} \sum_{r=0}^{k} \binom{k}{r} F_{j-k}^{(k-r)}(0) c_r$$

$$j = 0, 1, \ldots, N - 1 \tag{8.5-85}$$

In formulating these equations, account is taken of the vanishing of certain of the functions $F_j(t)$ according to Eqs. (8.5-79). The initial conditions (8.5-55) and (8.5-57) for the functions $\bar{v}_p(0)$ and $\bar{v}_i(0)$ have also been used to simplify the result. It should be noted that for $j < N - m$ the double sum in (8.5-85) vanishes. The joint solution of the sets of linear equations (8.5-70) and (8.5-85) may now be used to determine all necessary constants in the problem and hence to specify the function $u(t)$ completely.

As a final step, the quantity $W(t)$ can now be expressed in terms of $u(t)$ over $0 \leq t \leq T$ by Eq. (8.5-47). The techniques for computing the required derivatives of $u(t)$ over the interior of this interval have already been discussed. At the end points, however, delta-function terms arise from discontinuity in the derivative $u^{(m)}(t)$.

To handle this situation, we first express $W(t)$ in the form

$$W(t) = W_0(t) + \sum_{i=0}^{N-m-1} [A_i \delta^{(i)}(t) + B_i \delta^{(i)}(t - T)] \qquad (8.5\text{-}86)$$

where $W_0(t)$ is continuous at 0 and T. For any function $g(t)$ possessing, say, N continuous derivatives, we have

$$\int_0^T g(t) \sum_{i=0}^{N-m-1} [A_i \delta^{(i)}(t) + B_i \delta^{(i)}(t - T)] \, dt$$

$$= \sum_{i=0}^{N-m-1} (-1)^i [A_i g^{(i)}(0) + B_i g^{(i)}(T)] \qquad (8.5\text{-}87)$$

Turning now to the expression (8.5-47) for $W(t)$,

$$\int_0^T g(t) L_t^* u(t) \, dt = \int_0^T g(t) W_0(t) \, dt$$

$$+ \lim_{\epsilon \to 0} \left[\int_{-\epsilon}^{\epsilon} g(t) L_t^* u(t) \, dt + \int_{T-\epsilon}^{T+\epsilon} g(t) L_t^* u(t) \, dt \right] \qquad (8.5\text{-}88)$$

and we now wish to identify the bracketed terms in (8.5-88) with the expression (8.5-87).

By means of Eq. (8.5-19), we find

$$\int_{-\epsilon}^{\epsilon} g(t) L_t^* u(t) \, dt = \int_{-\epsilon}^{\epsilon} u(t) L_t g(t) \, dt - P_L[g(t), u(t)]_{-\epsilon}^{\epsilon} \qquad (8.5\text{-}89)$$

In the limit as ϵ approaches zero, the integral term on the right-hand side vanishes since $u(t)$ and $L_t g(t)$ are both continuous. For the bilinear concomitant we have, from (8.5-20),

$$P_L(g, u) = \sum_{i=0}^{N-1} \frac{d^i g}{dt^i} \sum_{j=0}^{N-1-i} \sum_{r=0}^{j} (-1)^j \binom{j}{r} \frac{d^r u}{dt^r} \frac{d^{j-r}}{dt^{j-r}} \beta_{N-1-i-j} \qquad (8.5\text{-}90)$$

Writing

$$\Delta_0 u^{(r)} = \lim_{\epsilon \to 0} [u^{(r)}(\epsilon) - u^{(r)}(-\epsilon)] = \bar{u}^{(r)}(0) - \tilde{u}^{(r)}(0) \quad (8.5\text{-}91)$$

and noting that by the continuity properties of $u(t)$

$$\Delta_0 u^{(r)} = 0 \qquad r = 0, 1, \ldots, m - 1 \quad (8.5\text{-}92)$$

we have

$$\lim_{\epsilon \to 0} P_L[g(t), u(t)]^{\epsilon}_{-\epsilon} = \sum_{i=0}^{N-m-1} g^{(i)}(0) \sum_{j=m}^{N-1-i} \sum_{r=m}^{j} (-1)^j \binom{j}{r} \Delta_0 u^{(r)} \beta^{(j-r)}_{N-1-i-j}(0) \quad (8.5\text{-}93)$$

A comparison with Eq. (8.5-87) then yields for A_i the value

$$A_i = \sum_{j=m}^{N-1-i} \sum_{r=m}^{j} (-1)^{i+j+1} \binom{j}{r} \Delta_0 u^{(r)} \beta^{(j-r)}_{N-1-i-j}(0) \quad (8.5\text{-}94)$$

By a similar calculation

$$B_i = \sum_{j=m}^{N-1-i} \sum_{r=m}^{j} (-1)^{i+j+1} \binom{j}{r} \Delta_T u^{(r)} \beta^{(j-r)}_{N-1-i-j}(T) \quad (8.5\text{-}95)$$

where

$$\Delta_T u^{(r)} = \lim_{\epsilon \to 0} [u^{(r)}(T + \epsilon) - u^{(r)}(T - \epsilon)] = -\bar{u}^{(r)}(T) \quad (8.5\text{-}96)$$

8.6 Prediction and Filtering in the Presence of Gaussian Interference

In this section we outline an approach to the theory of optimum prediction and filtering which, at least for a restricted class of problems, appears to remove many of the limitations of the conventional theory. In particular, we find it possible to consider more general error criteria than the rms condition usually employed, and are led to consider certain predictors or filters which are nonlinear. The results are achieved by making special assumptions concerning the nature of the signal and noise; in particular, we consider only Gaussian noise and certain standardized forms of signal. For the class of cases considered, our results give absolute optimum prediction and filtering.

Our approach is in large part heuristic rather than rigorous; we bypass certain potentially difficult questions of existence and convergence of solutions. The principal aim here is to lay a groundwork of ideas for future consideration.

The ideas which are basic to our method can for the most part be illustrated by a relatively simple problem. Let a target start from the origin on the x axis at time $t = 0$, with a randomly selected constant velocity. Then

$$x(t) = vt \qquad t \geqq 0 \quad (8.6\text{-}1)$$

where v is a random variable. Let

$$z(t) = x(t) + y(t) \tag{8.6-2}$$

where $y(t)$ is a member of a Gaussian random process and is statistically independent of v. On the basis of observed values of $z(t)$ over the time interval $0 \leq t \leq T$, we wish to make an accurate determination of the future value of $x(T + T_1)$.

We assume the probability density function of v to be known; specifically we define $h(v)$ by

$$h(v_0)\, dv = \mathrm{Pr}\ (v_0 < v \leq v_0 + dv) \tag{8.6-3}$$

We further assume knowledge of the spectral density or correlation function of the interference $y(t)$. In specifying an "accurate" determination of $x(T + T_1)$, we shall mean the following: Let $P(z)$ denote symbolically a prediction operator; that is, an arbitrary set of rules which assigns to each function $z(t)$, $0 \leq t \leq T$, a "predicted value of x" which is the number $P(z)$. The prediction error ϵ is

$$\epsilon = P(z) - x(T + T_1)$$

Let $\phi(\epsilon)$ be a nonnegative function such that $\phi = 0$ implies $\epsilon = 0$. We then specify as the optimum or "most accurate" predictor that which minimizes the mathematical expectation or average of $\phi(\epsilon)$ over a large number of trials. In conventional theory

$$\phi(\epsilon) = \epsilon^2$$

We may introduce other functions of interest, however, such as

$$\phi(\epsilon) = |\epsilon| \qquad \text{or} \qquad \phi(\epsilon) = 1 - e^{-\epsilon^2}$$

Before attacking the main problem, we consider first the following case. Let a set of discrete points $(t_1, t_2, \ldots, t_n)$ be assigned, and let it be supposed that we are given the n numbers $z(t_1), z(t_2), \ldots, z(t_n)$, and only these. A general "predictor" $P(z)$ will then be an ordinary function $P(z_1, z_2, \ldots, z_n)$ of the n variables $z_k = z(t_k)$, $(k = 1, \ldots, n)$. In other words, with each such set of numbers z_k we wish to associate a number $P(z_1, \ldots, z_n)$ in such manner that $E[\phi(\epsilon)]$ is a minimum, where

$$\epsilon = P(z_1, \ldots, z_n) - x(T + T_1) \tag{8.6-4}$$

Here $z_k = x_k + y_k$, where the random variables y_k satisfy an n-dimensional Gaussian distribution. Writing

$$M = \|\phi_{ij}\| = \|E[y(t_i)y(t_j)]\|$$

we denote by M_{ij}^{-1} the general element of the inverse matrix M^{-1} and by $|M|$ the determinant of M.

The expectation in question, taking into account the fact that v is a random variable, is given by (8.6-1) to (8.6-4), in the form

$$E[\phi(\epsilon)] = (2\pi)^{-n/2}|M|^{-\frac{1}{2}} \int_{-\infty}^{\infty} dy_1 \cdots \int_{-\infty}^{\infty} dy_n \int_{-\infty}^{\infty} dv\, h(v)$$
$$\times \left[\exp\left(-\frac{1}{2} \sum_{i,j} M_{ij}^{-1} y_i y_j\right) \right]$$
$$\times \phi[P(y_1 + vt_1, \ldots, y_n + vt_n) - v(T + T_1)]$$

Our problem is considered solved if we can find the function P which gives this integral a minimum value.

For this purpose we introduce the change of variable

$$u_k = y_k + vt_k \qquad k = 1, 2, \ldots, n$$

giving

$$E[\phi(\epsilon)] = (2\pi)^{-n/2}|M|^{-\frac{1}{2}} \int_{-\infty}^{\infty} du_1 \cdots \int_{-\infty}^{\infty} du_n \int_{-\infty}^{\infty} dv\, h(v)$$
$$\times \left\{ \exp\left[-\frac{1}{2} \sum_{i,j} M_{ij}^{-1}(u_i - vt_i)(u_j - vt_j)\right] \right\}$$
$$\times \phi[P(u_1, \ldots, u_n) - v(T + T_1)]$$

Now consider the integral

$$J(u_1, \ldots, u_n) = \int_{-\infty}^{\infty} dv\, h(v)$$
$$\times \left\{ \exp\left[-\frac{1}{2} \sum_{i,j} M_{ij}^{-1}(u_i - vt_i)(u_j - vt_j)\right] \right\}$$
$$\times \phi[P(u_1, \ldots, u_n) - v(T + T_1)] \qquad (8.6\text{-}5)$$

For each combination of values $(u_1, \ldots, u_n)$ all quantities in (8.6-5) except P are fixed; for any such particular combination we may thus regard P as a parameter. Since

$$E[\phi(\epsilon)] = (2\pi)^{-n/2}|M|^{-\frac{1}{2}} \int_{-\infty}^{\infty} du_1 \cdots \int_{-\infty}^{\infty} du_n\, J(u_1, \ldots, u_n) \qquad (8.6\text{-}6)$$

it follows that the optimum function $P_0(u_1, \ldots, u_n)$ is that quantity which minimizes $J(u_1, \ldots, u_n)$ for each combination of values $(u_1, \ldots, u_n)$.

To determine the general form of the optimum predictor, let

$$A = \sum_{i,j} M_{ij}^{-1} t_i t_j$$
$$B = \sum_{i,j} M_{ij}^{-1} t_i u_j$$
$$C = \sum_{i,j} M_{ij}^{-1} u_i u_j$$

Noting that $M_{ij}^{-1} = M_{ji}^{-1}$ we have

$$\sum_{i,j} M_{ij}^{-1}(u_i - vt_i)(u_j - vt_j) = Av^2 - 2Bv + C$$

Then

$$J = e^{-C/2} \int_{-\infty}^{\infty} h(v) \exp\left[-\tfrac{1}{2}(Av^2 - 2Bv)\right]\phi[P - v(T + T_1)]\,dv \qquad (8.6\text{-}7)$$

Examination of the integrand of (8.6-7) shows that only B and P depend upon $(u_1, \ldots, u_n)$. The function P which minimizes J for each $(u_1, \ldots, u_n)$ must therefore depend upon $(u_1, \ldots, u_n)$ only through the quantity B. In other words, we have established the following basic proposition.

The optimum predictor $P_0(u_1, \ldots, u_n)$ can be expressed in the form

$$P_0(u_1, u_2, \ldots, u_n) = H_0\left(\sum_{i,j} M_{ij}^{-1}t_i u_j\right)$$

The function $H_0(B)$ depends upon the nature of the function $h(v)$ and upon $\phi(\epsilon)$; it also depends parametrically upon A and upon $(T + T_1)$. The important point, however, is that the optimum predictor P_0 depends upon $(u_1, u_2, \ldots, u_n)$ only as a function of a certain linear combination of these variables.

To lend further strength to this proposition, we consider the special case in which

$$\phi(\epsilon) = \epsilon^2$$

and

$$h(v) = \frac{1}{\sqrt{2\pi}\sigma} \exp\left(-\frac{v^2}{2\sigma^2}\right)$$

We then have

$$
\begin{aligned}
J &= \frac{e^{-C/2}}{\sqrt{2\pi}\sigma} \int_{-\infty}^{\infty} \exp\left\{-\tfrac{1}{2}[(A + 1/\sigma^2)v^2 - 2Bv]\right\}[P - v(T + T_1)]^2\,dv \\
&= \frac{\exp\left\{-\tfrac{1}{2}[C - B^2\sigma^2/(1 + A\sigma^2)]\right\}}{\sqrt{2\pi(1 + A\sigma^2)}} \int_{-\infty}^{\infty} \exp\left(-\frac{w^2}{2}\right) \\
&\qquad\qquad \times \left[P - (T + T_1)\left(\frac{B\sigma^2}{1 + A\sigma^2} + \frac{w\sigma}{\sqrt{1 + A\sigma^2}}\right)\right]^2\,dw \\
&= \frac{\exp\left\{-\tfrac{1}{2}[C - B^2\sigma^2/(1 + A\sigma^2)]\right\}}{\sqrt{2\pi(1 + A\sigma^2)}} \\
&\qquad \times \left\{\int_{-\infty}^{\infty} \exp\left(-\frac{w^2}{2}\right)\left[P - (T + T_1)\frac{B\sigma^2}{1 + A\sigma^2}\right]^2\,dw \right. \\
&\qquad\qquad \left. + \int_{-\infty}^{\infty} \exp\left(-\frac{w^2}{2}\right)\left[(T + T_1)\frac{w\sigma}{\sqrt{1 + A\sigma^2}}\right]^2\,dw\right\} \qquad (8.6\text{-}8)
\end{aligned}
$$

In the last form of this relation use is made of the fact that

$$\int_{-\infty}^{\infty} w \exp\left(-\frac{w^2}{2}\right) dw = 0$$

Examination of (8.6-8) shows that for the mean-squared error criterion with $h(v)$ normal, the optimum predictor is given explicitly by

$$P_0 = L_0 = (T + T_1)\frac{\sigma^2}{1 + A\sigma^2} B \qquad (8.6\text{-}9)$$

We thus have the (well-known) result that the optimum predictor in this case is linear. In addition, however, we have identified B to within a constant of proportionality with this optimum linear predictor. This fact is important since in many cases the optimum linear predictor in the mean-squared error sense may be readily determined by other means.

We may conveniently summarize our results thus far derived for the discrete case as follows:

1. The optimum predictor for the mean-squared error case with normal $h(v)$ depends linearly upon the variables u_j and is given by (8.6-9). We denote this quantity by $L_0(u)$.

2. The general (h,ϕ) optimum predictor depends upon the variables u_j only through the linear combination involved in $L_0(u)$. Specifically, the general optimum predictor is given by

$$P_0(u_1, \ldots, u_n) = H_0\left[\frac{1 + A\sigma^2}{\sigma^2(T + T_1)} L_0(u)\right] \qquad (8.6\text{-}10)$$

where the function $H_0(x)$ depends parametrically upon A and $T + T_1$, and is that which minimizes, for each x, the integral

$$\int_{-\infty}^{\infty} h(v) \exp\left[-\tfrac{1}{2}(Av^2 - 2vx)\right]\phi[H(x) - v(T + T_1)]\, dv \qquad (8.6\text{-}11)$$

Before taking up the question of the passage to the limit to the continuous case, we wish here to replace the function t of Eq. (8.6-1) by a more general quantity. Let $g(t)$ be a preassigned function, and set

$$x(t) = vg(t)$$

where v is a random variable as before. Our previous results may then be carried through with no more than formal changes. We have the following result: Let

$$A = \sum_{i,j} M_{ij}^{-1} g(t_i)g(t_j)$$

$$B = \sum_{i,j} M_{ij}^{-1} g(t_i)u_j$$

$$C = \sum_{i,j} M_{ij}^{-1} u_i u_j$$

Then the optimum predictor is given by

$$P_0(u_1, \ldots, u_n) = H_0\left[\sum_{i,j} M_{ij}^{-1}g(t_i)u_j\right]$$

where $H_0(x)$ minimizes, for each x, the integral

$$\int_{-\infty}^{\infty} h(v) \exp\left[-\tfrac{1}{2}(Av^2 - 2vx)\right]\phi[H(x) - vg(T + T_1)]\, dv$$

The optimum mean-squared predictor for normal $h(v)$ is again linear and is given explicitly by

$$L_0(u) = \frac{\sigma^2}{1 + A\sigma^2}\, g(T + T_1)\sum_{i,j} M_{ij}^{-1}g(t_i)u_j$$

We wish, now, to consider the following situation: Let

$$t_k = k\Delta \qquad k = 0, 1, 2, \ldots, n \tag{8.6-12}$$

where $n\Delta = T$, and T is a fixed number. As n approaches infinity, the points t_k become progressively more dense in the interval $0 \leq t \leq T$. Can we in any sense assume that our previous results are convergent to well-defined continuous operators?

We offer only heuristic arguments at this point. We remark, however, that from the practical standpoint we would seriously mistrust the application of any prediction operator which could not be approximated by one that was discrete. We further show that the requirement of convergence is at least plausible mathematically.

Our argument starts with the consideration of the double sum

$$\sum_{i=0}^{n} \sum_{j=0}^{n} M_{ij}^{-1}g(t_i)u(t_j) \tag{8.6-13}$$

in which t_i, t_j are defined by (8.6-12), and in which $g(t)$ and $u(t)$ are arbitrary continuous functions, possessing such derivatives as we might require. Let

$$p(t_j) = \sum_{i=0}^{n} M_{ij}^{-1}g(t_i) \qquad j = 0, 1, \ldots, n \tag{8.6-14}$$

We have

$$\sum_{j=0}^{n} M_{jk}p(t_j) = \sum_{i=0}^{n} g(t_i)\sum_{j=0}^{n} M_{ij}^{-1}M_{jk}$$

Since M and M^{-1} are inverse matrices, however,

$$\sum_{j=0}^{n} M_{ij}^{-1}M_{jk} = \begin{cases} 1 & \text{if } i = k \\ 0 & \text{if } i \neq k \end{cases}$$

Thus
$$\sum_{j=0}^{n} M_{jk} p(t_j) = g(t_k) \qquad k = 0, 1, \ldots, n$$

However,
$$M_{jk} = \phi(t_j, t_k)$$

where ϕ is the correlation function of $y(t)$. Thus the quantities $p(t_j)$ are to be determined as the solution to the $n + 1$ equations

$$\sum_{j=0}^{n} \phi(t_j, t_k) p(t_j) = g(t_k) \tag{8.6-15}$$

We now consider the integral equation

$$\int_{0}^{T} p_1(\tau) \phi(\tau, t) \, d\tau = g(t) \qquad 0 \leq t \leq T \tag{8.6-16}$$

Let it be supposed for the moment that this equation possesses a continuous solution $p_1(t)$ over $0 \leq t \leq T$. Comparing (8.6-15) and (8.6-16) we find it at least plausible to suppose that

$$\frac{p(t_j)}{\Delta} \approx p_1(t_j) \qquad j = 0, 1, 2, \ldots, n$$

for sufficiently large n (small Δ). From (8.6-13) and (8.6-14), we have

$$\sum_{i=0}^{n} \sum_{j=0}^{n} M_{ij}^{-1} g(t_i) u(t_j) = \sum_{j=0}^{n} p(t_j) u(t_j) \approx \sum_{j=0}^{n} p_1(t_j) u(t_j) \, \Delta$$
$$\approx \int_{0}^{T} p_1(\tau) u(\tau) \, d\tau$$

We therefore may provisionally assume in all subsequent work that

$$\lim_{n \to \infty} \sum_{i=0}^{n} \sum_{j=0}^{n} M_{ij}^{-1} g(t_i) u(t_j) = \int_{0}^{T} p_1(\tau) u(\tau) \, d\tau \tag{8.6-17}$$

where $p_1(t)$ satisfies the integral equation (8.6-16).

The integral equation (8.6-16) is identical to that developed and solved in previous sections of this chapter. Since the solutions previously derived involve delta functions, a certain amount of doubt might be cast on the validity of our approach to the limit, above. It is plausible to suppose, however, that limits such as (8.6-17) may exist even though $p(t_j)/\Delta$ does not approach a continuous function. This must of course be verified before the theory can be considered to be complete.

Assuming convergence, we note the following, without being rigorous:

1. In the discrete case the function $H_0(B)$ does not depend directly upon the number of points of subdivision, but only upon A and $g(T + T_1)$ as parameters.

2. Let $\lim A = A^{(0)} > 0$ and let $H_0(x)$ be a function (not necessarily unique in the general case) which minimizes for each x the integral

$$\int_{-\infty}^{\infty} h(v) \exp\left[-\tfrac{1}{2}(A^{(0)}v^2 - 2vx)\right]\phi[H(x) - vg(T + T_1)]\, dv \quad (8.6\text{-}18)$$

Then for each x, as the number n of points of subdivision increases,

$$\lim_{A \to A^{(0)}} \left\{ \min_{-\infty < H < \infty} \text{value} \int_{-\infty}^{\infty} h(v) \exp\left[-\tfrac{1}{2}(Av^2 - 2vx)\right]\phi[H - vg(T + T_1)]\, dv \right\}$$

$$= \int_{-\infty}^{\infty} h(v) \exp\left[-\tfrac{1}{2}(A^{(0)}v^2 - 2vx)\right]\phi[H_0(x) - vg(T + T_1)]\, dv$$

assuming only very mild restrictions on $h(v)$ and $\phi(\epsilon)$. The implication of this statement is the following. If we consider the class of discrete predictors and assume the limit $A^{(0)}$ to exist, then there is a limiting value of $E[\phi(\epsilon)]$ which can be approached arbitrarily closely by a discrete predictor. Further, the function $H_0(x)$ which minimizes the limiting integral (8.6-18) is an acceptable function to use in the discrete case when A lies very near to its limiting value $A^{(0)}$.

We now consider the class of those general predictors which can be approximated by discrete predictors. We have the following further results:

3. Among this class of predictors, the optimum for the case of mean-squared error with normal h is linear and is given explicitly by

$$L_0(u) = \frac{\sigma^2}{1 + A^{(0)}\sigma^2} g(T + T_1) \int_0^T p_1(\tau)u(\tau)\, d\tau \quad (8.6\text{-}19)$$

where $$A^{(0)} = \int_0^T p_1(\tau)g(\tau)\, d\tau$$

4. Let $H_0(x)$ minimize (8.6-18) for each x. Then in the general (h, ϕ) case, an optimum predictor is

$$P_0(u) = H_0\left[\int_0^T p_1(\tau)u(\tau)\, d\tau\right]$$

With the preceding discussion as background, we now take up the most general case considered, in which

$$z(t) = \sum_{k=1}^{m} v_k g_k(t) + y(t)$$

Here the quantities $g_k(t)$ are preassigned functions [for example, $g_k(t) = t^k$] and the coefficients v_k are random variables with a known joint probability density function $h(v_1, v_2, \ldots, v_m)$. The function $y(t)$ is a Gaussian interference as before, and is statistically independent of the variables $(v_1, \ldots, v_m)$.

Let q_k be any linear function of $g_k(t)$, such as its derivative at time T, its predicted value at time $T + T_1$, or its integral.   We define the error ϵ by

$$\epsilon = P(z) - \sum_{k=1}^{m} v_k q_k$$

Our results will thus be understood to include prediction, differentiation, smoothing, etc., as special cases; for convenience in terminology, we use *predictor* as a generic term.

Proceeding as before, we have for the discrete case

$$E[\phi(\epsilon)] = (2\pi)^{-n/2}|M|^{-\frac{1}{2}} \int_{-\infty}^{\infty} dy_1 \cdots \int_{-\infty}^{\infty} dy_n \int_{-\infty}^{\infty} dv_1$$
$$\cdots \int_{-\infty}^{\infty} dv_m\, h(v_1, \ldots, v_m) \exp\left(-\frac{1}{2} \sum_{i,j} M_{ij}^{-1} y_i y_j\right)$$
$$\times \phi\left\{P\left[y_1 + \sum_k v_k g_k(t_1), \ldots, y_n + \sum_k v_k g_k(t_n)\right] - \sum_k v_k q_k\right\} \quad (8.6\text{-}20)$$

Writing

$$u_i = y_i + \sum_k v_k g_k(t_i) \qquad i = 1, \ldots, n$$

we find

$$E[\phi(\epsilon)] = (2\pi)^{-n/2}|M|^{-\frac{1}{2}} \int_{-\infty}^{\infty} du_1 \cdots \int_{-\infty}^{\infty} du_n\, J(u_1, \ldots, u_n)$$

where

$$J(u_1, \ldots, u_n) = \int_{-\infty}^{\infty} dv_1 \cdots \int_{-\infty}^{\infty} dv_m\, h(v_1, \ldots, v_m)$$
$$\times \phi\left[P(u_1, \ldots, u_n) - \sum_k v_k q_k\right]$$
$$\times \exp\left\{-\frac{1}{2} \sum_{i,j} M_{ij}^{-1} \left[u_i - \sum_{r=1}^{m} v_r g_r(t_i)\right]\left[u_j - \sum_{s=1}^{m} v_s g_s(t_j)\right]\right\}$$

The substitutions

$$A_{rs} = \sum_{i,j} M_{ij}^{-1} g_r(t_i) g_s(t_j)$$
$$B_r = \sum_{i,j} M_{ij}^{-1} g_r(t_i) u_j \qquad\qquad (8.6\text{-}21)$$
$$C = \sum_{i,j} M_{ij}^{-1} u_i u_j$$

give

$$J(u_1, \ldots, u_n) = e^{-C/2} \int_{-\infty}^{\infty} dv_1 \cdots \int_{-\infty}^{\infty} dv_m\, h(v_1, \ldots, v_m)$$
$$\times \phi\left[P(u) - \sum_k v_k q_k\right] \exp\left[-\frac{1}{2}\left(\sum_{r=1}^{m}\sum_{s=1}^{m} A_{rs} v_r v_s - 2 \sum_{r=1}^{m} v_r B_r\right)\right]$$

Since the integrand depends upon u only through P and the quantities $(B_1, B_2, \ldots, B_m)$, it follows that the optimum P has the form

$$H_0(B_1, B_2, \ldots, B_m)$$

By repetition of previous arguments, we have the following results:
Let $p_j(t)$ satisfy

$$\int_0^T \phi(t,\tau) p_j(\tau)\, d\tau = g_j(t) \qquad 0 \leq t \leq T \qquad j = 1, \ldots, m$$

and let

$$A_{rs}^{(0)} = \int_0^T p_r(\tau) g_s(\tau)\, d\tau$$

$$B_r^{(0)} = \int_0^T p_r(\tau) u(\tau)\, d\tau$$

For each point $(x_1, \ldots, x_m)$ let $H_0(x_1, \ldots, x_m)$ be such as to minimize the integral

$$\int_{-\infty}^{\infty} dv_1 \cdots \int_{-\infty}^{\infty} dv_m\, \phi \left[H(x_1, \ldots, x_m) - \sum_{r=1}^m v_r q_r \right]$$

$$\times h(v_1, \ldots, v_m) \exp \left[-\tfrac{1}{2} \left(\sum_{r=1}^m \sum_{s=1}^m A_{rs}^{(0)} v_r v_s - 2 \sum_{r=1}^m v_r x_r \right) \right] \qquad (8.6\text{-}22)$$

Then the optimum predictor is given by

$$P_0(u) = H_0(B_1^{(0)}, B_2^{(0)} \ldots, B_m^{(0)})$$

In general, the above results define the optimum predictor only implicitly. For the case $\phi(\epsilon) = \epsilon^2$, however, the function H_0 can be given trivially in a closed form. Differentiation of the integral (8.6-22) with respect to H gives, upon equating the result to zero,

$$H_0(x_1, x_2, \ldots, x_m)$$

$$= \frac{\displaystyle\sum_{r=1}^m q_r \int_{-\infty}^{\infty} dv_1 \cdots \int_{-\infty}^{\infty} dv_m \left\{ v_r h(v_1, \ldots, v_m) \right.}{\displaystyle\int_{-\infty}^{\infty} dv_1 \cdots \int_{-\infty}^{\infty} dv_m \left\{ h(v_1, \ldots, v_m) \right.}$$
$$\qquad\qquad \frac{\left. \times \exp\left[-\tfrac{1}{2}\left(\sum A_{rs}^{(0)} v_r v_s - 2 \sum v_r x_r \right) \right] \right\}}{\left. \times \exp\left[-\tfrac{1}{2}\left(\sum A_{rs}^{(0)} v_r v_s - 2 \sum v_r x_r \right) \right] \right\}}$$

$$(8.6\text{-}23)$$

In particular, for the case $m = 1$,

$$H_0(x) = q \frac{\displaystyle\int_{-\infty}^{\infty} v h(v) \exp\left[-\tfrac{1}{2}(A^{(0)} v^2 - 2vx) \right] dv}{\displaystyle\int_{-\infty}^{\infty} h(v) \exp\left[-\tfrac{1}{2}(A^{(0)} v^2 - 2vx) \right] dv} \qquad (8.6\text{-}24)$$

Having determined the optimum predictor for a given problem, it is often convenient to be able to calculate the quantity $E[\phi(\epsilon)]$ associated with this optimum. Our aim here is to make this task somewhat less formidable than might be indicated by previous formulas. We assume in doing this that the calculation of the optimum function H_0 has been accomplished. Equation (8.6-20) may then be written in the form

$$\min E[\phi(\epsilon)] = (2\pi)^{-n/2}|M|^{-\frac{1}{2}} \int_{-\infty}^{\infty} dy_1 \cdots \int_{-\infty}^{\infty} dy_n$$

$$\times \int_{-\infty}^{\infty} dv_1 \cdots \int_{-\infty}^{\infty} dv_m \, h(v_1, \ldots ,v_m) \exp\left(-\frac{1}{2}\sum_{i,j} M_{ij}^{-1} y_i y_j\right)$$

$$\times \phi\left[H_0\left(B_1' + \sum_s A_{1s}v_s, \ldots ,B_m' + \sum_s A_{ms}v_s\right) - \sum_r v_r q_r\right] \quad (8.6\text{-}25)$$

where
$$B_r' = \sum_{i,j} M_{ij}^{-1} g_r(t_i) y_j$$

and where A_{rs} is given by (8.6-21).

As n approaches infinity, the expression (8.6-25) becomes unmanageable, even though the number m may be small. We observe, however, that the quantities B_r' are random variables which are linear combinations of the Gaussian random variables y_j. The quantities B_r' thus themselves satisfy an m-dimensional Gaussian distribution, which we may indicate by the density function

$$(2\pi)^{-m/2}|K|^{-\frac{1}{2}} \exp\left(-\frac{1}{2}\sum_{r,s} K_{rs}^{-1} B_r' B_s'\right)$$

We also note that the variables B_r' and v_j are independent.

Since $\phi(\epsilon)$ can be made to depend by this device on the $2m$ variables $(B_1', \ldots , B_m', v_1, \ldots , v_m)$, we may rewrite the expression for $\min E[\phi(\epsilon)]$ in the form

$$\min E[\phi(\epsilon)] = (2\pi)^{-m/2}|K|^{-\frac{1}{2}} \int_{-\infty}^{\infty} dB_1' \cdots \int_{-\infty}^{\infty} dB_m' \int_{-\infty}^{\infty} dv_1$$

$$\cdots \int_{-\infty}^{\infty} dv_m \, h(v_1, \ldots ,v_m) \exp\left(-\frac{1}{2}\sum_{r,s} K_{rs}^{-1} B_r' B_s'\right)$$

$$\times \phi\left[H_0\left(B_1' + \sum_s A_{1s}v_s, \ldots ,B_m' + \sum_s A_{ms}v_s\right) - \sum_r v_r q_r\right] \quad (8.6\text{-}26)$$

The elements of the matrix K and the numbers A_{rs} depend upon n; under the supposition that these are suitably convergent, however, we may consider (8.6-26) as applicable to the continuous case as well as the discrete.

We now make the substitution

$$x_r = B_r' + \sum_s A_{rs}^{(0)} v_s \qquad r = 1, \ldots , m$$

to obtain

$$\min E[\phi(\epsilon)] = (2\pi)^{-m/2} |K|^{-\frac{1}{2}} \int_{-\infty}^{\infty} dx_1 \cdots \int_{-\infty}^{\infty} dx_m$$

$$\times \int_{-\infty}^{\infty} dv_1 \cdots \int_{-\infty}^{\infty} dv_m \, h(v_1, \ldots, v_m)$$

$$\times \exp\left[-\frac{1}{2} \sum_{i,j} K_{ij}^{-1} \left(x_i - \sum_r A_{ir}^{(0)} v_r \right) \left(x_j - \sum_s A_{js}^{(0)} v_s \right) \right]$$

$$\times \phi\left[H_0(x_1, \ldots, x_m) - \sum_r v_r q_r \right] \qquad (8.6\text{-}27)$$

In order to simplify this expression, we now examine the matrix K. Since by definition

$$K_{ij} = E[B_i' B_j']$$

and in the limiting case, as n becomes infinite,

$$B_r' = \int_0^T p_r(\tau) y(\tau) \, d\tau$$

we have

$$K_{ij} = E\left[\left\{ \int_0^T p_i(\tau) y(\tau) \, d\tau \right\} \left\{ \int_0^T p_j(\tau) y(\tau) \, d\tau \right\} \right]$$

$$= E\left[\int_0^T p_i(\tau_1) \, d\tau_1 \int_0^T p_j(\tau_2) y(\tau_1) y(\tau_2) \, d\tau_2 \right]$$

$$= \int_0^T p_i(\tau_1) \, d\tau_1 \int_0^T p_j(\tau_2) E[y(\tau_1) y(\tau_2)] \, d\tau_2$$

$$= \int_0^T p_i(\tau_1) \, d\tau_1 \int_0^T p_j(\tau_2) \phi(\tau_1, \tau_2) \, d\tau_2$$

$$= \int_0^T p_i(\tau_1) g_j(\tau_1) \, d\tau_1$$

$$= A_{ij}^{(0)}$$

Expansion of the exponent in (8.6-27) thus yields

$$-\frac{1}{2} \sum_{i=1}^{m} \sum_{j=1}^{m} K_{ij}^{-1} \left(x_i - \sum_{r=1}^{m} A_{ir}^{(0)} v_r \right) \left(x_j - \sum_{s=1}^{m} A_{js}^{(0)} v_s \right)$$

$$= -\frac{1}{2} \sum_{i=1}^{m} \sum_{j=1}^{m} K_{ij}^{-1} x_i x_j + \frac{1}{2} \sum_{r=1}^{m} v_r \sum_{j=1}^{m} x_j \sum_{i=1}^{m} K_{ij}^{-1} A_{ir}^{(0)}$$

$$+ \frac{1}{2} \sum_{s=1}^{m} v_s \sum_{i=1}^{m} x_i \sum_{j=1}^{m} K_{ij}^{-1} A_{js}^{(0)} - \frac{1}{2} \sum_{r=1}^{m} \sum_{s=1}^{m} v_r v_s \sum_{i=1}^{m} \sum_{j=1}^{m} K_{ij}^{-1} A_{ir}^{(0)} A_{js}^{(0)}$$

$$= -\frac{1}{2} \sum_{i=1}^{m} \sum_{j=1}^{m} A_{ij}^{-1} x_i x_j + \sum_{r=1}^{m} v_r x_r - \frac{1}{2} \sum_{r=1}^{m} \sum_{s=1}^{m} A_{rs}^{(0)} v_r v_s$$

Here free use is made of the symmetry of the matrices $A_{ij}^{(0)}$ and K_{ij}^{-1}.

Substitution of this result into (8.6-27) gives

$$\min E[\phi(\epsilon)] = (2\pi)^{-m/2} |A^{(0)}|^{-\frac{1}{2}} \int_{-\infty}^{\infty} dx_1 \cdots \int_{-\infty}^{\infty} dx_m$$
$$\times \exp\left[-\frac{1}{2} \sum_{r,s} (A^{(0)})_{rs}^{-1} x_r x_s\right] F(x_1, \ldots, x_m) \quad (8.6\text{-}28)$$

where

$$F(x_1, \ldots, x_m) = \int_{-\infty}^{\infty} dv_1 \cdots \int_{-\infty}^{\infty} dv_m\, h(v_1, \ldots, v_m)$$
$$\times \phi\left[H_0(x_1, \ldots, x_m) - \sum_r v_r q_r\right]$$
$$\times \exp\left[-\frac{1}{2}\left(\sum_{r,s} A_{rs}^{(0)} v_r v_s - 2 \sum_r v_r x_r\right)\right] \quad (8.6\text{-}29)$$

Comparison of (8.6-29) with (8.6-22), however, shows that $F(x_1, \ldots, x_m)$ is precisely that integral for which $H_0(x_1, \ldots, x_m)$ is the minimizing function. The quantity F may therefore be presumed to be known, and (8.6-28) relates the minimum $E[\phi(\epsilon)]$ to this function.

We note, incidentally, that the identification of the matrices K_{ij} and A_{ij} means that in using Eq. (8.6-26) in the continuous case we are assuming nothing new concerning convergence.

Example 8.6-1. We wish here to solve one very simple example, to illustrate the method. For convenience, we confine our study to the case of one variable v and further assume that the signal is confined to two discrete alternatives $v = +a$ and $v = -a$. Thus

$$h(v) = \frac{1}{2}[\delta(v + a) + \delta(v - a)]$$

We consider the mean-squared error case; Eq. (8.6-24) then gives the optimum H_0 in the explicit form

$$H_0(x) = q\, \frac{\frac{1}{2}a \exp\left[-\frac{1}{2}(Aa^2 - 2ax)\right] - \frac{1}{2}a \exp\left[-\frac{1}{2}(Aa^2 + 2ax)\right]}{\frac{1}{2}\exp\left[-\frac{1}{2}(Aa^2 - 2ax)\right] + \frac{1}{2}\exp\left[-\frac{1}{2}(Aa^2 + 2ax)\right]}$$
$$= aq \tanh ax \quad (8.6\text{-}30)$$

The optimum prediction for a particular signal plus noise combination $z(t)$ is thus

$$P(z) = aq \tanh\left[a \int_0^T p_1(\tau) z(\tau)\, d\tau\right]$$

The optimum linear prediction for this same case is a constant multiple of the quantity $\int_0^T p_1(\tau) z(\tau)\, d\tau$; in fact, since the determination of the best linear prediction in the least-squares sense depends upon $h(v)$ only through its standard deviation $\sigma = a$, it follows from (8.6-19) that

$$P_0(z) = \frac{a^2}{1 + A_0 a^2} q \int_0^T p_1(\tau) z(\tau)\, d\tau$$

We thus see that the general optimum predictor, in seeking to discriminate between the two discrete alternatives $\pm aq$, chooses the upper value if the optimum linear prediction gives a very large positive result, the lower value if the optimum linear prediction gives a very large negative result, and otherwise gives intermediate values.

It is of interest to compare expected mean-squared errors for the two predictors. For an arbitrary function $H(x)$

$$
\begin{aligned}
E[\epsilon^2] &= \frac{1}{\sqrt{2\pi A}} \int_{-\infty}^{\infty} \exp\left(-\frac{x^2}{2A}\right) dx \int_{-\infty}^{\infty} h(v)(H - qv)^2 \exp\left[-\frac{1}{2}(Av^2 - 2vx)\right] dv \\
&= \frac{1}{2\sqrt{2\pi A}} \int_{-\infty}^{\infty} \exp\left(-\frac{x^2}{2A}\right) \left\{(H + aq)^2 \exp\left[-\frac{1}{2}(Aa^2 + 2ax)\right]\right. \\
&\qquad\qquad\qquad\qquad \left. + (H - aq)^2 \exp\left[-\frac{1}{2}(Aa^2 - 2ax)\right]\right\} dx \\
&= \frac{\exp(-Aa^2/2)}{\sqrt{2\pi A}} \int_{-\infty}^{\infty} \exp\left(-\frac{x^2}{2A}\right) [H(x)^2 \cosh ax \\
&\qquad\qquad\qquad\qquad - 2aqH(x) \sinh ax + a^2 q^2 \cosh ax]\, dx
\end{aligned}
$$

For the optimum nonlinear case the substitution from (8.6-30) gives

$$
\begin{aligned}
E[\epsilon^2] &= \frac{a^2 q^2 \exp(-Aa^2/2)}{\sqrt{2\pi A}} \int_{-\infty}^{\infty} \frac{\exp(-x^2/2A)}{\cosh ax}\, dx \\
&= \frac{a^2 q^2 \exp(-\alpha^2/2)}{\sqrt{2\pi \alpha}} \int_{-\infty}^{\infty} \frac{\exp(-u^2/2\alpha^2)}{\cosh u}\, du
\end{aligned}
$$

where $\alpha^2 = a^2 A$. The corresponding optimum linear predictor is

$$
H_0(x) = \frac{a^2 q x}{1 + \alpha^2}
$$

giving

$$
\begin{aligned}
E[\epsilon^2]_{\text{linear}} &= \frac{a^2 q^2 \exp(-\alpha^2/2)}{\sqrt{2\pi \alpha}(1 + \alpha^2)^2} \int_{-\infty}^{\infty} \exp\left(-\frac{u^2}{2\alpha^2}\right) [u^2 \cosh u \\
&\qquad - 2(1 + \alpha^2)u \sinh u + (1 + \alpha^2)^2 \cosh u]\, du = \frac{a^2 q^2}{1 + \alpha^2}
\end{aligned}
$$

Since

$$
\frac{1}{\sqrt{2\pi \alpha}} \int_{-\infty}^{\infty} \frac{\exp(-u^2/2\alpha^2)}{\cosh u}\, du < \frac{1}{\sqrt{2\pi \alpha}} \int_{-\infty}^{\infty} \exp\left(-\frac{u^2}{2\alpha^2}\right) du = 1
$$

it is clear that for the optimum nonlinear predictor

$$
E[\epsilon^2] < a^2 q^2 \exp\left(-\frac{\alpha^2}{2}\right)
$$

For moderately large α (large signal-to-noise ratio), the improvement by use of the nonlinear predictor is quite significant.

We now consider briefly the case in which the signal depends upon the random variable v in an arbitrary manner, as indicated by

$$
z(t) = g(v,t) + y(t)
$$

Our results, although carried through for a single parameter v, can readily be extended to m such parameters.

Using previous techniques, we readily find for the discrete case

$$
E[\phi(\epsilon)] = (2\pi)^{-n/2}|M|^{-\frac{1}{2}} \int_{-\infty}^{\infty} du_1 \cdots \int_{-\infty}^{\infty} du_n\, J(u_1, \ldots, u_n)
$$

where

$$J(u_1, \ldots ,u_n) = \int_{-\infty}^{\infty} dv \, h(v) \phi[P(u) - q(v)]$$
$$\times \exp \left\{ -\frac{1}{2} \left[\sum_{i,j} M_{ij}^{-1} g(v,t_i) g(v,t_j) \right. \right.$$
$$\left. \left. - 2 \sum_{i,j} M_{ij}^{-1} g(v,t_i) u_j + \sum_{i,j} M_{ij}^{-1} u_i u_j \right] \right\} \quad (8.6\text{-}31)$$

Here we can no longer assert that the optimum predictor depends upon a certain linear combination of the quantities u_i, since the quantity $\Sigma M_{ij}^{-1} g(v,t_i) u_j$ now involves v as more than a simple multiplier. Equation (8.6-31) implies the optimum predictor, in the following sense: To each function u there corresponds a number $P_0(u)$ that minimizes J. In the general case, however, no direct characterization of the result in a convenient functional form is apparent.

For the special case $\phi(\epsilon) = \epsilon^2$, a closed solution is nevertheless easily obtained. Passing to the limit, we have for the continuous case

$$P_0(u) = \frac{\int_{-\infty}^{\infty} dv \, q(v) h(v) \exp \left\{ -\frac{1}{2}[A(v) - 2B(v,u)] \right\}}{\int_{-\infty}^{\infty} dv \, h(v) \exp \left\{ -\frac{1}{2}[A(v) - 2B(v,u)] \right\}}$$

where

$$A(v) = \int_0^T p_1(v,\tau) g(v,\tau) \, d\tau$$
$$B(v,u) = \int_0^T p_1(v,\tau) u(\tau) \, d\tau$$

and where $p_1(v,t)$ satisfies, for all v,

$$\int_0^T \phi(t,\tau) p_1(v,t) \, d\tau = g(v,t) \qquad 0 \leq t \leq T$$

The theory as outlined here contains several major gaps, and none of these appears to be easily filled at the present moment of writing. Among others, these include

1. A rigorous proof that our passage from the discrete to the continuous case is valid for a nontrivial class of situations. The development of a discrete analogue of some of the previous results of this chapter might be of aid in this step. However, deeper probabilistic considerations may be required to define the class of cases for which our results represent a true optimum, particularly in the definition of the precise sense in which discrete operators may be said to "approximate" continuous ones.

2. An extension to include random processes in the role as signals.

3. A practical technique for determination of the optimum function H_0. In cases involving more than one variable v, a direct numerical approach would appear extremely tedious.

In spite of these limitations, the theory seems to show promise. From the practical standpoint the lack of rigor in going from the discrete to the continuous case is not too serious. Certain optimum linear predictors can easily be seen to be well represented by discrete predictors. Since our theory permits construction of better discrete predictors which are nonlinear and involve the same linear operators, evidently our theory can give improved results even if a true optimum is unattainable.

EVALUATION OF AN INTEGRAL OCCURRING
IN THE ANALYSIS OF CERTAIN
NONLINEAR DEVICES

Several of the problems considered in Sec. 4.4 involve the computation of integrals of the form

$$I_{mn}(\alpha) = \int_0^\infty du_1 \int_0^\infty du_2 \, u_1^m u_2^n e^{-(u_1^2 + u_2^2 + 2\,u_1 u_2 \cos \alpha)} \tag{A-1}$$

We may obtain expressions for integrals of this type as follows.

From symmetry it follows that

$$I_{mn}(\alpha) = I_{nm}(\alpha) \tag{A-2}$$

so that we may assume $n \geq m$ without loss in generality. We also note that

$$\frac{dI_{mn}}{d\alpha} = \frac{dI_{mn}}{d(\cos \alpha)} \frac{d \cos \alpha}{d\alpha}$$
$$= 2 \sin \alpha \, I_{m+1,n+1}(\alpha) \tag{A-3}$$

Hence for $n \geq m$,

$$I_{mn}(\alpha) = \frac{1}{2^m} \left(\csc \alpha \frac{d}{d\alpha} \right)^m I_{0,n-m}(\alpha) \tag{A-4}$$

All integrals of this form can, therefore, be obtained by differentiation from the integral

$$I_{0k}(\alpha) = \int_0^\infty du_1 \int_0^\infty du_2 \, u_2^k e^{-(u_1^2 + u_2^2 + 2u_1 u_2 \cos \alpha)} \tag{A-5}$$

To evaluate this integral, we select a change of variable for which the integrand will factor into two functions of a single variable. This may be accomplished by writing

$$u_1^2 + u_2^2 + 2u_1 u_2 \cos \alpha = u_1^2 + 2u_1 u_2 \cos \alpha + u_2^2 \cos^2 \alpha + u_2^2 (1 - \cos^2 \alpha)$$
$$= (u_1 + u_2 \cos \alpha)^2 + (u_2 \sin \alpha)^2$$

Then if we define

$$v_1 = u_1 + u_2 \cos \alpha \qquad v_2 = u_2 \sin \alpha \tag{A-6}$$

the exponent in the integrand of Eq. (A-5) will reduce to a sum of squares.

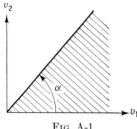

The elements of area in the (u_1, u_2) and (v_1, v_2) planes are related by

$$dv_1\, dv_2 = \frac{\partial(v_1, v_2)}{\partial(u_1, u_2)}\, du_1\, du_2$$
$$= \sin \alpha\, du_1\, du_2 \qquad (A\text{-}7)$$

The first quadrant $(u_1 \geqq 0,\ u_2 \geqq 0)$ in the (u_1, u_2) plane is transformed by (A-6) into a wedge-shaped region in the (v_1, v_2) plane, shown as the shaded area in Fig. A-1.

Therefore Eq. (A-5) is transformed by this means into the form

$$I_{0k}(\alpha) = (\csc \alpha)^{k+1} \int_0^\infty dv_2 \int_{v_2 \cot \alpha}^\infty v_2^k e^{-(v_1^2 + v_2^2)}\, dv_1 \qquad (A\text{-}8)$$

We now transform to polar coordinates by means of the relations

$$v_1 = r \cos \theta \qquad v_2 = r \sin \theta \qquad (A\text{-}9)$$

to obtain

$$I_{0k}(\alpha) = (\csc \alpha)^{k+1} \int_0^\alpha d\theta \int_0^\infty (r \sin \theta)^k e^{-r^2} r\, dr$$
$$= (\csc \alpha)^{k+1} \left[\int_0^\alpha (\sin \theta)^k\, d\theta \right] \left[\int_0^\infty r^{k+1} e^{-r^2}\, dr \right] \qquad (A\text{-}10)$$

The integrals in (A-10) can be obtained by use of a standard table. In particular,

$$I_{00}(\alpha) = \frac{\alpha}{2} \csc \alpha \qquad (A\text{-}11)$$

$$I_{01}(\alpha) = \frac{\sqrt{\pi}}{4} \csc^2 \alpha (1 - \cos \alpha) = \frac{\sqrt{\pi}}{4(1 + \cos \alpha)} \qquad (A\text{-}12)$$

$$I_{02}(\alpha) = \frac{\csc^3 \alpha}{4} (\alpha - \cos \alpha \sin \alpha) \qquad (A\text{-}13)$$

From (A-11) and (A-4), we have

$$I_{11}(\alpha) = \frac{1}{2} \csc \alpha \frac{d}{d\alpha} I_{00}(\alpha)$$
$$= \frac{\csc^2 \alpha}{4} (1 - \alpha \cot \alpha) \qquad (A\text{-}14)$$

$$I_{22}(\alpha) = \frac{1}{2} \csc \alpha \frac{d}{d\alpha} I_{11}(\alpha)$$
$$= \frac{\csc^3 \alpha}{8} [(\csc^2 \alpha + 2 \cot^2 \alpha) - 3 \cot \alpha] \qquad (A\text{-}15)$$

STATIONARY GAUSSIAN NOISE THROUGH A LIMITER

In Sec. 4.4, the correlation function of the output of a limiter whose input is a Gaussian random process is derived in terms of the input correlation function. This result is expressed by Eq. (4.4-42). If we introduce the notation

$$x = \frac{a}{\sqrt{\phi_{11}}} \qquad y = \frac{a}{\sqrt{\phi_{22}}} \tag{B-1}$$

$$P(x) = \sqrt{\frac{2}{\pi}} \int_0^x e^{-\alpha^2/2} \, d\alpha \tag{B-2}$$

we may write the output correlation function as

$$\frac{\phi_{ww}(t_1,t_2)}{\sqrt{\phi_{11}\phi_{22}}} = \rho P(x) P(y)$$

$$+ \frac{8}{\pi} e^{-(x^2+y^2)/2} \sum_{n=1}^{\infty} \frac{(\rho/2)^{2n+1}}{(2n+1)!} H_{2n-1}\left(\frac{x}{\sqrt{2}}\right) H_{2n-1}\left(\frac{y}{\sqrt{2}}\right) \tag{B-3}$$

It is doubtful whether the series part of this equation is expressible in closed form in terms of tabulated functions. However, we may establish the following relationship.

$$e^{-(x^2+y^2)/2} \sum_{n=0}^{\infty} \frac{(\rho/2)^n}{n!} H_n\left(\frac{x}{\sqrt{2}}\right) H_n\left(\frac{y}{\sqrt{2}}\right)$$

$$= \frac{1}{\sqrt{1-\rho^2}} \exp\left(-\frac{x^2 - 2xy\rho + y^2}{2(1-\rho^2)}\right) \tag{B-4}$$

If, in this equation we replace ρ by $-\rho$ and then add the resulting expression to Eq. (B-4), we succeed in eliminating the even powers of ρ and obtain the relation

$$e^{-(x^2+y^2)/2} \sum_{n=1}^{\infty} \frac{(\rho/2)^{2n-1}}{(2n-1)!} H_{2n-1}\left(\frac{x}{\sqrt{2}}\right) H_{2n-1}\left(\frac{y}{\sqrt{2}}\right)$$

$$= \frac{1}{\sqrt{1-\rho^2}} \exp\left[-\frac{1}{2}\left(\frac{x^2+y^2}{1-\rho^2}\right)\right] \sinh\left(\frac{xy\rho}{1-\rho^2}\right) \tag{B-5}$$

Let us denote by $G(x,y,\rho)$ the second term on the right-hand side of Eq. (B-3). Then from Eq. (B-5) we observe that $G(x,y,\rho)$ is obtainable simply as the solution of the following second-order differential equation.

$$\frac{\partial^2 G}{\partial \rho^2} = \frac{2}{\pi} \frac{1}{\sqrt{1 - \rho^2}} \exp\left[-\frac{1}{2}\left(\frac{x^2 + y^2}{1 - \rho^2}\right) \right] \sinh\left(\frac{xy\rho}{1 - \rho^2}\right) \qquad \text{(B-6)}$$

together with the initial conditions

$$G(x,y,0) = \frac{\partial}{\partial \rho} G(x,y,0) = 0 \qquad \text{(B-7)}$$

In practice, we are concerned almost exclusively with the case in which the input random noise has stationary properties. This condition is characterized by the fact that

$$\phi_{11} = \phi_{22} = \phi_0 \qquad \phi_{12} = \phi(\tau)$$

so that we have $x = y$ in Eqs. (B-6) and (B-7). Then Eq. (B-6) may be put in the following form.

$$\frac{\partial^2 G}{\partial \rho^2} = \frac{1}{\pi} \frac{1}{\sqrt{1 - \rho^2}} \left[\exp\left(-\frac{x^2}{1 + \rho}\right) - \exp\left(-\frac{x^2}{1 - \rho}\right) \right] \qquad \text{(B-8)}$$

The difficulty in solving such an equation by numerical methods arises from the singular nature of the right-hand side at $\rho = 1$. However, for the case of $\rho = 1$, the original problem may be solved directly by more conventional methods. The problem is to find the mean-squared output of a limiter whose input is a stationary Gaussian random noise.

The probability density function for the input noise is found from Eq. (4.4-5) to be

$$f_i(t) = \frac{1}{\sqrt{2\pi\phi_0}} e^{-t^2/2\phi_0} \qquad \text{(B-9)}$$

Since the magnitude of the output of the limiter can never exceed a, there is a nonzero probability that the output will equal $+a$ or $-a$. Thus, the distribution of the output will be of the mixed type discussed in Sec. 2.7 and the output density function will be given by

$$f_0(t) = \begin{cases} \delta(t + a) \int_{-\infty}^{-a} f_i(u)\, du & t \leq -a \\ f_i(t) & -a < t < a \\ \delta(t - a) \int_{a}^{\infty} f_i(u)\, du & t \geq a \end{cases} \qquad \text{(B-10)}$$

In terms of the notation of Eq. (B-2) this result may be expressed as

$$f_0(t) = \begin{cases} \delta(t + a) \, \tfrac{1}{2}[1 - P(x)] & t \leq -a \\ f_i(t) & -a < t < a \\ \delta(t - a) \, \tfrac{1}{2}[1 - P(x)] & t \geq a \end{cases} \qquad \text{(B-11)}$$

Finally, the ratio between the mean-squared output of the limiter and the mean-squared input is obtained, using Eq. (2.8-5) as the second moment of the distribution of the output random process. We have

$$\frac{\phi_{ww}(0)}{\phi_0} = \frac{1}{\phi_0} \int_{-\infty}^{\infty} t^2 f_0(t)\, dt$$

$$= \frac{a^2}{\phi_0} [1 - P(x)] + \frac{1}{\phi_0 \sqrt{2\pi\phi_0}} \int_{-a}^{a} t^2 e^{-t^2/2\phi_0}\, dt \quad \text{(B-12)}$$

The integral of Eq. (B-12) may be evaluated in terms of $P(x)$ by means of the following artifice. In Eq. (B-2) replace the variable of integration α by $t\sqrt{h}$. Then we have

$$\int_0^{x/\sqrt{h}} e^{-t^2 h/2}\, dt = \sqrt{\frac{\pi}{2}}\, P(x)\, \frac{1}{\sqrt{h}} \quad \text{(B-13)}$$

Differentiating both sides of this expression with respect to the parameter h, we obtain

$$\int_0^{x/\sqrt{h}} t^2 e^{-t^2 h/2}\, dt = \sqrt{\frac{\pi}{2}}\, P(x)\, \frac{1}{h^{3/2}} - \frac{x}{h^{3/2}}\, e^{-x^2/2} \quad \text{(B-14)}$$

Writing $1/\phi_0$ for h and using a symmetrical interval for the integral, we have

$$\int_{-a}^{a} t^2 e^{-t^2/2\phi_0}\, dt = \sqrt{2\pi}\, P(x)\phi_0^{3/2} - 2x\phi_0^{3/2} e^{-x^2/2} \quad \text{(B-15)}$$

Thus, Eq. (B-12) may be written as

$$\frac{\phi_{ww}(0)}{\phi_0} = x^2[1 - P(x)] + P(x) - \sqrt{\frac{2}{\pi}}\, xe^{-x^2/2} \quad \text{(B-16)}$$

Finally, from Eqs. (B-3) and (B-15) we have

$$G(x,x,1) = x^2[1 - P(x)] + P(x) - \sqrt{\frac{2}{\pi}}\, xe^{-x^2/2} - P(x)^2 \quad \text{(B-17)}$$

Let us return now to the problem of the numerical integration of Eq. (B-8). For automatic machine computation it is convenient to write Eq. (B-8) as a set of four simultaneous first-order equations as follows.

$$y_1 = \pi G(x,x,\rho)$$

$$\frac{dy_1}{d\rho} = y_2$$

$$\frac{dy_2}{d\rho} = \frac{1}{\sqrt{1 - \rho^2}}\, (y_3 + y_4) \quad \text{(B-18)}$$

$$\frac{dy_3}{d\rho} = \frac{x^2}{(1 + \rho)^2}\, y_3$$

$$\frac{dy_4}{d\rho} = -\frac{x^2}{(1 - \rho)^2}\, y_4$$

The appropriate initial conditions are

$$y_1(0) = y_2(0) = 0 \qquad y_3(0) = -y_4(0) = e^{-x^2} \qquad \text{(B-19)}$$

The correlation function ratio may then be written as

$$\frac{\phi_{ww}(\tau)}{\phi_0} = \rho(\tau)P(x)^2 + \frac{1}{\pi} y_1[x,\rho(\tau)] \qquad \text{(B-20)}$$

TABLE I $\phi_{ww}(\tau)/\phi_0$ AS A FUNCTION OF ρ AND x FOR THE EXACT LIMITER

ρ	$x = 0.2$	$x = 0.4$	$x = 0.6$	$x = 0.8$	$x = 1.0$	$x = 1.2$	$x = 1.4$	$x = 1.6$	$x = 1.8$	$x = 2.0$
0.05	0.00126	0.00483	0.0102	0.0166	0.0233	0.0296	0.0352	0.0396	0.0431	0.0456
0.10	0.00252	0.00968	0.0204	0.0332	0.0466	0.0593	0.0703	0.0793	0.0862	0.0911
0.15	0.00378	0.0145	0.0307	0.0499	0.0700	0.0890	0.106	0.119	0.129	0.137
0.20	0.00506	0.0194	0.0410	0.0667	0.0925	0.119	0.141	0.159	0.172	0.182
0.25	0.00635	0.0244	0.0514	0.0836	0.117	0.149	0.176	0.199	0.216	0.228
0.30	0.00765	0.0294	0.0619	0.101	0.141	0.179	0.212	0.238	0.259	0.274
0.35	0.00898	0.0345	0.0725	0.118	0.165	0.209	0.247	0.278	0.302	0.319
0.40	0.0103	0.0396	0.0833	0.135	0.189	0.239	0.283	0.318	0.345	0.365
0.45	0.0117	0.0449	0.0943	0.153	0.213	0.270	0.319	0.359	0.389	0.411
0.50	0.0131	0.0503	0.106	0.171	0.238	0.301	0.355	0.399	0.432	0.457
0.55	0.0146	0.0559	0.117	0.189	0.263	0.332	0.392	0.440	0.476	0.502
0.60	0.0161	0.0617	0.129	0.208	0.289	0.364	0.428	0.480	0.520	0.548
0.65	0.0177	0.0677	0.141	0.227	0.315	0.396	0.465	0.521	0.564	0.594
0.70	0.0194	0.0739	0.154	0.247	0.341	0.428	0.502	0.562	0.608	0.641
0.75	0.0212	0.0806	0.167	0.267	0.368	0.461	0.540	0.604	0.652	0.687
0.80	0.0232	0.0877	0.181	0.288	0.396	0.494	0.578	0.645	0.696	0.733
0.85	0.0253	0.0955	0.196	0.310	0.424	0.528	0.617	0.687	0.741	0.780
0.90	0.0278	0.104	0.212	0.333	0.454	0.563	0.656	0.730	0.786	0.826
0.95	0.0308	0.114	0.229	0.358	0.484	0.598	0.695	0.772	0.831	0.873
1.00	0.0358	0.126	0.249	0.384	0.516	0.635	0.736	0.816	0.877	0.920

TABLE II $\phi_{ww}(\tau)/\phi_0$ AS A FUNCTION OF ρ AND x FOR THE APPROXIMATE LIMITER

ρ	$x = 0.6$	$x = 0.8$	$x = 1.0$	$x = 1.2$	$x = 1.4$	$x = 1.6$	$x = 1.8$	$x = 2.0$
0.10	0.01886	0.02979	0.04022	0.04952	0.05744	0.06400	0.06939	0.07378
0.20	0.03787	0.05974	0.08059	0.09917	0.11499	0.12810	0.13884	0.14762
0.30	0.05718	0.09002	0.12127	0.14910	0.17276	0.19237	0.20844	0.22157
0.40	0.07695	0.12080	0.16244	0.19946	0.23088	0.25691	0.27824	0.29568
0.50	0.09739	0.15228	0.20429	0.25038	0.28946	0.32182	0.34833	0.37000
0.60	0.11874	0.18473	0.24703	0.30206	0.34864	0.38719	0.41877	0.44460
0.70	0.14131	0.21845	0.29090	0.35467	0.40856	0.45312	0.48965	0.51953
0.80	0.16558	0.25384	0.33621	0.40843	0.46936	0.51974	0.56104	0.59485
0.90	0.19231	0.29145	0.38334	0.46360	0.53122	0.58714	0.63302	0.67062
1.00	0.22277	0.33212	0.43276	0.52045	0.59533	0.65547	0.70569	0.74691

The equations in (B-18) were solved using a Runge-Kutta-type integration procedure. This process, of course, breaks down near the point $\rho = 1$. However, from a value of ρ near $\rho = 1$ it is possible to extrapolate the solution by appropriate difference formula techniques.

In Table I, $\phi_{ww}(\tau)/\phi_0$ is tabulated as a function of ρ for various values of x. The interval used in the integration procedure was 0.05. The exact value of $\phi_{ww}(0)/\phi_0$ corresponding to $\rho = 1$, as obtained from Eq. (B-16), agreed with the extrapolated solution of the differential equations to at least three significant figures in every case.

Table II gives an abbreviated tabulation of similar data for the approximate limiter studied in Sec. 4.4.

APPENDIX C

ANALOGUE COMPUTERS

C.1 Introduction

An electronic analogue computer is a machine designed primarily for solving systems of ordinary differential equations of both the linear and nonlinear type. There are many different types of such machines which are available commercially. In analogue devices the dependent variables are represented by voltages or shaft rotations which are made to vary as a function of time in such a way that at any particular instant of time the magnitude of these voltages or rotations is proportional to the desired solution of the mathematical equations under consideration.

The analogue computer may be distinguished from the digital computer in that the latter is a device which solves mathematical problems by working with numbers and sequentially performing elementary arithmetical operations. Thus, it is to be expected that digital machines will, in general, be the more accurate of the two but that the analogue machine, in many cases, will be the easier to program and use.

Most analogue machines on the market today fall into either of two categories, the *real-time* computer and the *repetitive* computer. Solutions obtained on real-time equipment are generated at a rate which is usually of the order of magnitude of from several seconds to several minutes. On the other hand, a high-speed repetitive computer solves a given problem many times in 1 second and displays the solution on a cathode-ray oscilloscope. The repetitive computer has the advantage of permitting the operator to explore a large range of parameter values in a relatively short period of time but, generally speaking, it seldom attains the accuracy of the slower type of machine.

C.2 Theory of Operation of the Linear Computing Elements

The basic unit of the electronic analogue computer is the high-gain d-c amplifier. Such amplifiers may be used for adding, integrating, or, sometimes, differentiating voltages, depending on the kinds of impedances used in the feedback path and as input to the grid. We shall now consider the elementary theory of operation of the d-c amplifier when used to perform each of these operations.

1. *The Summing Amplifier.* Let A be the forward gain of the amplifier, E_g the voltage at the grid, E_i the input voltage, and E_o the output

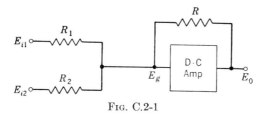

Fig. C.2-1

voltage. Consider the arrangement shown in Fig. C.2-1. Assuming that the amplifier draws no grid current, we have

$$\frac{E_{i1} - E_g}{R_1} + \frac{E_{i2} - E_g}{R_2} = \frac{E_g - E_o}{R} \tag{C.2-1}$$

$$E_o = -AE_g \tag{C.2-2}$$

Eliminating E_g from these two equations and using the fact that A is very large, we have approximately

$$E_o = -\left(\frac{R}{R_1} E_{i1} + \frac{R}{R_2} E_{i2}\right) \tag{C.2-3}$$

Thus by appropriately choosing the ratios of the feedback resistance to the input resistances, this arrangement may be used to sum voltages each of which is multiplied by a different input gain.

2. *The Integrating Amplifier.* A d-c amplifier may be used as an integrator by replacing the feedback resistor R by a condenser C in Fig. C.2-1. Again assuming that the amplifier operates with a nonconducting grid, we have

$$E_g - E_o = \frac{1}{C} \int_0^t \left(\frac{E_{i1} - E_g}{R_1} + \frac{E_{i2} - E_g}{R_2}\right) dt + E_{ic} \tag{C.2-4}$$

where E_{ic} is the initial voltage on the condenser. Since Eq. (C.2-2) is again valid we obtain approximately

$$E_o = -\frac{1}{R_1 C} \int_0^t E_{i1}\, dt - \frac{1}{R_2 C} \int_0^t E_{i2}\, dt - E_{ic} \tag{C.2-5}$$

3. *The Differentiating Amplifier.* Differentiation by means of analogue equipment is a difficult operation to perform in a satisfactory manner. The process of integration can be made quite accurate since it involves the successive additions of quantities of comparable size. However, differentiation requires the subtraction of nearly equal quantities which renders great precision unattainable.

A differentiator may be constructed, using the arrangement shown in Fig. C.2-2. It is left as an exercise to show that approximately we have

$$E_o = -RC \frac{dE_i}{dt} \tag{C.2-6}$$

On most commercial machines several input gains are provided for each of the integrating and summing amplifiers. In addition a number of linear potentiometers called *scale-factor potentiometers* or simply *pots* are provided which are used to multiply voltages by any constant factor between zero and one.

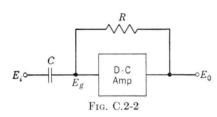

Fig. C.2-2

Let us consider a simple example of the use of an analogue computer for solving a system of linear constant-coefficient differential equations.

Example C.2-1. We wish to mechanize the solution of the following system of differential equations

$$\frac{d^2x}{dt^2} + 0.7 \frac{dx}{dt} + 0.5 \frac{dy}{dt} + 0.04x + 1.3y = 0$$

$$\frac{d^2y}{dt^2} + 1.6 \frac{dx}{dt} + 0.81 \frac{dy}{dt} + 5.2x + 0.4y = 0$$

with initial conditions

$$x(0) = 3 \qquad x'(0) = 0$$
$$y(0) = 8 \qquad y'(0) = 0$$

It is convenient to rewrite these equations in operational form with the highest-order derivative terms isolated on one side of the equation.

$$p^2x = -0.7px - 0.5py - 0.04x - 1.3y$$
$$p^2y = -1.6px - 0.81py - 5.2x - 0.4y$$

It is clear that all the lower-order derivatives including the dependent variables themselves may be obtained by integrating the highest-order derivative. Furthermore, when the equations are written in the above form, it is immediately evident that the highest-order derivatives are functions of all the lower-order terms. The analogue-computer block diagram for this system of equations is shown in Fig. C.2-3. It is important to observe that it is the feedback connections which mechanize the equal signs in the differential equations because it is these connections which compel the equipment to operate so as to equalize both sides of the equations.

In the diagram, squares are used to denote amplifiers, triangles to denote integrators, and circles to denote pots. The numbers opposite the arrowheads on the inputs to the amplifiers and integrators represent the gains into which the inputs are connected. The numbers on the pots represent their settings; i.e., the factor by which their input is multiplied to produce the output. For some purposes, during general theoretical discussions of simulator techniques, we occasionally use the circle symbol for a pot in the more general sense of representing an arbitrary constant or variable coefficient that may take on any set of positive or negative values. In this appendix, however, we use the pot symbol in the strict sense to denote a constant factor between zero and plus one.

The symbol of the form $IC = 3$ written beside an integrator denotes the initial voltage across its condenser, which is the value of the output of the integrator at the start of the run. Where no such symbol occurs, the initial condition is assumed to be zero.

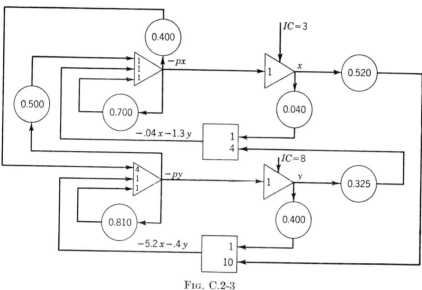

FIG. C.2-3

C.3 Theory of Operation of the Nonlinear Computing Elements

In many analogue computers the basic unit by which nonlinear operations are performed is the computing servomechanism. Each servo is a mechanical positioning device in which a shaft is rotated through an angle proportional to an input-voltage signal. Such servos may be used for multiplication and division of time-varying voltages as well as performing certain vector resolutions.

Mounted on each servo shaft is a feedback potentiometer as shown in Fig. C.3-1. Assume that $+100$ volts and -100 volts are applied to each end of the pot. Then if an input volt-

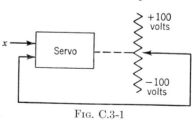

FIG. C.3-1

age x lies between $+100$ volts and -100 volts, the shaft will turn until the voltage picked off from the potentiometer equals x volts. The arm of the pot will then have moved $x/100$ of its total rotation from the center position to one end. In all block diagrams using servos the feedback pot will be omitted for convenience.

1. *Multiplication.* In addition to the feedback pot there may be a number of other potentiometers mounted on the shaft of each servo. The "high," "low," "center tap," and "arm" of each of these pots can be made available for interconnection with other computing elements. Multiplication of two voltages x and y is obtained with the arrangement shown in Fig. C.3-2. Since the arm is displaced through $x/100$ of its total rotation, the voltage picked off will be $x/100$ of y, or simply $xy/100$.

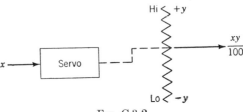

Fig. C.3-2

Several multiplications may be performed with a single servo by using one multiplying pot for each.

2. *Division.* The operation consisting of the division of one variable by another may be accomplished in several ways. Suppose the feedback path of a summing amplifier is broken. Without the feedback resistor, the amplifier is a high-gain phase-inverting amplifier which may be used for division in conjunction with a servo as shown in Fig. C.3-3.

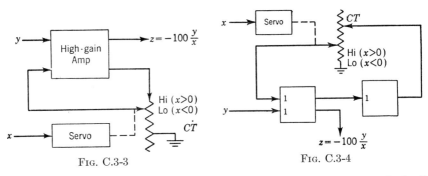

Fig. C.3-3   Fig. C.3-4

If z is the output of the amplifier, then $xz/100$ is the voltage picked off by the arm. Thus

$$\frac{xz}{100} + y = -\frac{z}{A} \cong 0$$

or simply $z = -100y/x$. In connecting the multiplying pot it should be kept in mind that a positive voltage into the servo drives the arm toward the high side of the pot.

Division may be accomplished without a high-gain amplifier using

positive feedback on the servo multiplying pot.   The arrangement for
this is shown in Fig. C.3-4.

3. *Vector Resolution.*   Vector resolution may be accomplished using
servos by mounting on their shafts trigonometric resolvers which are
used to generate sines and cosines of problem variables.   Alternately,
in place of resolvers, nonlinearly wound functional potentiometers are
often used.   Voltages across these pots are supplied externally through
two inputs which we shall denote by "*A* in" and "*B* in."   If the shaft of
the servo is then positioned at an angle θ and if the input voltages at A
and B are x and y, respectively, the outputs are $x \cos\theta$, $-x \sin\theta$, $y \cos\theta$,
$y \sin\theta$.   This is represented schematically in Fig. C.3-5.

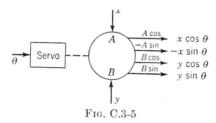

FIG. C.3-5

When a servo-resolver combination functions in this way, the servo is
said to be in the *rectangular* mode of operation.   This follows from geo-
metrical considerations.   If x and y are coordinates of a point P with
respect to a pair of rectangular axes, the quantities $(x \cos\theta + y \sin\theta)$
and $(-x \sin\theta + y \cos\theta)$ are the coordinates of the point P referred to a
pair of axes rotated through an angle θ.

The servo-resolver combination may also function in the *polar* mode
of operation.   The servo is driven so that $-x \sin\theta + y \cos\theta$ is forced
to be zero.   Then the angle through which the servo shaft has turned
will be $\theta = \tan^{-1}(y/x)$.   Furthermore, $x \cos\theta + y \sin\theta = x^2 + y^2$ for

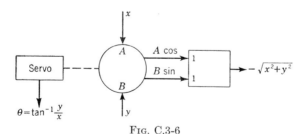

FIG. C.3-6

this value of θ.   This arrangement is represented schematically in Fig.
C.3-6.

4. *Function Generators.*   The generation of a voltage which is proportional to a given function may be accomplished by means of input tables.

The graph of the function is mounted on a rotating drum.   As the drum rotates, the curve is tracked either manually or automatically.   For automatic curve following, a linear resistance element is mounted parallel to the drum axis.   A wire is cemented to the curve to be tracked so that as the drum rotates in correspondence to the independent variable, the wire, acting as a wiper of a linear potentiometer, picks off the proper fraction of the voltage across the pot.   Since the voltage across the pot

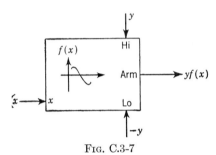

Fig. C.3-7

may itself be a problem variable, the output of the arm will be the product of this variable and the function on the table.   This function generator is represented schematically in Fig. C.3-7.

C.4   Scale-factor Techniques

In choosing scale factors for problem variables, two conflicting considerations arise.   On the one hand one would like the scales to be large enough so that the effect of stray voltages is minimized.   On the other hand the voltages must never exceed the operating range of the computing elements, which we shall assume is set at 100 volts.   Therefore, in choosing scale factors one must possess some information as to the possible range of values of the problem variables.   This knowledge may be obtained either from physical considerations of the problem to be solved or from a trial-and-error procedure.   In either case the following technique has been found to be quite useful.

After the basic block diagram has been drawn, each dependent variable appearing at the input or output of a computing element is given a literal scale.   Thus, if $v(t)$ were a problem variable representing a velocity measured in feet per second and if $v(t)$ appeared as the output of an integrator, then the scale at that point would be labeled arbitrarily as 1 volt = k feet per second.   Then starting from these points in the diagram, the scales at all other points may be determined from the requirements of the problem and from the characteristics of the various computing elements.   Specific details for this procedure will be discussed shortly.

There are two fundamental rules which must be observed in the scale-factoring process.

1. All inputs to a single amplifier must be at the same scale.

2. The scale of the input of a servo used for resolving is not arbitrary but is fixed during the design of the servo.   For example, a servo shaft may rotate through 2 degrees for each volt input in which case the input scale is fixed at 1 volt $= 2°$.

Thus, it is clear that a certain number of changes of scale will be required as we proceed from point to point in the block diagram.   This is usually accomplished by means of the scale-factor potentiometers.   For convenient reference we tabulate below some common operations performed by these pots.

Scale-factor potentiometers may be used for the following:

1. To change scale,

$$\xrightarrow[\;1^v\;=\;k\;\text{units}\;]{x(t)}\;\left(\dfrac{k}{m}\right)\;\xrightarrow[\;1^v\;=\;m\;\text{units}\;]{x(t)}$$

2. To multiply by a constant C,

$$\xrightarrow[\;1^v\;=\;k\;\text{units}\;]{x(t)}\;\left(C\right)\;\xrightarrow[\;1^v\;=\;k\;\text{units}\;]{Cx(t)}$$

3. To change scale and multiply by a constant C,

$$\xrightarrow[\;1^v\;=\;k\;\text{units}\;]{x(t)}\;\left(\dfrac{kC}{m}\right)\;\xrightarrow[\;1^v\;=\;m\;\text{units}\;]{Cx(t)}$$

4. To introduce a constant C as input,

$$100^v\;\longrightarrow\;\left(\dfrac{C}{100\,k}\right)\;\xrightarrow[\;1^v\;=\;k\;\text{units}\;]{C}$$

Example C.4-1.   Assume that A is an angle measured in milliradians and d is a distance measured in feet.   Let $d = AR$, where $R = 1000$ yards.   Then to convert from A, at a scale of 1 volt $= 5$ mils, to d, at a scale of 1 volt $= 25$ feet, we have

$$\xrightarrow[\;1^v\;=\;5\;\text{mils}\;]{A}\;\left(\dfrac{kR}{m}\right)\;\xrightarrow[\;1^v\;=\;25\;\text{feet}\;]{d\;=\;AR}$$

where
$$\frac{kR}{m} = \frac{5 \text{ mils} \times 1000 \text{ yards}}{25 \text{ feet}}$$
$$= \frac{0.005 \text{ radians} \times 3000 \text{ feet}}{25 \text{ feet}}$$
$$= 0.600$$

Notice that in all cases the pot values are nondimensional.

In performing the operations of multiplication and division one recalls the factors of 100 which appeared in the product and quotient. It is often convenient to eliminate these factors by declaring a change of scale at these points. Thus, referring to Fig. C.3-2, if x is at a scale of $1^v = k$ units and y is at a scale of $1^v = m$ units, the voltage at the arm may be taken to be xy at a scale of $1^v = 100\ km$ units. Applying the same argument to Figs. C.3-3 and C.3-4, the voltage representing the quotient may be taken as y/x at a scale of $1^v = m/100\ k$ units.

A slightly different scale-factoring problem arises in connection with the input tables. For this discussion let us refer to Fig. C.3-7. Suppose that the graph of $f(x)$ is plotted to a full scale of m units. We consider two important cases which may arise.

1. If y is a problem variable at the scale of $1^v = k$ units, then the voltage at the arm may be taken to be $yf(x)$ at a scale of $1^v = mk$ units.

2. If the voltage appearing across the "high" and "low" is a constant equal to k volts, then the voltage at the arm may be taken to be $f(x)$ at a scale of $1^v = m/k$ units.

Another important consideration in any scale-factoring problem is the choice of a proper time scale. Changes of time scale may be made within certain limits. When the time scale is changed, the voltages representing problem variables always remain proportional to these variables but the rate at which they change is altered. Thus, voltage changes may be speeded up or slowed down to improve the accuracy or the convenience of operation.

In choosing the proper time scale, we are again confronted with conflicting points of view. On the one hand the effect of drift in d-c integrators increases with time so that a short computing time seems desirable. On the other hand the mechanical elements, the computing servos, the input tables, and the recording equipment, are unable to operate at frequencies much higher than a few cycles per second. Furthermore, a short computing time usually implies high loop gains which may result in unstable computing circuits. In an effort to cope with these facts, it has been found to be helpful to assign a literal time scale just as was done in the case of the problem variables.

Time may enter a typical problem in any of the following three ways: (1) explicitly, (2) as the argument of a function to be generated, and (3) as the variable of differentiation or integration. In each of these cases a change in time scale may be treated by employing a different scale at the input and output of all the integrators. Thus if we let

$$t = a\tau$$

where t is problem time and τ is machine time or real time, then every second of problem time corresponds to $1/a$ seconds of machine time.

Therefore, a problem will run faster than real time if a is greater than one and will run slower than real time if a is less than one. If integrators are calibrated so that a 1-volt input will produce 1 volt per second output, a change in time scale may be accomplished conveniently by interpreting the scales at the integrators as shown below.

$$\xrightarrow[\overline{1^v = k \text{ units}}]{px} \triangleright \xrightarrow[\overline{1^v = ka \text{ units}}]{-x}$$

The selection of scale factors in any problem may be accomplished as described above. After assigning literal scales to all variables and reconciling them by appropriate scale changes, it is then a relatively easy matter to select specific scales. In making this selection, one is guided both by the physics of the problem to be solved and the nature of the equipment on which the problem is to be solved. When the programmer has a master block diagram from which to work and has not committed himself to any particular set of scales, the problem of arriving at an optimum simulation of his problem is considerably simplified.

Before considering an application of these techniques to a physical problem, one final point should be emphasized. In preparing the master block diagram, all scale changes are made with pots (or integrators for changes in time scale). However, when a choice of numerical scales is made, some pot values may turn out to be numbers larger than one. This situation may be handled by utilizing higher amplifier gains into which the pot is connected. Thus, if a pot value turns out to be 2, this gain may be accomplished by setting the pot at a value of 0.500 and following this by an amplifier gain of 4.

Example C.4-2. As an elementary application of the scale-factoring technique described above let us consider the following problem.

A missile and a target aircraft are both flying with constant velocity in the horizontal plane and are on a collision course. Referring to Fig. C.4-1, V_T and V_M are

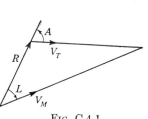

FIG. C.4-1

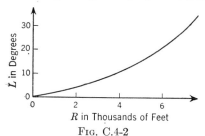

R in Thousands of Feet

FIG. C.4-2

the velocities of the target and the missile, respectively, R is the range from missile to target, L is the lead angle, and A is the angle of the line of sight. Let us assume that the lead angle L is given as a function of range R and that we wish to compute R and A as functions of time.

From the figure it is easy to establish the following two differential equations

$$\frac{dR}{dt} = V_T \cos A - V_M \cos L$$

$$\frac{dA}{dt} = \frac{V_M \sin L - V_T \sin A}{R}$$

The graph of L as a function of R is shown in Fig. C.4-2.

The computer block diagram for this problem is shown in Fig. C.4-3. One observes that a number of the scales at various locations in the diagram are not arbitrary. Thus, the scale at the input of the two resolving servos is $1^v = 2°$. The scale at the arm of the input table is fixed since full scale on the graph is $30°$ and the voltage drop from "high" to "low" is 100 volts. Furthermore, the scale on the x axis is fixed by the requirement that R is to vary from 0 to 6000 feet and that a full rotation of the drum requires a voltage change of 200 volts at the x input. (The pot labeled "bias" is used to align the drum so that the voltage representing R will position the drum at the proper location on the graph.)

Three literal scales were assigned. The quantities R and A each appear at the output of an integrator and these were given the scales of $1^v = k$ feet and $1^v = m$ radians, respectively. Also, the velocities V_T and V_M were assigned the arbitrary scale of $1^v = m$ feet per second in order to provide for additional flexibility.

The time scale at which the problem is to be run may be selected by choosing the value of a. One recalls that 1 second of machine time corresponds to a seconds of problem time.

Suppose that we now wish to solve a specific problem for which our parameters and initial conditions have the following values:

$$V_T = 300 \text{ ft/sec} \qquad R_0 = 4000 \text{ ft}$$
$$V_M = 500 \text{ ft/sec} \qquad A_0 = 30°$$

From the physical nature of the problem we know that R is going to decrease continuously. Thus, if we take $k = 50$, the initial voltage on the integrator which is generating R will be -80^v. Taking $m = 0.01$, the initial voltage on the integrator from which A is obtained is $30/57.3$ volts. If n is chosen to be 5, the voltage across the resolver pots will be as large as possible and, in addition, the settings of pots number 3 and 4 will each have the reasonable value of $a/10$.

With the above choice of scales the following pot settings are obtained.

Pot number	Setting
1	0.600
2	1.000
3	$a/10$
4	$a/10$
5	0.287
6	0.417
7	0.150

If now a time scale is selected, the problem is ready for solution.

C.5 A Useful Computing Technique

Let us consider the constant-coefficient linear system defined by

$$(p^n + a_1 p^{n-1} + \cdots + a_n)y = (b_0 p^m + b_1 p^{m-1} + \cdots + b_m)x \qquad \text{(C.5-1)}$$

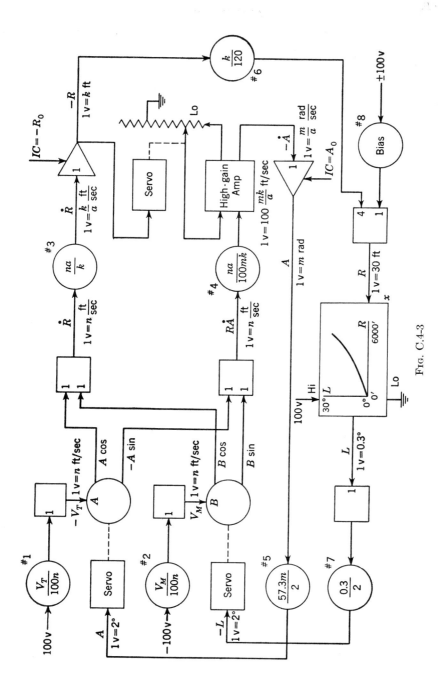

Fig. C.4-3

where $p \equiv d/dt$ is the usual derivative operator. This type of system is encountered quite often throughout the body of the text. It is possible to simulate this system using analogue equipment to obtain the output $y(t)$ even when the input function $x(t)$ is not known analytically and without calculating the derivatives of $x(t)$. We now show how this simulation is obtained for the special case $n = m = 2$. The extension to the more general problem is immediate.

Let us define an auxiliary system by

$$(p^2 + a_1 p + a_2)z = p^2 x \tag{C.5-2}$$

or, equivalently,

$$z - x = -\left(\frac{a_1}{p} + \frac{a_2}{p^2}\right)z \tag{C.5-3}$$

From the latter form the simulation is obtained immediately and is shown in Fig. C.5-1.

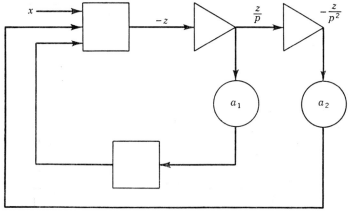

Fig. C.5-1

To obtain y, we note that

$$(b_0 p^2 + b_1 p + b_2)z = p^2 y \tag{C.5-4}$$

or, equivalently,

$$y = \left(b_0 + \frac{b_1}{p} + \frac{b_2}{p^2}\right)z \tag{C.5-5}$$

Referring to Fig. C.5-1, we note that the quantities z, z/p, and z/p^2 are all available as the outputs of amplifiers. Thus, the simulation of the complete system is obtained as shown in Fig. C.5-2.

It is seen that a direct connection exists between the input and output for this particular example. This is characteristic of all such systems of the form (C.5-1) for the case in which $m = n$.

It is clear that the simulation technique used above will not apply when the system has variable coefficients. If we write Eq. (C.5-2) in the operational form $Lz = p^2x$, then $z = L^{-1}p^2x$, where L^{-1} is the operator that is the inverse of L. Also writing Eq. (C.5-4) in the form $Mz = p^2y$, we have $y = p^{-2}ML^{-1}p^2x$ as the solution given by the formal block diagram of Fig. C.5-2. According to Eq. (C.5-1), however, we wish to solve the equation $Ly = Mx$, giving $y = L^{-1}Mx$. In general these two solutions are not equal except in the constant-coefficient case, since the

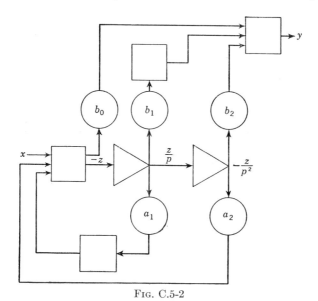

FIG. C.5-2

operators in question do not commute. In the general case we illustrate the necessary technique by considering the same problem as discussed above in which the coefficients are now functions of time.

The system, as described by the differential equation

$$\frac{d^2y}{dt^2} + a_1(t)\frac{dy}{dt} + a_2(t)y = b_0(t)\frac{d^2x}{dt^2} + b_1(t)\frac{dx}{dt} + b_2(t)x \quad \text{(C.5-6)}$$

may be written as a system of first-order differential equations as follows:

$$y = y_1 + F_0(t)x \quad \text{(C.5-7)}$$

$$\frac{dy_1}{dt} = y_2 + F_1(t)x \quad \text{(C.5-8)}$$

$$\frac{dy_2}{dt} = -a_1(t)y_2 - a_2(t)y_1 + F_2(t)x \quad \text{(C.5-9)}$$

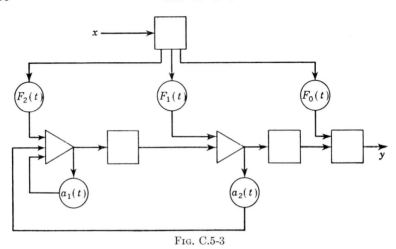

FIG. C.5-3

This procedure is discussed in Sec. 5.2.   The functions F_0, F_1, F_2 are combinations of the coefficients a_1, a_2, b_0, b_1, b_2, as given by Eq. (5.2-37). The simulation is then obtained immediately and is shown in Fig. C.5-3.

A CLASS OF ORTHOGONAL FUNCTIONS

In much of the work relating to the analysis and design of systems we are interested in approximating the spectral density $G(\omega)$ of a random process by a rational function of ω^2. Actually it turns out to be more convenient in practice to approximate the associated correlation function by a set of functions which possess rational Fourier transforms. There are several functions having this property, but here only the one which has been found to be the most convenient by the authors is discussed.

Consider a correlation function which is representable in the form

$$\phi(\tau) = \sum_{k=1}^{n} A_k e^{-c_k|\tau|} \tag{D-1}$$

The spectral density corresponding to this expression is

$$\begin{aligned}
G(\omega) &= \frac{2}{\pi} \int_0^{\infty} \phi(\tau) \cos \omega\tau \, d\tau \\
&= \frac{2}{\pi} \sum_{k=1}^{n} A_k \int_0^{\infty} e^{-c_k\tau} \cos \omega\tau \, d\tau \\
&= \frac{2}{\pi} \sum_{k=1}^{n} \frac{A_k c_k}{c_k^2 + \omega^2}
\end{aligned} \tag{D-2}$$

which has the desired property of being a rational function of ω^2. We now show that any correlation function may be approximated by an expression of the form of Eq. (D-1).

Let $\psi_n(t) (n = 1, 2, 3, \ldots)$ be a set of functions possessing the following properties.

$$\begin{aligned}
\int_0^{\infty} \psi_n(t)^2 \, dt &= 1 \qquad n = 1, 2, \ldots \\
\int_0^{\infty} \psi_m(t)\psi_n(t) \, dt &= 0 \qquad m \neq n
\end{aligned} \tag{D-3}$$

Such a set of functions is said to be normal and orthogonal. Now let $f(t)$ be an arbitrary function such that $\int_0^{\infty} f(t)^2 \, dt$ is finite, and let us attempt to approximate $f(t)$ in the least-squares sense by a sum of the form

$$\sum_{n=1}^{N} A_n \psi_n(t) \tag{D-4}$$

Writing

$$J = \int_0^\infty \left[f(t) - \sum_{n=1}^{N} A_n \psi_n(t) \right]^2 dt \tag{D-5}$$

we seek to choose the coefficients A_n in such manner that J is minimized.

Differentiating J with respect to an arbitrary coefficient A_k and using (D-3), we find

$$\begin{aligned}
\frac{\partial J}{\partial A_k} &= 2 \int_0^\infty \left[f(t) - \sum_{n=1}^{N} A_n \psi_n(t) \right] \psi_k(t) \, dt \\
&= 2 \left[\int_0^\infty f(t)\psi_k(t) \, dt - \sum_{n=1}^{N} A_n \int_0^\infty \psi_n(t)\psi_k(t) \, dt \right] \\
&= 2 \left[\int_0^\infty f(t)\psi_k(t) \, dt - A_k \right] \tag{D-6}
\end{aligned}$$

For a minimum, this derivative must be zero for each value of k; hence the best choice of coefficients is given by

$$A_k = \int_0^\infty f(t)\psi_k(t) \, dt \qquad k = 1, 2, \ldots, N \tag{D-7}$$

Each coefficient may thus be determined independently, without reference to the other coefficients or to the number N of terms chosen.

As the number N of terms in (D-4) approaches infinity, the minimum value of J must decrease. The sequence of functions $\psi_n(t)$ is said to be *complete*, provided that J approaches zero in the limit, for every function $f(t)$ whose integrated square is finite. In other words, the sequence is complete, provided that every such function $f(t)$ can be approximated to any desired degree of accuracy in the least-squares sense by some finite linear combination of the functions $\psi_n(t)$. The formal series

$$\sum_{n=1}^{\infty} A_n \psi_n(t)$$

need not converge in the ordinary sense, but is said to *converge in the mean* to $f(t)$.

To construct an orthogonal and normal sequence suited to our present application, let us start with the functions e^{-ct}, e^{-2ct}, e^{-3ct}, ... These functions are neither normal nor orthogonal; however we can systematically form linear combinations of these functions that possess the required properties. Let

$$u_1(t) = e^{-ct} \tag{D-8}$$

Then
$$\int_0^\infty u_1(t)^2 \, dt = \frac{1}{2c} \tag{D-9}$$

Consequently the function

$$\psi_1(t) = \sqrt{2c} \, e^{-ct} \tag{D-10}$$

satisfies

$$\int_0^\infty \psi_1(t)^2 \, dt = 1 \tag{D-11}$$

The function

$$u_2(t) = e^{-2ct} - \psi_1(t) \int_0^\infty \psi_1(\tau) e^{-2c\tau} \, d\tau \tag{D-12}$$

is orthogonal to $\psi_1(t)$, since by (D-11)

$$\int_0^\infty u_2(t)\psi_1(t) \, dt = \int_0^\infty e^{-2ct}\psi_1(t) \, dt$$
$$- \int_0^\infty \psi_1(t)^2 \, dt \int_0^\infty \psi_1(\tau) e^{-2c\tau} \, d\tau = 0 \tag{D-13}$$

From (D-10) and (D-12)

$$u_2(t) = e^{-2ct} - \tfrac{2}{3}e^{-ct} \tag{D-14}$$

Also
$$\int_0^\infty u_2(t)^2 \, dt = \frac{1}{36c} \tag{D-15}$$

Consequently the function

$$\psi_2(t) = \sqrt{36c}\, u_2(t) = \sqrt{c}\,(6e^{-2ct} - 4e^{-ct}) \tag{D-16}$$

is orthogonal to $\psi_1(t)$ and is also normalized.

In a similar way it follows that the function

$$u_3(t) = e^{-3ct} - \psi_1(t) \int_0^\infty \psi_1(\tau) e^{-3c\tau} \, d\tau - \psi_2(t) \int_0^\infty \psi_2(\tau) e^{-3c\tau} \, d\tau \tag{D-17}$$

is orthogonal to both $\psi_1(t)$ and $\psi_2(t)$. The function $\psi_3(t)$ may therefore be found by normalizing $u_3(t)$.

$$\psi_3(t) = \frac{u_3(t)}{\sqrt{\int_0^\infty u_3(\tau)^2 \, d\tau}}$$
$$= \sqrt{6c}\,(10e^{-3ct} - 12e^{-2ct} + 3e^{-ct}) \tag{D-18}$$

Continuing in this fashion the functions $\psi_n(t)$ may be computed one by one. It can be proved that the infinite sequence $\psi_n(t)$ thus derived forms a complete set.

To apply this procedure to the problem of approximating a correlation function by a sum of the form (D-1), the following steps are indicated:

1. If necessary, subtract a constant from $\phi(\tau)$ so that it approaches zero as $\tau \to \infty$.

2. Choose a reasonable value of c so that $e^{-c\tau}$ approaches zero at roughly the same rate as $\phi(\tau)$.

3. Using the functions $\psi_k(t)$, form the integrals

$$B_k = \int_0^\infty \phi(\tau)\psi_k(\tau)\, d\tau \tag{D-19}$$

4. The function $\phi(\tau)$ is then approximated in the least-squares sense by

$$\phi(\tau) \cong B_1\psi_1(|\tau|) + B_2\psi_2(|\tau|) + B_3\psi_3(|\tau|) + \cdots \tag{D-20}$$

5. Collecting terms with like exponents, $\phi(\tau)$ is given by the expression

$$\phi(\tau) \cong A_1 e^{-c|\tau|} + A_2 e^{-2c|\tau|} + \cdots \tag{D-21}$$

which is of the form (D-1) with $c_k = kc$.

Two remarks may be made on this procedure. In the first place, since the integrated square of a function in the time domain is proportional to the integrated squared magnitude of its Fourier transform in the frequency domain, it follows that the optimum least-squares approximation to $\phi(\tau)$ in the above sense also gives automatically the optimum least-squares approximation to $G(\omega)$ by a sum of the form (D-2). In the second place, this procedure might also be of use in the synthesis of linear systems possessing an assigned transient response. Thus if the weighting function, by the above techniques, can be approximated by an expression of the form

$$W(t) \cong A_1 e^{-ct} + A_2 e^{-2ct} + \cdots \qquad t \geq 0 \tag{D-22}$$

the corresponding transfer function is

$$Y(p) \cong \frac{A_1}{c + p} + \frac{A_2}{2c + p} + \cdots \tag{D-23}$$

It often happens in practice that the shape of a correlation function suggests an approximation by an exponentially damped cosine. Such a term has a rational Fourier transform as can be seen from the following calculation.

Let

$$\phi(\tau) = A e^{-a|\tau|} \cos b\tau \tag{D-24}$$

so that

$$G(\omega) = \frac{2}{\pi} A \int_0^\infty e^{-a\tau} \cos b\tau \cos \omega\tau \, d\tau$$

$$= \frac{A}{\pi} \int_0^\infty e^{-a\tau} \left[\cos (b - \omega)\tau + \cos (b + \omega)\tau \right] d\tau$$

$$= \frac{Aa}{\pi} \left[\frac{1}{a^2 + (b - \omega)^2} + \frac{1}{a^2 + (b + \omega)^2} \right]$$

$$= \frac{2}{\pi} Aa \frac{(a^2 + b^2) + \omega^2}{\omega^4 + 2(a^2 - b^2)\omega^2 + (a^2 + b^2)^2} \qquad \text{(D-25)}$$

which is a rational function of ω^2.

Thus, if a correlation function suggests an approximation of the form of Eq. (D-24) we may use a least-squares or trial-and-error technique to find the A, a, b in this expression. Then if we subtract this term from the original correlation function, the remaining function may be approximated by an expression of the form of Eq. (D-1). By proceeding in this way the number of terms necessary to obtain a good approximation to the correlation function may be significantly reduced.

In Table I are tabulated the values of the functions $\psi_n/\sqrt{c}$ for various values of ct and for $n = 1, \ldots, 5$. These functions

$$\frac{\psi_1}{\sqrt{c}} = \sqrt{2} \, e^{-ct}$$

$$\frac{\psi_2}{\sqrt{c}} = 6e^{-2ct} - 4e^{-ct}$$

$$\frac{\psi_3}{\sqrt{c}} = \sqrt{6} \, [10e^{-3ct} - 12e^{-2ct} + 3e^{-ct}]$$

$$\frac{\psi_4}{\sqrt{c}} = \sqrt{2} \, [70e^{-4ct} - 120e^{-3ct} + 60e^{-2ct} - 8e^{-ct}]$$

$$\frac{\psi_5}{\sqrt{c}} = \sqrt{10} \, [126e^{-5ct} - 280e^{-4ct} + 210e^{-3ct} - 60e^{-2ct} + 5e^{-ct}]$$

were computed for values of the argument from 0 to 10, as indicated.

TABLE I TABLE OF ORTHOGONAL FUNCTIONS

ct	$\dfrac{\psi_1}{\sqrt{c}}$	$\dfrac{\psi_2}{\sqrt{c}}$	$\dfrac{\psi_3}{\sqrt{c}}$	$\dfrac{\psi_4}{\sqrt{c}}$	$\dfrac{\psi_5}{\sqrt{c}}$
0.00	1.41421	2.00000	2.44949	2.82842	3.16227
0.01	1.40014	1.92099	2.23445	2.39460	2.42158
0.02	1.38621	1.84394	2.03004	1.99711	1.77456
0.03	1.37241	1.76880	1.83581	1.63331	1.21240
0.04	1.35876	1.69553	1.65138	1.30141	0.72746
0.05	1.34524	1.62410	1.47634	0.99923	0.31265
0.06	1.33185	1.55446	1.31034	0.72485	−0.03919
0.07	1.31860	1.48656	1.15302	0.47668	−0.33387
0.08	1.30548	1.42039	1.00402	0.25283	−0.57761
0.09	1.29249	1.35589	0.86304	0.05165	−0.77516
0.10	1.27963	1.29302	0.72974	−0.12827	−0.93164
0.11	1.26690	1.23177	0.60381	−0.28832	−1.05133
0.12	1.25429	1.17207	0.48495	−0.43001	−1.13891
0.13	1.24181	1.11392	0.37288	−0.55446	−1.19729
0.14	1.22945	1.05726	0.26731	−0.66303	−1.23054
0.15	1.21722	1.00207	0.16797	−0.75687	−1.24194
0.16	1.20511	0.94831	0.07462	−0.83693	−1.23373
0.17	1.19312	0.89595	−0.01298	−0.90426	−1.20892
0.18	1.18124	0.84496	−0.09512	−0.95986	−1.16997
0.19	1.16949	0.79532	−0.17199	−1.00467	−1.11869
0.20	1.15785	0.74698	−0.24381	−1.03950	−1.05733
0.21	1.14633	0.69993	−0.31084	−1.06518	−0.98792
0.22	1.13493	0.65413	−0.37323	−1.08233	−0.91165
0.23	1.12363	0.60955	−0.43122	−1.09186	−0.82994
0.24	1.11245	0.56617	−0.48499	−1.09432	−0.74438
0.25	1.10138	0.52397	−0.53473	−1.09036	−0.65612
0.26	1.09042	0.48290	−0.58062	−1.08061	−0.56608
0.27	1.07957	0.44296	−0.62282	−1.06551	−0.47516
0.28	1.06883	0.40410	−0.66151	−1.04568	−0.38428
0.29	1.05820	0.36632	−0.69683	−1.02157	−0.29413
0.30	1.04767	0.32958	−0.72894	−0.99365	−0.20532
0.31	1.03724	0.29386	−0.75801	−0.96232	−0.11857
0.32	1.02692	0.25914	−0.78416	−0.92801	−0.03408
0.33	1.01670	0.22540	−0.80755	−0.89100	0.04767
0.34	1.00659	0.19261	−0.82828	−0.85177	0.12614
0.35	0.99657	0.16074	−0.84651	−0.81051	0.20128
0.36	0.98666	0.12979	−0.86232	−0.76764	0.27263
0.37	0.97684	0.09973	−0.87587	−0.72333	0.34013
0.38	0.96712	0.07054	−0.88726	−0.67790	0.40369
0.39	0.95749	0.04219	−0.89659	−0.63157	0.46301

TABLE I TABLE OF ORTHOGONAL FUNCTIONS (*Continued*)

ct	$\dfrac{\psi_1}{\sqrt{c}}$	$\dfrac{\psi_2}{\sqrt{c}}$	$\dfrac{\psi_3}{\sqrt{c}}$	$\dfrac{\psi_4}{\sqrt{c}}$	$\dfrac{\psi_5}{\sqrt{c}}$
0.40	0.94797	0.01468	−0.90397	−0.58458	0.51828
0.41	0.93853	−0.01202	−0.90951	−0.53712	0.56914
0.42	0.92920	−0.03793	−0.91328	−0.48940	0.61583
0.43	0.91995	−0.06307	−0.91540	−0.44152	0.65830
0.44	0.91080	−0.08745	−0.91594	−0.39373	0.69655
0.45	0.90173	−0.11110	−0.68952	−0.34613	0.73065
0.46	0.89276	−0.13403	−0.67207	−0.29886	0.76053
0.47	0.88388	−0.15625	−0.65433	−0.25205	0.78657
0.48	0.87508	−0.17778	−0.63634	−0.20581	0.80855
0.49	0.86638	−0.19864	−0.61813	−0.16023	0.82680
0.50	0.85775	−0.21885	−0.91500	−0.11542	0.84132
0.51	0.84922	−0.23842	−0.91266	−0.07147	0.85231
0.52	0.84077	−0.25736	−0.90899	−0.02840	0.85988
0.53	0.83240	−0.27569	−0.90407	0.01365	0.86413
0.54	0.82412	−0.29342	−0.89798	0.05468	0.86515
0.55	0.81592	−0.31058	−0.89078	0.09461	0.86329
0.56	0.80780	−0.32716	−0.88254	0.13342	0.85851
0.57	0.79976	−0.34319	−0.87332	0.17104	0.85096
0.58	0.79181	−0.35868	−0.86319	0.20745	0.84093
0.59	0.78393	−0.37364	−0.85220	0.24263	0.82846
0.60	0.77613	−0.38809	−0.84042	0.27655	0.81368
0.61	0.76840	−0.40203	−0.82790	0.30921	0.79684
0.62	0.76076	−0.41548	−0.81467	0.34056	0.77796
0.63	0.75319	−0.42845	−0.80081	0.37061	0.75730
0.64	0.74569	−0.44095	−0.78636	0.39938	0.73490
0.65	0.73827	−0.45300	−0.77135	0.42682	0.71096
0.66	0.73093	−0.46460	−0.75584	0.45297	0.68555
0.67	0.72366	−0.47576	−0.73986	0.47780	0.65893
0.68	0.71645	−0.48651	−0.72345	0.50134	0.63107
0.69	0.70933	−0.49684	−0.70667	0.52359	0.60218
0.70	0.70227	−0.50676	−0.59972	0.54456	0.57240
0.71	0.69528	−0.51630	−0.58115	0.56429	0.54176
0.72	0.68836	−0.52545	−0.56244	0.58275	0.51045
0.73	0.68151	−0.53422	−0.54362	0.59999	0.47853
0.74	0.67473	−0.54263	−0.52471	0.61600	0.44613
0.75	0.66802	−0.55069	−0.50573	0.63083	0.41332
0.76	0.66137	−0.55840	−0.48670	0.64448	0.38024
0.77	0.65479	−0.56577	−0.46764	0.65699	0.34693
0.78	0.64827	−0.57281	−0.44858	0.66836	0.31349
0.79	0.64182	−0.57953	−0.42952	0.67863	0.28002

Table I   Table of Orthogonal Functions (Continued)

ct	$\dfrac{\psi_1}{\sqrt{c}}$	$\dfrac{\psi_2}{\sqrt{c}}$	$\dfrac{\psi_3}{\sqrt{c}}$	$\dfrac{\psi_4}{\sqrt{c}}$	$\dfrac{\psi_5}{\sqrt{c}}$
0.80	0.63544	−0.58594	−0.41049	0.68782	0.24655
0.81	0.62911	−0.59204	−0.39151	0.69594	0.21320
0.82	0.62285	−0.59785	−0.37258	0.70305	0.18004
0.83	0.61666	−0.60336	−0.35373	0.70915	0.14710
0.84	0.61052	−0.60860	−0.33497	0.71427	0.11444
0.85	0.52025	−0.61356	−0.31631	0.71844	0.08216
0.86	0.50995	−0.61825	−0.29776	0.72170	0.05026
0.87	0.49986	−0.62268	−0.27933	0.72404	0.01884
0.88	0.48996	−0.62686	−0.26104	0.72553	−0.01208
0.89	0.48026	−0.63079	−0.24289	0.72618	−0.04245
0.90	0.60445	−0.63448	−0.22489	0.72601	−0.07224
0.91	0.59843	−0.63794	−0.20706	0.72506	−0.10141
0.92	0.59248	−0.64117	−0.18941	0.72335	−0.12994
0.93	0.58658	−0.64418	−0.17192	0.72090	−0.15776
0.94	0.58074	−0.64697	−0.15463	0.71775	−0.18490
0.95	0.57497	−0.64955	−0.13753	0.71392	−0.21129
0.96	0.56924	−0.65193	−0.12063	0.70943	−0.23691
0.97	0.56358	−0.65411	−0.10393	0.70432	−0.26179
0.98	0.55797	−0.65609	−0.08745	0.69861	−0.28583
0.99	0.55242	−0.65789	−0.07118	0.69233	−0.30909
1.00	0.54692	−0.65950	−0.05512	0.68549	−0.33154
1.02	0.54148	−0.66220	−0.02372	0.67028	−0.37387
1.04	0.53609	−0.66423	0.00679	0.65314	−0.41288
1.06	0.53076	−0.66563	0.03635	0.63427	−0.44846
1.08	0.52548	−0.66643	0.06497	0.61385	−0.48063
1.10	0.47075	−0.66666	0.09260	0.59206	−0.50940
1.12	0.46142	−0.66636	0.11926	0.56904	−0.53483
1.14	0.45229	−0.66557	0.14493	0.54496	−0.55696
1.16	0.44333	−0.66430	0.16962	0.51996	−0.57588
1.18	0.43455	−0.66259	0.19333	0.49418	−0.59166
1.20	0.42595	−0.66046	0.21605	0.46776	−0.60440
1.22	0.41751	−0.65795	0.23781	0.44080	−0.61421
1.24	0.40925	−0.65507	0.25860	0.41343	−0.62123
1.26	0.40114	−0.65185	0.27844	0.38577	−0.62554
1.28	0.39320	−0.64832	0.29734	0.35789	−0.62730
1.30	0.38541	−0.64448	0.31532	0.32991	−0.62663
1.32	0.37778	−0.64037	0.33240	0.30191	−0.62366
1.34	0.37030	−0.63600	0.34858	0.27397	−0.61853
1.36	0.36297	−0.63139	0.36389	0.24616	−0.61137
1.38	0.35578	−0.62656	0.37835	0.21855	−0.60231

TABLE I TABLE OF ORTHOGONAL FUNCTIONS (*Continued*)

ct	$\dfrac{\psi_1}{\sqrt{c}}$	$\dfrac{\psi_2}{\sqrt{c}}$	$\dfrac{\psi_3}{\sqrt{c}}$	$\dfrac{\psi_4}{\sqrt{c}}$	$\dfrac{\psi_5}{\sqrt{c}}$
1.40	0.34873	-0.62152	0.39198	0.19121	-0.59151
1.42	0.34183	-0.61630	0.40479	0.16418	-0.57907
1.44	0.33506	-0.61090	0.41681	0.13753	-0.56513
1.46	0.32843	-0.60534	0.42807	0.11130	-0.54983
1.48	0.32192	-0.59963	0.43857	0.08553	-0.53327
1.50	0.31555	-0.59379	0.44834	0.06026	-0.51559
1.52	0.30930	-0.58783	0.45741	0.03552	-0.49689
1.54	0.30317	-0.58176	0.46579	0.01134	-0.47730
1.56	0.29717	-0.57559	0.47351	-0.01224	-0.45691
1.58	0.29129	-0.56934	0.48059	-0.03521	-0.43583
1.60	0.28552	-0.56301	0.48705	-0.05756	-0.41415
1.62	0.27986	-0.55660	0.49292	-0.07926	-0.39198
1.64	0.27432	-0.55014	0.49820	-0.10031	-0.36940
1.66	0.26889	-0.54363	0.50293	-0.12069	-0.34650
1.68	0.26357	-0.53708	0.50713	-0.14039	-0.32335
1.70	0.25835	-0.53049	0.51081	-0.15941	-0.30003
1.72	0.25323	-0.52387	0.51399	-0.17774	-0.27661
1.74	0.24822	-0.51723	0.51671	-0.19539	-0.25316
1.76	0.24330	-0.51058	0.51896	-0.21235	-0.22974
1.78	0.23848	-0.50391	0.52077	-0.22863	-0.20640
1.80	0.23376	-0.49725	0.52217	-0.24423	-0.18321
1.82	0.22913	-0.49058	0.52317	-0.25915	-0.16021
1.84	0.22459	-0.48392	0.52378	-0.27341	-0.13744
1.86	0.22015	-0.47728	0.52403	-0.28700	-0.11495
1.88	0.21579	-0.47065	0.52393	-0.29994	-0.09278
1.90	0.21152	-0.46404	0.52349	-0.31224	-0.07096
1.92	0.20733	-0.45746	0.52274	-0.32391	-0.04953
1.94	0.20322	-0.45090	0.52168	-0.33495	-0.02850
1.96	0.19920	-0.44438	0.52034	-0.34538	-0.00792
1.98	0.19525	-0.43789	0.51872	-0.35521	0.01220
2.00	0.19139	-0.43144	0.51685	-0.36446	0.03184
2.02	0.18760	-0.42503	0.51473	-0.37314	0.05099
2.04	0.18388	-0.41866	0.51238	-0.38125	0.06962
2.06	0.18024	-0.41234	0.50981	-0.38882	0.08772
2.08	0.17667	-0.40607	0.50703	-0.39586	0.10529
2.10	0.17317	-0.39984	0.50406	-0.40239	0.12232
2.12	0.16974	-0.39367	0.50091	-0.40841	0.13879
2.14	0.16638	-0.38755	0.49758	-0.41395	0.15470
2.16	0.16309	-0.38149	0.49409	-0.41901	0.17006
2.18	0.15986	-0.37549	0.49045	-0.42361	0.18485

APPENDIX D

TABLE I   TABLE OF ORTHOGONAL FUNCTIONS (*Continued*)

ct	$\dfrac{\psi_1}{\sqrt{c}}$	$\dfrac{\psi_2}{\sqrt{c}}$	$\dfrac{\psi_3}{\sqrt{c}}$	$\dfrac{\psi_4}{\sqrt{c}}$	$\dfrac{\psi_5}{\sqrt{c}}$
2.20	0.15669	−0.36954	0.48667	−0.42777	0.19908
2.22	0.15359	−0.36365	0.48276	−0.43149	0.21274
2.24	0.15055	−0.35782	0.47872	−0.43481	0.22585
2.26	0.14757	−0.35206	0.47457	−0.43772	0.23840
2.28	0.14464	−0.34635	0.47032	−0.44024	0.25040
2.30	0.14178	−0.34071	0.46596	−0.44239	0.26186
2.32	0.13897	−0.33514	0.46152	−0.44419	0.27277
2.34	0.13622	−0.32963	0.45700	−0.44563	0.28315
2.36	0.13352	−0.32418	0.45240	−0.44675	0.29300
2.38	0.13088	−0.31880	0.44774	−0.44754	0.30234
2.40	0.12829	−0.31348	0.44301	−0.44803	0.31116
2.42	0.12575	−0.30823	0.43823	−0.44822	0.31949
2.44	0.12326	−0.30305	0.43340	−0.44814	0.32733
2.46	0.12082	−0.29794	0.42853	−0.44778	0.33469
2.48	0.11842	−0.29289	0.42362	−0.44717	0.34159
2.50	0.11608	−0.28790	0.41868	−0.44631	0.34802
2.52	0.11378	−0.28299	0.41372	−0.44522	0.35401
2.54	0.11153	−0.27814	0.40873	−0.44391	0.35956
2.56	0.10932	−0.27335	0.40372	−0.44238	0.36469
2.58	0.10715	−0.26864	0.39870	−0.44065	0.36941
2.60	0.10503	−0.26399	0.39367	−0.43873	0.37372
2.62	0.10295	−0.25940	0.38864	−0.43663	0.37765
2.64	0.10091	−0.25488	0.38360	−0.43435	0.38120
2.66	0.09891	−0.25043	0.37857	−0.43191	0.38439
2.68	0.09696	−0.24604	0.37354	−0.42932	0.38722
2.70	0.09504	−0.24171	0.36852	−0.42658	0.38971
2.72	0.09315	−0.23745	0.36352	−0.42371	0.39186
2.74	0.09131	−0.23326	0.35853	−0.42071	0.39370
2.76	0.08950	−0.22912	0.35355	−0.41759	0.39524
2.78	0.08773	−0.22505	0.34860	−0.41435	0.39647
2.80	0.08599	−0.22104	0.34366	−0.41101	0.39742
2.82	0.08429	−0.21710	0.33876	−0.40757	0.39810
2.84	0.08262	−0.21321	0.33388	−0.40404	0.39851
2.86	0.08098	−0.20939	0.32903	−0.40043	0.39866
2.88	0.07938	−0.20562	0.32420	−0.39674	0.39858
2.90	0.07781	−0.20192	0.31942	−0.39297	0.39826
2.92	0.07627	−0.19827	0.31466	−0.38914	0.39772
2.94	0.07476	−0.19469	0.30994	−0.38525	0.39697
2.96	0.07328	−0.19116	0.30526	−0.38131	0.39601
2.98	0.07183	−0.18768	0.30062	−0.37731	0.39486

TABLE I TABLE OF ORTHOGONAL FUNCTIONS (*Continued*)

ct	$\dfrac{\psi_1}{\sqrt{c}}$	$\dfrac{\psi_2}{\sqrt{c}}$	$\dfrac{\psi_3}{\sqrt{c}}$	$\dfrac{\psi_4}{\sqrt{c}}$	$\dfrac{\psi_5}{\sqrt{c}}$
3.00	0.07040	−0.18427	0.29601	−0.37327	0.39352
3.02	0.06901	−0.18091	0.29145	−0.36919	0.39201
3.04	0.06764	−0.17760	0.28693	−0.36508	0.39033
3.06	0.06630	−0.17435	0.28245	−0.36093	0.38849
3.08	0.06499	−0.17116	0.27801	−0.35676	0.38650
3.10	0.06370	−0.16801	0.27362	−0.35257	0.38437
3.12	0.06244	−0.16492	0.26927	−0.34836	0.38210
3.14	0.06120	−0.16188	0.26497	−0.34413	0.37970
3.16	0.05999	−0.15890	0.26072	−0.33989	0.37718
3.18	0.05880	−0.15596	0.25651	−0.33565	0.37455
3.20	0.05764	−0.15307	0.25235	−0.33140	0.37182
3.22	0.05650	−0.15023	0.24824	−0.32714	0.36898
3.24	0.05538	−0.14744	0.24417	−0.32289	0.36605
3.26	0.05428	−0.14470	0.24016	−0.31865	0.36303
3.28	0.05321	−0.14201	0.23619	−0.31441	0.35994
3.30	0.05215	−0.13936	0.23227	−0.31018	0.35676
3.32	0.05112	−0.13676	0.22840	−0.30596	0.35352
3.34	0.05011	−0.13421	0.22458	−0.30175	0.35021
3.36	0.04912	−0.13169	0.22080	−0.29757	0.34684
3.38	0.04814	−0.12923	0.21708	−0.29339	0.34342
3.40	0.04719	−0.12680	0.21341	−0.28924	0.33995
3.42	0.04626	−0.12442	0.20978	−0.28512	0.33643
3.44	0.04534	−0.12208	0.20620	−0.28101	0.33287
3.46	0.04444	−0.11978	0.20268	−0.27693	0.32928
3.48	0.04356	−0.11753	0.19920	−0.27288	0.32565
3.50	0.04270	−0.11531	0.19577	−0.26885	0.32200
3.52	0.04185	−0.11313	0.19238	−0.26485	0.31832
3.54	0.04103	−0.11100	0.18905	−0.26089	0.31462
3.56	0.04021	−0.10890	0.18576	−0.25695	0.31090
3.58	0.03942	−0.10683	0.18253	−0.25305	0.30717
3.60	0.03864	−0.10481	0.17933	−0.24918	0.30342
3.62	0.03787	−0.10282	0.17619	−0.24535	0.29967
3.64	0.03712	−0.10087	0.17309	−0.24155	0.29591
3.66	0.03639	−0.09895	0.17004	−0.23778	0.29215
3.68	0.03566	−0.09707	0.16703	−0.23406	0.28839
3.70	0.03496	−0.09522	0.16407	−0.23037	0.28464
3.72	0.03427	−0.09341	0.16116	−0.22672	0.28088
3.74	0.03359	−0.09162	0.15829	−0.22310	0.27714
3.76	0.03292	−0.08988	0.15547	−0.21953	0.27340
3.78	0.03227	−0.08816	0.15268	−0.21599	0.26968

TABLE I   TABLE OF ORTHOGONAL FUNCTIONS (*Continued*)

ct	$\dfrac{\psi_1}{\sqrt{c}}$	$\dfrac{\psi_2}{\sqrt{c}}$	$\dfrac{\psi_3}{\sqrt{c}}$	$\dfrac{\psi_4}{\sqrt{c}}$	$\dfrac{\psi_5}{\sqrt{c}}$
3.80	0.03163	−0.08647	0.14995	−0.21250	0.26596
3.82	0.03100	−0.08482	0.14725	−0.20904	0.26227
3.84	0.03039	−0.08320	0.14460	−0.20563	0.25859
3.86	0.02979	−0.08160	0.14199	−0.20225	0.25493
3.88	0.02920	−0.08004	0.13942	−0.19892	0.25128
3.90	0.02862	−0.07850	0.13690	−0.19563	0.24766
3.92	0.02805	−0.07700	0.13441	−0.19237	0.24406
3.94	0.02750	−0.07552	0.13197	−0.18916	0.24049
3.96	0.02695	−0.07407	0.12956	−0.18599	0.23694
3.98	0.02642	−0.07264	0.12720	−0.18286	0.23341
4.00	0.02590	−0.07124	0.12487	−0.17978	0.22992
4.02	0.02538	−0.06987	0.12259	−0.17673	0.22645
4.04	0.02488	−0.06853	0.12034	−0.17372	0.22301
4.06	0.02439	−0.06720	0.11813	−0.17076	0.21960
4.08	0.02391	−0.06591	0.11595	−0.16783	0.21622
4.10	0.02343	−0.06464	0.11381	−0.16495	0.21287
4.12	0.02297	−0.06339	0.11171	−0.16211	0.20956
4.14	0.02251	−0.06216	0.10965	−0.15930	0.20627
4.16	0.02207	−0.06096	0.10762	−0.15654	0.20302
4.18	0.02163	−0.05978	0.10562	−0.15382	0.19980
4.20	0.02120	−0.05863	0.10366	−0.15113	0.19662
4.22	0.02078	−0.05749	0.10173	−0.14849	0.19347
4.24	0.02037	−0.05638	0.09984	−0.14588	0.19036
4.26	0.01997	−0.05529	0.09798	−0.14332	0.18728
4.28	0.01957	−0.05421	0.09615	−0.14079	0.18423
4.30	0.01918	−0.05316	0.09435	−0.13830	0.18123
4.32	0.01880	−0.05213	0.09258	−0.13585	0.17825
4.34	0.01843	−0.05112	0.09085	−0.13343	0.17532
4.36	0.01807	−0.05013	0.08915	−0.13106	0.17241
4.38	0.01771	−0.04915	0.08747	−0.12872	0.16955
4.40	0.01736	−0.04820	0.08583	−0.12641	0.16672
4.42	0.01701	−0.04726	0.08421	−0.12415	0.16393
4.44	0.01668	−0.04634	0.08262	−0.12192	0.16117
4.46	0.01635	−0.04544	0.08107	−0.11972	0.15845
4.48	0.01602	−0.04456	0.07954	−0.11756	0.15577
4.50	0.01570	−0.04369	0.07803	−0.11543	0.15312
4.52	0.01539	−0.04284	0.07656	−0.11334	0.15051
4.54	0.01509	−0.04200	0.07511	−0.11129	0.14793
4.56	0.01479	−0.04119	0.07368	−0.10926	0.14539
4.58	0.01450	−0.04038	0.07229	−0.10727	0.14289

TABLE I   TABLE OF ORTHOGONAL FUNCTIONS (*Continued*)

ct	$\dfrac{\psi_1}{\sqrt{c}}$	$\dfrac{\psi_2}{\sqrt{c}}$	$\dfrac{\psi_3}{\sqrt{c}}$	$\dfrac{\psi_4}{\sqrt{c}}$	$\dfrac{\psi_5}{\sqrt{c}}$
4.60	0.01421	−0.03959	0.07091	−0.10531	0.14042
4.62	0.01393	−0.03882	0.06957	−0.10339	0.13798
4.64	0.01365	−0.03806	0.06824	−0.10149	0.13559
4.66	0.01338	−0.03732	0.06694	−0.09963	0.13322
4.68	0.01312	−0.03659	0.06567	−0.09780	0.13089
4.70	0.01286	−0.03588	0.06442	−0.09600	0.12860
4.72	0.01260	−0.03518	0.06319	−0.09423	0.12634
4.74	0.01235	−0.03449	0.06198	−0.09249	0.12411
4.76	0.01211	−0.03382	0.06080	−0.09078	0.12192
4.78	0.01187	−0.03315	0.05963	−0.08910	0.11976
4.80	0.01163	−0.03251	0.05849	−0.08745	0.11763
4.82	0.01140	−0.03187	0.05737	−0.08582	0.11554
4.84	0.01118	−0.03125	0.05627	−0.08423	0.11347
4.86	0.01096	−0.03064	0.05519	−0.08266	0.11145
4.88	0.01074	−0.03004	0.05413	−0.08112	0.10945
4.90	0.01053	−0.02945	0.05309	−0.07961	0.10748
4.92	0.01032	−0.02887	0.05207	−0.07812	0.10555
4.94	0.01011	−0.02831	0.05107	−0.07666	0.10364
4.96	0.00991	−0.02775	0.05009	−0.07522	0.10177
4.98	0.00972	−0.02721	0.04913	−0.07381	0.09993
5.00	0.00952	−0.02667	0.04818	−0.07242	0.09812
5.10	0.00862	−0.02416	0.04371	−0.06586	0.08949
5.20	0.00780	−0.02188	0.03964	−0.05985	0.08156
5.30	0.00705	−0.01981	0.03595	−0.05438	0.07427
5.40	0.00638	−0.01794	0.03259	−0.04938	0.06760
5.50	0.00577	−0.01624	0.02954	−0.04483	0.06149
5.60	0.00522	−0.01470	0.02677	−0.04068	0.05590
5.70	0.00473	−0.01331	0.02425	−0.03691	0.05080
5.80	0.00428	−0.01205	0.02197	−0.03347	0.04614
5.90	0.00387	−0.01091	0.01991	−0.03035	0.04190
6.00	0.00350	−0.00987	0.01803	−0.02752	0.03803
6.10	0.00317	−0.00894	0.01633	−0.02495	0.03451
6.20	0.00287	−0.00809	0.01479	−0.02261	0.03131
6.30	0.00259	−0.00732	0.01339	−0.02049	0.02839
6.40	0.00234	−0.00662	0.01212	−0.01856	0.02575
6.50	0.00212	−0.00600	0.01098	−0.01681	0.02334
6.60	0.00192	−0.00543	0.00994	−0.01523	0.02115
6.70	0.00174	−0.00491	0.00900	−0.01379	0.01917
6.80	0.00157	−0.00444	0.00814	−0.01249	0.01737
6.90	0.00142	−0.00402	0.00737	−0.01131	0.01574

Table I   Table of Orthogonal Functions (*Continued*)

ct	$\dfrac{\psi_1}{\sqrt{c}}$	$\dfrac{\psi_2}{\sqrt{c}}$	$\dfrac{\psi_3}{\sqrt{c}}$	$\dfrac{\psi_4}{\sqrt{c}}$	$\dfrac{\psi_5}{\sqrt{c}}$
7.00	0.00128	−0.00364	0.00667	−0.01024	0.01426
7.10	0.00116	−0.00329	0.00604	−0.00927	0.01291
7.20	0.00105	−0.00298	0.00546	−0.00839	0.01169
7.30	0.00095	−0.00269	0.00495	−0.00760	0.01059
7.40	0.00086	−0.00244	0.00448	−0.00688	0.00959
7.50	0.00078	−0.00221	0.00405	−0.00623	0.00868
7.60	0.00070	−0.00200	0.00367	−0.00564	0.00786
7.70	0.00064	−0.00181	0.00332	−0.00510	0.00712
7.80	0.00057	−0.00163	0.00300	−0.00462	0.00644
7.90	0.00052	−0.00148	0.00272	−0.00418	0.00583
8.00	0.00047	−0.00134	0.00246	−0.00378	0.00528
8.10	0.00042	−0.00121	0.00222	−0.00342	0.00478
8.20	0.00038	−0.00109	0.00201	−0.00310	0.00432
8.30	0.00035	−0.00099	0.00182	−0.00280	0.00391
8.40	0.00031	−0.00089	0.00165	−0.00253	0.00354
8.50	0.00028	−0.00081	0.00149	−0.00229	0.00320
8.60	0.00026	−0.00073	0.00135	−0.00208	0.00290
8.70	0.00023	−0.00066	0.00122	−0.00188	0.00262
8.80	0.00021	−0.00060	0.00110	−0.00170	0.00237
8.90	0.00019	−0.00054	0.00100	−0.00154	0.00215
9.00	0.00017	−0.00049	0.00090	−0.00139	0.00194
9.10	0.00015	−0.00044	0.00082	−0.00126	0.00176
9.20	0.00014	−0.00040	0.00074	−0.00114	0.00159
9.30	0.00012	−0.00036	0.00067	−0.00103	0.00144
9.40	0.00011	−0.00033	0.00060	−0.00093	0.00130
9.50	0.00010	−0.00029	0.00054	−0.00084	0.00118
9.60	0.00009	−0.00027	0.00049	−0.00076	0.00107
9.70	0.00008	−0.00024	0.00045	−0.00069	0.00096
9.80	0.00007	−0.00022	0.00040	−0.00062	0.00087
9.90	0.00007	−0.00020	0.00036	−0.00056	0.00079

EVALUATION OF AN INTEGRAL OCCURRING
IN MEAN-SQUARED ERROR ANALYSIS
OF LINEAR SYSTEMS

In one type of mean-squared error analysis discussed in Secs. 5.4 and 5.5 the following integral is encountered:

$$I_n = \frac{1}{2\pi j} \int_{-\infty}^{\infty} \frac{g_n(\omega)}{h_n(\omega)h_n(-\omega)} \, d\omega \qquad \text{(E-1)}$$

where
$$h_n(\omega) = a_0\omega^n + a_1\omega^{n-1} + \cdots + a_n \qquad \text{(E-2)}$$
$$g_n(\omega) = b_0\omega^{2n-2} + b_1\omega^{2n-4} + \cdots + b_{n-1} \qquad \text{(E-3)}$$

[Observe that only even powers of ω are used in the polynomial $g_n(\omega)$ since the contribution to the integral of any odd-power term in the numerator of Eq. (E-1) is zero.]

The polynomial coefficients of Eq. (E-2) are postulated to be such that the coefficient of the leading term a_0 is different from zero, and that the roots $\omega_1, \omega_2, \ldots, \omega_n$ of this polynomial all lie in the upper half plane. For the moment we also require that the roots all be distinct. The integrand of Eq. (E-1) may then be written as a partial fraction expansion of the form

$$\frac{g_n(\omega)}{h_n(\omega)h_n(-\omega)} = \sum_{k=1}^{n} A_k \left(\frac{1}{\omega - \omega_k} - \frac{1}{\omega + \omega_k} \right) \qquad \text{(E-4)}$$

Then, according to the Cauchy residue theorem of complex function theory the integral I_n has the value

$$I_n = \sum_{k=1}^{n} A_k \qquad \text{(E-5)}$$

The problem now is to find an expression for the A_k's in terms of the polynomial coefficients of Eqs. (E-2) and (E-3).

Equation (E-4) may be written as

$$g_n(\omega) = \sum_{k=1}^{n} A_k \left[\frac{h_n(\omega)}{\omega - \omega_k} h_n(-\omega) + \frac{h_n(-\omega)}{-\omega - \omega_k} h_n(\omega) \right] \qquad \text{(E-6)}$$

and by division it is clear that

$$\frac{h_n(\omega)}{\omega - \omega_k} = \sum_{r=1}^{n} B_{rk}\omega^{n-r} \tag{E-7}$$

It is important to note that each of the quantities B_{rk} in general depends upon k except the first which is simply

$$B_{1k} = a_0 \tag{E-8}$$

Then, from Eqs. (E-2) and (E-7), we have

$$\frac{h_n(\omega)}{\omega - \omega_k} h_n(-\omega) + \frac{h_n(-\omega)}{-\omega - \omega_k} h_n(\omega) = \sum_{s=0}^{n} \sum_{r=1}^{n} a_s B_{rk}(-1)^{n-s}\omega^{2n-s-r}$$

$$+ \sum_{s=0}^{n} \sum_{r=1}^{n} a_s B_{rk}(-1)^{n-r}\omega^{2n-s-r} = 2 \sum_{m=1}^{n} \sum_{r=1}^{2m} a_{2m-r}B_{rk}(-1)^{r+n}\omega^{2n-2m} \tag{E-9}$$

In the above expression it is understood that $a_s = 0$ for $s < 0$ or $s > n$ and $B_{rk} = 0$ for $r > n$. We now substitute Eqs. (E-9) and (E-3) into Eq. (E-6) to obtain

$$\sum_{m=1}^{n} b_{m-1}\omega^{2n-2m} = 2(-1)^n \sum_{m=1}^{n} \omega^{2n-2m} \left(\sum_{k=1}^{n} A_k \sum_{r=1}^{2m} a_{2m-r}(-1)^r B_{rk} \right) \tag{E-10}$$

The result is an identity between two polynomials in ω and thus coefficients of like powers of ω must be equal. Equating these coefficients, we obtain

$$\sum_{k=1}^{n} A_k \sum_{r=1}^{2m} a_{2m-r}(-1)^r B_{rk} = (-1)^n \frac{b_{m-1}}{2} \qquad m = 1, 2, \ldots, n \tag{E-11}$$

For simplification let us define

$$C_r = \frac{(-1)^{r+1}}{a_0} \sum_{k=1}^{n} A_k B_{rk} \tag{E-12}$$

Then, from Eqs. (E-5) and (E-8), we see that

$$C_1 = I_n \tag{E-13}$$

so that Eq. (E-11) becomes

$$a_{2m-1}I_n + \sum_{r=2}^{2m} a_{2m-r}C_r = (-1)^{n+1}\frac{b_{m-1}}{2a_0} \qquad m = 1, 2, \ldots, n \tag{E-14}$$

This is a set of n linear algebraic equations in the quantities I_n, C_2, C_3, ..., C_n which may be solved for I_n by the method of determinants.

The final result may be summarized as

$$I_n = \frac{(-1)^{n+1}}{2a_0} \frac{N_n}{D_n} \tag{E-15}$$

where
$$D_n = |d_{mr}| \qquad d_{mr} = a_{2m-r} \tag{E-16}$$

and with the numerator determinant N_n the same as the denominator except that its first column is replaced by $b_0, b_1, \ldots, b_{n-1}$.

Furthermore, this result is true even when two zeros of $h(\omega)$ coincide since the integral I_n is a continuous function of the coefficients of $h_n(\omega)$ and hence is a continuous function of the zeros of $h_n(\omega)$. It should be noted that D_n is the Hurwitz determinant of $h_n(\omega)$ and thus will not vanish.

MATHEMATICAL PROOF OF THE METHOD
OF ADJOINT SYSTEMS

Let us consider a simulated system which is composed exclusively of "integrators," "summers," and time-varying "scale factors." For simplicity, we shall assume integrators and summers to have unit gain and positive sign, while the scale factors may be constant or time-varying with either positive or negative sign. Let the integrators and summers be numbered from 1 to m and from $m + 1$ to n, respectively. Then if x_i is the output of integrator i, x_α the output of summer α, and $f(t)$ the input, such a system may be represented mathematically by the set of differential equations

$$\frac{dx_i}{dt} = a_{ij}(t)x_j(t) + a_{i\alpha}(t)x_\alpha(t) + F_i(t)f(t) \tag{F-1}$$

together with a set of algebraic equations

$$x_\alpha(t) = b_{\alpha j}(t)x_j(t) + F_\alpha(t)f(t) \tag{F-2}$$

where $i, j = 1, \ldots, m$ and $\alpha = m + 1, \ldots, n$.

For convenience of notation, we use the summation convention on repeated indices. That is, in place of writing $\sum_{j=1}^{m} a_{ij}(t)x_j(t)$, we omit the summation symbol and write $a_{ij}(t)x_j(t)$. The repeated subscript j serves to indicate that j is an index of summation. Furthermore, we postulate that all repeated Latin letter indices are to be summed over the range from 1 to m while repeated Greek letter indices have the range $m + 1$ to n.

Equations (F-1) and (F-2) may be written as a set of differential equations alone by substituting Eq. (F-2) into Eq. (F-1) to obtain

$$\frac{dx_i}{dt} = [a_{ij}(t) + a_{i\alpha}(t)b_{\alpha j}(t)]x_j(t) + [F_i(t) + a_{i\alpha}(t)F_\alpha(t)]f(t) \tag{F-3}$$

In a more compact notation

$$\frac{dx_i}{dt} = A_{ik}(t)x_k(t) + f_i(t) \tag{F-4}$$

Let $X_{ij}(t)$ be a nonsingular matrix solution of the homogeneous equation so that

$$\frac{dX_{ij}}{dt} = A_{ik}(t)X_{kj}(t) \tag{F-5}$$

In such a case an inverse matrix exists, denoted by $X_{jk}^{-1}(t)$, such that

$$X_{ij}(t)X_{jk}^{-1}(t) = X_{ij}^{-1}(t)X_{jk}(t) \equiv \delta_{ik} \tag{F-6}$$

where δ_{ik} is the well-known Kronecker delta symbol which is unity if $i = k$ and zero if $i \neq k$. By differentiating Eq. (F-6) and using Eq. (F-5) it is seen that $X_{jk}^{-1}(t)$ is the matrix solution of the equation

$$\frac{dX_{jk}^{-1}}{dt} = -X_{jr}^{-1}(t)A_{rk}(t) \tag{F-7}$$

If we premultiply Eq. (F-4) by $X_{jr}^{-1}(t)$, postmultiply Eq. (F-7) by $x_k(t)$, and add the results, we obtain easily

$$\frac{d}{dt}[X_{jk}^{-1}(t)x_k(t)] = X_{jk}^{-1}(t)f_k(t) \tag{F-8}$$

Integrating Eq. (F-8) and premultiplying both sides by $X_{ij}(t)$ there results

$$x_i(t) = \int^t X_{ij}(t)X_{jk}^{-1}(\tau)f_k(\tau)\,d\tau \tag{F-9}$$

Therefore, the matrix weighting function for the system defined by Eq. (F-4) is given by

$$W_{(x)ik}(t,\tau) = X_{ij}(t)X_{jk}^{-1}(\tau) \tag{F-10}$$

As a particular example, if we set $f_i(t) = B_i(t)f(t)$ as in Eq. (F-3), we obtain

$$x_i(t) = \int^t X_{ik}(t)X_{kj}^{-1}(\tau)B_j(\tau)f(\tau)\,d\tau \tag{F-11}$$

Therefore, the weighting function for the output of the ith integrator is simply

$$W_i(t,\tau) = \begin{cases} X_{ik}(t)X_{kj}^{-1}(\tau)B_j(\tau) & \tau < t \\ 0 & \tau > t \end{cases} \tag{F-12}$$

It is the behavior of $W_i(t,\tau)$ as a function of τ for fixed t that we wish to study.

Let us now consider the following system of differential equations

$$\frac{dy_k}{dt} = -y_i(t)A_{ik}(t) + g_k(t) \tag{F-13}$$

whose homogeneous part is the adjoint of the corresponding homogeneous part of Eq. (F-4). By postmultiplying Eq. (F-13) by $X_{kj}(t)$, premultiplying Eq. (F-5) by $y_i(t)$, adding the results, and integrating, we obtain

$$y_i(t) = \int^t g_k(\tau) X_{kj}(\tau) X_{ji}^{-1}(t) \, d\tau \qquad (F\text{-}14)$$

Thus, the matrix weighting function associated with the system defined by Eq. (F-13) is given by

$$W_{(y)ki}(t,\tau) = X_{kj}(\tau) X_{ji}^{-1}(t) \qquad (F\text{-}15)$$

Let us suppose that we wish to compute the quantity $W_r(T,\tau)$ as a function of τ for some fixed values of r and T. In Eq. (F-14) set $g_k(t) = \delta_{rk}\delta(t - T)$. Then $y_i(t) = X_{rj}(T) X_{ji}^{-1}(t)$ is the response of the adjoint system at time t to a unit impulse at time T. Let this response be multiplied by $B_i(t)$ (and summed over i). By a change in dummy indices we have

$$y_i(t) B_i(t) = X_{rk}(T) X_{kj}^{-1}(t) B_j(t) \qquad T < t \qquad (F\text{-}16)$$

If i is replaced by r and t by T in Eq. (F-12), we obtain

$$W_r(T,\tau) = X_{rk}(T) X_{kj}^{-1}(\tau) B_j(\tau) \qquad T > \tau \qquad (F\text{-}17)$$

These two expressions are formally identical [with τ replaced by t in Eq. (F-17)]; however, they hold over different intervals of the time axis. To overcome this difficulty, let us observe that the expressions composing the right-hand sides of Eqs. (F-16) and (F-17) are well-defined functions for all values of the arguments since they merely represent combinations of solutions of a nonsingular homogeneous differential equation satisfying certain initial conditions. Therefore, denoting these quantities by $W_r^*(T,\tau)$ and $y_i^*(t) B_i(t)$, the new functions thus defined agree with the results of the appropriate unit-impulse tests for the values of the argument indicated by Eqs. (F-16) and (F-17). Thus, $W_r^*(t,\tau)$ is defined over the t, τ plane and it is the value of this function along the line L_1 shown in Fig. F-1 in which we are interested. The shaded portion of the t, τ plane indicates only those values of W_r^* which have physical significance in terms of unit-impulse response. The response of the adjoint system, as given by Eq. (F-16), is also defined over the entire t, τ plane; the values of $y_i^*(t) B_i(t)$, corresponding to a unit impulse applied to the adjoint system at time T, are along the dotted line L_2' of Fig. F-2. The desired values, however, are those along the line L_2, since these are equal to the values of W_r^* in a corresponding position along L_1. However, the line L_2 lies outside the region of physical interpretation of the weighting function for the adjoint system. This may be remedied by effecting a reversal in time in the adjoint system. The response will then be $y_i^*(-t) B_i(-t)$ and in the t, τ plane of Fig. F-3 these values will lie along the line L_3. The line L_3 now lies within the physical region.

It is convenient to regard the input to our new system as occurring at time $t = 0$ rather than $t = -T$. This can be accomplished by a shift in the origin of time. That is, if we utilize the adjoint system reversed in time and replace t by $t - T$ we will have a system whose response to a unit impulse initiated at time $t = 0$ will result in values along the line L_4 of Fig. F-4 which are correspondingly the same as those of W_r^* along the line L_1 of Fig. F-1.

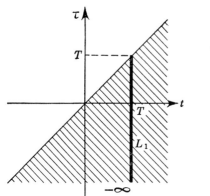

Fig. F-1   Representation of $W_r^*(t, \tau)$ in t, τ plane.

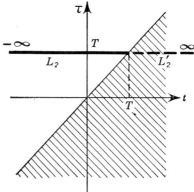

Fig. F-2   Representation of $y_i^*(t)B_i(t)$ in t, τ plane.

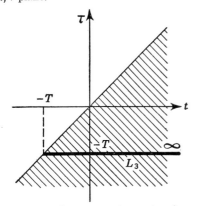

Fig. F-3   Representation of $y_i^*(-t)$ $B_i(-t)$ in t, τ plane.

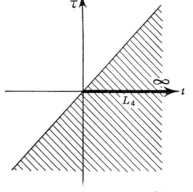

Fig. F-4   Representation of $y_i^*(T - t)$ $B_i(T - t)$ in t, τ plane.

To summarize, we wish to construct an appropriate modified system to be used in generating $W_r(t,\tau)$ continuously as a function of τ for a fixed value of $t = T$. This may be accomplished by first simulating the adjoint system and replacing t by $T - t$. Then, an impulse input to this system at time zero yields the desired result.

A rule for simulating the adjoint of a linear time-varying system can be stated quite simply after the following argument. The equations corre-

sponding to Eq. (F-3) for the adjoint system run backward in time and
with a shift in the origin of time of an amount T are given by

$$\frac{d}{dt} y_i(T - t) = y_j(T - t)[a_{ji}(T - t)$$
$$+ a_{j\alpha}(T - t)b_{\alpha i}(T - t)] + \delta_{ri}\delta(t) \quad \text{(F-18)}$$

This may be written as a set of differential and algebraic equations as
follows.

$$\frac{d}{dt} y_i(T - t) = y_j(T - t)a_{ji}(T - t) + y_\alpha(T - t)b_{\alpha i}(T - t) + \delta_{ri}\delta(t) \quad \text{(F-19)}$$

$$y_\alpha(T - t) = y_j(T - t)a_{j\alpha}(T - t) \quad \text{(F-20)}$$

A schematic diagram for Eqs. (F-1) and (F-2) in terms of "integrators,"
"summers," and time-varying "scale factors" is shown in Fig. F-5 while
a similar representation for Eqs. (F-19) and (F-20) is given in Fig. F-6.

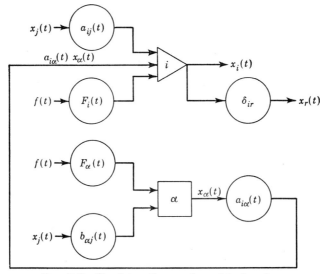

FIG. F-5   Simulator diagram for original system.

These diagrams are to be interpreted by means of the summation convention.   There will be m integrators and $n - m$ summers connected
as shown.   In Fig. F-5 the integrator for which $i = 1$ will have x_1 as its
output and will have (1) m inputs, x_1a_{11}, x_2a_{12}, . . . , $x_m a_{1m}$; (2) $n - m$
inputs, $x_{m+1}a_{1,m+1}$, $x_{m+2}a_{1,m+2}$, . . . , $x_n a_{1n}$; and (3) one input, $F_1(t)f(t)$.
Also, the summer for which $\alpha = m + 1$ will have x_{m+1} as its output and
will have (1) m inputs, $x_1b_{m+1,1}$, $x_2b_{m+1,2}$, . . . , $x_m b_{m+1,m}$, and (2) one input,
$F_{m+1}(t)f(t)$.   The other integrators and summers are connected in a sim-
ilar manner.   Here $x_r(t)$ is the output of the system for which the weighting function is desired and r may be any integer from 1 to m.   In Fig. F-6
a unit impulse is initiated at time $t = 0$ and the responses $y_i(T - t)$ are

shown to be multiplied by $F_i(T - t)$ and $y_\alpha(T - t)$ by $F_\alpha(T - t)$ because it is precisely the sum of these products that gives $y_i(T - t)B_i(T - t)$ as the desired weighting $W_r(T,t)$ for the original system as a function of t.

A comparison of Figs. F-5 and F-6 shows a very simple relation to exist between the original and the modified system. For example, in Fig. F-5 it is seen that integrator 2 is an input to integrator 1 through the factor a_{12}, and in Fig. F-6 the corresponding connection requires integrator 1 to be an input to integrator 2 through the same factor a_{12}. It is easily

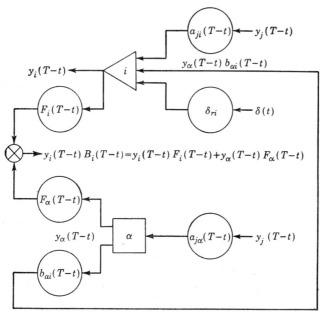

FIG. F-6   Simulator diagram for modified system.

verified that this interchanging of the roles of input and output is characteristic of all the connections. Therefore, the following general rule may be formulated:

"A schematic diagram of the system whose weighting function we desire is formed using only 'integrators,' 'summers,' and time-varying 'scale factors.' (Any linear lumped-parameter system may, of course, be so represented.) Then the corresponding diagram for the modified system is simulated by reversing the roles of inputs and outputs for each of the three basic elements and replacing the argument t in the time-varying coefficients by $T - t$. If the output of the rth integrator is the quantity for which the weighting function is desired, then the impulse input in the modified system should be introduced into the rth integrator and the appropriate outputs recorded."

The direct application of this technique to a simple second-order system is shown in Figs. 6.4-1 and 6.4-2.

DERIVATION OF OPTIMUM TIME-VARYING PARAMETER
FOR FIRST-ORDER PROBLEM

In Sec. 6.6 the problem of minimizing the mean-squared error for a first-order system is attacked empirically by the method of steepest descents. To provide a point of reference, the same problem is solved analytically in this appendix, giving a formal result which is then justified rigorously.

Let $y(t)$ satisfy

$$\frac{dy}{dt} + a(t)y = a(t)f(t) \qquad 0 \leq t \leq 1 \tag{G-1}$$

with
$$y(0) = y_0 \tag{G-2}$$

Let $f(t)$ belong to a stationary random process, with a correlation function given by

$$\phi(\tau) = c_0^2 e^{-\beta|\tau|} \tag{G-3}$$

Let y_0 be a random variable, statistically independent of $f(t)$, and with zero mean. The general solution to (G-1) and (G-2) may be written in the form

$$y(t) = y_0 w(t) + w(t) \int_0^t \frac{a(\tau)f(\tau)}{w(\tau)} d\tau \tag{G-4}$$

where
$$w(t) = \exp\left[- \int_0^t a(\tau)\, d\tau \right] \tag{G-5}$$

In particular, the mean-squared value of $y(1)$ is given by

$$\overline{y(1)^2} = \overline{y_0^2} w(1)^2 + w(1)^2 \int_0^1 \frac{a(\tau_1)}{w(\tau_1)} d\tau_1 \int_0^1 \frac{a(\tau_2)}{w(\tau_2)} \phi(\tau_2 - \tau_1) d\tau_2 \tag{G-6}$$

The problem is so to select $a(t)$ as to minimize $\overline{y(1)^2}$.

Rather then work directly with the expression (G-6) as it stands, it is convenient to employ the preliminary transformation

$$u(t) = \exp\left[\int_0^t a(\tau)\, d\tau \right] = \frac{1}{w(t)} \tag{G-7}$$

Noting that

$$u'(t) = \frac{du}{dt} = a(t)u(t) = \frac{a(t)}{w(t)} \tag{G-8}$$

Eq. (G-6) may be expressed in the form

$$\overline{y(1)^2} = \frac{\overline{y_0^2}}{u(1)^2} + \frac{c_0^2}{u(1)^2} \int_0^1 u'(\tau_1)\,d\tau_1 \int_0^1 u'(\tau_2) e^{-\beta|\tau_2 - \tau_1|}\,d\tau_2 \tag{G-9}$$

From Eq. (G-8),

$$a(t) = \frac{u'(t)}{u(t)} \tag{G-10}$$

Thus if $u(t)$ is any differentiable function such that

$$u(0) = 1 \qquad u(t) > 0 \qquad 0 \le t \le 1 \tag{G-11}$$

a corresponding quantity $a(t)$ is definable. In seeking to minimize the quantity $\overline{y(1)^2}$ as given by (G-9), it is therefore sufficient to find the best function $u(t)$ with the required properties.

Applying variational methods to (G-9), let $u(t)$ take on an increment $\delta u(t)$ such that

$$\delta u(0) = 0 \tag{G-12}$$

The variation in $\overline{y(1)^2}$ is

$$\delta \overline{y(1)^2} = -2 \frac{\overline{y_0^2}}{u(1)^3} \delta u(1) - 2 \frac{c_0^2}{u(1)^3} \delta u(1) \int_0^1 u'(\tau_1)\,d\tau_1$$
$$\times \int_0^1 u'(\tau_2) e^{-\beta|\tau_2 - \tau_1|}\,d\tau_2 + 2 \frac{c_0^2}{u(1)^2} \int_0^1 \delta u'(\tau_1)\,d\tau_1$$
$$\times \int_0^1 u'(\tau_2) e^{-\beta|\tau_2 - \tau_1|}\,d\tau_2 \tag{G-13}$$

By an integration by parts, using (G-12)

$$\int_0^1 \delta u'(\tau_1)\,d\tau_1 \int_0^1 u'(\tau_2) e^{-\beta|\tau_2 - \tau_1|}\,d\tau_2 = \delta u(1) \int_0^1 u'(\tau_2) e^{-\beta|\tau_2 - 1|}\,d\tau_2$$
$$- \int_0^1 \delta u(\tau_1) \left[\frac{d}{d\tau_1} \int_0^1 u'(\tau_2) e^{-\beta|\tau_2 - \tau_1|}\,d\tau_2 \right] d\tau_1 \tag{G-14}$$

Substitution of this result into (G-13) yields

$$\delta \overline{y(1)^2} = \delta u(1) \left[-\frac{2\overline{y_0^2}}{u(1)^3} - \frac{2c_0^2}{u(1)^3} \int_0^1 u'(\tau_1)\,d\tau_1 \int_0^1 u'(\tau_2) e^{-\beta|\tau_2 - \tau_1|}\,d\tau_2 \right.$$
$$\left. + \frac{2c_0^2}{u(1)^2} \int_0^1 u'(\tau_2) e^{-\beta|\tau_2 - 1|}\,d\tau_2 \right]$$
$$- \frac{2c_0^2}{u(1)^2} \int_0^1 \delta u(\tau_1) \frac{d}{d\tau_1} \left[\int_0^1 u'(\tau_2) e^{-\beta|\tau_2 - \tau_1|}\,d\tau_2 \right] d\tau_1 \tag{G-15}$$

If $u(t)$ gives a minimum $\overline{y(1)^2}$, the quantity (G-15) must vanish for every choice of $\delta u(t)$. Thus after simplification

$$-\overline{y_0^2} - c_0^2 \int_0^1 u'(\tau_1)\, d\tau_1 \int_0^1 u'(\tau_2)e^{-\beta|\tau_2-\tau_1|}\, d\tau_2$$

$$+ c_0^2 u(1) \int_0^1 u'(\tau_2)e^{-\beta|\tau_2-1|}\, d\tau_2 = 0 \quad \text{(G-16)}$$

and

$$\frac{d}{d\tau_1}\int_0^1 u'(\tau_2)e^{-\beta|\tau_2-\tau_1|}\, d\tau_2 = 0 \qquad 0 \leq \tau_1 \leq 1 \quad \text{(G-17)}$$

From (G-17),

$$\int_0^1 u'(\tau)e^{-\beta|\tau-t|}\, d\tau = K \qquad 0 \leq t \leq 1 \quad \text{(G-18)}$$

or some constant K. Equation (G-16) then gives

$$-\overline{y_0^2} - c_0^2 \int_0^1 u'(\tau_1)K\, d\tau_1 + c_0^2 u(1)K = 0 \quad \text{(G-19)}$$

or

$$-\overline{y_0^2} - c_0^2 K[u(1) - u(0)] + c_0^2 u(1)K = 0 \quad \text{(G-20)}$$

Noting that $u(0) = 1$, Eq. (G-20) yields for K the value

$$K = \frac{\overline{y_0^2}}{c_0^2} \quad \text{(G-21)}$$

The function $u'(t)$ is thus to be determined as the solution to the integral equation

$$\int_0^1 u'(\tau)e^{-\beta|\tau-t|}\, d\tau = \frac{\overline{y_0^2}}{c_0^2} \quad \text{(G-22)}$$

A solution to this relation may be verified by inspection. Let

$$u'(t) = A + B\delta(t) + C\delta(t - 1) \quad \text{(G-23)}$$

Then $\quad A \int_0^1 e^{-\beta|\tau-t|}\, d\tau + Be^{-\beta t} + Ce^{-\beta(1-t)} = \frac{\overline{y_0^2}}{c_0^2} \qquad 0 \leq t \leq 1 \quad$ (G-24)

giving

$$\frac{2A}{\beta} + e^{-\beta t}\left(B - \frac{A}{\beta}\right) + e^{-\beta(1-t)}\left(C - \frac{A}{\beta}\right) = \frac{\overline{y_0^2}}{c_0^2} \qquad 0 \leq t \leq 1 \quad \text{(G-25)}$$

The requirement that (G-25) be satisfied identically in t gives

$$A = \frac{\beta}{2}\frac{\overline{y_0^2}}{c_0^2} \qquad B = \frac{1}{2}\frac{\overline{y_0^2}}{c_0^2} = C \quad \text{(G-26)}$$

Thus

$$u'(t) = \frac{1}{2}\frac{\overline{y_0^2}}{c_0^2}[\beta + \delta(t) + \delta(t - 1)] \quad \text{(G-27)}$$

Integration of this relation gives

$$u(t) = \begin{cases} 1 & t = 0 \\ 1 + \dfrac{1}{2}\dfrac{\overline{y_0^2}}{c_0^2} + \dfrac{\beta}{2}\dfrac{\overline{y_0^2}}{c_0^2}t & 0 < t < 1 \\ 1 + \dfrac{2 + \beta}{2}\dfrac{\overline{y_0^2}}{c_0^2} & t = 1 \end{cases} \qquad \text{(G-28)}$$

From (G-10), $a(t)$ is then found to be

$$a(t) = \frac{\dfrac{1}{2}\dfrac{\overline{y_0^2}}{c_0^2}[\beta + \delta(t) + \delta(t-1)]}{u(t)}$$

$$= \frac{\dfrac{1}{2}\dfrac{\overline{y_0^2}}{c_0^2}[\beta + \delta(t) + \delta(t-1)]}{1 + \displaystyle\int_0^t \dfrac{1}{2}\dfrac{\overline{y_0^2}}{c_0^2}[\beta + \delta(\tau) + \delta(\tau-1)]\,d\tau} \qquad \text{(G-29)}$$

Physically, this result is somewhat surprising. In effect, the theory calls for a very high coefficient for a very short period of time both at the beginning and end of the time interval, with a coefficient given in between by

$$a(t) = \frac{\dfrac{\beta}{2}\dfrac{\overline{y_0^2}}{c_0^2}}{\left[1 + \dfrac{1}{2}\dfrac{\overline{y_0^2}}{c_0^2}\right] + \dfrac{\beta}{2}\dfrac{\overline{y_0^2}}{c_0^2}t} \qquad \text{(G-30)}$$

The singular character of the solution throws considerable doubt on its validity. We shall nevertheless prove rigorously that the proper interpretation of this result in terms of a limiting process does in fact lead to a unique solution to the problem.

As a final calculation, the minimum value of $\overline{y(1)^2}$ is derived from (G-9). Substitution from (G-22) and (G-28) gives

$$\overline{y(1)^2} = \frac{\overline{y_0^2}}{u(1)^2} + \frac{c_0^2}{u(1)^2}\int_0^1 u'(\tau_1)\frac{\overline{y_0^2}}{c_0^2}\,d\tau_1$$

$$= \frac{\overline{y_0^2}}{u(1)^2}[1 + u(1) - u(0)]$$

$$= \frac{\overline{y_0^2}}{u(1)} = \frac{\overline{y_0^2}}{1 + \dfrac{2 + \beta}{2}\dfrac{\overline{y_0^2}}{c_0^2}} \qquad \text{(G-31)}$$

In particular, for $\beta = 1 = c_0^2$,

$$\overline{y(1)^2} = \frac{\overline{y_0^2}}{1 + \frac{3}{2}\overline{y_0^2}} \qquad \text{(G-32)}$$

for the optimum system.

As the first step in proof of these formal results we establish the following:

LEMMA.   Let $v(t)$ belong to $L_1(0,1)$ and let $\beta > 0$.   Then

$$\int_0^1 v(t_1) \, dt_1 \int_0^1 v(t_2)e^{-\beta|t_2-t_1|} \, dt_2 \geq \frac{2}{2+\beta}\left[\int_0^1 v(t) \, dt\right]^2 \qquad \text{(G-33)}$$

PROOF.   Assume first that the result is valid whenever $\int_0^1 v(t) \, dt \neq 0$. We then may prove it for $\int_0^1 v(t) \, dt = 0$ by replacing $v(t)$ by $v(t) + \epsilon x(t)$, with $\int_0^1 x(t) \, dt \neq 0$, and letting ϵ approach zero.   Since each side of the inequality holds for all nonvanishing ϵ and is continuous in ϵ, the inequality must hold for $\epsilon = 0$ as well.   As a result of this argument, we may normalize the problem by assuming

$$\int_0^1 v(t) \, dt = 1 \qquad \text{(G-34)}$$

We next note that

$$e^{-\beta|t_2-t_1|} = \int_{-\infty}^{\infty} K(t_1 - \tau)K(t_2 - \tau) \, d\tau \qquad \text{(G-35)}$$

where

$$K(t) = \begin{cases} 0 & t < 0 \\ \sqrt{2\beta} \, e^{-\beta t} & t > 0 \end{cases} \qquad \text{(G-36)}$$

Thus for any $v(t)$

$$\int_0^1 v(t_1) \, dt_1 \int_0^1 v(t_2)e^{-\beta|t_2-t_1|} \, dt_2$$

$$= \int_0^1 v(t_1) \, dt_1 \int_0^1 v(t_2) \, dt_2 \int_{-\infty}^{\infty} K(t_1 - \tau)K(t_2 - \tau) \, d\tau$$

$$= \int_{-\infty}^{\infty} d\tau \left[\int_0^1 v(t)K(t - \tau) \, dt\right]^2 \geq 0 \quad \text{(G-37)}$$

For any two functions $x(t)$, $y(t)$ of L_1, let

$$F(x,y) = \int_0^1 x(t_1) \, dt_1 \int_0^1 y(t_2)e^{-\beta|t_2-t_1|} \, dt_2 \qquad \text{(G-38)}$$

We note that $F(x,y) = F(y,x)$.   Also, let

$$v_\epsilon(t) = \begin{cases} \dfrac{1}{(\beta + 2)\epsilon} & 0 \leq t \leq \epsilon \\[2mm] \dfrac{\beta}{(\beta + 2)(1 - 2\epsilon)} & \epsilon < t < 1 - \epsilon \\[2mm] \dfrac{1}{(\beta + 2)\epsilon} & 1 - \epsilon \leq t \leq 1 \end{cases} \qquad \text{(G-39)}$$

We show that for any $v(t)$ satisfying (G-34),

$$F(v,v_\epsilon) = \frac{2}{\beta + 2} + O\left(\epsilon \int_0^1 |v(t)| \, dt\right) \qquad \text{(G-40)}$$

For this purpose we note that

$$(\beta + 2) \int_0^1 v_\epsilon(\tau) e^{-\beta|t-\tau|} \, d\tau$$

$$= \frac{1}{\epsilon} \int_0^\epsilon e^{-\beta|t-\tau|} \, d\tau + \frac{\beta}{1 - 2\epsilon} \int_\epsilon^{1-\epsilon} e^{-\beta|t-\tau|} \, d\tau + \frac{1}{\epsilon} \int_{1-\epsilon}^1 e^{-\beta|t-\tau|} \, d\tau \quad \text{(G-41)}$$

However,

$$\left| \frac{1}{\epsilon} \int_0^\epsilon e^{-\beta|t-\tau|} \, d\tau - e^{-\beta t} \right| = \left| \frac{1}{\epsilon} \int_0^\epsilon (e^{-\beta|t-\tau|} - e^{-\beta t}) \, d\tau \right| \leq e^{\beta\epsilon} - 1$$

$$0 \leq t \leq 1 \quad \text{(G-42)}$$

Similarly,

$$\left| \frac{1}{\epsilon} \int_{1-\epsilon}^1 e^{-\beta|t-\tau|} \, d\tau - e^{-\beta(1-t)} \right| \leq e^{-\beta(1-t)}(e^{\beta\epsilon} - 1) \leq e^{\beta\epsilon} - 1$$

$$0 \leq t \leq 1 \quad \text{(G-43)}$$

Finally,

$$\left| \frac{\beta}{1 - 2\epsilon} \int_\epsilon^{1-\epsilon} e^{-\beta|t-\tau|} \, d\tau - [2 - e^{-\beta t} - e^{-\beta(1-t)}] \right|$$

$$= \left| \frac{\beta}{1 - 2\epsilon} \int_\epsilon^{1-\epsilon} e^{-\beta|t-\tau|} \, d\tau - \beta \int_0^1 e^{-\beta|t-\tau|} \, d\tau \right| \leq 4\beta\epsilon \quad \text{(G-44)}$$

Thus

$$(\beta + 2) \int_0^1 v_\epsilon(\tau) e^{-\beta|t-\tau|} \, d\tau = 2 + O(\epsilon) \quad \text{(G-45)}$$

uniformly for $0 \leq t \leq 1$.

From (G-38) and (G-45), together with (G-34), we have

$$F(v, v_\epsilon) = \int_0^1 v(t_1) \left[\frac{2}{\beta + 2} + O(\epsilon) \right] dt_1$$

$$= \frac{2}{\beta + 2} + \int_0^1 |v(t) O(\epsilon)| \, dt$$

$$= \frac{2}{\beta + 2} + O\left(\epsilon \int_0^1 |v(t)| \, dt \right) \quad \text{(G-46)}$$

as indicated by (G-40).   In particular,

$$F(v_\epsilon, v_\epsilon) = \frac{2}{\beta + 2} + O(\epsilon) \quad \text{(G-47)}$$

Now let $v(t)$ satisfy (G-34), and assume that

$$F(v, v) < \frac{2}{\beta + 2} \quad \text{(G-48)}$$

Let θ be an arbitrary real number, and set

$$v_1(\theta, \epsilon, t) = (1 - \theta)v(t) + \theta v_\epsilon(t) \quad \text{(G-49)}$$

Also let

$$f_\epsilon(\theta) = F[v_1(\theta,\epsilon,t), v_1(\theta,\epsilon,t)] \qquad \text{(G-50)}$$

By direct calculation from (G-38) and (G-49),

$$f_\epsilon(\theta) = (1 - \theta)^2 F(v,v) + 2\theta(1 - \theta)F(v,v_\epsilon) + \theta^2 F(v_\epsilon,v_\epsilon) \qquad \text{(G-51)}$$

Then

$$\frac{d^2}{d\theta^2} f_\epsilon(\theta) = 2F(v,v) - 4F(v,v_\epsilon) + 2F(v_\epsilon,v_\epsilon)$$

$$= 2\left[F(v,v) - \frac{2}{\beta + 2}\right] + O(\epsilon) + O\left[\epsilon \int_0^1 |v(t)| \, dt\right] \qquad \text{(G-52)}$$

Taking ϵ so small that the right-hand member of (G-52) is negative, we may then choose θ so large that $f_\epsilon(\theta)$ is negative also. From (G-37) and (G-50) this is impossible, however, showing that (G-48) is false. We thus have

$$F(v,v) \geqq \frac{2}{\beta + 2} \qquad \text{(G-53)}$$

which is equivalent to the desired result (G-33).

Turning now to the main problem, let

$$u_\epsilon(t) = 1 + \frac{\beta + 2}{2} \frac{\overline{y_0^2}}{c_0^2} \int_0^t v_\epsilon(\tau) \, d\tau \qquad \text{(G-54)}$$

For an arbitrary absolutely continuous positive function $u(t)$ such that

$$u(0) = 1 \qquad \text{(G-55)}$$

let

$$G(u) = \overline{y(1)^2} = \frac{\overline{y_0^2}}{u(1)^2} + \frac{c_0^2}{u(1)^2} \int_0^1 u'(\tau_1) \, d\tau_1 \int_0^1 u'(\tau_2) e^{-\beta|\tau_2 - \tau_1|} \, d\tau_2 \qquad \text{(G-56)}$$

For the particular choice $u = u_\epsilon$, we have

$$u_\epsilon(1) = 1 + \frac{\beta + 2}{2} \frac{\overline{y_0^2}}{c_0^2} \qquad \text{(G-57)}$$

from (G-39) and (G-54). Also

$$\overline{y_0^2} + c_0^2 \int_0^1 u'_\epsilon(\tau_1) \, d\tau_1 \int_0^1 u'_\epsilon(\tau_2) e^{-\beta|\tau_2 - \tau_1|} \, d\tau_2 = \overline{y_0^2} + \left(\frac{\beta + 2}{2}\right) \frac{2(\overline{y_0^2})^2}{c_0^2} F(v_\epsilon,v_\epsilon)$$

$$= \overline{y_0^2} + \frac{\beta + 2}{2} \frac{(\overline{y_0^2})^2}{c_0^2} + O(\epsilon) \qquad \text{(G-58)}$$

Thus

$$\lim_{\epsilon \to 0} G(u_\epsilon) = \frac{\overline{y_0^2}}{1 + \dfrac{\beta + 2}{2} \dfrac{\overline{y_0^2}}{c_0^2}} \qquad \text{(G-59)}$$

To complete the proof, we now show that

$$G(u) \geq \frac{\overline{y_0^2}}{1 + \dfrac{\beta + 2}{2}\,\dfrac{\overline{y_0^2}}{c_0^2}} \tag{G-60}$$

for every suitable function $u(t)$.

From (G-56) and the lemma, we have

$$G(u) \geq \frac{1}{u(1)^2}\left\{\overline{y_0^2} + \frac{2c_0^2}{2 + \beta}\left[\int_0^1 u'(t)\,dt\right]^2\right\}$$

$$= \frac{1}{u(1)^2}\left\{\overline{y_0^2} + \frac{2c_0^2}{2 + \beta}\,[u(1) - 1]^2\right\} \tag{G-61}$$

The right-hand member of this relation, considered as a function of the positive variable $u(1)$, possesses a unique minimum at

$$u(1) = 1 + \frac{\beta + 2}{2}\,\frac{\overline{y_0^2}}{c_0^2} \tag{G-62}$$

and this minimum value is precisely the right-hand member of (G-60).

We have thus established the result, in the following sense. The particular function $u_\epsilon'(t)$ [which can be regarded as approximating the function $u'(t)$ of (G-27)] is such that $\lim_{\epsilon \to 0} G(u_\epsilon)$ is less than or equal to the value of $G(u)$ for any other suitable function $u(t)$. In this sense, then, the delta-function result actually defines an optimum.

SOLUTION OF THE EQUATION $P(x) = 0$

Before the procedure developed in Sec. 7.5 can be carried out in practice it is necessary to find the roots of the equation $P(x) = 0$, where $P(x)$ is defined by Eq. (7.5-11). From the form of $P(x)$ it is possible to locate approximately the positive real roots in many cases. For example, if each of the B's and C's is positive, and if each of the b's and c's is real, then the function has the form shown in Fig. H-1. Therefore, in this case, there will exist exactly $m + p - 1$ distinct real roots. Actually, it is possible to formulate a general rule which is applicable even when all B's and C's are not of the same sign. We first arrange the b's and c's, which are regarded as a single group of positive numbers, in increasing order of magnitude and examine the signs of the corresponding B's and C's. From an inspection of the various possibilities illustrated in Figs. H-1 through H-6, the following rule may be deduced:

"Count the number of changes in sign of the coefficients when the coefficients are reordered as described. If the number of changes is even, there can be at most that number of complex roots with positive real parts. If the number of changes is odd, there can be at most one less than that number of complex roots with positive real parts."

In this way not only the number of real roots but also their approximate location often can be determined so that the labor involved in finding these as well as the other roots is considerably reduced. However, since two real roots may occur between consecutive b's and c's, it seems to be impossible to get a lower bound on the number of complex roots from this kind of argument.

For real correlation functions there cannot exist a pair of pure imaginary roots of Eq. (7.5-11). This can be seen from the following argument. The power spectral density $G_1(\omega)$ of the total input to our filter (signal + noise) is found from

$$G_1(\omega) = \frac{2}{\pi} \int_0^\infty \phi(\tau) \cos \omega\tau \, d\tau$$

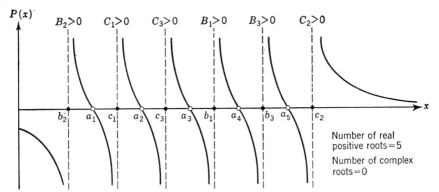

FIG. H-1   Typical form of $P(x)$ when all coefficients are positive.

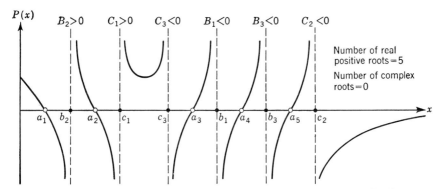

FIG. H-2   Typical form of $P(x)$ when coefficients have one change in sign

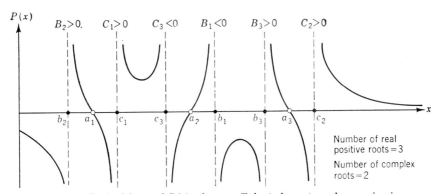

FIG. H-3   Typical form of $P(x)$ when coefficients have two changes in sign.

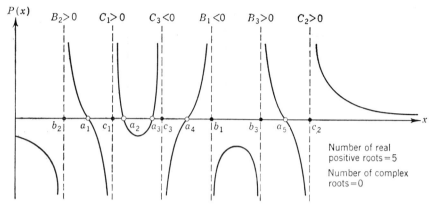

FIG. H-4 Typical form of $P(x)$ when coefficients have two changes in sign.

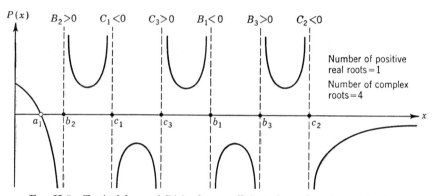

FIG. H-5 Typical form of $P(x)$ when coefficients have five changes in sign.

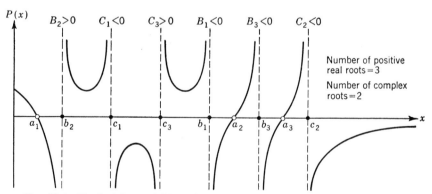

FIG. H-6 Typical form of $P(x)$ when coefficients have three changes in sign.

Using Eq. (7.5-7), we obtain

$$G_1(\omega) = \frac{2}{\pi}\left(\sum_{j=1}^{m}\frac{b_jB_j}{\omega^2 + b_j^2} + \sum_{k=1}^{p}\frac{c_kC_k}{\omega^2 + c_k^2}\right)$$

Since the power spectral density is a measure of the amount of energy contained in the input at various frequencies, it must always be positive. If this expression for $G_1(\omega)$ is compared with $P(x)$ in Eq. (7.5-11), we see that pure imaginary roots of $P(x)$ would imply pure real roots of $G_1(\omega)$, which is clearly impossible.

At this point it is necessary to interject a note of caution. It is possible to approximate a true correlation function in such a way that although the approximation may seem quite satisfactory, it nevertheless may give rise to a negative power density at some frequencies. This could be detected immediately from the fact that $P(x)$ would then possess pure imaginary roots. In many cases this can be avoided by making certain that $G_1(\omega)$ is of the same sign at zero frequency as it is at very large frequencies. Therefore, an easy rule to apply is the following:

"In choosing an approximation to the correlation functions, care must be exercised to ensure that the quantities

$$\sum_{j=1}^{m}\frac{B_j}{b_j} + \sum_{k=1}^{p}\frac{C_k}{c_k} \quad \text{and} \quad \sum_{j=1}^{m}b_jB_j + \sum_{k=1}^{p}c_kC_k$$

are of the same sign."

DELTA-FUNCTION TERMS IN THE SOLUTION
OF A CERTAIN INTEGRAL EQUATION

In this appendix we wish to justify, by a physical argument, the inclusion of delta-function terms and their derivatives at each of the end points $t = 0$ and $t = T$ in the solution of the integral equation (8.4-1). For this purpose let us consider the following problem.

A taut string of infinite length is held fixed at its ends and is subject to an elastic restraint against vertical deflection. If $\rho(x)$ is a distribution of load applied to the string producing a small deflection $y(x)$, then the deflection is determined as the solution of the boundary-value problem

$$\frac{d^2y}{dx^2} - \beta^2 y = \rho(x) \tag{I-1}$$

$$y(-\infty) = y(+\infty) = 0$$

where β is a constant related to the elastic restraint coefficient and the tension in the string. Alternately, the deflection is given explicitly by

$$y(x) = \int_{-\infty}^{\infty} K(x - \xi)\rho(\xi)\,d\xi \tag{I-2}$$

where $K(x - \xi)$, the Green's function of the problem, is given by

$$K(x - \xi) = -\frac{1}{2\beta}\,e^{-\beta|x-\xi|} \tag{I-3}$$

Suppose now that $y(x)$ is prescribed over the interval $0 \leq x \leq X$ and we are required to determine the load distribution $\rho(x)$ to be applied in this interval only which would produce the desired deflection. The relation (I-2) then becomes an integral equation for ρ with limits 0 and X on the integral. For example, to produce a constant deflection in this interval it is clear physically that one must apply concentrated loads at the end points together with a uniform load distribution throughout the interval. Thus for $y(x) = -1$, the solution of Eq. (I-2) is readily seen to be

$$\rho(x) = \beta[\beta + \delta(x) + \delta(X - x)] \tag{I-4}$$

More generally, for an arbitrary $y(x)$ one would expect concentrated loads at the end points in order to produce the required deflection.

416

For a more complicated example, consider the problem of the deflection of an infinite beam on an elastic foundation.   If the shear stress and bending moment are zero at the ends, then the deflection is determined as the solution of the boundary-value problem

$$\frac{d^4y}{dx^4} + \beta^2 y = -\rho(x) \tag{I-5}$$

$$y''(-\infty) = y'''(-\infty) = y''(\infty) = y'''(\infty) = 0$$

where β is a constant related to the elastic restraint coefficient and Young's modulus for the beam.   The Green's function for this problem is

$$K(x - \xi) = -\frac{1}{16\beta\sqrt{2\beta}}[\exp(-\sqrt{2\beta}\,|x - \xi|)(\cos\sqrt{2\beta}\,|x - \xi|$$
$$- \sin\sqrt{2\beta}\,|x - \xi|)] \tag{I-6}$$

so that the deflection again is given by Eq. (I-2).   Now if $y(x)$ is prescribed in the interval $0 \leq x \leq X$, the required load $\rho(x)$ would necessarily consist of a concentrated shear force and bending moment at each of the end points of the interval together with a continuous distribution of load in between.   Thus, $\rho(x)$ would contain the terms $\delta(x)$, $\delta'(x)$, $\delta(T - x)$, and $\delta'(T - x)$.

As a consequence of the above discussion the string problem and the beam problem may be considered the mechanical analogues of certain filtering problems.   Thus, a stationary random process possessing a correlation function proportional to the Green's function of Eq. (I-3) is obtained by passing a white noise through a first-order filter whose transfer function is given by

$$Y(p) = \frac{1}{p + \beta} \tag{I-7}$$

Similarly, the transfer function associated with the Green's function of Eq. (I-6) is seen to be

$$Y(p) = \frac{1}{p^2 + 2\beta p + \beta} \tag{I-8}$$

That there is an upper limit to the number of δ-function terms and their derivatives at the end points in the solution of Eq. (8.4-1) is a consequence of the following argument.   To such an integral equation, with a kernel expressible as a sum of exponentials, we may always associate a certain prediction problem.   The kernel may be considered as the correlation function of a certain random process whose spectral density is a rational function of frequency.   Thus, the transfer function of the associated shaping filter will be a rational function of p with numerator m and denominator N such that $m \leq N$.   As a consequence the optimum predictor weighting function cannot contain a derivative of a δ-function higher than $N - m + 1$. Otherwise, by passing white noise through the shaping filter and predictor in cascade, the output would be a white noise or a differentiated white noise, both of which have infinite mean-squared values.

To summarize, we have given arguments made plausible by physical reasoning to show that the solution of Eq. (8.4-1) must contain δ-function terms and their derivatives at each of the end points of the interval. Furthermore, we have shown that there can be no more than $N - m = n$ such δ-function terms contained in the solution.

INVERSION OF A CERTAIN MATRIX

It is the purpose of this appendix to demonstrate that the inverse of the matrix A_{NN}, defined by Eq. (8.4-51), is correctly given by Eq. (8.4-57). For this purpose let us define the two matrices $E_{NN}^{(1)}$ and $E_{NN}^{(2)}$ by

$$E_{NN}^{(1)} = \left\| \begin{array}{cc} T_{nn}^{(1)} & O_{nm} \\ R_{mn}^{(1)} D_{nn} & D_{mm}^{(1)} \end{array} \right\| \tag{J-1}$$

$$E_{NN}^{(2)} = \left\| \begin{array}{cc} T_{nn}^{(2)} & -T_{nn}^{(2)} R_{nm}^{(2)} \\ O_{mn} & D_{mm}^{(2)} \end{array} \right\| \tag{J-2}$$

Each of the indicated submatrices is defined in the computational procedure of Sec. 8.4 with the exception of $T_{nn}^{(1)}$. The matrix $T_{nn}^{(1)}$ is triangular with zeros above the main diagonal. The element in the first row and first column is a one. The other elements are given by

$$\prod_{r=1}^{i}{}^{i} \frac{1}{\gamma_j - \gamma_r}$$

If we can show that

$$E_{NN}^{(1)} A_{NN} E_{NN}^{(2)} = \left\| \begin{array}{cc} I_{nn} & O_{nm} \\ O_{mn} & M_{mm}^{(2)} \end{array} \right\| \tag{J-3}$$

then the inverse A_{NN}^{-1} will be given by

$$A_{NN}^{-1} = E_{NN}^{(2)} \left\| \begin{array}{cc} I_{nn} & O_{nm} \\ O_{mn} & M_{mm}^{(2)-1} \end{array} \right\| E_{NN}^{(1)} \tag{J-4}$$

Carrying out the matrix multiplication indicated in Eq. (J-4), the formula for the inverse as given by Eq. (8.4-57) will follow. Thus, the problem at hand will be solved if we can establish Eq. (J-3).

If we perform the multiplication indicated in Eq. (J-3), we see at once that our problem is that of establishing the following as identities:

$$I_{nn} = T_{nn}^{(1)} V_{nn}^{(1)} T_{nn}^{(2)}$$
$$O_{nm} = -T_{nn}^{(1)} V_{nn}^{(1)} T_{nn}^{(2)} R_{nm}^{(2)} + T_{nn}^{(1)} M_{nm}^{(1)} D_{mm}^{(2)}$$
$$O_{mn} = (R_{mn}^{(1)} D_{nn} V_{nn}^{(1)} + D_{mm}^{(1)} V_{mn}^{(2)}) T_{nn}^{(2)}$$
$$M_{mm}^{(2)} = -(R_{mn}^{(1)} D_{nn} V_{nn}^{(1)} + D_{mm}^{(1)} V_{mn}^{(2)}) T_{nn}^{(2)} R_{nm}^{(2)}$$
$$+ (R_{mn}^{(1)} D_{nn} M_{uu}^{(1)} + D_{mm}^{(1)} M_{mm}^{(2)}) D_{mm}^{(2)}$$

or, equivalently,

$$\text{I.} \quad I_{nn} = T_{nn}^{(1)} V_{nn}^{(1)} T_{nn}^{(2)} \tag{J-5}$$

$$\text{II.} \quad R_{nm}^{(2)} = T_{nn}^{(1)} M_{nm}^{(1)} D_{mm}^{(2)} \tag{J-6}$$

$$\text{III.} \quad O_{mn} = R_{mn}^{(1)} D_{nn} V_{nn}^{(1)} + D_{mm}^{(1)} V_{mn}^{(2)} \tag{J-7}$$

$$\text{IV.} \quad M_{mm}^{(2)} = (R_{mn}^{(1)} D_{nn} M_{nm}^{(1)} + D_{mm}^{(1)} M_{mm}^{(2)}) D_{mm}^{(2)} \tag{J-8}$$

Proof of I. First let us observe that

$$V_{nn}^{(1)} T_{nn}^{(2)} = \| P_j(\gamma_i) \| \tag{J-9}$$

where we have defined

$$P_1(\gamma_i) = 1 \qquad P_j(\gamma_i) = \prod_{r=1}^{j-1} (\gamma_i - \gamma_r) \tag{J-10}$$

Since both of the matrices $T_{nn}^{(1)}$ and $V_{nn}^{(1)} T_{nn}^{(2)}$ are triangular matrices with zeros above the main diagonal, their product will have the same form. The rest of the elements in the product are

$$\sum_{u=j}^{i} \frac{\displaystyle\prod_{r=1}^{j-1} (\gamma_u - \gamma_r)}{\displaystyle\prod_{s=1}^{i} (\gamma_u - \gamma_s)} = \sum_{u=j}^{i} \frac{1}{\displaystyle\prod_{s=j}^{i} (\gamma_u - \gamma_s)} \qquad 1 \leq j \leq i$$

Clearly, the elements along the main diagonal are one's and the result will follow if we can show that

$$\sum_{u=j}^{i} \frac{1}{\displaystyle\prod_{s=j}^{i} (\gamma_u - \gamma_s)} = 0 \qquad j < i \tag{J-11}$$

To prove this, let us define the following analytic function of the complex variable z

$$F(z) = \frac{1}{\displaystyle\prod_{s=j}^{i} (z - \gamma_s)} \qquad j < i \tag{J-12}$$

which has simple poles at $z = \gamma_j, \gamma_{j+1}, \ldots, \gamma_i$ and is analytic at infinity. The residues at each of these poles are easily found to be

$$R(\gamma_u) = \frac{1}{\displaystyle\prod_{s=j}^{i} (\gamma_u - \gamma_s)} \tag{J-13}$$

Now, following the same arguments that were used in establishing Eq. (8.4-79), we have the proof.

Proof of II. Since

$$M^{(1)}_{nm} D^{(2)}_{mm} = \left\| \prod_{r=1}^{n} {}^{i} (\alpha_j - \gamma_r) \right\| \tag{J-14}$$

we have

$$T^{(1)}_{nn} M^{(1)}_{nm} D^{(2)}_{mm} = \left\| \sum_{u=1}^{i} \frac{\prod_{s=1}^{n} {}^{u} (\alpha_j - \gamma_s)}{\prod_{r=1}^{i} {}^{u} (\gamma_u - \gamma_r)} \right\| \tag{J-15}$$

As before we use complex variable techniques to establish Eq. (J-6). We define

$$F(z) = \frac{\prod_{s=1}^{n} (\alpha_j - \gamma_s)}{(\alpha_j - z) \prod_{r=1}^{i} (z - \gamma_r)} \tag{J-16}$$

which has simple poles at $z = \alpha_j, \gamma_1, \gamma_2, \ldots, \gamma_i$ with residues given by

$$R(\gamma_u) = \frac{\prod_{s=1}^{n} {}^{u} (\alpha_j - \gamma_s)}{\prod_{r=1}^{i} {}^{u} (\gamma_u - \gamma_r)} \qquad u = 1, 2, \ldots, i \tag{J-17}$$

$$R(\alpha_j) = \begin{cases} -\prod_{s=i+1}^{n} (\alpha_j - \gamma_r) & i = 1 \text{ or } 2 \text{ or } \ldots n-1 \\ -1 & i = n \end{cases} \tag{J-18}$$

Using the same argument, we have the proof.

Proof of III. We have

$$R^{(1)}_{mn} D_{nn} V^{(1)}_{nn} = \sum_{u=1}^{n} \frac{\gamma_u^{j-1}}{(\gamma_u - \rho_i) \prod_{r=1}^{n} {}^{u} (\gamma_u - \gamma_r)} \tag{J-19}$$

and

$$D^{(1)}_{mm} V^{(2)}_{mn} = \left\| \frac{\rho_i^{j-1}}{\prod_{r=1}^{n} (\rho_i - \gamma_r)} \right\| \tag{J-20}$$

The desired result will follow as before by considering the analytic function

$$F(z) = \frac{z^{j-1}}{(z - \rho_i) \prod_{r=1}^{n} (z - \gamma_r)} \tag{J-21}$$

which has simple poles at $z = \rho_i, \gamma_1, \gamma_2, \ldots, \gamma_n$ with residues given by

$$R(\gamma_u) = \frac{\gamma_u^{j-1}}{(\gamma_u - \rho_i) \prod_{r=1}^{u} (\gamma_u - \gamma_r)} \qquad u = 1, 2, \ldots, n \qquad \text{(J-22)}$$

$$R(\rho_i) = \frac{\rho_i^{j-1}}{\prod_{r=1}^{n} (\rho_i - \gamma_r)} \qquad\qquad \text{(J-23)}$$

Proof of IV.   We have

$$R_{mn}^{(1)} D_{nn} M_{nm}^{(1)} D_{mm}^{(2)} = \left\| \sum_{u=1}^{n} \frac{1}{\gamma_u - \rho_i} \prod_{r=1}^{u} \left(\frac{\alpha_j - \gamma_r}{\gamma_u - \gamma_r} \right) \right\| \qquad \text{(J-24)}$$

and

$$D_{mm}^{(1)} M_{mm}^{(2)} D_{mm}^{(2)} = \left\| \frac{1}{\alpha_j - \rho_i} \prod_{r=1}^{n} \left(\frac{\alpha_j - \gamma_r}{\rho_i - \gamma_r} \right) \right\| \qquad \text{(J-25)}$$

Equation (J-8) follows by considering the analytic function

$$F(z) = \frac{\prod_{r=1}^{n} (\alpha_j - \gamma_r)}{(z - \rho_i)(\alpha_j - z) \prod_{r=1}^{n} (z - \gamma_r)} \qquad \text{(J-26)}$$

which has simple poles at $z = \rho_i, \alpha_j, \gamma_1, \gamma_2, \ldots, \gamma_n$ with

$$R(\gamma_u) = \frac{1}{\gamma_u - \rho_i} \prod_{r=1}^{u} \left(\frac{\alpha_j - \gamma_r}{\gamma_u - \gamma_r} \right) \qquad \text{(J-27)}$$

$$R(\rho_i) = \frac{1}{\alpha_j - \rho_i} \prod_{r=1}^{n} \left(\frac{\alpha_j - \gamma_r}{\rho_i - \gamma_r} \right) \qquad \text{(J-28)}$$

$$R(\alpha_j) = - \frac{1}{\alpha_j - \rho_i} \qquad\qquad \text{(J-29)}$$

To complete this appendix, it is necessary to show that the inverses of the matrices $V_{nn}^{(1)}$ and $M_{mm}^{(2)}$ are correctly given by Eqs. (8.4-8) and (8.4-10). From Eq. (J-5) it follows that

$$V_{nn}^{(1)-1} = T_{nn}^{(2)} T_{nn}^{(1)} \qquad \text{(J-30)}$$

However, it is easier to verify Eq. (8.4-8) by another method.   Let us define

$$Q_j(x) = \prod_{r=1}^{n} {}^{j} (\gamma_r - x) \qquad \text{(J-31)}$$

Then the result of multiplying $V_{nn}^{(1)}$ by the expression given in Eq. (8.4-8) is simply

$$\left\| \frac{Q_j(\gamma_i)}{Q_j(\gamma_j)} \right\|$$

Clearly, $Q_j(\gamma_i) = 0$ for $i \neq j$ and $Q_j(\gamma_j) \neq 0$ so that the product matrix thus obtained is the identity matrix. This completes the proof.

To obtain the inverse of the matrix $M_{mm}^{(2)}$, we verify that the determinant of this matrix satisfies the difference equation

$$|M_{kk}^{(2)}| = \frac{\displaystyle\prod_{r=1}^{k-1} \frac{(\rho_r - \rho_k)(\alpha_k - \alpha_r)}{(\alpha_k - \rho_r)}}{\displaystyle\prod_{s=1}^{k} (\alpha_s - \rho_k)} |M_{k-1,k-1}^{(2)}| \qquad \text{(J-32)}$$

by first subtracting the kth row of the determinant $|M_{kk}^{(2)}|$ from each of the other rows and then subtracting the kth column from each of the other columns. We may now use an inductive argument to show that

$$|M_{mm}^{(2)^*}| = \frac{\displaystyle\prod_{s=1}^{m-1} \prod_{r=s+1}^{m} (\rho_r - \rho_s)(\alpha_s - \alpha_r)}{\displaystyle\prod_{s=1}^{m} \prod_{r=1}^{m} (\alpha_r - \rho_s)} \qquad \text{(J-33)}$$

Thus, Eq. (J-33) is readily established for $m = 2$. Furthermore, one shows, without difficulty, that the expression given in Eq. (J-33) satisfies the difference equation (J-32).

From the form of the matrix $M_{mm}^{(2)}$ it is clear that the minor determinant for the ith row and the jth column of $M_{mm}^{(2)}$ is obtained from Eq. (J-33) by omitting the factors containing either α_j or ρ_i. Finally, the inverse of the matrix $M_{mm}^{(2)}$ is obtained as the transposed matrix of the cofactors of the elements of $M_{mm}^{(2)}$ divided by the determinant of $M_{mm}^{(2)}$.

BIBLIOGRAPHY

As stated in the introduction, the authors have preferred to gather together in one place a brief commentary on the literature references used in preparing this text. Isolated footnotes are not, unfortunately, always well suited to the task of orienting the reader to matters other than a specific point of discussion. Here we wish not only to summarize the specific sources of our material, but also to suggest further reading in areas we have left relatively untouched. In the latter instance we may perhaps cite only one of several possible references. We do this with implied apologies to those authors whose papers have been omitted, even though equally relevant; however, our purpose is to indicate that certain bodies of information exist, rather than to attempt to guide the reader in areas with which we are not ourselves thoroughly familiar.

The discussion is organized for the most part according to chapters. We begin, however, by noting certain references which, because of either their historical importance or their broad scope, deserve separate comment.

General References

Engineering books that relate at least in part to the theory of random processes and its applications include James, Nichols, and Phillips (15), Tsien (35), and Lawson and Uhlenbeck (23).[1] Wax (39) has recently edited a collection of six classic papers on random processes, written, for the most part, in the early 1940s. Wiener (40,41) gave, with his elegant theory of optimum prediction and filtering of stationary processes, a strong impetus to the development in this field. More recently Doob (10) has presented a rigorous mathematical treatise on the fundamental theory of random processes. His applications are generally apart from the main fields of interest in this text; however, his book is of considerable importance in the development of basic theory. Finally, we must cite Stumpers (34) who has given a recent (1953) bibliography of 46 pages in length covering random processes, information theory, and closely related fields.

Chapter 2

For further reading on the general subject of probability theory, see Feller (12), Cramér (6), or Kolmogoroff (17). Feller concentrates exclusively on discrete sample spaces and for this reason his treatment is mathematically the least sophisticated of the three. His approach is both elegant and readable, and countless stimulating illustrations and problems are given. Cramér devotes considerable space to the theory of sets of real numbers and Lebesgue integration before considering probability theory as such. Kolmogoroff's treatment is more abstract than that of the others, and represents a concise and sophisticated presentation of the basic mathematical notions underlying probability theory.

Several of the more interesting examples given in Chap. 2 are due to Kac (16).

[1] Numbers in parentheses refer to the List of References at the end of this section.

424

Chapter 3

Most of the material in Secs. 3.1 to 3.6 is covered in other texts with perhaps slightly less emphasis on nonstationary processes. See, for example, James, Nichols, and Phillips (15), Tsien (35), and Lawson and Uhlenbeck (23). With respect to the fundamental definition of power spectral density, Page (30), Turner (37), and Lampard (18) have defined an instantaneous power spectrum, valid for nonstationary processes. Our relation (3.6-34) defining the power spectrum of a nonstationary process is equivalent to the time average of the instantaneous power spectrum defined by these authors. The analysis of the random step function given in Sec. 3.7 is based upon calculations by Phillips (15, pp. 300–304).

Practical problems associated with the computation of correlation functions and spectra from experimental data have been discussed by several authors including Tukey (36), Spetner (33), and Ross (32). The material in Sec. 4.3 of this text is also relevant. The symposium containing Tukey's paper also includes several others of general interest.

The reader interested in the rigorous mathematical foundations of the theory of random processes is again referred to Doob (10).

Chapter 4

The Gaussian random process has been widely studied and used in applications, particularly in nonlinear problems in the electronics and communications field. Most of the material in Chap. 4 is generally available elsewhere, and is introduced in the text to illustrate the variety of applications of basic theory.

Our development of the properties of the shot effect in Sec. 4.1 generally follows that of Rice (31). Much of the material of Sec. 4.4 is drawn from the same source, including the evaluation in Appendix A of a special class of integrals occurring in nonlinear problems. Numerous other nonlinear applications have been given in the literature; see, for example, Middleton (25,26). The use of differential equation methods in Appendix B to sum the series occurring in the limiter problem is due to Battin.

The automatic tracking problem of Sec. 4.5, and our treatment of it, have been adapted by Laning from the closely related problem of the average density of the zeros of a Gaussian random process as discussed by Rice (*loc. cit.*). An alternate approach to this problem, not yet fully explored, is indicated by the following. Let $\{x(t)\}$ be a Gaussian process, $\dot{x}$ its derivative, and let Y be a random variable given by

$$ Y = \frac{1}{\sqrt{2\pi}\,\epsilon} \int_a^b |\dot{x}(t)| \, \exp\left[-\frac{x(t)^2}{2\epsilon^2} \right] dt $$

Then the limit of Y as ϵ approaches zero is the number of zero's of $x(t)$ in (a,b). By a formal calculation

$$ E[Y^n] = (2\pi)^{-n/2}\epsilon^{-n} \int_a^b dt_1 \cdots \int_a^b dt_n \, E\left[\prod_{k=1}^n |\dot{x}(t_k)| \, \exp\left\{ -\sum_{i=1}^n \frac{x(t_i)^2}{2\epsilon^2} \right\} \right] $$

For $n = 1$ or 2 the expectation in the integrand can readily be computed, and the limit taken as ϵ approaches zero. In this way, one can determine not only the mean value but also the mean-squared value of the number of zero's in a given interval, and thus derive a limited amount of information about their distribution.

Other applications of the Gaussian process include problems in the reception of modulated carriers in noise [e.g., Blachman (2), Middleton (27)] and in the detection of pulsed signals [e.g., Middleton (28), Davis (8)]. Further extensions of basic theory are given by Middleton (29) and others.

Chapter 5

Much of the material in this chapter is available in previous texts; see, for example, James, Nichols, and Phillips (15). The concept of the generalized transfer function, for time-variable linear systems mentioned in Sec. 5.2 and applied in Chap. 6, has been studied recently by Zadeh (42 to 46) and others. The evaluation of the integral studied in Sec. 5.5 and Appendix E was first given by Phillips (15). Mersman (24) later showed how the results of Phillips could be presented in determinant form. The simplified derivation presented in Appendix E is due to Battin. To the best of our knowledge the simulator techniques discussed in Sec. 5.6 are original with the authors.

Chapter 6

The techniques of Sec. 6.2 are due to Frey (13). A related discussion has been given recently by Lampard (19). The frequency methods presented in Sec. 6.3 are original; however, the relation (6.3-19) for obtaining mean-squared output in terms of the input spectral density and the generalized transfer function is due to Zadeh (42). The adjoint method has been previously described by Laning and Battin (21). The material given in Sec. 6.5 represents a generalization of results first presented by Duncan (11). So far as is known, the application of the well-known steepest-descents method to the optimization of variable-parameter systems is original.

Chapter 7

The original work on this problem was done by Wiener (40,41). It should be noted that the material presented here represents only a fraction of that treated by Wiener; his methods embrace a considerably broader field of applications than those which we consider. Sections 7.3 and 7.5 represent two attempts to simplify the presentation and technique of the Wiener theory, and are due, respectively, to Bode and Shannon (4) and to Battin (1).

A recent paper by Vowels (38) has given an extension to the Wiener theory that is worthy of comment. By solving a variational problem in which a certain number of the integrals $\int W(t)\,dt$, $\int t W(t)\,dt$, $\int t^2 W(t)\,dt$, . . . are constrained to take on specified constant values, he is led to a modified form of the Wiener-Hopf equation. The solution to this equation then yields optimum filters possessing (say) specified position and velocity error coefficients. This technique may be of value in certain instances where a portion of the data (e.g., a low-frequency nonrandom signal) does not readily fit into the standard theory.

Chapter 8

Sections 8.1 to 8.5 represent an attempt to formulate in a unified way a class of problems that have been studied by several previous authors. The matrix techniques of Sec. 8.4 for solution to the integral equation in the stationary case are due to Battin. The first solution to the nonstationary integral equation of Sec. 8.5 was presented informally by Giever (14) and subsequently modified and formalized by Battin. The material as presented here represents an entirely new approach developed at a later date by Laning. Earlier attacks on these problems include the work of Blackman, Bode, and Shannon (3), Zadeh and Ragazzini (48,49), Dolph and Woodbury (9), Booton (5), Davis (7,8) and Laning and Frey (22).

The material of Sec. 8.6 is taken more or less intact from Laning (20). An alternate approach to the nonlinear problem has been given by Zadeh (47).

List of References

1. Battin, R. H.: "A Simplified Approach to the Wiener Optimum Filter Theory," Report R-38, M.I.T. Instrumentation Laboratory, Cambridge, Mass., August, 1952.
2. Blachman, N. M.: The Demodulation of a Frequency-modulated Carrier and Random Noise by an FM Receiver, *J. Appl. Phys.*, vol. 20, p. 38, 1949.
3. Blackman, R. B., H. W. Bode, and C. E. Shannon: "Data-smoothing and Prediction in Fire Control Systems," Research and Development Board, August, 1948.
4. Bode, H. W., and C. E. Shannon: A Simplified Derivation of Linear Least Square Smoothing and Prediction Theory, *Proc. IRE*, vol. 38, pp. 417–425, April, 1950.
5. Booton, R. C.: An Optimization Theory for Time-varying Linear Systems with Non-stationary Statistical Inputs, *Proc. IRE*, vol. 40, pp. 977–981, 1952.
6. Cramér, H.: "Mathematical Methods of Statistics," Princeton University Press, Princeton, N.J., 1946.
7. Davis, R. C.: On the Theory of Prediction of Non-stationary Stochastic Processes, *J. Appl. Phys.*, vol. 23, pp. 1047–1053, September, 1952.
8. Davis, R. C.: On the Detection of Sure Signals in Noise, *J. Appl. Phys.*, vol. 25, pp. 76–82, January, 1954.
9. Dolph, C. L., and M. A. Woodbury: On the Relation between Green's Functions and Covariances of Certain Stochastic Processes and Its Application to Unbiased Linear Prediction, *Trans. Am. Math. Soc.*, vol. 72, pp. 519–550, May, 1952.
10. Doob, J. L.: "Stochastic Processes," John Wiley & Sons, Inc., New York, 1953.
11. Duncan, D. B.: Response of Linear Time-dependent Systems to Random Inputs, *J. Appl. Phys.*, vol. 24, pp. 609–611, May, 1953.
12. Feller, W.: "An Introduction to Probability Theory and Its Applications," John Wiley & Sons, Inc., New York, 1950.
13. Frey, E. J.: Engineering Memorandum E-111 (Classified), M.I.T. Instrumentation Laboratory, Cambridge, Mass., October, 1951.
14. Giever, J. B.: Personal Communication, November, 1953.
15. James, H. F., N. B. Nichols, and R. S. Phillips: "Theory of Servomechanisms," M.I.T. Radiation Laboratory Series, vol. 25, McGraw-Hill Book Company, Inc., New York, 1947.
16. Kac, M.: Lectures on Probability, given at Massachusetts Institute of Technology, Cambridge, Mass., July–August, 1951.
17. Kolmogoroff, A. N.: "Foundations of the Theory of Probability," Chelsea Publishing Company, New York, 1950.
18. Lampard, D. G.: Generalization of the Wiener-Khintchine Theorem to Non-stationary Processes, *J. Appl. Phys.*, vol. 25, pp. 802–803, June, 1954.
19. Lampard, D. G.: The Response of Linear Networks to Suddenly Applied Stationary Random Noise, *Trans. IRE on Circuit Theory*, vol. CT-2, pp. 49–57, March, 1955.
20. Laning, J. H., Jr.: "Prediction and Filtering in the Presence of Gaussian Interference," Report R-27, M.I.T. Instrumentation Laboratory, Cambridge, Mass., October, 1951.
21. Laning, J. H., Jr., and R. H. Battin: An Application of Analog Computers to the Statistical Analysis of Time-variable Networks, *Trans. IRE on Circuit Theory*, vol. CT-2, pp. 44–49, March, 1955. Also presented at Project Cyclone Symposium II on Simulation and Computing Techniques, Reeves Instrument Corp., New York, May, 1952.
22. Laning, J. H., Jr., and E. J. Frey: "Filtering of Linear Combinations of Analytic

Functions in the Presence of Gaussian Interference," Report R-51, M.I.T. Instrumentation Laboratory, Cambridge, Mass., March, 1953.

23. Lawson, J. L., and G. E. Uhlenbeck: "Threshold Signals," M.I.T. Radiation Laboratory Series, vol. 26, McGraw-Hill Book Company, Inc., New York, 1950.

24. Mersman, W. A.: Evaluation of an Integral Occurring in Servomechanism Theory, *Pacific J. Math.*, vol. 2, pp. 627–632, 1952.

25. Middleton, D.: The Response of Biased, Saturated Linear and Quadratic Rectifiers to Random Noise, *J. Appl. Phys.*, vol. 17, pp. 778–801, October, 1946.

26. Middleton, D.: Some General Results in the Theory of Noise Through Non-linear Devices, *Quart. Appl. Math.*, vol. 5, pp. 445–498, January, 1948.

27. Middleton, D.: The Spectrum of Frequency-modulated Waves after Reception in Random Noise—I, *Quart. Appl. Math.*, vol. 7, pp. 129–174, 1949; II, *ibid.*, vol. 8, pp. 59–80, 1950.

28. Middleton, D.: Statistical Criteria for the Detection of Pulsed Carriers in Noise —I, II, *J. Appl. Phys.*, vol. 24, pp. 371–379, 1953.

29. Middleton, D.: On the Theory of Random Noise. Phenomenological Models—I, *J. Appl. Phys.*, vol. 22, pp. 1143–1152, September, 1951; II, *ibid.*, pp. 1153–1163.

30. Page, C. H.: Instantaneous Power Spectra, *J. Appl. Phys.*, vol. 23, pp. 103–106, January, 1952.

31. Rice, S. O.: Mathematical Analysis of Random Noise, *Bell System Tech. J.*, vol. 23, pp. 282–332, July, 1944; vol. 24, pp. 46–156, January, 1945. Also included in Wax (39).

32. Ross, D. T.: "Improved Computational Techniques for Fourier Transformation," Report 7138-R-5, M.I.T. Servomechanisms Laboratory, Cambridge, Mass., June, 1954.

33. Spetner, L. M.: Errors in Power Spectra Due to Finite Sample, *J. Appl. Phys.*, vol. 25, pp. 653–659, May, 1954.

34. Stumpers, F. L.: "A Bibliography of Information Theory (Communication Theory—Cybernetics)," M.I.T. Research Laboratory of Electronics, Cambridge, Mass., February, 1953.

35. Tsien, H. J.: "Engineering Cybernetics," McGraw-Hill Book Company, Inc., New York, 1954.

36. Tukey, J. W.: "Sampling Theory of Power Spectrum Estimates," Symposium on Applications of Autocorrelation Analysis to Physical Problems, Woods Hole, Mass., June, 1949. ONR Publication NAVEXOS-P-735.

37. Turner, C. H. M.: On the Concept of an Instantaneous Power Spectrum, and Its Relationship to the Autocorrelation Function, *J. Appl. Phys.*, vol. 25, pp. 1347–1351, November 1954.

38. Vowels, R. E.: The Application of Statistical Methods to Servomechanisms, *Australian J. Appl. Sci.*, vol. 4, pp. 469–488, 1953.

39. Wax, N.: "Selected Papers on Noise and Stochastic Processes," Dover Publications, New York, 1954.

40. Wiener, N.: "The Extrapolation, Interpolation, and Smoothing of Stationary Time Series with Engineering Applications," John Wiley & Sons, Inc., New York, 1949.

41. Wiener, N.: "Cybernetics: Control and Communication in the Animal and the Machine," John Wiley & Sons, Inc., New York, 1948.

42. Zadeh, L. A.: Frequency Analysis of Variable Networks, *Proc. IRE*, vol. 38, pp. 291–299, March, 1950.

43. Zadeh, L. A.: The Determination of the Impulsive Response of Variable Networks, *J. Appl. Phys.*, vol. 21, pp. 642–645, July, 1950.

44. Zadeh, L. A.: Circuit Analysis of Linear Varying-parameter Networks, *J. Appl. Phys.*, vol. 21, pp. 1171–1177, November, 1950.
45. Zadeh, L. A.: On Stability of Linear Varying-parameter Systems, *J. Appl. Phys.*, vol. 22, pp. 402–405, April, 1951.
46. Zadeh, L. A.: Initial Conditions in Linear Varying-parameter Systems, *J. Appl. Phys.*, vol. 22, pp. 782–786, July, 1951.
47. Zadeh, L. A.: Optimum Nonlinear Filters, *J. Appl. Phys.*, vol. 24, pp. 396–404, April, 1953.
48. Zadeh, L. A., and J. R. Ragazzini: An Extension of Wiener's Theory of Prediction, *J. Appl. Phys.*, vol. 21, pp. 645–655, July, 1950.
49. Zadeh, L. A., and J. R. Ragazzini: Optimum Filters for the Detection of Signals in Noise, *Proc. IRE*, vol. 40, pp. 1223–1231, October, 1952.

INDEX